FORMULAS, METHODS, TIPS and DATA for home and workshop

A POPULAR SCIENCE BOOK

FORMULAS, METHODS, TIPS and DATA for home and workshop

by Kenneth M. Swezey

updated and expanded by
Robert Scharff

POPULAR SCIENCE

Success and safety in the use of tools or in compounding or using formulas depend largely on the operator's skill and knowledge in handling tools and chemicals. To promote both success and safety, techniques in this book have been described in unusual detail, and precautions in handling chemicals that may be hazardous if improperly used have been explicitly pointed out. These instructions and precautions should be followed faithfully. Because the actual manipulation of the materials and processes described in the book are entirely in the hands of the operator, however, neither author nor publisher can guarantee the results of any instructions or formulas. Therefore each of them expressly disclaims any responsibility for injury to persons or property through their use.

Published by Grolier Book Clubs, Inc.

Library of Congress Catalog Card Number: 68-54377
ISBN: 1-55654-003-5

First edition, 1969, eleven printings
Second edition, revised and expanded, 1979

Fourth Printing, 1987

Manufactured in the United States of America

Contents

Editor's Foreword

This second edition of the late Kenneth M. Swezey's 1969 original has been updated and greatly expanded by Robert Scharff, a long-time friend and associate of Swezey's.

Swezey drew the materials for the original edition from the huge collection of notes, books, and personal experiences he used in the preparation of magazine articles on chemistry, physics, and the home workshop—and in the writing of his books *After Dinner Science, Science Magic, Chemistry Magic,* and *Science Shows You How.* Swezey died in 1972.

Robert Scharff, himself a widely known author and editorial director, first met Swezey in 1952, when both men were working on books for McGraw-Hill. Scharff recalls, "Ken Swezey could give you a formula for anything. If he didn't have it in his head, he could work it up for you in an hour. He had more information in his head—and files—than any man I have ever met. I just couldn't see this book die. That's the reason I wanted to update it. It was the best book of its type and I hope I was able to keep it up to Ken's standards."

Preface
to the First Edition

This is a book of practical but often hard-to-find information for anybody who likes to do things for himself. Its purpose is to put at your fingertips the special technique, the needed table, the right formula to help solve all sorts of problems that crop up constantly around the home and in the workshop.

Some of the methods and formulas may save you money. Others may help you do a better job or make a special product you can't buy ready-made. Still others may just satisfy your curiosity or enable you to carry out a project you have always wanted to undertake but didn't know quite how to.

As you can see from the table of contents, the book covers an exceptionally wide range. Included, of course, are the everyday basic and more familiar methods, hints, and tables you would expect to find in any comprehensive home and workshop data book. Beyond these, however, are hundreds of lesser known and more specialized techniques, uncommon tables, and useful formulas that have been selected and adapted from technical and professional literature as well as from personal experience, many of which appear in no other book of this type. If, therefore, you can't locate a wanted item by title in the table of contents, don't give up until you have double-checked for it in the index.

One help you should not overlook is the table "Conversions of Common Units," beginning on page 567. In this table—compiled especially for this book—units of weight, area, volume, power, velocity, and so on are listed in simple alphabetical order, with the units you may wish to convert to, and the number you should use to make the conversion, immediately adjacent. Another table in the same chapter will enable you to convert from spoons, cups, and other household measures to more conventional ones. A third table will help you convert from specialized and unusual units, ranging from cubits and furlongs to Angstrom units and light-years.

The formulas in this book are only those that might be actually useful around the home and shop, that are relatively easy to make with home equipment, and that are either better than, or cheaper but just as good as, proprietary products that serve the same purpose.

Most of the basic ingredients needed for preparing these formulas are well-known and are easily obtainable from the local grocery, hardware, paint, or drugstore, or from the supermarket. You may soon discover, however, that many others that were once readily available in such stores have either disappeared or are now sold only in disguise as specialty products under proprietary names and at a considerable markup in price. But don't give up! You can usually still get these products under their own names and at reasonable cost by sleuthing a little among sources that cater to special trades or industries.

Another complication may also at first discourage you. To protect inexperienced persons—especially children—from poisons and other products that may be hazardous if improperly used, federal and state laws now prohibit the sale without prescription of many additional common chemicals that were once freely obtainable in drug and other stores that sell directly to the general public. Again, most of such chemicals can be bought by any responsible adult from chemical supply houses and from dealers to industry or to specialty trades in which the chemicals are routinely used.

To help you find some of the elusive materials, a chapter full of sources begins on page 636.

Kenneth M. Swezey

Acknowledgments

Below is a listing of the organizations that helped with the preparation of the original and revised editions:

U.S. Army Corps of Engineers
U.S. Bureau of Mines
U.S. Consumer Product Safety Commission
U.S. Department of Agriculture
U.S. Department of Health, Education and Welfare
U.S. Department of the Interior
U.S. Fish and Wildlife Service
U.S. Food and Drug Administration
U.S. Forest Products Laboratory
U.S. Occupational Safety and Health Administration
U.S. Public Health Service
U.S. Secret Service
National Bureau of Standards
N.Y. State College of Agriculture, Cornell University
N.Y. State College of Home Economics, Cornell University
University of Wisconsin, College of Agriculture
N.Y. Zoological Society
Air-Conditioning and Refrigeration Institute
American Dental Association
American Red Cross
American Society of Heating, Refrigeration and Air-Conditioning Engineers
National Better Business Bureau
National Board of Fire Underwriters
National Fire Protection Association
National Safety Council
American Brush Manufacturers Association
American Gas Association
American Petroleum Institute
American Plywood Association
Asphalt Roof Manufacturers Association
Best Foods
Bethlehem Steel Corporation
Borden Chemical Company
Calgon Corporation

(Continued)

California Redwood Association
Church & Dwight Company
Commercial Solvents Corporation
Diamond Crystal Salt Company
Dow Chemical Company
E. I. DuPont de Nemours & Company
Eastman Kodak Company
ESB, Inc. (formerly the Electric Storage Battery Company)
Esso, Inc.
Fisher Scientific Company
Ford Motor Company
General Aniline & Film Corporation
Heath Company
Home Ventilating Institute
Honeywell Inc.
International Nickel Company
International Salt Company
Walter Kidde & Company
Knape & Vogt Manufacturing Company
Landers-Segal Color Company
Lead Industries Association
Mallinckrodt Chemical Works
Marble Institute of America
Morton Salt Company
National Flaxseed Processors Association
National Lead Company
National Lime Association
National Paint and Coating Association
Pennsalt Chemicals Corporation
Pittsburgh Plate Glass Company
Portland Cement Association
Pyrofax Gas Corporation
Radio Corporation of America
Rockwell International Corporation
Rose-X Chemical Company
Shell Chemical Company
Small Homes Council
Velsicol Chemical Corporation
Vermont Marble Company
Western Wood Products Association
Wool Bureau, Inc.
William Zinsser & Company

FORMULAS, METHODS, TIPS and DATA for home and workshop

Wood: Selection, Finishing, Preservation

HOW YOU ARE CHARGED FOR LUMBER

Lumber is sold by the board-foot measure. A board foot is equal to a piece 1 inch thick and 12 inches square. If you know the board-foot price, you can find the cost of any size or shape of lumber by using this formula (thickness and width are in inches and length is in feet):

$$\frac{\text{Thickness} \times \text{width} \times \text{length}}{12} = \text{board feet}$$

Thus a 2 × 4-inch piece of lumber that is 12 feet long would contain 8 board feet:

$$\frac{2 \times 4 \times 12}{12} = 8$$

Lumber is always quoted at a specified price per M (thousand) board feet. For example, if it was quoted at $220 per M board feet, it would be charged for at the rate of $.22 per foot ($\frac{\$220}{1000} = \$.22$). Thus the 8 feet from the formula above would be multiplied times $.22 for a cost of $1.76. The number of board feet in lumber of various sizes and lengths is given in the lumber calculator table on the next page.

LUMBER CALCULATOR

Size in inches	8-foot	10-foot	12-foot	14-foot	16-foot
1 × 2	1⅓	1⅔	2	2⅓	2⅔
1 × 3	2	2½	3	3½	4
1 × 4	2⅔	3⅓	4	4⅔	5⅓
1 × 5	3⅓	4⅙	5	5⅚	6⅔
1 × 6	4	5	6	7	8
1 × 8	5⅓	6⅔	8	9⅓	10⅔
1 × 10	6⅔	8½	10	11⅔	13⅓
1 × 12	8	10	12	14	16
1¼ × 4	3⅓	4⅙	5	5⅚	6⅔
1¼ × 6	5	6¼	7½	8¾	10
1¼ × 8	6⅔	8⅓	10	11⅔	13⅓
1¼ × 10	8⅓	10 5/12	12½	14 7/12	16⅔
1¼ × 12	10	12½	15	17½	20
2 × 4	5⅓	6⅔	8	9⅓	10⅔
2 × 6	8	10	12	14	16
2 × 8	10⅔	13⅓	16	18⅔	21⅓
2 × 10	13⅓	16⅔	20	23⅓	26⅔
2 × 12	16	20	24	28	32
4 × 4	10⅔	13⅓	16	18⅔	21⅓
4 × 6	16	20	24	28	32
4 × 8	21⅓	26⅔	32	37½	42⅔
4 × 10	26⅔	33⅓	40	46⅔	53⅓
4 × 12	32	40	48	56	64
6 × 6	24	30	36	42	48
6 × 8	32	40	48	56	64

It must be remembered, however, that prices are based on *nominal* or original rough sizes rather than *actual* dimensions as sold. In the case of softwoods, the actual thickness and width depend upon whether the pieces are rough-sawed or planed smooth, green or dry. For instance, a green, rough-sawed board 1 inch thick is actually ¾ inch thick if dry and dressed; it is 25/32 inch thick if it is green (above 19-percent moisture content) and dressed. If the lumber is grade-marked, the stamp will indicate whether the piece was green or dry when it was dressed to size. The table at the top of page 3 gives the nominal and actual average sizes of commonly used softwood lumber.

NOMINAL AND ACTUAL SIZES OF SOFTWOODS

	THICKNESSES Actual (inches)			FACE WIDTHS Actual (inches)	
Nominal (rough) size*	Minimum dry**	Dressed green	Nominal (rough) size*	Minimum dry**	Dressed green
1	3/4	25/32	2	1 1/2	1 9/16
1 1/4	1	1 1/32	3	2 1/2	2 9/16
1 1/2	1 1/4	1 9/32	4	3 1/2	3 9/16
2	1 1/2	1 9/16	6	5 1/2	5 5/8
3	2 1/2	2 9/16	8	7 1/4	7 1/2
4	3 1/2	3 9/16	10	9 1/4	9 1/2
			12	11 1/4	11 1/2

* Thickness sometimes is expressed as 4/4, 5/4, etc.

** Dry lumber has been seasoned to a moisture content of 19 percent or less.

In softwoods, thickness less than 1 inch is charged as a full inch, though in hardwoods the prices vary. The amount of size reduction of hardwoods depends partly on the standards used by the planing mill and partly on the amount of finishing (also called "dressing"). A piece may be dressed on one side only (S1S) or on both sides (S2S) and/or on one edge (S1E) or both edges (S2E). In the accompanying table, it should be kept in mind that the widths of hardwoods vary with various grades.

NOMINAL AND ACTUAL SIZES OF HARDWOODS

Nominal (rough) size	Surfaced 1 Side (S1S)	Surfaced 2 Sides (S2S)
3/8"	1/4"	3/16"
1/2"	3/8"	5/16"
5/8"	1/2"	7/16"
3/4"	5/8"	9/16"
1"	7/8"	1 13/16"
1 1/4"	1 1/8"	1 1/16"
1 1/2"	1 3/8"	1 5/16"
2"	1 13/16"	1 3/4"
3"	2 13/16"	2 3/4"
4"	3 13/16"	3 3/4"

Lumber is also worked or *milled* to produce popular molded shapes for specific purposes, such as for baseboards, doweling, etc. Milled lumber also is dimensioned, but the dimensions may or may not refer to thickness and width. Each shape is dimensioned in a manner necessitated by its usage. When buying milled pieces, you must learn, in each case, what the dealer's dimensions specify (usually, but not always, obvious). Milled lumber is always sold by the *lineal foot* or the piece, based on its length. A lineal-foot measurement, of course, refers to the real length of a board, measured in feet.

HOW WOOD IS GRADED

When a lumber dealer refers to "boards," he means stock less than 2 inches thick and usually more than 6 inches wide. Narrower boards are "strips."

Dimension lumber, also called *framing* lumber, includes structural pieces from 2 to 5 inches thick, used for studs, joists, and rafters. Lumber 5 inches thick or more is *timber.*

Each type is sold in various grades according to the size, number, and kind of defects found in them. Softwoods and hardwoods are graded differently; there is no relation between softwood and hardwood grades.

SOFTWOOD LUMBER GRADES

SELECT

(Lumber of good appearance and finishing qualities)

Suitable for Natural Finishes

GRADE A (also called No. 1 Clear). Free of defects. Because of cost, this grade is not stocked in all lumberyards.

GRADE B (also called No. 2 Clear). Allows a few small defects and blemishes. (A slightly higher category—B & Better—is sold by lumberyards. While not an "official" grade, it contains a few pieces of Grade A, but the majority is Grade B. This is slightly more expensive than Grade B itself.)

Suitable for Paint Finishes

GRADE C. Allows a limited number of small defects or blemishes that can be covered with paint. Some pieces can even take a natural finish.

GRADE D. Allows any number of defects or blemishes that do not detract from a finish appearance, especially when painted.

COMMON

(Lumber containing defects or blemishes which detract from a finish appearance, but which is suitable for general utility and construction use.)

Lumber Suitable for Use Without Waste

NO. 1 COMMON (also called Construction Grade). Good, sound, watertight lumber with tight knots (none larger than 2 inches and rarely on edges) and limited blemishes. No warp, splits, checks, or decay.

NO. 2 COMMON (also called Standard Grade). Allows larger and coarser defects than No. 1, but is considered graintight lumber.

Lumber Permitting Waste

NO. 3 COMMON (Also called Utility Grade). Allows larger and coarser defects than No. 2 and occasional knotholes.

NO. 4 COMMON (also called Economy Grade). Low-quality lumber admitting the coarsest defects, such as decay and knotholes.

NO. 5 COMMON. Practically waste lumber, good only for use as a filler, and then with considerable waste.

HARDWOOD LUMBER GRADES

Hardwood grading is not consistent for all trees, nor in all parts of the country. On the whole, however, the grades are as follows:

FIRSTS: Lumber that is 91⅔-percent clear on both sides; considered the best possible for cabinetwork.

SECONDS: Lumber that is 83⅓-percent clear on both sides; still very good for most cabinetwork.

FIRSTS & SECONDS: A selection that must contain not less than 20-percent firsts.

SELECTS (in alder, ash, beech, birch, cherry, chestnut, mahogany, maple, sycamore, and walnut only): Lumber that is 90-percent clear on one side only (other side not graded). Good for most cabinetwork, with some waste.

SAPS (in poplar only): Approximately the same as select above.

NO. 1 COMMON: One side only, 66⅔-percent clear. With waste, good for interior and less demanding cabinetwork.

NO. 2 COMMON: One side only, 50-percent clear. Okay for painting, some paneling and flooring.

STAINED SAPS (in poplar only): Equivalent to No. 2 common, above.

NO. 3A COMMON: One side only, 33⅓-percent clear.

NO. 3B COMMON: One side only, 25-percent clear.

SOUND-WORMY (in chestnut only): A No. 1 above but with wormholes.

Notes: Hardwoods are supposed to be free of warp, wind, bad splits, and checks. "Clear" refers to the number of clear cuttings that can be obtained.

COMMON HOME-WORKSHOP WOODS

Name of Wood	Hardness	Strength	Stability	Weight	Rot resistance	Split resistance	Working quality for hand tools	Shaping	Turning	Mortising	Planing and jointing	Nailing	Gluing	Sanding	Cost
Alder	medium	weak	G	light	F	F	G	F	F	F	G	G	G	F	medium
Ash, white	medium	medium	E	medium heavy	F	G	P	E	F	F	G	G	F	E	medium
Balsa	soft	weak	G	light	P	E	E	P	P	P	G	E	E	P	low
Basswood	soft	weak	G	light	P	E	E	P	P	F	G	E	E	P	medium
Beech	hard	medium	P	heavy	P	G	F	F	F	G	F	P	G	G	medium
Birch	hard	strong	G	heavy	P	G	P	E	G	E	G	P	F	F	high
Butternut	soft	weak	E	light	F	F	G	F	G	F	G	F	G	F	medium
Cedar, red	soft	weak	G	medium	E	P	G	P	P	F	F	P	G	P	medium
Cherry	medium	medium	G	heavy	F	P	G	E	E	E	E	F	E	E	high
Chestnut	soft	weak	E	light	E	P	G	G	E	G	G	G	E	E	high
Cottonwood	soft	weak	G	light	P	E	E	P	P	P	G	E	E	P	low
Cypress	soft	medium	G	light	E	F	F	P	P	P	G	F	F	F	medium
Elm	medium	medium	P	medium heavy	F	G	F	P	P	G	P	E	F	G	medium
Fir, Douglas	medium	medium strong	F	medium heavy	G	F	F	P	P	G	G	G	G	F	medium
Fir, white		low		light	G	G	G	P	P	G	G	G	G	G	low
Gum, red	medium	medium	P	medium	F	G	G	F	E	F	F	G	E	F	medium

Hickory	hard	strong	G	heavy	P	F	P	F	G	E	G	P	G	E	medium
Lauan	medium	medium	E	medium	G	P	G	F	G	F	G	G	E	P	medium
Magnolia	soft	weak	F	medium	F	G	G	G	F	P	G	E	E	G	medium
Mahogany	medium	medium	E	medium heavy	F	P	G	E	E	E	G	G	E	G	high
Maple, hard	hard	strong	G	heavy	P	P	P	E	E	E	F	P	F	G	high
Maple, soft	medium	medium	F	medium	F	G	G	F	F	P	P	F	G	G	medium
Oak, red	hard	strong	E	heavy	P	F	P	F	G	E	E	G	G	E	medium
Oak, white	hard	strong	E	heavy	F	F	P	G	G	E	E	G	G	E	high
Pine, ponderosa	soft	weak	G	light	F	P	E	G	G	F	G	E	E	F	low
Pine, sugar	soft	weak	G	light	F	P	E	G	G	F	G	E	E	P	low
Pine, white	soft	weak	G	light	F	P	E	G	G	F	G	E	E	G	low
Pine, yellow	hard	strong	F	heavy	G	P	F	G	P	G	G	F	F	F	medium
Poplar	soft	weak	G	medium	P	G	E	P	G	F	G	E	E	P	medium
Redwood	soft	medium	E	medium	E	G	G	G	F	P	G	G	E	P	medium
Spruce	soft	weak	G	light	F	F	G	G	G	F	G	G	G	G	medium
Sycamore	medium	medium	P	heavy	F	G	G	P	G	E	P	E	G	P	medium
Walnut	medium	strong	E	heavy	G	F	G	G	E	E	G	F	E	E	high
Willow	soft	weak	G	light	G	G	G	F	F	F	F	G	G	G	low

(E = Excellent, G = Good, F = Fair, P = poor)

By looking over lumber grades carefully, you can choose the cheapest one that will do for your purpose. Don't buy the most expensive clear grade if you're going to cover it with paint. On the other hand, a low, knot-filled grade may be fine for rustic paneling.

If you're building a garage or addition to your house, you'll need a high grade that has good strength. Local building codes may specify grades that must be used; check these before starting construction.

CHOOSING THE BEST WOOD FOR THE JOB

Careful shopping will enable you to suit the wood you buy to the job you intend it for. Woods have widely different characteristics. Woods like redwood and cypress stand up well and are easy to work, but they are too soft to take a fine finish. Birch and maple finish beautifully, but aren't easy to work without power tools. They also are more susceptible to moisture damage and decay. The table on pages 6 and 7 will help you choose the woods that have the qualities you need for each job.

Woods that sand smooth and take a high, hard finish are listed as "excellent." Those that require more work and take softer, duller finishes are listed as "good," "fair," or "poor." Strength won't matter much in woods used for paneling, or those that are supported by a framework, but can be very important in structural woods or furniture parts such as table legs. Hardness, or density, can be roughly translated into "dentability." In general the hardest woods make the best cabinets and table tops.

HOW WOODS WEATHER

The accompanying table shows how woods stand up under age and weather. Only those with very high decay resistance should be used unpainted outdoors. But many lower-rated woods will last well under outdoor conditions if treated with preservative, or if they are varnished or painted. Woods with high shrinkage aren't necessarily a bad choice if you make sure they are dry. "Checking" (small cracks) and "cupping" (warping) are defects found in woods exposed to the weather. How much a wood cups or checks helps determine its suitability for exterior uses, as in house siding.

CHANGES DUE TO WEATHERING

Wood	Resistance to decay	Amount of shrinkage	Color becomes	Conspicuous checking	Cupping
Ash, white	low	medium	dark gray	yes	very high
Aspen	low	medium high	light gray	no	medium
Basswood	low	high	light gray	yes	medium
Birch	low	medium high	light gray	yes	very high
Cedar, red	very high	low	dark gray	no	low
Chestnut	high	medium	dark gray	yes	high
Cottonwood	low	medium high	light gray	yes	very high
Cypress	very high	medium low	silvery gray	no	low
Fir, Douglas	medium	medium	dark gray	yes	medium
Fir, white	low	medium	dark gray	yes	medium
Gum, red	medium	medium	light gray	yes	very high
Hemlock, Eastern	low	medium	light gray	yes	medium
Hemlock, Western	low	medium	light gray	yes	medium
Hickory	low	high	light gray	yes	very high
Larch	medium	medium high	dark gray	yes	medium
Maple	low	high	light gray	yes	very high
Oak, red	low	medium high	dark gray	yes	very high
Oak, white	high	medium low	dark gray	yes	very high
Pine, Eastern white	medium	low	light gray	yes	medium
Pine, ponderosa	low	medium low	light gray	yes	medium
Pine, sugar	medium	low	light gray	yes	medium
Pine, Western white	medium	medium high	light gray	yes	medium
Pine, yellow	medium	medium high	dark gray	yes	medium
Poplar	low	medium	light gray	no	high
Redwood	very high	medium low	dark gray	no	low
Spruce	low	medium	light gray	yes	medium
Walnut	high	medium	dark gray	yes	high

HOW TO USE PLYWOOD

Plywood is made of a number of thin sheets of wood glued together with the grain of the adjacent layers perpendicular. The grain of the two outside plies must be parallel to provide stability. This gives the panel nearly equalized strength and minimizes dimensional changes. The thin layers of wood, called plies, usually are "peeled" from a log as veneer. In some instances the veneer is sliced from the log. The veneer is cut into various lengths, dried, selected or graded, then glued together to make a sheet or panel of plywood.

Both softwood and hardwood plywoods are available. Softwood plywood is extensively used in building construction; hardwood plywood is used for cabinetwork and furniture; both are used for paneling. Softwood and hardwood plywood are classified by grade and type. Grade is determined by the quality or condition of the separate plies and the appearance of the face plies; type refers to the durability of the adhesive bond between the plies.

Softwood Plywood

Softwood plywood is manufactured from several species of wood, of which Douglas fir is the most common. Some of the other species used in significant quantity include Southern yellow pine, Western larch, Western hemlock, Sitka spruce, commercial white firs, Alaska and Port Orford cedar, and California redwood.

SIZE. Plywood is most readily available in sheets or panels 4 feet wide by 8 feet long. Lengths up to 16 feet are available, but not always stocked. Widths range from 24 to 60 inches, with 48 inches being most common.

THICKNESS. Plywood is manufactured in thicknesses of ¼ inch to 1⅛ inches. A special ⅛ inch plywood is also available for model making and similar uses. There always will be an odd number of plies, the minimum number being three.

PRODUCT STANDARD. Construction and industrial plywood is manufactured in accordance with U.S. Product Standard PS 1. American Plywood Association grade-trademarks (shown here) are positive identification of plywood manufactured in conformance with PS 1 and with rigid quality standards of the Association.

TYPES. Two types of softwood plywood are available: exterior (waterproof) and interior (moisture-resistant); within each type there are several grades.

Exterior-type plywood is used when the wood will come into contact with excessive moisture and water, such as in boats, outdoor fences, combination sheathing and siding for houses, and outdoor furniture. This type of plywood is manufactured with phenolic or resorcinol-type adhesives that are insoluble in water.

Interior-type plywood will withstand occasional wetting during construction, but should not be permanently exposed to the elements. Within the interior-type classification there are two levels of adhesive durability: (1) interior with interior glue, which may be used where the plywood will not be subject to prolonged moisture conditions or extreme humidity and (2) interior with exterior waterproof glue for use where prolonged but temporary exposures to moisture are expected. Because lower veneer grades are permitted for inner plies of interior plywood, however, these panels are not equal in durability to fully exterior plywood and should not be exposed to continuous moisture conditions.

GROUP. All appearance grades are identified in the APA grade-trademark with a group number that refers to species. Plywood is manufactured from over 70 wood species of varying strength that have been classified under PS 1 into five groups (see table on page 12). Each species within a given group meets a common criterion for that group. The strongest woods are found in Group 1 (the lower the group number, the greater the stiffness and strength). The group number in APA grade-trademarks is based on the species used for the face or back of the panel. Where face and back veneers are not from the same species, the number is based on the weaker group, except for decorative and sanded panels ⅜ inch or less, which are identified by face-species group.

GRADES. The presence or absence of defects in the face or surface plies determines the grade of the plywood. The quality of the veneer is graded N (best), A, B, C, and D (poorest). N grade is a special-order veneer for use as a natural finish. In A-A grade plywood, for instance, both faces are of A quality; in C-D grade, one face is of C quality and the other of D quality. Only minor surface defects and limited patches are permitted in Grade A quality, and the face must be sanded. Grade B allows some appearance defects and permits more patching than Grade A as long as the surface is sanded smooth. Grades C and D permit knots, knotholes, and some splits, with larger defects permitted in the D grade. Some manufacturers produce plywood with an improved C veneer called C-plugged. A special grade of plywood, which usually has the second ply repaired, is used for underlayment. Only plywood bearing the "underlayment" or "Sturd-I-Floor" grade stamps should be used for that purpose.

The inner plies may be of any grade, although D is commonly used interior type plywood. C is the lowest-grade veneer permitted for exterior type, and defects in the inner plies of marine plywood for boat hulls must be patched and repaired.

CLASSIFICATION OF SPECIES (Softwood and Hardwood)

Group 1	Group 2		Group 3	Group 4	Group 5
Apitong (a),(b)	Cedar, Port Orford	Maple, Black	Alder, Red	Aspen	Basswood
Beech	Cypress	Mengkulang (a)	Birch, Paper	Bigtooth	Fir, Balsam
American	Douglas Fir 2 (c)	Meranti, Red (a),(b)	Cedar, Alaska	Quaking	Poplar, Balsam
Birch	Fir	Mersawa (a)	Fir, Subalpine	Cativo	
Sweet	California Red	Pine	Hemlock, Eastern	Cedar	
Yellow	Grand	Pond	Maple, Bigleaf	Incense	
Douglas Fir 1 (c)	Noble	Red	Pine	Western Red	
Kapur	Pacific Silver	Virginia	Jack	Cottonwood	
Keruing (a),(b)	White	Western White	Lodgepole	Eastern	
Larch, Western	Hemlock, Western	Spruce	Ponderosa	Black (Western Poplar)	
Maple, Sugar	Lauan	Red	Spruce	Pine	
Pine	Almon	Sitka	Redwood	Eastern white	
Caribbean	Bagtikan	Sweetgum	Spruce	Sugar	
Ocote	Mayapis	Tamarack	Black		
Pine, Southern	Red Lauan	Yellow-poplar	Engelmann		
Loblolly	Tangile		White		
Longleaf	White Lauan				
Shortleaf					
Slash					
Tanoak					

KEY TO SYMBOLS

(a) Each of these names represents a trade group of woods consisting of a number of closely related species.
(b) Species from the genus Dipterocarpus are marketed collectively, Apitong if originating in the Philippines, Keruing if originating in Malaysia or Indonesia.
(c) Douglas fir from trees grown in the states of Washington, Oregon, California, Idaho, Montana, Wyoming, and the Canadian provinces of Alberta and British Columbia shall be classed as Douglas fir No. 1. Douglas fir from trees grown in the states of Nevada, Utah, Colorado, Arizona and New Mexico shall be classed as Douglas fir No. 2.
(d) Red Meranti shall be limited to species having a specific gravity of 0.41 or more based on green volume and oven dry weight.

COMMON GRADES OF PLYWOOD

EXTERIOR

Grade (exterior)	Face	Back	Inner plies	Uses
A-A	A	A	C	Outdoors, where appearance of both sides is important
A-B	A	B	C	Alternate for A-A, where appearance of one side is less important; face is finish grade
A-C	A	C	C	Soffits, fences, base for coatings
B-C	B	C	C	For utility uses such as farm buildings, some kinds of fences, etc., base for coatings
303 Siding	C (or better)	C	C	Panels with variety of surface texture and grooving patterns; for siding, fences, paneling, screens, etc.
T 1–11	C	C	C	Special ⅝-inch siding panel with deep parallel grooves; available unsanded, textured, or MDO surface
C-C (plugged)	C (plugged)	C	C	Excellent base for tile and linoleum, backing for wall coverings, high-performance coatings
C-C	C	C	C	Unsanded, for backing and rough construction exposed to weather
B-B Plyform	B	B	C	Concrete forms; reuse until wood literally wears out
MDO	B	B or C	C	Medium Density Overlay—ideal base for paint; for siding, built-ins, signs, displays
HDO	A or B	A or B	C-plugged or C	High Density Overlay—hard surface; no paint needed; for concrete forms, cabinets, counter tops, tanks

(Continued)

COMMON GRADES OF PLYWOOD ***(continued)***

INTERIOR

Grade (interior)	Face	Back	Inner plies	Uses
A-A	A	A	D	Cabinet doors, built-ins, furniture where both sides will show
A-B	A	B	D	Alternate of A-A, face is finish grade, back is solid and smooth
A-D	A	D	D	Finish grade face for paneling, built-ins, backing
B-D	B	D	D	Utility grade; for backing, cabinet sides, etc.
C-D	C	D	D	Sheathing and structural uses such as temporary enclosures, subfloor; unsanded
Underlayment	C-plugged	D	C[1] and D	For separate underlayment under tile, carpeting
Sturd-I-Floor	C-plugged	D	C[1] and D	For combination subfloor-underlayment under tile, carpeting

[1] Special construction to resist indentation from concentrated loads.

ENGINEERED GRADES. Structural I and Structural II grades have been recently added to the better grades. They are unsanded grades made with exterior adhesives, and stronger woods, and are for use in engineered applications, such as stressed-skin panels, box beams, gusset plates for trusses, etc.

IDENTIFICATION INDEX. This is a pair of numbers separated by a slash in the APA grade-trademark on unsanded grades.

The index number tells you the panel's basic construction capabilities at a glance. The number on the left refers to the maximum recommended spacing in inches for supports when the panel is used for roof decking with face grain across supports. The number on the right refers to the recommended maximum spacing in inches for supports when the panel is used for residential subflooring with face grain across supports. [For example, an index number of 32/16 means the panel can be used for roof decking with supports spaced up to 32 inches "on center" (o.c.) and for subfloors on supports spaced up to 16 inches o.c.] A number "0" on the right of the slash means the panel should not be used for subflooring. No reference to the index number is needed when the panel is to be used for wall sheathing.

SPAN INDEX. The grade-trademarks for APA Sturd-I-Floor and APA 303 plywood siding products contain Span Index numbers indicating the recommended maximum support or framing spans for normal installations. In the case of Sturd-I-Floor, the Span Index gives the maximum floor joist spacing with plywood face grain perpendicular to supports. Spans are given in inches "on center" (o.c.). Typical Sturd-I-Floor Span Indexes are 16 o.c., 20 o.c., 24 o.c., and 48 o.c. For 303 plywood siding, on the other hand, the Span Index gives the maximum stud spacing (or nail column spacings when applied over plywood sheathing) with plywood face grain *parallel* to supports, the most common application. Span Indexes for 303 siding are 16 o.c. and 24 o.c.

Hardwood Plywood

The species used in the face plies identifies hardwood plywood—that is, black walnut plywood would have one or both face plies of black walnut. Some of the more common species used in hardwood plywood are cherry, oak, birch, black walnut, maple, and gum among the native woods; mahogany, lauan, and teak in the imported category. A major difference in the manufacture of softwood and hardwood plywood is the use of a solid "core" or extra-thick middle ply in some hardwood panels.

VENEER-CORE. Veneer-core plywood is manufactured with layers of wood veneer joined in the standard manner. It is intended for such uses as paneling, sheathing, and furniture parts, or when the plywood might be bent or curved.

LUMBER-CORE. Lumber-core plywood contains a thick core made by edge-gluing several narrow strips of solid wood. This core forms the middle section to which veneer crossbands and face plies are glued. Lumber-core plywood is manufactured for specific uses such as tabletops, built-in cabinets, and fixtures and doors where butt hinges are specified.

PARTICLEBOARD-CORE. In this plywood the core is an aggregate of wood particles bonded together with a resin binder. Face veneers are usually glued directly to the core, although crossbanding is sometimes used. Particleboard-core plywood is used in manufacturing furniture and is particularly adaptable for table, desk, and cabinet tops.

SIZE. Hardwood plywood is most commonly sold in panels 4 × 8 feet, although it is possible to have plywood made in almost any desired size.

THICKNESS. Hardwood plywood is manufactured in three, five, seven, and nine plies with thicknesses ranging from ⅛ inch to 1 inch. The table shows the most common thickness dimensions for the different number of plies.

Number of plies	Plywood thickness (inches)			
3	⅛	3/16	¼	
5	¼	⅜	½	⅝
7	⅝	¾		
9	¾	1		

TYPES. The following four types of hardwood plywood are available:

1. Type I is manufactured with waterproof adhesives and is used in areas where it will come in contact with water.
2. Type II is manufactured with water-resistant adhesives and is used in areas where it will not ordinarily be subjected to contact with water. However, it can be used in areas of continued dampness and excessive humidity.
3. Type III is manufactured with moisture-resistant adhesives and is intended for use in areas where it will not come in contact with any water. It can be subjected to some dampness and excessive humidity.
4. Technical has the same adhesive specifications as Type I but varies in thickness and arrangement of plies.

GRADES. Hardwood plywood is manufactured in six specific grades. As in softwood plywood, each face must be specified.

Specialty grade (SP). This is a plywood made to order to meet the specific requirements of a particular buyer. Plywood of this grade usually entails special matching of the face veneers.

Premium grade (#1). The veneer on the face is fabricated for matched joints, and contrast in color and grain is avoided.

Good grade (#1). The veneer on the face is fabricated to avoid sharp contrasts in color and grain.

Sound grade (#2). The veneer on the face is not matched for color or grain. Some defects are permissible, but the face is free of open defects and is sanded and smooth. It is usually used for surfaces to be painted.

Utility grade (#3). Tight knots, discoloration, stain, wormholes, mineral streaks, and some slight splits are permitted in this grade. Decay is not permitted.

Backing grade (#4). This grade permits larger defects. Grain and color are not matched, and the veneer is used primarily as the concealed face. Defects must not affect strength or serviceability of the panel made from it. At the manufacturer's option, this face can be of some species other than the exposed face.

When ordering plywood—either softwood or hardwood—be guided by the following questions:

Do you want veneer, lumber, or particleboard-core plywood?

What thickness will you need?

What panel size will be most economical?

Will you need one or both surfaces finished?

When you have answered these questions, you are ready to order plywood intelligently.

WOOD FLOORING

Softwood finish flooring costs less than most hardwood species and is often used to good advantage in bedroom and closet areas where traffic is light. It might also be selected to fit the interior decor. It is less dense than the hardwoods, less wear-resistant, and shows surface abrasions more readily. Softwoods most commonly used for flooring are Southern pine, Douglas fir, redwood, and Western hemlock.

The table on page 18 lists the grades and descriptions of softwood strip flooring. Softwood flooring has tongued-and-grooved edges and may be hollow-backed or grooved. Some types are also end-matched. Vertical-grain flooring generally has better wearing qualities than flat-grain flooring under hard usage.

Hardwoods most commonly used for flooring are red and white oak, beech, birch, maple, and pecan. The table lists grades, types, and sizes. Manufacturers supply both prefinished and unfinished flooring.

GRADE AND DESCRIPTION OF STRIP FLOORING

Species	Grain orientation	Thickness (inches)	Width (inches)	First grade	Second grade	Third grade
		SOFTWOODS				
Douglas fir and hemlock	edge grain	25/32	2⅜–5 3/16	B and better	C	D
	flat grain	25/32	2⅜–5 3/16	C and better	D	–
Southern pine	edge grain and flat grain	5/16–1 5/16	1¾–5 7/16	B and better	C and better	D (and No. 2)
		HARDWOODS				
Oak	edge grain	25/32	1½–3¼	Clear	Select	–
	flat grain	⅜	1½–2	Clear	Select	No. 1 Common
		½	1½–2			
Beech, birch, maple, and pecan*		25/32	1½–3¼			
		⅜	1½–2	First grade	Second grade	–
		½	1½–2			

*Special grades are available in which uniformity of color is a requirement.

Estimating Wood Flooring Requirements

To determine the board feet of flooring needed to cover a given space, first find the area in square feet (length times width). Where there are bay windows or other projections, allowance should be made for additional flooring. Once the square footage of an area is known, refer to the table on pages 20 and 21.

Preventing Cracks in New Wood Floors

Cracks that develop within a few weeks or months in a new, well-laid floor are the result of changes in the moisture content of the wood either before or just after the floor is laid. By taking proper precautions, you can prevent them.

The well-informed manufacturer generally sees that floor stock is properly dried and delivered in good condition to the retailer. The dealer, in turn, will store it under conditions that won't allow it to absorb moisture. Trouble usually starts, however, if the wood is delivered on a damp or rainy day, or if dry wood is laid in a cold, damp house in which the plaster or masonry has not thoroughly dried.

Boards swell when they absorb moisture and shrink when they dry. If flooring contains too much moisture when it is installed, cracks will open up soon after the house is occupied and heated. If, on the other hand, dry flooring is installed in a damp house, what is known technically as "compression set" will take place. As the boards swell, their edges press powerfully against each other, crushing the wood fiber and permanently compressing it; when they dry again, they leave cracks.

The cure for such cracks lies wholly in prevention. The rules are simple, but often overlooked:

1. Make sure the wood is dry when you lay it.
2. Do not lay it in a cold, damp house.
3. To retard moisture absorption, coat the floor with shellac, floor sealer, or varnish as soon as practicable.

HUMIDITY CONTROL. To keep indoor dampness low enough to prevent swelling of newly laid flooring, experts of the Forest Products Laboratory of the Department of Agriculture recommend that heat be maintained in a house from the time the workmen leave until they return the next workday, even during warm summer weather. If the heating plant has not already been installed, then a temporary stove should be used.

It is also good practice, they say, to open the bundles of flooring so that all surfaces are exposed to the air for at least 4 days. This allows time for the flooring to reach a moisture equilibrium with the air in the heated house before it is laid. The inside temperature should be kept at least 15° F above outdoor temperatures and should not be allowed to cool below about 70° F during the summer or 62° to 65° F when the outdoor temperatures are below freezing. Slightly higher temperatures will do no harm, but severe overheating should be avoided. After the floor has received its coating of protective finish, temperatures should be kept approximately what they will be when the house is occupied.

Besides preventing crack formation in the flooring, such heating will also permit better performance from mechanical sanders. In addition, it will prevent swelling and cracking of other interior woodwork and finish, such as doors, trim, and cabinets.

HOW DRY SHOULD FLOORING BE? It depends on where you live and to some extent what type of heating system you will use. With conventional heating systems, using warm air or hot water or steam radiators, flooring should be laid at an average moisture content of 8

ESTIMATING FLOORING REQUIREMENTS

Figures below show the number of board feet of various sizes of flooring required to cover square footage of floor space, as shown in the left most column.

Square feet of floor space	25/32 × 3¼	25/32 × 2¼	25/32 × 1½	½ × 2	½ × 1½	⅜ × 2	⅜ × 1½
10	13	14	16	13	14	13	14
20	26	28	31	26	28	26	28
30	39	42	47	39	42	39	42
40	52	56	62	52	56	52	56
50	65	70	78	65	70	65	70
60	78	83	93	78	83	78	83
70	91	97	109	91	97	91	97
80	104	111	124	104	111	104	111
90	117	125	140	117	125	117	125
100	129	139	155	130	139	130	139
200	258	277	310	260	277	260	277
300	387	415	465	390	415	390	415
400	516	553	620	520	553	520	553
500	645	692	775	650	692	650	692
600	774	830	930	780	830	780	830
700	903	969	1085	910	969	910	969
800	1032	1107	1240	1040	1107	1040	1107
900	1161	1245	1395	1170	1245	1170	1245
1000	1290	1383	1550	1300	1383	1300	1383

ESTIMATING FLOORING REQUIREMENTS ***(continued)***

	25/32 × 3¼	25/32 × 2¼	25/32 × 1½	½ × 2	½ × 1½	⅜ × 2	⅜ × 1½
Called	1 × 4	1 × 3	1 × 2¼	1 × 2½	1 × 2	1 × 2½	1 × 2
Lbs. per 1,000 board feet	2300	2100	2000	1350	1300	1000	1000
Size of nails used	8d	8d	8d	5d	5d	4d	4d
Nail spacing	10 to 12 inches on center			8 to 10 inches on center		6 to 8 inches on center	
No. pieces per bundle	8	12	12	18	18	24	24
To obtain board feet from bundle multiply by	2⅔	3	2¼	3¾	3	5	4

percent in most parts of the United States. This value is about midway between the highest and lowest values the flooring will attain during the different seasons.

The accompanying table will give you an indication of the moisture allowances for both dry and damp regions and for other parts of the country.

RECOMMENDED MOISTURE CONTENT FOR WOOD FLOORING AT TIME OF LAYING
(for dwellings with conventional heating systems)

Climatic region	Moisture content, percent	
	Average	*Individual pieces*
Semidesert region (Nevada, parts of California, Utah, and Arizona)	6	5 to 8
Damp southern coastal regions (from North Carolina to eastern coast of Texas, and on the southern coast of California)	11	9 to 12
Remainder of United States	8	6 to 9

Exceptions to these figures should be made for dwellings with radiant-heating systems in which heating pipes or coils are placed beneath the floor. Wood for flooring in such homes should be kiln dried and carefully protected from moisture absorption during both storage and installation. Its average moisture content should be about 2 percent lower than that indicated in the table.

TEST FOR MOISTURE CONTENT. Large lumber manufacturers test the moisture content of their lumber by means of electric moisture meters. You can make your own test with the help of a fairly accurate scale and your kitchen oven.

Cut a small specimen, preferably not smaller than 9 square inches, from the flooring. Weigh it accurately to find its original weight. Dry it in an oven maintained at a temperature of 212° to 221° F until the wood stops losing weight. The lowest weight of the specimen is its oven-dry weight. You can then compute the original moisture content of the wood by this formula:

$$\frac{\text{Original weight} - \text{oven-dry weight}}{\text{Original weight}} \times 100$$

The answer is the moisture content in percent.

SANDING WOOD

Sanding is the most important operation in preparing the wood for a finish. It must be done to remove tool marks and to smooth the surface so that the reflective properties of the finishing materials will accentuate the full beauty of the wood grain. By taking time to do a good job of sanding, using correct procedures and selected grades of abrasives, you can produce a finish of professional appearance and quality.

Sandpaper

The term *sandpaper*, meaning paper coated with abrasive particles, had its birth many years ago, probably when sand was actually used in that way. Today, modern "sandpapers," now called "coated abrasives," are available in a number of different types in several different shapes, sizes, and grades of grit. In choosing sandpaper, it is important to choose the right coating and appropriate fineness of grit.

FLINT. This old-timer is a soft, yellowish quartz mineral that looks much like sand. It is the cheapest material but cuts slowly and wears out quickly. Its chief usefulness today is for cleaning painted, resinous, or waxy surfaces that would clog any paper and require frequent replacement.

GARNET. This is the hardest of natural abrasives. Although it is more than twice as expensive as flint paper, it cuts better and lasts five times as long. It is a favorite with woodworkers for fine sanding.

ALUMINUM OXIDE. This is a hard, tough synthetic mineral made in the electric furnace. Available in the form of sheets, belts, and discs, aluminum oxide paper is fast becoming the most widely used all-around paper.

SILICON CARBIDE. Another product of the electric furnace, this is the hardest of all common abrasives. Materials coated with it are used in finishing metal, stone, and plastic. The finest grades are used either dry or mixed with water or rubbing oil for polishing varnish, shellac, and lacquer finishes.

What Grit Size to Use

Modern abrasives come in grits as fine as baby powder and as coarse as gravel. The old grading system, using arbitrary numbers from an ultra-coarse 4 up to a super-fine 10/0, is inadequate for the wide range of present abrasives and is being replaced by a system based on mesh sizes that grains must pass through. Leaving out sizes too coarse for smoothing purposes, the accompanying table shows the corresponding numbers for all classifications.

GRADE AND GRIT NUMBERS OF ABRASIVES

	Aluminum oxide or silicon oxide	Garnet	Flint
Super fine	12/0–600	10/0–400	
	11/0–500	9/0–320	
	10/0–400	8/0–280	
Extra fine	9/0–320		
	8/0–280		
	7/0–240	7/0–240	
Very fine	6/0–220	6/0–220	4/0
	5/0–180	5/0–180	3/0
Fine	4/0–150	4/0–150	
	3/0–120	3/0–120	
	2/0–100	1/0–100	0
Medium	1/0–80	1/0–80	½
	½–60	½–60	1
Coarse	1–50	1–50	1½
	1½–40	1½–40	2
Very coarse	2–36	2–36	2½
	2½–30	2½–30	3
	3–24	3–24	

In finishing wood, you might use 60 grit for coarse sanding, 80 for smoothing, and 120 to 220 for finishing. On metal, you would probably use no coarser grit than 80 and, in some cases, run up to the very finest. Smoothing paints or other fine finishes, on wood or metal, will require very fine grits. The first coat might be smoothed with 220 grit, the second with 320, and the third with 400. You might use light oil with the last rubbing.

At the other extreme is floor sanding, where 30 grit may be used for removing the old finish, 40 or 50 for smoothing, and 80 or 100 for final sanding and a professional-looking job.

POWER-SANDING GRITS

OLD-FLOOR SANDING GRITS

Floor	Operation	Grade of abrasive paper
Covered with varnish, shellac, paint, etc.	first cut second cut final cut	coarse 3⅓ (20) medium fine 1½ (40) extra fine 2/0 (100)

NEW-FLOOR SANDING GRITS

Species of wood	Operation	Grade of abrasive paper
Hardwood: oak, maple, beech, birch, pecan	first cut second cut final sanding	medium coarse 2 (36) fine 1 (50) extra fine 2/0 (100)
Softwood: pine, fir	first cut second cut final sanding	medium fine 1½ (40) fine 1 (50) extra fine 2/0 (100)

Coated abrasives can also be used for sharpening tools. For average sharpening, the grit sizes will be about the same as the grinding wheels used for the same purpose, say 40 or 50 grit for rough sharpening and 100 or 120 for finishing.

For work on specialized materials such as glass, marble, gems, and plastics, it would be best to consult a textbook on the proper grits for each particular substance.

Closed or Open Coating?

Abrasive papers come in two types of coatings. Closed-coat papers have tightly packed grains that cover the entire surface; open-coat papers have grains that cover only 50 to 70 percent of the surface. The closed-coat cuts faster but is more apt to become clogged when used on soft materials. Use open-coat on soft or gummy woods, paint, and other finishes, and on some soft metals and plastics. Open-coat papers are usually made only in grit 80 (1/0) and finer.

The backing to which the abrasive particles are glued may be paper, cloth, a cloth-paper combination, fiber, or a fiber-cloth combination. For home-workshop work, paper and cloth backings are generally used. The others are used mostly in industrial applications. Cloth and paper backings (except flint) also come in waterproof versions (sometimes called wet or dry) that permit wet sanding.

Paper backing comes in four weights, which are designated as A, C,

D, and E. The A grade includes the fine-grit lightweight papers known as *finishing papers*. The C and D grades, known as *cabinet*, are mediumweight papers with abrasive particles of medium fineness. The E grade, known as *roll stock*, is heavyweight with stiff paper backing and is used only occasionally in handwork.

In cloth backings, the J grade, the lighter of the two commonly available cloth backings, is used for finishing shaped work. The X grade is heavier and stronger and is used for flat or shaped work in power tools. As a rule of thumb, use either cloth or paper backing in a weight light enough to bend as much as necessary without cracking. When cracking occurs, switch from paper to cloth or to the next heavier weight in either type. Since paper backing is the cheapest, use it wherever it will stand up. A general classification and recommendation for grades to be used on various types of work is given in the accompanying table.

RECOMMENDED GRADES OF PAPER

Handwork	Backing	Grit number	Grade number	Word description
Rough sanding and shaping	D	60 or 80	1/2 or 1/0	medium
Preparatory sanding on softwood	A	100 to 150	2/0 to 4/0	fine
Preparatory sanding on hardwood	A	120 or 150	3/0 or 4/0	fine
Finish sanding on softwood	A	180 or 220	5/0 or 6/0	very fine
Finish sanding on hardwood	A	220 to 280	6/0 to 8/0	very fine to extra fine
Dry-sanding sealers and finishes between coats	A	220 to 280	6/0 to 8/0	very fine to extra fine
Wet-sanding sealers and finishes between coats	J or X	220 to 280	6/0 to 8/0	very fine to extra fine
Rubbing down after finish coat	J	280 to 400	8/0 to 10/0	extra fine to super fine

Sandpaper is available in many forms other than the common sandpaper sheets. Most abrasives can be bought in continuous rolls of various widths and backings for use with hand sanders, for sanding in lathes, and for wrapping on special-purpose mandrels. They also come in discs, drums, and belts for use with various types of power sanding tools.

Which Abrasive for What?

The object here is to choose the one that cuts fastest and most efficiently with a given material. The accompanying table will serve as a guide.

ABRASIVES FOR DIFFERENT MATERIALS

	Aluminum oxide	Silicon carbide	Garnet
Ceramics (to shape and sand)		X	
Floors (to sand)		X	
Gems (to cut and shape)		X	
Glass (to shape and sand)		X	
Leather (to shape and sand)	X	X	
Metals, hard (to shape and sand)	X		
Metals, soft (to shape and sand)	X	X	
Metals, hard (to polish)	X		
Metals (to remove rust and dirt)	X		
Paint (to smooth)	X	X	
Plastics (to shape and sand)		X	
Wood (to hand-shape and sand)			X
Wood (to power-shape and sand)	X		X
Tools (to sharpen)	X		

Other Finishing Abrasives

STEEL WOOL. Available in rolls or pads, this is familiar to almost everyone as an aid in cleaning food from pots and pans, rust from tools, and paint and varnish from anything in paint-removal jobs. Pads of finer grade are sold in hardware, paint, and craft stores for the final finishing of wood. Steel wool is graded as follows:

No. 3 The coarsest grade, rarely used in finishing work
No. 2 Should be used on rough lumber only
No. 1 The coarsest grade that should be used on furniture
No. 1/0 The most commonly used of all grades for general cleaning and smoothing
No. 2/0 Used for rough smoothing
No. 3/0 The fine grade, often used for final smoothing
No. 4/0 The very fine grade, used for between-coat smoothing
No. 5/0 The extra-fine grade, used for top-coat rubbing
No. 6/0 The super-fine grade, used for top-coat rubbing

PUMICE. This is a time-honored abrasive powder of volcanic origin used for rubbing down the final finish coat. It comes in four grades, with 4/0 the finest and 0 the coarsest. Lubricate it with water or oil.

ROTTENSTONE. A decomposed siliceous limestone, this is softer and finer than pumice and is sometimes used after it to give a higher sheen.

BLEACHING WOOD

To produce blond, champagne, lime, straw, or other popular light finishes, wood must be bleached first. This process removes the natural coloring matter in wood without damaging the fibers. Light-colored, even-grained woods are best for bleaching, though such dark woods as walnut and mahogany bleach successfully. Individual pieces of wood or veneer that are abnormally dark or that contain dark streaks known as mineral streaks may also be bleached to match the surrounding wood. If varnish, stain, or other finishing material is present on wood surfaces to be bleached, it must be removed completely before bleaching is started. Even waxy materials left on the wood by varnish removers may interfere with the action of the bleaching chemicals. A final sanding before bleaching is desirable in such cases.

Knowing the characteristics of the wood to be bleached is important. Some woods bleach easily; others do not.

BLEACHING QUALITIES OF WOODS

Ash (fairly easy)	Lauan, or Philippine (fairly easy)
Basswood (difficult)	Mahogany (easy)
Beech (fairly easy)	Locust (difficult)
Birch (easy)	Magnolia (easy)
Cedar (no)	Maple (fairly easy)
Cherry (difficult)	Oak (easy)
Chestnut (difficult)	Pine, white (no)
Cypress (difficult)	Pine, yellow (no)
Douglas fir (no)	Poplar (difficult)
Ebony (difficult)	Redwood (no)
Gum (fairly easy)	Rosewood (difficult)
Hemlock (no)	Spruce (no)
Holly (easy)	Sycamore (easy)
Korina (easy)	Teakwood (fairly easy)
Lacewood (fairly easy)	Walnut (fairly easy)

In small-scale work, or in bleaching selected areas such as mineral streaks, the bleaching solutions are usually applied with a cloth swab, sponge, or brush. In large-scale production work, they are sometimes applied with a spray gun. The gun should have a glass-solution container, and all metal parts that come in contact with the solution should be of stainless steel or other corrosion-resistant alloy. (*Caution:* Many bleaching chemicals are injurious to the skin and eyes. Therefore goggles, rubber gloves, and aprons should be worn when applying them, particularly those containing oxalic acid. If any is spilled on your skin, wash the part thoroughly under running water. Also, do large bleaching jobs outdoors over bare ground, or protect the floor and surroundings from spilled solutions.)

Commercial Wood Bleaches

These ready-prepared bleaches should be applied as directed by their manufacturer. Many of these are based on commercial hydrogen peroxide and are fairly expensive. They are very powerful and are the only satisfactory bleaches for light tones on dark wood. The best and most thorough-working wood bleaches are the so-called "two-solution" bleaches, although one-solution commercial bleaches are available.

Oxalic Acid Bleach

Oxalic acid, which comes as white crystals, is one of the oldest bleaching agents. It is used where a comparatively mild bleaching action will suffice. Prepare this bleach as needed by dissolving from 3 to 4 ounces of the acid in each quart of hot water. Do this in glass, earthenware, or enameled steel vessels. Several applications may be made, until the desired color is reached. Then neutralize the acid by swabbing the surface with a solution of 3 ounces of borax per gallon of water. Finally rinse with hot water and wipe dry.

Bleach for Walnut

Black walnut may be bleached by first coating with a solution of 6 ounces of sodium bisulfite in 1 gallon of water. After this dries, apply a second coat consisting of 8 ounces of oxalic acid in 1 gallon of water. After this dries, wash with hot water and neutralize with solution of 3 ounces of borax in 1 gallon of water. Rinse with hot water and dry.

GENERAL WOOD-CHARACTERISTIC AND FINISHING TABLE

Wood	Natural color	Grain figure	Stain		Filler		Natural finish	Bleach	Paint
			Type	*Color*	*Weight +*	*Color*			
Alder	pink to brown	plain or figured	oil or water	red or brown	none	none	yes	yes	yes
Amaranth	purple	plain or stripe	none	none	8	match wood	yes	no	no
Ash	white to brown	plain	any	any	1.5 to 2	white or brown	yes	yes	yes
Aspen	light straw	plain or stripe	water	amber	none	none	yes	no	yes
Avodire	white to cream	stripe	none	none	8	match wood	yes	yes*	no
Basswood	cream	mild	water	red or brown	none	none	no	yes*	yes
Beech	white to brown	mild	water	red or brown	8	red or brown	no	yes	yes
Birch	cream	mild	any	walnut or mahogany	none or 7	natural or brown	yes	yes	yes
Bubinga	pale red to flesh red	plain to figured	water	red or brown	12 to 14	red or brown	yes	no	no
Butternut	amber and cream	like walnut	water	walnut or oak	12 to 14	medium brown	yes	yes	no
Cedar	red and cream	knotty or stripe	none	none	none	none	yes	no	no
Cherry	red to brown	fine	water	red or brown	6 to 8	brown, red, or black	yes	no	no

Chestnut	gray-brown	heavy grain	oil[s]	red or brown	15	red or brown	yes	yes	yes
Cypress	brown and cream	plain or figured	water or oil[s]	red or brown	none	none	yes	no	yes
Ebony	dark brown to black	plain or stripe	water	red or brown	none	none	yes	no	no
Elm	cream to brown	heavy grain	water	red or brown	12 to 14	dark brown	yes	no	yes
Fir (Douglas)	cream	wild	oil[s]	brown	none	none	no	no	yes
Gaboon	golden to pinkish tan	plain or stripe	water	red or brown	none	none	yes	no	no
Gum (red)	cream and red	plain or figured	any	red or brown	none or 4 to 6	match wood	yes	yes	yes
Hemlock	light reddish brown	plain	water or oil[s]	red or brown	none	none	no	no	yes
Hickory	white to cream	straight	water	red or brown	15	brown	yes	yes	no
Holly	white	mild	water	amber	none	none	yes	yes*	yes
Kelobra	brown	plain or stripe	water	dark brown	12 to 14	dark brown	yes	yes	no
Korina	creamy gray	plain or stripe	water	red or brown	12 to 14	red or brown	yes	yes	no
Lacewood	light brown	flake	water	oak	12 to 14	dark brown	yes	yes	no

+ Weight designates number of pounds of filler plastic per gallon of thinner.

* Generally not necessary because of the light color of the wood.

[s] Penetrating oil stain may also be used. Non-grain-raising stains may be substituted for water stains throughout.

(Continued)

GENERAL WOOD-CHARACTERISTIC AND FINISHING TABLE *(continued)*

Wood	Natural color	Grain figure	Stain		Filler		Natural finish	Bleach	Paint
			Type	*Color*	*Weight +*	*Color*			
Lauan	brown to red-brown	stripe	water or oil[s]	red or brown	18	red, brown, or black	yes	yes	no
Locust	golden brown	wild	water or oil[s]	brown	12 to 16	brown	yes	no	yes
Magnolia	light to dark yellowish brown	plain	water or oil[s]	brown	none	none	yes	yes	yes
Mahogany	brown to red-brown	stripe	water	red or brown	12	red, brown, or black	yes	yes	no
Maple	cream	varied	water or oil[s]	maple	none	none	yes	yes	yes
Oak (red)	red to brown	plain or flake	water	light green	15	brown	no	yes	yes
Oak (white)	white to pale brown	plain or flake	water	brown	15	brown	yes	yes	yes
Orientalwood	light brown	stripe	water	amber or brown	12	brown	yes	no	no
Padauk	golden red to crimson	stripe or mottle	none	none	14 to 16	red or brown	yes	no	no
Pine (white)	white to cream	very mild	water or oil	brown	none	none	no	no	yes

Pine (yellow)	cream to yellow	mild	water or oil	brown	none	none	yes	no	yes
Poplar	white	mild	water or oil	red or brown	none	none	no	no	yes
Primavera	white to yellow	stripe	water	amber	12	natural	yes	yes	no
Redwood	red	mild	oil	red	none	none	yes	no	yes
Rosewood	red to brown	stripe to varied	water	red	12 to 15	dark red to black	yes	no	no
Sapeli	medium brown	stripe	water	red or brown	10	dark brown	yes	yes	no
Spruce	white	plain	water or oil	amber or brown	none	none	no	no	yes
Sycamore	white to pink	flake	water	amber or brown	none	none	yes	yes*	yes
Teakwood	golden brown	plain or figured	water or oil	brown	16	natural or brown	yes	yes	no
Tigerwood	golden brown	stripe	water	dark brown	8 to 12	dark brown	yes	yes	no
Tupelo	pale to brownish gray	plain	water	brown	none to 7	brown	yes	yes	yes
Walnut	cream and dark brown	varied	water	dark brown	12 to 15	brown to black	yes	yes	no
Zebrawood	tan with brown stripe	heavy stripe	water	light oak	12	natural	yes	no	no

+ Weight designates number of pounds of filler plastic per gallon of thinner.

* Generally not necessary because of the light color of the wood.

§ Penetrating oil stain may also be used. Non-grain-raising stains may be substituted for water stains throughout.

Bleach for French Walnut Finish

This is a two-solution specialty bleach to precede a French or a Huguenot walnut finish, though it may be used with other woods. Make the first solution by dissolving 1 ounce of potassium permanganate in 1 gallon of water. Apply this purplish liquid liberally. While still wet, apply the second solution, which consists of 3 ounces of sodium bisulfite in 1 gallon of water. The purplish tint will vanish and the wood will be considerably lighter than it was originally. Rinse the surface, let it dry, and then sand lightly.

Sodium Hydrosulfite Bleach

A simple bleach can be made by dissolving 3 ounces of sodium hydrosulfite in 1 quart of water. This chemical is commonly used for removing dyes from textiles, and is the color remover supplied with some brands of household dyes (read label). Repeatedly wet the wood with this solution until the desired bleaching is obtained. Rinsing is not necessary.

Bleaching with Laundry Bleach

Ordinary chlorine laundry bleach—a 5- to 6-percent solution of sodium hypochlorite—is the basis for a simple bleach suited to many woods. Mix 8 ounces with a gallon of water. Apply it liberally, then let it dry. Repeat, if necessary, and then rinse.

Bleach for Mineral Streaks

For dark spots in maple, one recommendation calls for the use of 4 pounds of oxalic acid and 4 pounds of sodium hypophosphite per gallon of water, used hot. Neutralize with a solution of 4 pounds of borax in 1 gallon of water. Rinse with hot water, dry, and sand lightly.

Some mineral streaks in oak or other woods cannot be removed with ordinary bleaches. Many finishers paint these out with material tinted to match the surrounding bleached surfaces.

Bleaching Iron Stains in Oak

Oak sometimes becomes discolored with greenish or black stains where it comes in contact with iron in the presence of moisture. These result from the reaction of iron rust with the tannic acid present in oak. Their composition is insoluble black ferric tannate, the coloring matter in some inks.

Oxalic acid will reduce this to the colorless, water-soluble ferrous tannate. Give the surface several applications of a solution of 4 ounces of oxalic acid per quart of hot water. After the stains disappear, wash the wood thoroughly with warm water to remove both the acid and all ferrous tannate that might in time be oxidized back to the colored salt.

Iron stains on oak may be avoided by keeping all uncoated iron or steel off the wet wood.

Bleaching out Bluestain

Unsightly dark stains known as bluestain or sapstain often appear in the sapwood of woods of some species. They are caused by a type of fungi. Sodium hypochlorite laundry bleach (5 to 6 percent), diluted 8 ounces to 1 gallon of water, will reduce this staining if it is not too severe. This treatment is not recommended for oak or poplar.

Removing Glue Stains

Casein and vegetable glue stains can be removed almost entirely by swabbing them with a solution of 1 ounce of oxalic acid in 12 ounces of water. Rinse thoroughly with hot water and dry.

Bleached Effect Without Bleaching

A finish lighter in color than the natural color of the wood can be obtained by first applying a white or light-colored paint of very thin consistency, made with opaque pigments of the desired color. Such paint can be made by mixing enamel undercoater, flat wall paint, or even ordinary house paint with about twice its volume of a mixture of equal parts of boiled linseed oil and turpentine or mineral spirits. Another suitable mixture is wood sealer with enough color-in-oil or color-in-japan to give the required color and opacity. For a fast-drying material, lacquer enamel may be mixed with twice its volume of a clear lacquer.

The coloring material should be spread on the wood with a mop, brush, or spray gun, allowed to stand 5 to 10 minutes, and then wiped with clean rags to remove excess and leave only what sinks into the grain. Lacquer must be wiped immediately after applying, before it has time to harden. Wipe first across the grain and then parallel with the grain. When dry, apply further protective finish, such as clear wood sealer, varnish, or lacquer, as desired.

To Produce a Limed Finish

A limed effect, not quite as light as that produced by bleaching, can be developed by either of the following methods:

1. Mix thoroughly 1 pound of unslaked lime in 2 quarts of water. Apply this mixture to the surface of the smooth wood with a rough cloth, rubbing it into the pores of the grain as you would a wood filler. Wipe off excess by rubbing across the grain with another cloth and allow the surface to dry. Then apply a wash coat of shellac. After this has dried, finish with varnish or lacquer.
2. Mix 1¼ pounds white lead paste with ½ pound of fine silex and apply this filler to the smooth wood as mentioned in the procedure above. After it has set slightly, force the filler into the pores and wipe off excess by rubbing with a rough cloth across the grain. When thoroughly dry, apply a wash coat of shellac. Then finish with varnish or lacquer.

INTERIOR AND FURNITURE STAINS

Stain gives color to wood and enhances the beauty of the grain. No other step in finishing brings about so radical a change in the appearance of the wood. This change in hue or tone is caused by a chemical reaction of a liquid penetrating the surface of the wood and by coloring matter changing the color of a layer of wood near the surface but at the same time allowing the grain to be seen clearly. Staining should leave a transparent effect and should not obscure the surface with opaque material such as pigments.

You have considerable latitude in the selection of stains, for there are hundreds of types and colors. A convenient classification can be made by grouping the stains according to the solvent used in their manufacture, namely, water, oil, alcohol, and lacquer thinner. The stain color or dye can be purchased in dry powder form or in ready-mixed liquid form. Two exceptions are water stain and non-grain-raising stain which, because their solvent is water, are generally sold in a powder form.

Pigment Oil Stains

These oil stains are easy to prepare and use. They work best on soft woods of close grain, such as poplar, gum, and basswood; they have little effect on hardwoods. Their disadvantages are that they dim the grain a little, and they usually need to be sealed with a thin coat of shellac to prevent bleeding.

To promote even absorption, first wipe on the wood a coat of 1 part boiled linseed oil mixed with 3 parts gum turpentine, or 1 pound cut shellac.

MEDIUM FOR ALL COLORS

Boiled linseed oil	6 parts
Gum turpentine	2 parts
Japan drier	1 part

To this mixture, add the desired colors-in-oil, blended thoroughly with a little turpentine. The amount of the colors to be added will depend on the wood to be stained and on the shade desired. Test a stain for color on a sample or inconspicuous spot of the wood on which it is to be used. To see the true color, wait for it to dry.

GENERAL COLORS

Reds: turkey red, rose madder, rose pink, burnt sienna

Yellows: raw sienna, yellow ochre

Browns: burnt umber, vandyke brown, raw umber

Black: lampblack or ivory black

CHERRY

Dark: burnt sienna	
Light: burnt sienna	3 parts
raw sienna	2 parts

MAHOGANY

Red: burnt sienna	3 parts
rose pink	2 parts
burnt umber	½ part
Brown: sienna	3 parts
rose pink or maroon lake	1 part
vandyke brown or burnt umber	1 part

MAPLE

Yellow: raw sienna	3 parts
raw umber	1 part

Red: burnt sienna	4 parts
burnt umber	1 part
Reddish honeytone:	
raw sienna	1 part
burnt umber	1 part
OAK	
Light: raw sienna	4 parts
raw umber	1 pint
Dark: raw sienna	4 parts
burnt umber	1 part
Antique: raw sienna	8 parts
burnt umber	2 parts
lampblack	1 part
Mission: Ivory black	2 parts
rose pink	1 part
PINE	
Pumpkin pine: raw sienna	
small amount of ultramarine	
Honey pine: yellow ochre	
small amount of raw sienna	
EBONY	
Coach black	20 parts
Prussian blue	1 part
GRAY	
Zinc oxide white	
Lampblack, to get shade desired	
WALNUT	
Dark walnut: vandyke brown	6 parts
drop black	1 part
Rich dark brown: burnt umber	4 parts
vandyke brown	1 part
Yellowish brown: burnt umber	3 parts
raw umber	2 parts

Rich reddish brown: burnt umber	8 parts
burnt sienna	1 part

Apply the stain with a brush or cloth. Let it stand 2 or 3 minutes, then rub it with a soft cloth. Let the stain dry for at least 36 hours before smoothing with fine sandpaper or steel wool.

Penetrating Oil Stains

An easy way to make oil stains that will penetrate more deeply into the wood surface is simply to replace up to half of the linseed oil in any of the preceding formulas with the solvent toluol.

Another way to make penetrating stains is to dissolve oil-soluble dyes in a mixture of 5 parts toluol to 1 part painter's naphtha. Ordinarily about 1 ounce of dye is needed for each quart of liquid dye. Because oil-soluble dyes are made in an almost endless variety of trade-named colors, combinations to produce specific effects must be obtained by experiment, or from suggestions by individual dye suppliers. *Caution:* In using penetrating dyes containing toluol, have plenty of ventilation. The vapor of toluol is toxic, and the vapor of both toluol and naphtha is flammable.

Penetrating Spirit Stains

Stain powders soluble in alcohol make penetrating spirit stains. While the manufacturer's instructions should be followed to the letter, most spirit stains are mixed in a manner such as this: Mix 1 ounce of alcohol-soluble powder with 1 quart of hot denatured alcohol. The alcohol can be heated by placing the can in a pail of hot water away from the fire. One pint of white shellac should be added if the stain is to be used as a shading stain. Spirit stains are also available in ready-mixed liquid form with various blended solvent.

Water Stains

Water stains are especially good for hardwoods such as walnut, birch, maple, cherry, rosewood, and mahogany. They do not obscure the grain and they produce clear, rich colors that do not fade or bleed. They are not recommended for use on veneer, however, because they might loosen the glue.

You can get water stains in powder form in standard wood colors at large paint and craft stores or you can compound your own. In the former case, follow the directions on the package for mixing and application; in the latter, follow directions on the next page.

1. Moisten 1 ounce of dry aniline stain powder with hot water and stir to make a smooth paste. Use only soft or distilled water for mixing water stains, as hard water causes a change or loss of color.
2. Add the paste to 1 pint of hot water and stir well. Then add water to make 1 quart. Let stand for 24 hours.
3. Reduce the standard solution with a measured amount of hot water to make any lighter stain required. Test on wood similar to that to be stained. Mark the solution ration on the label.
4. Keep stock solutions of 1 ounce each of black, red, and yellow in 1-quart jars to use in shading new colors. Make a record of each mixture for future duplication.

Before application of water stain, sponge the wood with plain water and then dry it. This will raise tiny "whiskers" that should be removed with 3/0 or 4/0 steel wool or very fine finishing paper. Use a brush to apply the stain freely and evenly with the grain of the wood. Allow to dry slowly and thoroughly, away from heat, so that the wood will not warp or crack. Let it dry at least 24 hours. Then smooth very lightly once more with the finishing paper or steel wool. Be careful in smoothing edges, as it is very easy to remove color at such places.

Although all standard wood finish colors are obtainable in powder form, you may wish to mix your own water stain color or modify the color of a commercial mixture. Actually, with six powder colors, you can make almost any wood color you desire. Starting points for proportions are given in the table on the next page.

Non-Grain-Raising (NGR) Stains

Because water-soluble colors offer the best types of stain except for their grain-raising qualities, finishing manufacturers have developed stains in which powders are dissolved in a solvent other than water. Stains of this kind are known by various descriptive trade terms such as non-grain-raising, fast-to-light, and non-sand. Ready-mixed NGR stains are, of course, more expensive than water stains because of the solvent used. But you can mix your own by following this procedure: Add to 1 ounce of water-soluble stain powder 1 quart of Carbitol or Cellosolve. Keep in glass. Dilute as used with denatured alcohol, but not over 3 parts alcohol to 1 part stain.

NGR stains (sometimes called NFR, for "non-fiber-raising") are generally not recommended for fir, spruce, pine, and other woods that have a great variation in density between spring and summer growth because the resulting grain pattern will probably be too wild.

HOW TO MIX WOOD STAINS

Color*	Yellow (oak)	Orange (maple)	Red (mahogany)	Brown (walnut)	Dark blue	Black**
Sheraton mahogany (light red)		12	5		3	
Medium-red mahogany	2	6	6			3
Red mahogany		9	7		4	
Brown mahogany	2		2	11		1
Dark-red mahogany	2	6	7			4
Light walnut		8	1	4		4
Medium walnut		10		4		6
Oriental walnut		3		1		2
Modern walnut	5			8		1
Light oak	1	10			2	
Dark oak	2	10			5	
Golden oak		22	1		3	
Maple	4	10			1	
Honey maple	4	11		1	1	
Red cherry			12	8		1
Brown cherry	2		2	3		
Fruitwood	8	2		1		
Antique brown	2	8		11		1
Antique pine			2	9		1

* Light tints of same color can be obtained by diluting with proper solvent.

** Add dark colors last.

CHARACTERISTICS OF VARIOUS TYPES OF STAINS

	Water stain	Non-grain-raising stain	Penetrating oil stain	Pigment oil stain	Spirit stain
Coloring matter	water-soluble aniline powder	water-soluble aniline powder	oil-soluble aniline powder	pigment colors in oil	alcohol-soluble aniline powder
Solvent	water	carbitol or cellosolve plus alcohol	benzol, turpentine, etc.	benzol, turpentine, naphtha	denatured alcohol
Cost	low	high	medium	medium	high
Application	brush or spray	best sprayed, but can be brushed[a]	brush and wipe with cloth	brush and wipe	spray only
Grain raising	bad[b]	very little[c]	none	none	very little[c]
Clarity	excellent	excellent	fair	excellent	poor
Bleeding	none	none or very little	bad[e]	none	bad[d]
Permanence of color	excellent	excellent	fair	excellent	poor
Effect on top coats	none	possible slight bleeding	bleeds; must be sealed with shellac[e]	none[f]	bleeds[d]
Mixes with lacquer	no	yes	yes	no	yes
Mixes with varnish	no	yes	yes	yes	yes
Drying time	12 hours	10 minutes to 3 hours	24 hours[g]	3 to 12 hours[g]	10 to 15 minutes
Principal use	staining quality hardwoods	same as water stain; also for refinishing	staining softwoods	softwoods; also as a glaze coat or wiping stain	patching and quick work

[a] Some types, factory-mixed in liquid form, dry very quickly and are difficult to brush smoothly.

[b] Water solvent causes wood fibers to lift. Work must be resanded smooth when dry. The addition of up to 25-percent Carbitol or Cellosolve will help correct this fault.

[c] Alcohol solvent absorbs moisture from air, causing slight grain raising in muggy weather.

[d] Refers to own-mix stain. Some factory-mixed stains of the alcohol series are strictly nonbleeding.

[e] Seal with shellac when used under varnish. Do not use under lacquer.

[f] Refers to factory-mixed product, made with specially treated oils to work under lacquer.

[g] Use benzol as solvent for fast drying. Retard drying with turpentine or turpentine substitute.

Tobacco Stain for Pine

To give new pine paneling and furniture an "old pine-finish look," the tobacco-stain method works well.

Break up 1 plug of chewing tobacco in a jar and add 1 pint of clear household ammonia. Cover the jar tightly and let stand for about a week. Wipe surface and end grain of wood with a damp cloth just before applying stain, to ensure even penetration. Strain liquid though a piece of old but clean nylon stocking, and mop several coats of it on the wood with a lintless cloth. Allow to dry 24 hours. Then rub lightly with fine steel wool. Dust with dry cloth and finally with a tack rag.

This stain dries lighter than it appears when wet; it shows up darker again, however, after it has been shellacked, varnished, or waxed.

Stains for Maple

All maple finishes should be clean, thin, and transparent. Sand wood clean with 4/0 finishing paper; sponge with clean water, but avoid touching with the hands; dry; sand clean again with the finishing paper, then use one of the following water-stain formulas. The colors mentioned are standard water-soluble wood stains sold in powder form.

HONEY MAPLE	
Canary yellow, concentrated	½ ounce
Orange	¾ ounce
Hot water	1 gallon

AMBER MAPLE	
Add to the preceding formula:	
Jet black	¼ ounce

COTTAGE MAPLE	
Add to the amber maple formula:	
Scarlet	¼ ounce

New Stains with Household Dyes

Everyday household dyes used generally for textiles not only can be used to pinch-hit for regular water stains but also to obtain exciting and off-beat decorator color effects on furniture, craft work, and other home projects in wood. If you are tired of such old standbys as oak, walnut, and maple, these dyes will enable you to try your hand with items in rose pink, tangerine, and Kelly green!

If you use Rit dye, dissolve 1 package of a single color, or an equivalent amount of mixed colors, in 1 pint of hot—but not boiling—water. (If you use a different brand, experiment for yourself. Begin by trying twice the concentration of dye ordinarily used for textiles.) Test the color on hidden parts of the wood to be dyed. If the color is too light, add more dye; if too dark, add hot water.

As with all water stains, be sure the wood to be dyed is clean, free of grease, and sanded smooth. Sponge the surface evenly with water and wipe. When thoroughly dry, smooth with 3/0 or 4/0 steel wool or sandpaper. Apply the dye solution, while still warm, with a brush, sponge, or soft cloth. Let dry 24 hours, sand lightly with 4/0 finishing paper, and finish as you would any other water-dyed surface.

STAINS FOR OUTDOOR USE

Stains used for wood shingles, rough siding, outbuildings, and fences are essentially greatly diluted linseed oil paints. In addition to ordinary paint ingredients, they often contain coal-tar creosote to kill microorganisms, and asbestine—a species of hydrated magnesium silicate or talc—as an extender.

On rough wood they are cheaper than paint and sometimes give service twice as long. Unlike stains for interior use, exterior stains contain only pure, finely divided opaque pigments, with iron oxide, chrome, and carbon pigments being the most durable. The following formulations all use the same basic medium with different combinations of pigment and asbestine to vary the color.

MEDIUM FOR ALL COLORS

Raw linseed oil	36 fluid ounces
Coal-tar creosote	16 fluid ounces
Turpentine	16 fluid ounces
Japan drier	8 fluid ounces

To make a stain of any of the following colors grind thoroughly the specified dry pigment and asbestine with one-half of the linseed oil in the above formula, adding the oil slowly and grinding continuously until it is uniformly mixed. Mix together the other ingredients, and then add them, while stirring, to the combined pigments.

DARK RED STAIN

Indian red dry color	14½ ounces
Asbestine	1½ ounces

LIGHT RED STAIN	
Venetian red dry color	14½ ounces
Asbestine	1½ ounces
MAHOGANY STAIN	
Raw sienna dry color	13 ounces
Asbestine	2½ ounces
DARK BROWN STAIN	
Burnt umber dry color	14½ ounces
Asbestine	1½ ounces
BROWN STAIN	
Raw umber dry color	14½ ounces
Asbestine	1½ ounces
GOLDEN OAK STAIN	
Raw sienna dry color	13 ounces
Asbestine	2½ ounces
GREEN STAIN	
Chrome green dry color	15 ounces
Asbestine	¾ ounce
YELLOW GREEN STAIN	
Chrome green dry color	11 ounces
Yellow ochre dry color	4 ounces
Asbestine	½ ounce
OLIVE GREEN STAIN	
Chrome green dry color	15 ounces
Lampblack	⅛ ounce
Asbestine	½ ounce

(Continued)

GRAY STAIN

Lithopone	9½ ounces
Whiting	4 ounces
Asbestine	2 ounces
Lampblack	⅛ ounce

EMERGENCY SHINGLE STAIN. To improvise a shingle stain of a special color, mix 1 gallon of outside paint with 1 gallon of turpentine or mineral spirits and 1 gallon of linseed oil.

Natural Wood Finish for Exterior

Owners of houses of Western red cedar, redwood, or other woods of interesting color and grain figure, often desire a durable finish that will preserve the character of the natural wood. Commercially available finishes that form a clear film, however, do not bond well and are susceptible to cracking and peeling. They therefore must be renewed frequently.

The following oil-base penetrating stain was developed by the Forest Products Laboratory of the U.S. Department of Agriculture to overcome this disadvantage. Tests indicate that one application on planed surfaces of bevel siding of redwood or Western red cedar fully exposed to the weather would last at least 3 years before renewal. The finish should last 1 or 2 years longer on siding that receives some shelter. As it merely wears or erodes away, it may then be reapplied without further treatment. The following formula will make slightly less than 5 gallons of finish.

Paraffin wax	1 pound
Zinc stearate	2 ounces
Turpentine or mineral spirits paint thinner	1 gallon
Pentachlorophenol, concentrate, 10:1	½ gallon
Boiled linseed oil	3 gallons

To the foregoing mixture, the following pigments must be added to produce the colors mentioned:

LIGHT REDWOOD

Burnt sienna in oil	2 pints

CEDAR	
Burnt sienna in oil	1 pint
Raw umber in oil	1 pint

DARK REDWOOD	
Burnt sienna in oil	⅓ pint
Raw umber in oil	⅓ pint
Indian red iron oxide in oil	⅔ pint
Additional turpentine or mineral spirits	1 pint

By varying the proportions of the burnt sienna and raw umber colors-in-oil, other shades may be produced. Raw umber produces a dark brown, burnt sienna gives a red, and Indian red iron oxide gives a darker red. These components contain iron oxide pigments, which are the most durable of all pigments. By using other colors, or smaller amounts of those specified, the life of the present finish will be shortened.

Pentachlorophenol, commonly called "penta," is used widely as a preservative to protect a finish from mildew. It may be obtained at a paint store, lumberyard, or mail-order house. Zinc stearate may be bought at a drugstore.

To prepare the finish, melt the paraffin and zinc stearate in the top unit of a double boiler. Stir until completely melted and combined. Then, with vigorous stirring, slowly add the mixture to the turpentine or mineral spirits. *Caution:* Perform the latter operation outdoors or in a well-ventilated room, and far from sparks or flame. Turpentine and mineral spirits are flammable and their concentrated vapors are not healthful to breathe.

When the mixture has cooled to room temperature, add the penta concentrate and the linseed oil. Then gradually stir in the pigments until the color is uniform.

A single application of the finish by brush or spray is recommended. On a smooth surface, a gallon should cover 400 to 500 square feet; on rough, 200 to 250 square feet. It may be used over other penetrating natural finishes that have been worn until they need renewal. Varnish films must be removed before applying the finish. In good drying weather, it should dry to a low luster within 24 hours.

This finish was designed particularly for siding, but has been used satisfactorily on wood fences, lawn furniture, and sun decks. It does not provide sufficient protection for exterior millwork, such as frames, window sash, and doors, which should be painted.

Penetrating Stain for Rough and Weathered Wood

Simply by doubling the amount of pigment in the dark redwood finish mentioned above, forest products experts of the University of Wisconsin have developed a moisture-resistant, long-lasting, and economical finish for exterior surfaces that had always been difficult to paint.

The new finish is excellent for rough-sawn and weathered lumber with "fuzzy" surfaces. Because of its penetration, it also works well on dense, smooth woods, such as exterior plywood and knotty or flat-grained boards of oak, pine, and fir, from which paint peels. It is an effective finish for wood that has been neglected until the paint has fallen off and the raw wood is exposed to the weather.

One coat of the fortified stain properly applied to rough wood should last 8 to 10 years. Due to less penetration, it should last about 3 years on smooth planed surfaces. It will not blister, crack, peel, or scale, even if moisture penetrates into the wood.

You can make the finish from scratch by adding ⅓ of a pint each of burnt sienna and raw umber in oil, and ⅔ of a pint of Indian red iron oxide, to the formula given for the dark redwood stain in the section "Natural Wood Finish for Exterior," which precedes this section.

You can also make a satisfactory version by thinning premium-quality red barn paint with linseed oil and water-repellent wood preservative. The paint should contain about 55-percent pigment, at least one-third of which should be ferric oxide. The vehicle should contain about 85-percent linseed, soybean, or other "drying" oil. Thin this paint with 2 gallons of boiled linseed oil and 2 gallons of paintable water-repellent wood preservative to a gallon of paint.

Apply only one coat of the fortified stain, at the rate of 200 to 250 square feet per gallon on rough surfaces and 400 to 500 square feet on smooth surfaces, using a brush or spray gun. Apply immediately to rough wood, but let smooth wood weather several months before application. Apply when the wood is dry, and the temperature above 40° F. To prevent lap marks, stain the full length of boards without stopping for more than 5 minutes.

WOOD FILLERS

For a fine finishing job on many woods, a filler should be used after the stain has dried. The purpose of a filler is to close the cells or tiny crevices in open-grained woods. Close-grained woods are often finished without the use of fillers.

Fillers can be obtained in two forms—paste and liquid. Paste fillers, used on open-grained woods, are either semitransparent or opaque; liquid fillers, normally used on close-grained woods, are transparent. In general, fillers should be as transparent as possible so as not to hide the natural color and beauty of the wood. However, opaque fillers have their place in wood finishing when special effects such as two-tone finishes are desired.

If fillers are not used, finishing materials such as varnish, shellac, paint, or lacquer will sink in and produce a rippled effect. Even though several coats of finishing material are applied and rubbed down, the rippled effect is likely to remain. The rubbing down of each coat serves as a substitute for a filler, but this operation is slower than filling the surface before applying the finish.

FILLER MIX REQUIRED FOR VARIOUS WOODS

No filler needed	Thin filler	Medium filler	Heavy filler
Aspen	Alder	Amaranth	Ash
Basswood	Beech	Avodire	Bubinga
Cedar	Birch	Butternut	Chestnut
Cypress	Cherry	Korina	Elm
Ebony	Gum	Mahogany	Hickory
Fir	Maple	Orientalwood	Kelobra
Gaboon	Sycamore	Primavera	Lacewood
Hemlock	Tupelo	Rosewood	Lauan
Holly		Sapeli	Locust
Magnolia		Tigerwood	Oak
Pine		Walnut	Padauk
Poplar		Zebrawood	Teakwood
Redwood			
Spruce			

Paste Fillers

Paste fillers are made of various formulations. They can be purchased in many stain colors as well as in natural (semitransparent) and white. Paste fillers are usually sold under the name of "wood fillers" and in cans of 1, 5, 10, and 25 pounds. One pound will fill about 40 square feet of surface.

Before use, paste fillers should be thinned to the desired consistency with gum turpentine or naphtha, the amount of dilution depending on the size of the pores to be filled. Obviously, large pores require a thicker mix than small ones. Mix only enough filler for the job at hand, as the thinned filler thickens after a few hours and becomes useless. Mixing by exact weight is always good practice. Refer to the table below for mixing proportions for various quantities of filler. The term *heavy mix* does not mean a heavy-bodied material; actually, the consistency is no thicker than varnish.

PROPORTIONS FOR MIXING VARIOUS QUANTITIES OF FILLER

Approximate amount needed*	Paste	Thinner
	HEAVY MIX (16-pound base)	
2 gallons	16 pounds	1 gallon
5 pints	5 pounds	2½ pints
2 quarts	1 quart	1 quart
1 pint	1 pound	½ pint
½ pint	½ pound	4 ounces
	MEDIUM MIX (12-pound base)	
1 gallon, 3 quarts	12 pounds	1 gallon
3 quarts	5 pounds	3 pints, 5 ounces
2 quarts, 10 ounces	1 quart	2 pints, 10 ounces
1 quart, 5 ounces	1 pint	1 pint, 5 ounces
1 pint, 20 ounces	1 pound	10½ ounces
9 ounces	½ pound	5¼ ounces
	THIN MIX (8-pound base)	
1½ gallons	8 pounds	1 gallon
1 gallon	5 pounds	5 pints
3 quarts	1 quart	2 quarts
3 pints	1 pint	2 pints
1½ pints	1 pound	1 pint
12 ounces	½ pound	½ pint

* One pint of thinned filler covers approximately 36 square feet.

The first step in mixing is to spade the unmixed paste with a putty knife, then add a very small amount of thinner and stir. After the first mixing, add increasingly larger amounts of thinner and stir until the mix is the proper consistency. Do not add a lot of thinner at the start, as this makes mixing much harder. Use naphtha for thinning when the filler is to set up quickly for wiping; use turpentine to hold the coat open longer. A small amount of boiled linseed oil can be added to hold the coat open for 30 to 40 minutes. The reverse of this—a very quick setting filler—can be obtained by adding a small amount of japan drier.

The natural paste filler, which is usually light gray, may be colored by adding a small amount of oil stain or colors-in-oil. For changing natural filler to walnut, for instance, add a little raw umber ground in oil or japan drier. Vandyke brown will give a slightly redder color than raw umber. For mahogany, add lampblack and a little raw and burnt sienna. To test tinting, apply the filler to a scrap of stained wood and then a lacquer or varnish coat over it to get an idea of the color obtained when the surface is finished. For green, gray, white, and other colors, follow the same general procedure, except use colors-in-oil. Dry powder colors mixed in turpentine or oil-soluble aniline colors thinned with turpentine are sometimes used for colors in paste fillers. A shade of color may often be had by using a pigment stain or a penetrating wood stain as it comes from the can. Remember that the filler should be approximately the same color as the surface to which it is applied, except when the final finish is opaque. Otherwise, the filler might show through a transparent finish, if the filler is not correctly applied or properly wiped off.

If you wish to prepare your own paste filler, one much-used formula consists of ½ pint of boiled linseed oil, 4 ounces of japan drier, and 1 pint of turpentine. Mix these liquids and then add fine silica until you have a very thick paste that is well mixed. Put the paste through a paint mill, or mix it thoroughly with a paddle and strain through a wire screen. Thin with naphtha or turpentine to a thick brushing consistency. It should be just thin enough to pour out of a pot. Tinting colors should be broken up with turpentine or benzine and strained before adding them to the filler. While in use, the filler should be stirred every few minutes, because the heavy pigment settles rapidly to the bottom. To overcome this, add cornstarch (10 to 20 percent of the weight of the silica used), or add up to 25 percent of asbestine (silicate of magnesia). These materials will keep the filler pigment suspended in the oil.

Liquid Fillers

For close-grained woods like maple and birch, use liquid filler or paste filler thinned to a liquid consistency. Transparent liquid fillers are available in pint, quart, half-gallon, and gallon cans.

Commercial liquid fillers composed of glass oil, hard oil, or other cheap varnishes are not dependable. Some of the cheap fillers bleach out white in time and make a mottled, cloudy appearance under the varnish. Some are brittle and crack easily. However, when made of first-class varnish by a well-known manufacturer, they are excellent.

For mixing liquid filler yourself, the following formula may be used: 1 gallon of good rubbing varnish, 1 quart of turpentine, 1 pint of japan drier, and 2½ pounds of silica. Mix the silica well with a little of the varnish, then add the other liquids and mix them thoroughly. Grind the whole batch through a paint mill, if one is at hand, or mix it with a paddle. After it is thoroughly mixed, let it stand for 2 or 3 days, and then strain through muslin. Thin the mixture to easy brushing consistency with turpentine. Stir the filler occasionally while you are using it to keep the silica in suspension; it may settle to the bottom. It should dry flat, but not dead flat. Use less silica to avoid the dead-flat appearance.

Apply either a paste or liquid filler with a brush or rough cloth, using a circular motion and rubbing it well into the pores. After the surface has dulled over from evaporation of the turpentine, carefully remove excess filler by scraping with the edge of a card followed by wiping the wood across the grain with burlap. After 24 hours, touch up lightly with 6/0 finishing paper.

COVERING-CAPACITY SPECIFICATIONS*

Material	Square feet per gallon	Material	Square feet per gallon
Bleaching solutions	250–300	Spirit stain	250–300
Lacquer	200–300	Shellac	300–350
Lacquer sealer	250–300	Rubbing varnish	450–500
Paste wood filler	36–50 (per pound)	Flat varnish	300–350
Liquid filler	250–400	Paste wax	125–175
Water stain	350–400	Liquid wax	600–700
Oil stain	300–350	Non-grain-raising stain	275–325
Pigment oil stain	350–400	Paint	650–750

* General average—will vary considerably, depending on thickness of coat application to porous or non-porous surface, etc.

WOOD FINISHING WITH VARNISH

Varnish makes an excellent transparent finish on wood; it is unequaled for depth or build and possesses good durability and hardness. It is made by mixing synthetic resins in oil-derived vehicles, along with driers and other chemicals. Since modern synthetic resin varnishes can be formulated to meet specific conditions by changing or mixing to achieve precise differences in hardness, scuff resistance, clarity, and chemical or water resistance, manufacturers are constantly changing products. For instance, one company recently marketed an excellent varnish by combining alkyd and vinyl resins and the result was a product that contained the good properties of both.

While the synthetic varnishes vary as to their formulations, there are certain characteristics of the resins that will help to predict the finish. For example, the polyurethane, acrylic, and vinyl types of varnish produce the clearest finish and show very little color change in the wood tone. On the other hand, phenolic varnish tends to turn yellow more readily in the same manner that natural-resin varnishes do.

Polyurethane varnish has the highest resistance to abrasion and is most resistant to ordinary chemicals and water. For instance, tests show that polyurethane lasts 25 percent longer than first-quality spar varnishes—the old standard for varnish life—in exterior use. It has double the service life of first-grade natural varnishes when used on interior surfaces. While alkyds and phenolics are only slightly less resistant to abrasion and chemicals, they tend to be brittle. For this reason, they will usually scratch "white" and may show a series of fine cracks over a period of time if the wood is subjected to wide variations in humidity.

To be assured of a well-finished surface, purchase the varnish of reliable manufacturers. Never buy a cheap varnish. A small quantity of varnish covers a large area and a cheap grade will never result in a good or lasting finish. The number-one rule of success with synthetic varnishing is to read the container label *very* carefully, since instructions sometimes run counter to much common practice with "older," regular varnishes that were used for a long time.

WOOD FINISHING WITH SHELLAC

Although shellac's popularity as a top-coat finish has decreased in recent years, it is still one of the most convenient, attractive, and useful finishes for the home handyman. It is easy to apply, is ready for a second coat in an hour or two, and may be washed from brushes and rollers with nothing but ammonia in warm water.

Shellac dries to a varnishlike transparent film. It is sold in solid granular form or as a liquid when dissolved in alcohol. The liquid shellac is ready for use and is available in three stages of purification: orange, bleached (or white), and dewaxed. *Orange shellac* consists of partially refined shellac flakes dissolved in alcohol. It has a pronounced reddish brown color and is cloudy in appearance. *White* or *bleached shellac* is a similar solution but is made from bleached resin. *Dewaxed shellac* is usually light in color, but, unlike the other two, it is wax-free and thus perfectly clear.

The three forms are very much alike. However, white (clear) shellac is best for most work and is essential for blond finishes. Orange shellac is used for dark wood or over darkly stained woods. Intermixing white and orange shellac to obtain color effects is not advisable. Should deeper colors be desired to tone a finish where the stain does not seem exactly right, a transparent toner may be used. It can be made by mixing alcohol-soluble powder stain with alcohol and adding it to the shellac as required. The same method can be used to darken lacquer and varnish finishes, using lacquer-soluble and oil-soluble powder respectively. A shellac may be medium or high gloss, depending on the number of coats applied. It may be steel-wooled or rubbed with pumice and oil to a pleasing low sheen.

What "Pound Cut" Means

This term describes the pounds of dry shellac dissolved in 1 gallon of alcohol solvent. For example, a standard 4-pound cut is made dissolving 4 pounds of bleached shellac in 1 gallon of alcohol. (In 1 gallon of 4-pound cut shellac there would be a little less than 3 pounds of dry resin.)

RATIOS TO USE TO THIN SHELLAC

Original cut	Desired cut	MIXING RATIO Alcohol	Shellac
5-lb cut	4-lb cut	1 part	to 4 parts
5-lb cut	3-lb cut	1 part	to 2 parts
5-lb cut	2-lb cut	1 part	to 1 part
5-lb cut	1-lb cut	2 parts	to 1 part
5-lb cut	½-lb cut	7 parts	to 1 part
4-lb cut	3-lb cut	1 part	to 4 parts
4-lb cut	2-lb cut	3 parts	to 4 parts
4-lb cut	1-lb cut	3 parts	to 1 part
4-lb cut	½-lb cut	5 parts	to 1 part
3-lb cut	2-lb cut	2 parts	to 5 parts
3-lb cut	1-lb cut	4 parts	to 3 parts
3-lb cut	½-lb cut	4 parts	to 1 part

Thinning

A coat of 4- or 5-pound cut shellac would be too thick to penetrate and to develop a good bond with wood. For most end uses, shellac must be diluted to a 2- or 3-pound cut before application. For French polishing and for a wash coat under stains, it must be diluted to a ½- or 1-pound cut. As a thinner, use only denatured alcohol that is recommended on the label for this purpose.

Storage and Test for Drying

Liquid shellac tends to deteriorate with long storage, so don't buy more than you need at a time. Also don't expose it to heat. Shellac is too old for use when it refuses to dry. If in doubt, test a sample by coating it on a scrap of clean wood. If the shellac dries to a hard film, it is still good. If it doesn't, throw it out. Adding alcohol won't help.

Uses of Shellac

At one time, shellac was one of the most widely used floor finishes. Today, because of the new synthetic varnishes, we seldom see shellacked floors, but shellac is still used for a number of projects.

FURNITURE, WALL PANELING, WOODWORK. Sand smooth. Apply 3-pound shellac, with full brush, following grain of wood, and with minimum of brushing. After 3 hours sand lightly with extra-fine paper and wipe free of dust. Apply second coat using same technique. Do not sand. Do not put heavy objects on surface for at least 48 hours.

If a semidull finish is wanted, gently burnish second coat with fine steel wool. For a flat finish, rub down with fine powdered pumice and oil. Waxing will increase the water- and wear-resistance of any finish. Let last coat of shellac dry 24 to 48 hours. Then apply paste wax and buff.

RAW WOOD TO BE PAINTED. On soft wood such as pine, 1 coat of 3-pound cut seals off pores of the wood and prevents finish coat from striking in to leave an uneven finish.

UNDERCOAT FOR VARNISH. One coat of 3-pound shellac serves as an excellent undercoat for conventional varnishes. Shellac's quick dry shortens finishing cycle and reduces amount of varnish needed. Note: Do not use under urethanes.

SEALING KNOTS AND SAPPY STREAKS IN NEW WOOD. Apply 1 or 2 coats of 3-pound cut.

WASH COAT UNDER STAINS. One coat of 1-pound shellac assures uniform surface and controls penetration of stain.

UNDERCOAT FOR WAX FINISH. Wood that is to have an all-wax finish should first be sealed with a coat of 3-pound cut. This prevents dirt from being ground into the wood.

FRENCH POLISHING. This is one of the most beautiful and lasting of finishes. Sanded and stained surface must be completely dry. Then wipe on a 1-pound shellac with a soft lintless cloth rolled into a ball. Dip the ball into the shellac and rub on the wood in rapid straight strokes, exerting only light pressure. On drying, rub the wood with 4/0 steel wool or 7/0 sandpaper. The surface can be sprinkled lightly with very fine powdered pumice before sanding. Continuous coats are applied with sanding or steel wooling every third coat until a light glow appears.

At this point add several drops of boiled linseed oil to the shellac mixture and continue application, but with a rotary motion. Add more oil by degrees with subsequent coats until a deeply glowing finish is achieved. Ordinarily eight to twelve coats will be required.

OUTSIDE APPLICATION. One or two coats of shellac spot seals knots and sappy streaks. Cover with exterior paint for protection against the weather.

WOOD FINISHING WITH LACQUERS

The original "lacquer" is an Oriental product made by Chinese and Japanese artists from the sap of a plant closely related to our poison ivy. Some of the finer Oriental furniture pieces were finished with over 300 coats of these lacquers and have lasted for centuries.

The principal feature of lacquers is the rapid drying (fully hardened in 30 minutes to 2 hours), and there is no dust problem when using lacquers. The film is hard, durable, and waterproof, and won't become soft or sticky at high temperatures. Of all the top finishes, lacquers also darken wood the least. This is especially true when a lacquer lightener is employed, which will leave the wood almost at its sanded color. While most lacquers are sprayed, slower-drying brushing lacquers are available.

The basic lacquer finishing procedure does not differ materially from the basic varnish procedure. It is simply a case of stain, fill, and lacquer, instead of stain, fill, and varnish. The quality of the lacquer finish is dependent upon the spraying or brushing technique.

The best lacquer finishes, from bare wood to final finish, are made as follows:

1. Sponge work with warm water. Add 2 ounces of dextrin per gallon of water if desired. Allow to dry 1 hour before continuing.
2. Sand with fine paper. Dust.
3. Stain with water stain of desired color. Let dry 12 hours.
4. Shellac wash coat (7 parts alcohol to 1 part shellac). Let dry 30 minutes.
5. Sand with fine paper. Dust.
6. Fill with paste wood filler stain. Wipe clean. Let dry 4, 24, or 48 hours, depending on type of filler. Follow manufacturer's recommendations.
7. Spray one coat clear gloss lacquer. Let dry 2 to 4 hours.
8. Scuff with very fine paper or 3/0 steel wool (list continues).

DRYING-TIME SPECIFICATIONS*

Material	Touch	Recoat	Rub
Lacquer	1–10 minutes	1½–3 hours	16–24 hours
Lacquer sealer	1–10 minutes	30–45 minutes	1 hour
Paste wood filler		24–48 hours	
Paste wood filler (quick dry)		3–4 hours	
Water stain	1 hour	12 hours	
Oil stain	1 hour	24 hours	
Spirit stain	zero	10 minutes	
NGR stain	2 minutes	15 minutes	
Penetrating resin finishes	15–45 minutes	3–4 hours	4 hours
Pigment oil stain	1 hour	12 hours	
Pigment oil stain (quick dry)	1 hour	3 hours	
Shellac	15 minutes	2 hours	12–18 hours
Shellac (wash coat)	2 minutes	30 minutes	
Varnish (spar)	1½ hours	18–24 hours	24–48 hours
Varnish (synthetic)	½ hour	4 hours	12–48 hours

* Average time. Different products will vary.

9. Spray second coat of clear gloss lacquer. Let dry 4 hours.
10. Scuff with very fine paper or 4/0 steel wool.
11. Spray third coat of clear gloss lacquer. Let dry overnight.
12. Rub to satin finish.

LINSEED OIL FINISH

A rubbed linseed oil finish requires patience and "elbow grease" to apply, but develops a beautiful, durable, mellow luster on stained or raw wood that many consider the most attractive of all finishes. Although not highly water-resistant, this finish will withstand hot dishes and is less likely to show scratches than a varnish finish. It may be kept in condition just by rubbing on more oil.

Use either straight boiled linseed oil or 2 parts boiled linseed oil diluted with 1 part gum turpentine. Spread the oil liberally over the surface with a thick pad of folded cloth. Allow this to sink in until no more is absorbed. Rub again with the same pad, making an effort to work additional oil into the pores of the wood. Use clean cloths to wipe off surplus oil, allow to dry overnight, and then repeat the whole process. The greater the number of coats, the more attractive and durable the finish will be. For most pieces, a minimum of three coats is recommended. (*Caution:* At the end of the day, burn used rags or store them under water; otherwise they might catch fire spontaneously.)

SOLVENT FOR FINISHING MATERIALS

The following is a summary of the various materials of many solvents or thinners used with various finishing products.

BRONZE POWDERS. These are not soluble, but are held in suspension by lacquer, varnish, shellac, etc. Best results are obtained by using a special bronzing liquid that can be bought in either a varnish or lacquer formula.

FILLER, PASTE WOOD. Can be mixed with turpentine, naphtha (benzine), or a half-and-half mixture of turpentine and gasoline.

FILLER, QUICK-DRY. Same as above. Naphtha usually recommended.

FILLER STAIN. Same as above. The addition of 20 percent benzol or toluol will ensure better penetration of the stain.

LACQUER. Usually a blended mixture that can be purchased in fast-, medium-, or slow-drying type, and sold under the general name of lacquer thinner. A standard formula for clear lacquers is butyl acetate 23 percent, ethyl acetate 8 percent, toluol 69 percent. A standard formula for pigmented lacquers is butyl acetate 28 percent, ethyl acetate 29 percent, butyl alcohol 26 percent, toluol 17 percent.

LACQUER SEALER. Lacquer thinner.

RUBBING COMPOUND. Can be lubricated with water, soapy water, naphtha, low-test gasoline, or kerosene. It is advisable to follow the manufacturer's recommendations.

STAIN, PENETRATING OIL. Naphtha, turpentine, benzol, toluol.

STAIN—NON-GRAIN-RAISING. Special.* Many brands can be reduced with denatured alcohol. Some types reduce with butyl alcohol (butanol).

STAIN, PIGMENT OIL. Naphtha, turpentine.

STAIN, SPIRIT. Denatured alcohol.

SHELLAC. Denatured alcohol. Wood alcohol. Butanol. Denatured alcohol is probably the best, in view of price and workability. It should be no less than 190 proof.

SYNTHETICS. Special.* Toluol can be used for most products.

VARNISH, OIL. Turpentine.

VARNISH, SYNTHETIC. Some synthetic varnishes require special reducers. Many can be thinned with turpentine; others with toluol and other materials.

"Special*" indicates that a special blended solvent is provided by the manufacturer and should be used for best results.

HOW TO REPAIR WOOD FINISHES

Badly worn furniture may require complete refinishing. If, however, it is just soiled from everyday use, or it is marred merely by minor scratches, water marks, cigarette burns, and other local blemishes, it may be wonderfully improved by one of the following treatments.

Cleaning

This may be all that is needed to revive the luster and character of an oil, varnish, or lacquer finish. (Shellac must be given special treatment, which will be described separately.) Here is a cleaning mixture suggested by the College of Home Economics, at Cornell University:

Warm water	1 quart
Boiled linseed oil	3 tablespoons
Turpentine	1 tablespoon

Keep the mixture warm in a double boiler. Rub the finish with a soft cloth dampened with it. Then wipe the surface dry and polish with a dry cloth.

Dullness is difficult to remove from varnish or enamel of poor quality. To increase the luster, apply a thin coat of paste wax and buff well; or use the following mixture:

Boiled linseed oil	2 parts
Turpentine	1 part

Rub this polish well into the surface and buff briskly with a clean dry cloth until the finish is dry and shiny.

White Spots

On oil, varnish, and lacquer finishes, white spots are caused by heat, moisture, or alcohol. In most cases you can remove them by rubbing the finish carefully with a thin paste of finely powdered pumice in light mineral or machine oil.

Rub the mixture over the spot, using your fingertips or a piece of felt. Wipe the surface clean with a dry cloth. To remove any remaining oil, wash the surface with a cloth moistened with detergent suds. If the pumice leaves a dull spot, polish it with rottenstone and oil.

Repairing Shellac

Ordinarily a shellac finish is easily maintained by cleaning with a damp cloth or waxing. For stubborn stains, use mild soap and water. Rinse and dry. Water spots can generally be removed by rubbing gently with a cloth moistened with alcohol. (If the surface is waxed, first remove the wax with turpentine.)

If damage is too severe for this remedy, or the finish is burned or scratched, remove the old film in the affected area with fine sandpaper or pumice and oil. Then apply two or more coats of spray shellac or 3-pound-cut liquid shellac. When dry, buff with No. 00 steel wool until new finish blends with the old.

Scratches

The cleaning solution described above often makes scratches less noticeable. More serious scratches may require further treatment.

Fine scratches can usually be removed by softening the finish and letting it flow together. Use alcohol for shellac, turpentine for varnish, lacquer thinner for lacquer. Dab the solvent on with a fine artist's brush.

Where the stain is damaged, it can be restored with fine-tipped touch-up applicators that come in many colors. Dark woods also respond to repeated rubbing with liquid shoe polish or stain waxes. You might also rub a small amount of oil color into the scratch to color it and then cover with a quick-drying varnish, or mix the varnish directly with the oil color before application. Here are some suggestions for matching colors:

Reds: Turkey red, rose madder, rose pink, burnt sienna.

Yellows: Raw sienna, French ocher.

Browns: Burnt umber, Vandyke brown, raw umber.

Blacks: Lampblack, ivory black.

Walnut: Use either burnt umber or Vandyke brown. Raw umber, a yellowish brown, is sometimes added.

Mission oak: Raw umber.

Brown oak: Burnt umber alone or with a little raw sienna.

Golden oak: Raw sienna, a little burnt umber.

Maple: Burnt sienna for the redder maples; raw sienna for the yellow maples. Mix for blends.

Red mahogany: Turkey red, rose madder, or rose pink; add a little burnt umber or black, if needed.

Brown mahogany: Burnt umber, with a very little red, if needed.
Dark mahogany: Use one of the mahogany reds with black added.
Cherry: Burnt sienna. Add a little burnt umber and one of the mahogany reds, if needed.

Deep Scratches

These can be filled with stick shellac in the same way as for burns (see below). Build up the shellac to the height of the masking tape, then shave it down with a razor blade and polish with fine pumice.

A Temporary Scratch Repair

Do this with a wax crayon of a color to match the finish. Rub in, clean off the excess, then polish with wax. This works especially well on enamel.

Small Dents

These can often be raised by steaming the wood, thus swelling the compressed fibers. Remove the surface wax with turpentine so moisture can penetrate the wood. Lay a blotter over the dent and keep it wet for several hours to saturate the wood.

Apply heat to the dent with an electric iron. Do this by placing a metal bottle cap on the blotter, directly over the dent, and resting the iron on the cap. This concentrates the heat, steaming the dent. If the dent won't swell, remove the finish and try steaming again. If this won't work, use the filling method that follows.

Cigarette Burns, Scars, and Cracks

These need more drastic treatment. If burned, clean out the burn thoroughly, scraping away all damaged fibers with a knife edge or razor blade. Then smooth the wood with a small piece of fine sandpaper or steel wool, feathering the edges into the good wood.

Fill deep scars with wood paste filler or stiff spackling compound until the recess is almost flush with the surrounding surface. Shallow burns can be built up with coats of varnish or shellac, depending on furniture's finish, without the filler.

Mask the area around the scar with masking tape. Cover the filler with stick shellac in a color to match the furniture. Melt the shellac in an alcohol flame and smooth it on with a small spatula. Remove the tape and shave the shellac flush with a razor blade. Rub gently with very fine steel wool, or pumice and oil, to smooth the patch and the surrounding surface. Apply wax or polish.

Instead of using shellac, you may fill large scars with spackling compound mixed with oil color to match the finish. Make the compound a little darker than the finish, however, because it lightens as it dries. When thoroughly dry, smooth down the patch with fine steel wool or very fine abrasive paper. Varnish or shellac.

Removing Silicone Polish

Modern liquid furniture polishes containing silicone compounds are often a blessing to the housewife. These tough chemicals, related to sand, effectively repel water and resist staining and oxidation. Because they also repel the liquids in many present-day paints and varnishes, they can be a bane to the retoucher or refinisher. Every trace of silicone must be removed before the new finish can be successfully applied.

The best way to do this is to wash the surface with a silicone solvent, such as turpentine, xylol, or tuluol. After wiping the surface dry with a clean cloth, wash it again with a fresh cloth. Even after washing, it is best to apply a barrier coat of shellac or other sealer before you apply the final finish.

If you intend to use an old-fashioned oil and resin finish, the washing need not be done. In this case the oil in the finish will dissolve and blend with the silicone.

Tack Rag for Furniture Finishing

In varnishing and enameling furniture and other woodwork, it is important to keep the surface clean just ahead of the brush. A practical means for doing this is to use a so-called "tack rag." This may be purchased or made. To prepare one, use lintless cloth such as an old handkerchief, which is especially good because of its hemmed edges. Dip it in water, wringing quite dry, then sprinkle it lightly with varnish from a brush. Refold and rewring so the varnish permeates the cloth. Keep it rolled in sheet plastic or waxed paper when not in use to prevent drying out. Should this occur, sprinkle with water and wring out again.

MILDEW TREATMENT FOR WOOD

Conditions that favor the growth of surface mold on unpainted wooden parts of buildings and on stored wood are warmth, dampness, and poor ventilation. Because new, unseasoned lumber contains considerable natural moisture, it should be avoided if possible where such conditions prevail.

Under similar conditions, the molds of mildew also feed on the oils and minerals in paint, causing a dirty-looking discoloration. Indoor wood surfaces coated with varnish, enamel, or hard-surfaced paints, if kept reasonably dry, resist these molds fairly well. Softer paints on outdoor surfaces mildew more readily, the molds even penetrating to the wood.

Mildew-resistant paints containing fungicides can be bought ready-made, as can fungicides that can be mixed with ordinary paints. Linseed oil paint containing zinc oxide, used as a top coat, also inhibits the mildew fungi.

To prevent and cure mildew on house paint, the Forest Service of the U.S. Department of Agriculture recommends these steps:

1. In warm damp climates where mildew occurs frequently, use a paint containing zinc oxide for top coats over the primer coat. (Zinc oxide, however, makes a paint too brittle for a priming coat.)
2. For mild cases of mildew, use a prepared paint containing a mildewcide (a poison for mildew fungi), or mix a mildewcide in regular paint.
3. Ideally, to cure mildew, remove the mildew from the old paint surface and apply a paint that contains zinc oxide or a mildewcide.
4. To kill the fungi and clean an area for repainting, scrub the paint surface with the following solution:

Trisodium phosphate	6 ounces (¾ cup)
Household detergent	2 ounces (¼ cup)
Sodium hypochlorite, 5% solution (household bleach)	1 quart
Warm water	3 quarts

When clean, rinse thoroughly with fresh water from a hose. Avoid splashing the solution on shrubbery or grass; it may do harm. Repaint with a zinc-oxide paint or one containing a fungicide.

HOW TO COMBAT BLUE STAIN

Blue stain is a blue-black discoloration of wood that may also discolor paint applied over it. Blue stain is caused by certain fungi that grow in sapwood and use part of this wood for their food. It is not decay, although the conditions that lead to its growth may favor decay-producing fungi also. The main condition is an excess of moisture, produced by contact with moist ground or constant exposure to rain, dew, or water vapor.

If it does not penetrate too deeply, blue stain can be removed temporarily by sanding or by treating with a solution of household liquid chlorine bleach. Permanent cure, however, depends on keeping moisture out of the wood. Treat unpainted wood with a water-repellent preservative. Provide protection against excess water and water vapor for other wood.

PRESERVING WOODEN FENCE POSTS

The life of wooden fence posts and other outdoor timber can often be more than doubled by treating them with chemicals that inhibit decay. There are so many possible treatments that it is hard to make a choice. The advertising of commercial or "pattented" preservatives and processes makes the choice harder. Often the products with secret formulas are made to appear less expensive than they really are by recommending such sparing use that they are ineffective. The most common chemicals used as wood preservatives, and their ratings according to various characteristics, are shown on the accompanying table.

WOOD PRESERVATIVES

Preservative	Toxicity	Odor	Color	Paintability	Soil contact	Permeability
Creosote	***	*	*	*	***	***
Penta	***	**	***	***	***	***
Water-soluble preservatives	***	***	**	***	**	**

* = usable   ** = better   *** = best

The two methods that follow on page 66 are simple, proved, and inexpensive ones suggested by the Forest Products Laboratory of the Department of Agriculture.

Cold Soaking

This consists in submerging posts for 1 to 2 days or longer in a solution of pentacholorophenol, or of copper naphthenate in fuel oil. A "penta" solution should contain 5 percent of this chemical by weight. A copper naphthenate water-soluble solution should contain the equivalent of at least 1 percent of copper metal by weight. You can buy both of these preservatives in concentrated solutions, with accompanying directions for proper dilution. This treatment works best with round pine posts that are well seasoned. Posts so treated with the penta solution have averaged more than 20 years of service.

End-Diffusion Treatment

This is a simple and inexpensive method for use on green unpeeled posts. It consists in standing such posts, freshly cut, in a container of a measured quantity of a water-soluble solution of zinc chloride or chromated zinc chloride. These chemicals are cheap, can be bought as dry powder or concentrated solution, and are not dangerous to people or animals.

Use a 15- to 20-percent solution of either. About 5 pounds, or about ½ gallon, is recommended for each cubic foot of post treated. Allow the posts to stand with butts down in the solution until approximately three-fourths of the solution has been absorbed, which may take from 1 to 10 days. Then turn them over and let the tops absorb the rest of the solution. Store at least 30 days before setting in ground.

HOW TO STOP "DRY ROT"

The decay of wood is caused by decay fungi, and these microscopic plants can't work in wood without moisture. Although decayed wood may be dry in the final stages, it is not so while the fungi are doing the damage. For this reason there is actually no such thing as "dry rot."

Often, however, the term is applied to decay that is found in house lumber many feet from the nearest possible source of moisture. When such decay occurs, it is apt to be caused by one of the water-conducting fungi. Between two layers of wood, such as a floor and subfloor, these fungi may produce thick rootlike strands that are capable of carrying moisture for considerable distances. Vapor barriers or ventilation may limit their spread, but may not stop their activity entirely.

The first thing to do to control these fungi is to trace them back to the source of their moisture and cut off the connection. Usually the moisture comes up from the ground, using a brace, frame, wooden concrete form, or a grade stake as a bridge to let the fungus climb from moist soil to a joist or sill. Sometimes a joist is in direct contact with a tree stump that has been left under the house. In other cases the source from which the fungus is bringing its moisture may not be so easily located. These special fungi sometimes get their moisture directly from the soil through strands of mycelium, or vegetative fibers, that may grow a foot or more over the surface of foundation walls, or through cracks in loosely built masonry.

If any wood has already been made useless by the decay, replace it with wood that is sound and dry. If you are sure you have eliminated the sources of moisture that started the decay, replace only the wood that has been weakened. If there is any doubt, it is safer to remove also the apparently sound wood 2 feet in each direction from the part obviously decayed, and to replace it with wood that has been thoroughly impregnated with a preservative (see paragraph on "Cold Soaking" in previous item on preserving fence posts). Before installing the new wood, give all adjacent old wood and masonry surfaces a heavy treatment with a similar preservative.

2

Paints and Painting

PAINTING HOUSE EXTERIORS

The paint on your house will cost less, look better, and be far easier to maintain if you choose and apply it according to a few tried and tested rules. When painting a new wood house or any other outside wood surfaces, there are three recommended steps:

Step 1. Treat with Water-Repellent Preservative

Protect the wood against penetration of rain and heavy dew by applying a water-repellent preservative solution before painting. If you'd rather not do this yourself, you can buy lumber already treated and retreat cut ends on the job with a preservative solution sold at most paint and building-supply dealers. It is especially important that window sash and trim be treated.

Or you can apply the solution to untreated wood with a brush. Be careful to brush it well into lap and butt joints of trim and siding. Old houses can be treated effectively after paint has been removed. Allow 2 warm, sunny days for adequate drying of the treatment before painting.

Step 2. Apply a Priming Coat

The first or prime coat is the most important coat of paint to be applied to wood. For this coat, and for spot priming bare wood areas when repainting, experts at the U.S. Forest Products Laboratory find that a linseed oil-base paint adheres best to the wood and makes the best foundation for subsequent coats. It may contain lead or titanium pigments, but should not contain zinc oxide, which forms a hard and inflexible film that may crack itself and also crack later paint layers.

Apply the primer thickly enough so you can't see the grain of the wood. If you use ready-made paint, follow the spreading rates recommended by the manufacturer. This rate should be approximately 400 to 450 square feet per gallon with a paint that contains at least 85-percent solids by weight. The prime coat should not be porous, which would permit capillary flow of rain and dew through the paint film.

If the second coat is to be an exterior emulsion or latex paint, a primer of the type just mentioned is still necessary. The primer should be applied both to new wood and to painted surfaces that are badly weathered. It would be extremely unwise to apply emulsion-base paint directly to bare wood or to an undercoat that is chalking or deteriorated.

Step 3. Apply Finish Coats over Primer

For a smooth and durable finish, keep the following points in mind:

- Use a high-quality paint; cheap paints are more costly in the end. Finish coats can be of the linseed oil, alkyd, or latex type.
- Apply two topcoats, particularly to areas that are fully exposed to the weather such as the south side of the house. A two-coat job of low-quality paint may last only 3 years, but a three-coat job with good-quality paint may last as long as 10 years.
- To avoid peeling of one coat of paint from another, apply topcoats within 2 weeks after the primer. Do not prime in the fall and delay topcoats until spring. It is better to treat with a water-repellent preservative and delay all painting until spring.
- To avoid temperature blistering, do not apply oil-base paints on a cool surface that will be heated by the sun within a few hours. Follow the sun around the house.
- To reduce the wrinkling and flattening of oil-base paint and watermarks on latex paint, do not paint late in the evenings of cool spring and fall days when heavy dews frequently form.

Applying today's paints has become such an easy job that the first piece of advice is a warning: Don't spread it too much. When a can of paint says "one gallon covers 400 square feet" it means that the contents will cover that much. It also means don't try to get more than 400 feet, or you'll end up with a coating that is too thin. This is particularly true of the most modern paints that are thicker than ever in the can, but spread more easily than before.

The quickest and easiest exterior painting involves three steps that guarantee complete and uniform coverage:

1. Brush under the edge of the strips, running the brush edgewise.
2. Dip the brush and dab the paint along the face of the strip in patches about 4 inches apart.
3. Brush out the dabs, smoothing the paint lengthwise along the strip. Brush into the preceding "dip" to smooth the joining area. Brush out at the far edge, to produce a "feather" that will accept the next "dip" smoothly.

Where siding meets trim, work paint well into the joint, then pull out the excess by putting the tips of the brush in the joint and stroking away from it. Two or three pulling-out strokes will prevent a deposit of paint in the joint that is too thick and likely to crack.

Most modern house paints are formulated for use on the trim and the body of the house. Therefore, if the trim and the rest of the house are the same color, paint them at the same time and save ladder moving. If the trim is a different color, or if you insist on a special trim paint, it is easiest to do the trim first, because of some tricky techniques involved.

Paint the face of the trim and the edges, if you don't care if a little trim paint slops over on the siding. It is easy to cover it when you do the siding because you can work the brush into the joint more easily when the area the brush rests on is the siding—not that little edge of the trim. In fact, if there should be any reason why you must paint the body before the trim, let the house paint color cover that tiny edge, and use the trim paint only on the flat, easy-to-paint areas of the trim where a roller will save you time.

How to Repaint

A repainted job is only as good as the old paint beneath it. Here are some general rules to observe:

1. Before repainting, wash old, glossy, and unweathered surfaces with a detergent, washing soda, or trisodium phosphate solution, or roughen it well with steel wool to remove contaminants that may prevent adhesion of the next coat. Failure to do this is a common cause of intercoat peeling.

2. Repaint only when the old paint has weathered to the extent that it no longer covers or protects the wood. Where paint is peeling and wood surfaces are exposed, remove loose paint from adjacent areas. Treat with water-repellent preservative and spot prime with the housepaint primer described above. Remove excess chalk or old paint with steel wool. The paint in protected areas of the house may need cleaning only by washing.
3. For the topcoats, use any high-quality exterior paint reputed to give good service.

Other Outdoor Paint Jobs

Besides the wooden clapboard siding of a house, there will probably be wood trim, shingles, porch floors, metalwork, brick, concrete, and other items to be decorated and protected. Each of these may require a different type of paint, varnish, or other coating material.

Shingles of various decorative woods may have a pleasing natural grain that you will want to preserve. These may be coated merely with a clear water-repellent preservative or with a pigmented stain (See Chapter 1). Wood trim, such as window sashes, shutters, and doors, may be given finish coats of colored high-gloss or semigloss exterior enamel.

MASONRY SURFACES. Brick, cement, stucco, and cinder block can be brightened and protected with a variety of paint products. One of the newest ideas in painting brick is a clear coating that withstands weather yet allows the natural surface of the brick to show through. Cement-based and rubber-based paints, as well as alkyd, vinyl, and emulsion coatings, are also used on many types of masonry. Almost all exterior house paints may be applied to masonry, however, when surface preparations are made properly.

METAL SURFACES. Iron and steel surfaces should be primed with a rust-inhibiting paint such as red-lead, zinc chromate, or special aluminum paint. Finish coats may be of any good house paint or exterior enamel. Although copper building materials do not rust, they give off a corrosive wash that may discolor surrounding areas and so should be coated with a clear weatherproof varnish. Aluminum, like copper, does not rust in a conventional way, but gets oxidized and stained if not coated.

Porches, floors, and steps are subjected to unusually heavy traffic and so must be coated with a paint designed for durability. You can buy special porch and deck paints that that will stand up well under this hard use. Wooden porches, floors, and steps can be primed with a thinned version of the top coat. Cement and concrete ones may have to be primed with an alkali-resisting paint.

Even though there are a number of different types of paint, selection need not be too much of a problem. First consider the type of surface. Are you painting wood, metal, or masonry? Some paints can be used on all three; others on two. The condition of the surface may also be important. Old chalky surfaces, for example, are not generally a sound base for latex or water-base paints.

Next consider any special requirements. For example, nonchalking paint may be advisable where chalk rundown would discolor adjacent brick or stone surfaces. Or if mildew is a problem in your area, you may use mildew-resistant paint. Lead-free paints may be used in areas where sulfur fumes cause staining of paints containing lead pigments.

Color is a third consideration, but it is mostly a matter of personal preference. Some colors are more durable than others, and some color combinations are more attractive than others. Your paint dealer can help you with decisions on color durability and combinations.

"House paint" is the commercial term for exterior paints mixed with many different formulations. It is the most widely used type of paint. Formulations are available for use on all surfaces and for all special requirements such as chalk or mildew resistance. White is the most popular color.

Exterior paint comes in both oil-base and latex (water-base) types. The vehicle of oil-base paint consists usually of linseed oil plus turpentine or mineral spirits as the thinner. Latex paint contains water as the vehicle thinner; its vehicle consists of fine particles of resin emulsified or held in suspension in water.

Another type of water-base paint has a vehicle consisting of a soluble linseed oil dissolved in water. This paint has the properties of both oil-base and water-base paints.

The advantages of latex paints include easier application, faster drying, usually better color retention, and resistance to alkali and blistering. Also, they can be applied in humid weather and to damp surfaces. Brush and tool cleanup is simpler because it can be done with water.

Many paint dealers custom-mix paints to any shade you have in mind. Custom mixes run a little higher in price than "standard" colors, however. For this reason, check the color cards of several manufacturers to see if you can find a standard shade that suits your fancy and saves you money. Colors can also be tinted, as described later in this chapter.

Estimating Paint Needed

Of the several common methods of computing the amount of paint a house will take, the simplest is this: Multiply the height of the eaves times the linear distance around the house. If there are wings with lower eaves, compute the body of the house and the wings separately, then add.

If the house has gable ends, add 2 feet to the height of the eaves. If it has a gambrel roof, add 4 feet to the height of the eaves.

Do not subtract for windows, unless they are very large, since the paint you save on the area occupied by windows is normally needed for board edges, eaves, soffits, etc.

Roof dormers typically take 100 square feet of paint.

If your house has an overhang no greater than a foot or so, ignore it. More overhang should be computed on the basis of eave-line distance times overhang.

When you have the total square footage, divide it by the number of square feet per gallon given on the label of the paint. This figure varies from product to product, so check labels carefully and remember that square footages are not so much a "boast" about how far the paint will stretch as they are a warning not to stretch too far.

Trim paint is hard to figure in the above manner, since computation of square feet on the irregular shapes and surfaces of trim is just about impossible. However, a gallon of trim paint will take care of the average house. Even if 3 quarts would do it, there is little economy over buying a gallon, and you can always use the leftover paint for touching up. On the other hand, if your best guess is that a gallon won't quite do it, buy a gallon and a quart, and make a deal with the paint store to return the quart if you don't need it.

Floor paint, for porches, terraces, patios, and the like, is simple enough to figure on a pure square-foot basis. For odds and ends such as black wrought-iron railings, carriage lamps, etc., your guess is as good as anyone's. Remember that a little left over, stored away on a shelf in the garage, is excellent insurance against damage that should be touched up.

Causes and Remedies for Paint Failure

When exterior paint fails, not only is it necessary to correct the condition but it is more important to figure out what caused it. Otherwise, it will surely happen again.

(*Text continues on page 78*)

WHICH OUTDOOR PAINTS TO USE WHERE

	House paint (oil alkyd)	Cement powder paint	Exterior clear finish	Aluminum paint	Wood stain	Roof coating	Trim paint	Porch and deck paint	Primer or undercoater	Metal primer	House paint (latex)	Water-repellent preservative
MASONRY												
Asbestos cement	X								X		X	
Brick	X	X		X					X		X	X
Cement and cinder block	X	X		X					X		X	
Concrete/Masonry porches and floors								X			X	
Coal-tar-felt roof						X						
Stucco	X	X		X					X		X	
METAL												
Aluminum windows	X			X			X			X	X	
Steel windows	X			X			X			X	X	
Metal roof	X*									X	X*	

Metal siding	X*		X*		X*			X	X*	
Copper surfaces		X								
Galvanized surfaces	X*		X*		X*			X	X*	
Iron surfaces	X*		X*		X*			X	X*	
WOOD										
Clapboard	X*		X				X		X*	
Natural wood siding and trim		X		X						
Shutters and other trim	X*				X*		X		X*	
Wood frame windows	X*		X		X*		X		X*	
Wood porch floor						X				
Wood shingle roof				X						X

X* indicates that a primer sealer, or fill coat, may be necessary before the finishing coat (unless the surface has been previously finished).

GUIDE TO BODY AND TRIM COLORS

If the roof of your house is	you can paint the body, as below.	Pink	Bright red	Red-orange	Tile red	Cream	Bright yellow	Light green	Dark green	Gray-green	Blue-green	Light blue	Dark blue	Blue-gray	Violet	Brown	White
		And you can paint the trim or shutters and doors as below.															
Gray	White	X	X	X	X	X	X	X	X	X	X	X	X	X	X		
	Gray	X	X	X	X		X	X	X	X	X	X	X	X	X		X
	Cream-yellow		X		X		X		X	X							X
	Pale green				X		X		X	X							X
	Dark green	X				X	X	X									X
	Putty			X	X				X	X			X	X		X	
	Dull red	X				X		X						X			X
Green	White	X	X	X	X	X	X	X	X	X	X	X	X	X	X	X	
	Gray			X		X	X	X									X
	Cream-yellow		X		X			X	X	X						X	X
	Pale green			X	X		X		X								X
	Dark green	X		X		X	X	X									X
	Beige				X				X	X	X		X	X			
	Brown	X				X	X	X									X
	Dull red					X		X		X							X
	White		X		X				X		X			X			
	Light gray		X		X				X								X

Red	Cream-yellow		X		X						X		X	X			X
	Pale green		X		X												X
	Dull red					X		X		X	X						X
Brown	White			X	X		X	X	X	X	X		X	X	X	X	
	Buff				X				X	X	X					X	
	Pink-beige				X				X	X						X	X
	Cream-yellow				X				X	X	X					X	
	Pale green								X	X						X	
	Brown			X		X	X										X
Blue	White			X	X		X					X	X				
	Gray			X		X						X	X				X
	Cream-yellow			X	X								X	X			
	Blue			X		X	X					X					X

BLISTERS. Most exterior paint blisters are caused by moisture. The moisture that creates these blisters comes from a variety of sources. For one thing, water vapor is generated inside the house, from cooking, bathing, and so forth. It will try to migrate outside the house, but when it becomes trapped inside it can push the paint film right off the wall. This will cause blisters, and in the advanced stage, peeling.

The remedy for this paint problem is to provide an escape for the moisture. High moisture areas, such as the kitchen, bath, and laundry rooms, can be equipped with exhaust fans. Even opening windows during high moisture times will remove some of the moisture. Also, you can vent the walls with various commercial products. An example is a miniature, 1-inch-diameter plastic vent. Drill holes through the siding and insert these vents between pairs of studs, about 5 inches below ceiling level and beneath windows. Also, you can buy vents about the size of nails. These are driven in place with a hammer.

Moisture can get behind paint film through cracks or improper openings in the house. Loose or missing caulk, loosely joined window and door frames and corner butts, insufficient flashing, roof damage, and missing shingles are examples. Another prime entry point for moisture is siding that is too close (within 6 inches) to the ground. It sucks up moisture by capillary action.

If the house has cracks or openings, seal them up; if siding is too low, a vapor barrier installed between it and the house foundation will reduce the problem greatly.

When you have blisters or peelings, remove all the loose paint with a scraper and sand down the edges of the remaining "craters" with medium-grade sandpaper. If you have a lot of scraping to do, use the disc sander on your electric drill. Another method is the use of heat to soften the paint, making it easy to scrape off. Never use a blowtorch for this job. Paint and hardware stores sell an electric paint remover that gets hot enough to do its softening job, but not hot enough to start a fire. Some makes combine the heating element and the scraper in a single tool.

ALLIGATORING. This occurs when the paint has split up into segments and resembles alligator skin. This happens most often when two coats of paint are not compatible, which usually means that they do not swell and shrink at the same rate with changes in temperature. As a result, the top layer of paint develops cracks every which way, to make up for the difference in swell and shrink.

If the cracks in the paint are very fine, you may be able to escape by just repainting with a compatible paint. If not, you'll have to remove the paint to bare wood because the segments will eventually curl up at the edges and flake off, taking off whatever is on top with them.

CHALKING. Here, pigment washes out of the paint, and onto anything that is below it. There are three causes for this:

1. The paint does not contain adequate binders.
2. Badly weathered surfaces were not primed properly so that the wood absorbs the binders, leaving the pigment to wash away.
3. The paint was applied during freezing weather or below the temperature limit specified on the label.

The answer is proper priming (with a paint that will stick) and painting. If the chalking is really bad, brush it off the surface first. A certain amount of chalking is normal with some oil-base housepaints. It is deliberate in their formulation since the slow, gradual chalking washes away and keeps the surface looking clean. In addition, it prevents undue buildup of paint, as succeeding coats go on.

CRAWLING. This is characterized by the paint puddling up much as water would on a greasy plate. In fact, the cause is usually grease—a heavy accumulation of oily, greasy dirt, usually in protected areas, such as under the porch or eaves. The solution is simple: wash off all grease and oily deposits.

SPOTTING. This is characterized by a loss of gloss and color in spots and is commonly caused by paint being spread too thinly—skimping on application. The symptoms may appear right after the paint is applied on up to a few weeks.

There is no real solution to this problem, at least when it occurs over previously painted surfaces. Gradually, the spotting will disappear with age. Do not apply another coat of paint too soon; this can build up an excessively thick paint film that might lead to serious problems.

CRACKING. When cracking occurs the paint is starting to segment, but is not as pronounced as with alligatoring. The cause is usually having used a paint that has dried to an excessively hard finish and normal expansion and contraction of the house cracks it.

The only sure solution is taking the paint off down to bare wood. If you want to take a chance, you can wire-brush the cracks to remove as much curling-up paint as possible, then repaint.

WRINKLING. Here, the paint looks as if it were crumpled and then smoothed flat on the wall. The common cause of the problem is the paint is applied too thick and is not properly brushed out. If you have this problem, sand the affected areas smooth with a belt sander using an open-coat sandpaper, such as 60 or 80 grit. Keep the sander moving so you don't make any gouges.

TO PREVENT BLEEDING OF STAIN. When paint or enamel is applied over a surface already treated with oil stain or varnish stain, the oil in the new finish tends to dissolve the stain. This, in turn, discolors the new coating.

To find out if such bleeding will occur on a given project, make a test by painting a small area. The stain may bleed through immediately, but it is better to wait 3 or 4 days before deciding to continue.

If the stain does come through it is best to first remove as much as possible by washing the surface with turpentine or benzine if it is an oil stain, or with denatured alcohol if it is an alcohol stain.

BACK PRIMER FOR UNPAINTED WOOD. On new construction—to help preserve the wood and seal out moisture—it is best to give a priming coat of paint to the back surfaces and edges of siding, plywood panels, and flooring before it is put in place. For such priming give one coat of the same primer that is going to be used on the structure.

Ladder Safety

The most dangerous phase of house painting involves the use of a ladder. For safety's sake observe the following precautions:

1. Make sure that the ladder is not defective. Check the rungs and rails carefully. Any cracked wood or loosened metal should be repaired before the ladder is used. Check any ropes and pulleys also to make sure that they are securely fastened and work properly. Check the locking mechanism to be certain that it works freely. It is a good idea to keep this well oiled at all times.
2. To raise a straight or extension ladder, brace one end against the house foundation, a step, or a curb. Raise the other end and walk in, working the hand alternately rung after rung. Be sure that the ladder is positioned firmly both on the ground and on the top, never against a window or screen or a weak gutter. If the ground is soft or the surface is macadam, install metal cleats at the base. You can avoid ladder pitching by placing a plank under the base or legs, or by driving a stake into the ground, set firmly against the bottom rung. Keep in mind that a stepladder is firmly footed

only when the spreader is fully opened and press-locked. Do not try to climb a step ladder in any other position; it will probably topple or slip.

3. Check the angle of a straight or extension ladder against the wall. It should be set so that its foot is away from the wall one-fourth of the distance to the point of support. Remember that if the base is too far away from the wall, the rungs might not be able to support the weight; if the base is too close to the wall, then the ladder might topple backwards. If you use scaffolding, make sure that it is secure.
4. Always face the ladder when climbing up or down. Hold on with both hands. Carry tools and supplies in your pocket or haul them up with a line. Keep your shoes clean when climbing. It is always wise to scrape off any dirt or mud; corrugated or square rungs add to safety, but not with dirty shoes.
5. Be sure that the paint bucket, tools, and other objects are secure when you are on a ladder or scaffolding. Falling objects can injure persons walking below.
6. Do not overreach when painting. Move the ladder frequently rather than risk a fall. A good rule is to keep your belt buckle between the rails.
7. Lean toward the ladder when working. If you must have both hands free to do a job, then "lock" yourself to the ladder. Slip one leg over a rung and hold the rung below with the heel of your shoe. But keep one hand free, ready to grab the ladder just in case. Never "push off" when painting a spot directly under the ladder—that is, do not shove the ladder away from the wall and let it momentarily "float." It is during this time that a gust of wind could carry the ladder away.
8. Never stand with both feet on the top level. On a stepladder it is wise not to go higher than the second step from the top; on a straight ladder the third step from the top is the highest you should go. If you must go higher, get a longer ladder.
9. Watch out for and avoid any electrical wiring within the area of work. This is especially important if you are using a metal ladder.
10. When painting second roofs, do not rest or place the ladder on the tar or shingles of the first roof. Tar melts and shingles are prone to sliding. Nail a 1×2 brace into the roof; this will prevent the ladder's legs from sliding. Always wear rubber-soled shoes when on rooftops.
11. No matter where the job, avoid setting a ladder up in front of a

door—for if someone opens the door, down you go. If you must work in front of a door, then have a helper stand in front of the locked door.

12. If it is necessary to move the ladder a short distance, place your foot against the base and pull on the rungs until the ladder is vertical. Slip your arm through the space between the rungs at about shoulder height and hold the ladder against your side. Use your other hand to brace the ladder. Walk slowly, watching the top (now and then, for you also must watch your step on the ground) to make sure that the ladder remains vertical. To carry a ladder horizontally, lift it at its center of gravity, and put it over one shoulder. Keep the front end raised so that it is at least 5 to 6 feet off the ground.

INTERIOR PAINTING

Many different kinds and formulations of paints and other finishes are available for interior use, and new ones frequently appear on the market. Use the table on pages 84–85 as a general guide in making your selection. For a more specific selection consult your paint dealer. Reputable paint dealers keep abreast of the newest developments in the paint industry and stock the newest formulations. "Dripless" paint is an example of a fairly recent development. It has a jelled consistency in the can, but it loses that form when picked up on a brush or roller and spreads evenly and smoothly. It is particularly convenient when painting a ceiling.

The usual interior paint job consists of painting wallboard or plaster walls and ceilings, woodwork, and wood windows and doors. For these surfaces you need to choose first between solvent-thinned paint (commonly called oil-base paint) and water-thinned paint (commonly called latex paint, but not necessarily latex), and then between a gloss, semigloss, or flat finish. (Enamels, which are made with a varnish, or resin, base instead of the usual linseed-oil vehicle, are included under the broad oil-paint grouping.)

Oil-base paints are very durable, are highly resistant to staining and damage, can withstand frequent scrubbings, and give good one-coat coverage. Many latex paints are advertised as having similar properties.

The main advantages of latex paint are easier application, faster drying, and simpler tool cleanup. The brushes, rollers, and other equipment can be easily cleaned with water. Both oil-base paint and latex paint are now available in gloss, semigloss, and flat finishes. Glossy finishes look shiny and clean easily. Flat finishes show dirt more readily but absorb light and thus reduce glare. Semigloss finishes have properties of both glossy and flat finishes.

Because enamel is durable and easy to clean, semigloss or full-gloss enamel is recommended for woodwork and for the walls of kitchens, bathrooms, and laundry rooms. For the walls of nurseries and other playrooms, either oil-base or latex semigloss enamel paint is suggested. Flat paint is generally used for the walls of living rooms, dining rooms, and other nonwork or nonplay rooms.

Interior Color

Paints are available in a wide range of colors and shades. Dealers usually carry color charts showing the different possibilities. Some of the colors are ready mixed; others have to be mixed by adding or combining different colors.

Color selection is mostly a matter of personal preference. Here are some points to keep in mind in selecting your colors:

1. Light colors make a small room seem larger. Conversely, dark colors make an overly large room appear smaller.
2. Bright walls in a large room detract from otherwise decorative furnishings.
3. Ceilings appear lower when darker than the walls and higher when lighter than the walls.
4. Paint generally dries to a slightly different color or shade. For a preview of the final color, brush a little of the paint on a piece of clean, white blotting paper. The blotting paper will immediately absorb the wet gloss, and the color on the paper will be about the color of the paint when it dries on the wall.
5. Colors often change under artificial lighting. Look at color swatches both in daylight and under artificial lighting.

Psychological Effects of Colors

The colors you select for the various rooms in your home will reflect your personality as well as your good taste. But your color selection will also create an emotional feeling about your home that will help form the opinion your visitors will have about you and your family.

PSYCHOLOGICAL SIGNIFICANCE

Red-Orange. Heat; stimulation; activity; richness; splendor; dignity.

WHICH INTERIOR PAINTS TO USE WHERE

	Aluminum paint	Casein	Cement-base paint	Emulsion paint (including latex)	Enamel	Flat paint	Floor paint or enamel	Floor varnish	Interior varnish	Metal primer	Rubber-base paint (not latex)	Sealer or undercoater	Semigloss paint	Shellac	Stain	Wax (emulsion)	Wax (liquid or paste)	Wood sealer
FLOORS																		
Asphalt tile																	X*	
Concrete																X*	X*	
Linoleum							X							X		X	X	
Vinyl and rubber							X	X								X	X	
Wood							X*	X*									X	
MASONRY																		
Old	X	X	X	X	X*	X*					X	X	X*					
New			X	X	X*	X*					X	X	X*					
METAL																		
Heating ducts	X				X*	X*				X	X		X*					
Radiators	X				X*	X*				X	X		X*					

STAIRS																
Treads						X	X						X	X		
Risers				X*	X*			X		X		X*	X	X		
WALLS AND CEILINGS																
Kitchen and bathroom			X	X*						X	X	X*				
Plaster		X	X		X*					X	X	X*				
Wallboard		X	X		X*					X	X	X*				
Wood paneling			X*		X*			X								
Wood trim			X*	X*	X*			X		X	X	X*	X	X	X	X
WINDOWS																
Aluminum	X			X*	X*				X	X		X*				
Steel	X			X*	X*				X	X		X*				
Wood sill				X*				X			X			X		

X* indicates that a primer or sealer may be necessary before the finishing coat, unless the surface has been previously finished.

Pink. Daintiness; gaiety; animation. Slightly stimulating. (Use in masses in bedroom or nursery.)

Yellow–Yellow-Green. Dryness; crispness; relaxation; warmth; light; cheer.

Green-Blue. Coldness; spaciousness; passivity; tranquillity.

Violet, Lavender. Coolness; limpness; dullness; daintiness; reservation; feminity. (Lavender may be used in bedrooms.)

Brown. Warmth.

DECORATIVE USES AND EFFECTS

Red. Stimulating or cheering to the melancholy or lazy; upsetting to the nervous or overactive; attention compelling. (Use in small quantities in dining room, library, kitchen.)

Blue. Soothing to the nervous; depressing to the morose. Inseparable mentally with illimitability—the cold immensity of space, infinity. It has an intellectual appeal. Symbolically, it is the color of truth, which is the result of calm reflection and never of heated argument.

Yellow. In certain hues, the sensation of glory, cheerfulness; in other variations, cowardice, cheapness. Connotes splendor, radiance, vividness. It is of great healing value to the brain. (Use in masses or small quantities, where light is poor.)

Green. Cooling, and productive of extreme reactions. Symbolic of serenity and rebirth; suggestive of hope.

Orange. Associated with life, well-being, energy. (Avoid bright orange in masses.)

Brown (Tan-Golden Brown). Depressing if used alone; best combined with orange, yellow, gold. (Use sparingly to avoid drabness, in living room, library.)

Purple (Plum, Mauve, Orchid). Associated with heroism, or with passion and mystery, pomp, gorgeousness. It has a soothing influence. (Use sparingly in living room, library.)

Black, White, Gray. Intensifies other colors in room.

Light-Reflecting Power of Paint

Colors may be used to give more light or more shadow as your decorative scheme and the type of room requires. The amount of light depends on the quantity of light reflected and absorbed. The more light reflected, the greater the visibility, reading and sewing advantages, etc. The following indicates the relative light-conserving powers (reflection) of colors:

	Percent
White	70–90
Ivories and creams	55–90
Light yellows	65–70
Light buffs	40–56
Light greens	40–50
Medium greens	15–30
Oranges	15–30
Medium blues	15–20
Dark blues	5–10
Medium grays	15–30
Red and maroons	3–18
Medium and dark browns	3–18
Black	1–4

How to Mix Custom Colors

As already mentioned, special colors of interior paint to suit your exact taste can be made in two ways. The first is to blend several different colors of ready-mixed paint. If you do this, be sure to use paints of the same brand and type. Never mix oil-base with emulsion or latex-type paints. Don't mix gloss paint with flat or semigloss, unless you deliberately want to reduce the gloss.

The second way is to tint a light-colored base paint with concentrated colors-in-oil. These may be used with almost all opaque surface coatings except lacquers and those thinned with water. They should not be used in large quantities in flat paints as they may produce glossy streaks.

Colors-in-oil come in both liquid and paste form. If you use the latter, first mix it with enough paint thinner so the mix pours smoothly.

When mixing special colors, be sure you mix enough for the whole job. If you intend to duplicate the color later, note down the amounts of the various colors used. Even if you do this, however, it is seldom possible to duplicate a batch exactly.

HOW TO MIX PAINT COLORS

This table suggests combinations of basic colors from which you can make hundreds of others. The base paint should in all cases have an oil base.

Color	Base paint	Colors-in-oil
Apple green	White	Light chrome green and orange chrome yellow
Apricot	Medium chrome yellow	Venetian red and carmine lake; for light tint, lighten with white
Browns	Venetian red	Ochre and lampblack in proportions according to shades of brown wanted
Café au lait	Burnt umber	Yellow ochre, Venetian red, and white
Canary	Lemon chrome yellow	White
Chartreuse	Lemon chrome yellow	Medium chrome green
Colonial yellow	White	Medium chrome yellow and a touch of orange chrome yellow
Copper	Medium chrome yellow	A little burnt sienna
Coral pink	Vermilion	White and medium chrome yellow
Cream and buff	White	For cream, add ochre For buffs, also add burnt umber
Crimson	Toluidine red	For very rich hue, add crimson lake
Ecru	White	Ochre, burnt sienna, and lampblack
Electric blue	Ultramarine blue	White and raw sienna
Emerald	Light chrome green	
Fawn	White	Medium chrome yellow, Venetian red, and burnt umber
French gray	White	Lampblack with touch of ultramarine blue and madder lake or carmine
Gray	White	Lampblack to obtain desired shade, plus color, if wanted
Ivy green	Ochre	Lampblack and Prussian blue
Jonquil	White	Medium chrome yellow and touch of vermilion

Color	Base paint	Colors-in-oil
Lavender	White	Ivory black, ultramarine blue, touch of madder lake or carmine
Lemon	Lemon chrome yellow	
Marigold	Medium chrome yellow	White and orange chrome yellow
Maroon	Venetian red	Lampblack
Mauve	Ultramarine blue	White and madder lake
Navy blue	Ultramarine blue	Ivory black
Old gold	White	Medium chrome yellow, ochre, and a little burnt umber
Olive green	Lemon chrome yellow	Prussian blue and lampblack
Peach	White	Pale Indian red and chrome yellow
Pink	White	Any red desired
Plum	White	Indian red and ultramarine blue
Robin's egg blue	White	Prussian blue
Scarlet	Pale English vermilion or any scarlet-toned vermilion reds	
Sea green	White	Prussian blue, raw sienna
Shrimp	White	Venetian red, burnt sienna, and touch of vermilion
Sky blue	White	Prussian blue
Tan	White	Burnt sienna and touch of lampblack
Terra-cotta	Ochre	Venetian red and white, for some shades, also add Indian red
Turquoise	White	Prussian or phthalocyanine blue and pale chrome green
Violet	White	Lake red and ultramarine

Estimating Paint Quantity

To determine the amount of paint needed, measure the square feet of the wall area to be covered. The label usually indicates the number of square feet a gallon will cover when applied as directed.

To get the square feet of the wall area, measure the distance around the room, then multiply this figure by the distance from the floor to the ceiling. For example:

Your room is 12 by 15 feet and 8 feet high. Since $12 + 12 + 15 + 15 = 54$ feet, the distance around the room, multiply 54 by the height of the wall—$54 \times 8 = 432$ square feet of wall area.

Deduct the windows and doors that don't require paint. For example, in your room there is one door, 7 feet by 4 feet, and two windows, each one 5 feet by 3 feet. Multiply height by width to get the square feet.

$$7 \times 4 \times 1 = 28 \text{ square feet of door space}$$

$$5 \times 3 \times 2 = 30 \text{ square feet of window space}$$

Add these to get the total amount of space to be deducted from the room size—28 + 30 = 58 square feet. Subtract this from the total: 432 square feet − 58 square feet = 374 square feet of wall area to be painted. If the door is to be painted the same color as the walls, do not deduct the door area.

As mentioned earlier, be sure to buy enough paint to complete the job, especially if you are having colors mixed. Also keep in mind that unpainted plaster and wallboard soak up more paint than previously painted walls and therefore require more paint or primer.

Some paints are guaranteed to give one-coat coverage over all or most colors if applied as directed at a rate not exceeding the number of square feet specified on the label of the paint container.

How to Paint a Room

In general, walls, ceilings, woodwork, and other surfaces to be painted should be clean, dry, and smooth. But read the label on the paint can before you start painting; it may contain additional or special instructions for preparing the surface.

PREPARATION OF NEW SURFACES. New plaster walls should not be painted with oil-base paint until they have thoroughly cured—usually after about 2 months—and then a primer coat should be applied first. If it is necessary to paint uncured plaster, apply *one coat only* of a latex paint or primer. Latex, or water-base, paint will not be affected by the alkali in new plaster and will allow water to escape while the plaster dries. Subsequent coats of paint—either oil base or latex—can be added when the plaster is dry.

Unpainted plaster picks up and absorbs dirt and is difficult to clean. The one coat of latex paint or primer will protect it.

For new drywall, a latex primer or paint is recommended for the first coat. Solvent-thinned paints tend to cause a rough surface. After the first coat of latex paint, subsequent coats can be of either type.

Clean or dust new surfaces before you apply the first coat of primer or paint.

PREPARATION OF OLD SURFACES. The first step is to inspect the surface for cracks and mars. Fill small hairline cracks with spackling compound and larger cracks with special patching plaster. Follow the directions on the container label when using the patching material. When the patch is completely dry, sand it smooth and flush with the surrounding surface.

Nailheads tend to "pop out" in wallboard walls and ceilings. Countersink the projecting heads slightly and fill the hole with spackling compound. Sand the patch smooth when it is dry. It is desirable to prime newly spackled spots, particularly if you are applying only one coat.

Next, clean the surface of dirt and grease. A dry rag or mop will remove dust and some dirt. You may have to wash the surface with a household cleanser to remove stubborn dirt or grease.

Kitchen walls and ceilings are usually covered with a film of grease from cooking, which may extend to the walls and ceilings just outside the entrances to the kitchen, and bathroom walls and ceilings may have steamed-on dirt. The grease or dirt must be removed; the new paint will not adhere to it. To remove the grease or dirt, wash the surface with a strong household cleanser, turpentine, or mineral spirits.

The finish on kitchen and bathroom walls and ceiling is usually a gloss or semigloss. It must be "cut" so that the new paint can get a firm hold. Washing the surface with household cleanser or turpentine will dull the gloss, but, for best results, rub the surface with fine sandpaper or steel wool and then wipe the surface to remove the dust.

PAINTING SEQUENCE. Paint the ceilings first, walls second, then woodwork (doors, windows, and other trim). The place floors occupy in the sequence depends upon what is being done to them. If floors are simply being painted, they are done last; but if they are to be completely refinished, including sanding or scraping, do them first, then cover them with paper or drop cloths while painting the room.

CEILINGS. When using a roller for ceiling work, brush on a strip of paint around the entire perimeter of the ceiling. Roll the first stroke away from you (don't roll too fast or you will spatter the paint). Slow down as you reach the wall. Ease into the junction of wall and ceiling so as to get as little paint as possible on the wall.

If you are using a latex paint that doesn't show lap marks, paint a narrow strip around the entire perimeter of the ceiling. You'll fill in the center area later with your roller. If you are using an alkyd paint, it is best to work across the narrow dimension of the ceiling. Start in a corner and paint a narrow strip 2 or 3 feet wide against the wall. After loading your roller, roll on a strip of the same width, working from the unpainted area into a still-wet wall-side strip. When you get to the far side of the room, paint the area near the wall with a brush or roller and a paint guard. As you roll along, work backward into the wet edge of the previous strip. Crisscross your strokes to cover the area completely. Light strokes help to eliminate lap marks. It is a good idea to attach a tightly fitting cardboard disc around the handle of the roller to guard against any paint that may drip or run down the side of the roller.

When using a brush, also begin at a corner and paint a strip 2 to 3 feet wide across the ceiling. You may find it easier to brush on the paint and then cross-brush in the opposite direction, but always do the final brushing in the same direction. After you have completed the first strip, do another section about the same width. Continue in this manner until the ceiling is completed. Always work toward a wet edge of the last section to avoid lap marks.

You will find it easier to paint the ceiling if you place a 1½-inch plank of the proper height securely on the treads of two solidly footed, completely opened stepladders. This eliminates constant climbing up and down. An even easier method is to use a long-handled roller, which permits you to paint the ceiling while standing on the floor. You may have to use a ladder only to cut in the edges.

WALLS. Use the same basic procedure for painting the side walls as you did for the ceilings. When using a brush, start painting in a corner and complete a strip 2 to 3 feet wide from ceiling to baseboard, brushing from the unpainted into the painted area. Flat paint can be applied in wide overlapping arcs. When a few square feet have been covered, "lay off" with parallel upward strokes—that is, make all final brush-off strokes until one wall is completed. Leave the trim and woodwork until all walls are painted.

You can't do a smooth paint job in the corners with a standard 7- or 9-inch roller. Therefore, unless you plan to use a special corner roller, paint the corner, top of the wall next to the ceiling, and the bottom wall next to the baseboard with a wide brush before using the roller. When using any paint other than latex, remember to do this only as you are ready to paint each strip. If the corners are allowed to dry before the inner area is painted, lap marks will show.

To use the roller, start about 3 feet from the ceiling and roll up, then down. Roll across if necessary to fill in spots that you missed with the up and down motions. Always begin a strip by working from the dry area to the wet one.

TRIM AND BASEBOARDS. When painting a window, adjust it so you can paint the lower part of the upper sash. Then raise the upper sash almost to the top to finish painting it. The lower sash comes next. With the window open slightly at the top and bottom, it can be finished easily. Paint the recessed part of the window frame next, then the frame, and the window sill last. Spatters on the glass can be wiped off when wet, or removed with a razor blade when dry.

When painting a door, do the frame first, then paint the top, back, and front edges of the door itself. If the door is paneled, paint the panels and panel molding first, starting at the top. Keep a clean cloth handy to wipe off any paint that gets on the area surrounding the panels. Paint the rest of the door last, starting at the top.

The baseboards are painted last. A cardboard or plastic guard held flush against the bottom edge of the baseboard will protect the floor and prevent dirt from being picked up in the brush. Don't let paper or drop cloth touch the baseboard while the paint is wet.

Trim work is often painted with enamels and semigloss or gloss paints, which flow on more generously and with much less pressure than flat paints. Completing a small area at a time, brush on the paint with horizontal strokes, then level off with even, vertical strokes. Work quickly and never try to go back and touch up a spot that has started to set.

NATURAL FINISHES FOR TRIM. Some doors are attractive in their natural finish. However, they will discolor and soil easily unless protected. Your paint dealer can offer suggestions on how to finish and protect your doors. Many kinds of products are now on the market and new ones often appear.

The first step in finishing doors is to obtain the proper color tone. This is usually acquired by staining. However, sometimes no staining is required—the preservative finish is enough to bring out the desired color tone. With new doors, to help you make a decision, you can experiment on the trimmings or shavings.

The next step is sealing. One coat of shellac is usually adequate. When the shellac is dry, the surface should be sanded smooth, wiped free of dust, and varnished. Rubbing the surface with linseed oil, as is done in furniture finishing, provides a nice soft finish but requires more work. Also, surfaces so finished collect dust more readily.

For a natural finish of other interior trim, you need to specify the desired kind and grade of wood at the time of construction. This can add substantially to the construction costs.

Wood Floors and Their Finishes

You may want to refinish your wood floors to complement your paint job. This should be done before you paint.

Complete renewal of the floors requires a thorough removal of the old finish. This can be done by sanding or with paint and varnish remover. Sanding is probably the fastest and easiest method (see Chapter 1). Electric sanders can be rented. Be sure to sand with the grain of the wood until you have a clean, smooth surface. The table on pages 96–98 describes the method of applying the popular floor finishes.

Painting Concrete Floors

Concrete floors can be painted, but it is important to use an enamel that has good alkali resistance. There are good rubber-based, epoxy, and urethane types available. Also available and recommended are latex paints made especially for concrete floors.

Clean dirt and grease from concrete floors before you paint them. Trisodium phosphate is a good cleaner to use.

Slick concrete floors should be roughened slightly before they are painted. To roughen or etch the floor, treat it with a solution of 1 gallon of muriatic acid mixed in 2 gallons of water. (For more details on preparing a concrete floor for paint, see Chapter 4.) After treating, rinse the floor thoroughly and allow it to dry completely before you paint it.

Finishing Radiators and Pipes

1. Clean surface with sandpaper and steel scratch brush. Wipe with clean rags wet with naphtha or mineral spirits to remove all traces of oil and grease.
2. If new and unpainted, radiators should receive a first coat of standard metal primer that should be allowed to dry hard.
3. The finishing coats should be an eggshell or flat finish identical with that on the walls or woodwork of the room. Contrary to an opinion once popular, this type of paint permits the maximum radiation of heat. Aluminum and other metallic paints reduce radiation by reflecting heat into the radiator.
4. Allow the paint to dry completely before turning on the heat. Then bring the heat up slowly over a 12-hour period.

APPLICATOR TOOLS—HOW TO SELECT, USE, AND CLEAN

In order to do a good job with a minimum of trouble, choose the right tools and learn how to handle them properly. When painting your home, outside or inside, you have a choice among three tools: a brush, roller, or sprayer. Which one to use for the painting job you plan depends upon the surface to be painted.

Paint Brushes

The use of a brush assures good contact of paint with pores, cracks, and crevices. Brushing is particularly recommended for applying primer coats and exterior paints. It is also the most effective way of painting windows, doors, and intricate trim work. For spray work, window glass must be masked, a tedious affair for the most part.

SELECTING A BRUSH. Brush prices vary considerably; the greatest difference between one brush and another lies in the bristle stock, which may be made from either natural or synthetic sources. Natural bristle brushes are made with hog hair. This type of brush was originally recommended for applying oil-base paints, varnishes, lacquers, and other finishes, because natural fibers resist strong solvents.

Synthetic bristle brushes are made from a synthetic fiber, usually nylon. Today's nylon brushes are recommended for both latex (water-soluble) and oil-base paints, because this tough synthetic fiber absorbs less water than natural bristles do, while also resisting most strong paint and lacquer solvents. In addition, nylon bristles are easier to clean than natural bristles.

Brush quality determines painting ease, plus the quality of the finished job. A good brush holds more paint, controls dripping and spattering, and applies paint more smoothly to minimize brush marks. To assure that you are buying a quality brush, check the following factors:

1. Flagged bristles have split ends that help load the brush with more paint, while permitting the paint to flow on more smoothly. Cheaper brushes will have less flagging, or none at all.
2. Tapered bristles also help paint flow and provide smooth paint release. Check to see that the base of each bristle is thicker than the tip. This helps give the brush tip a fine painting edge for more even and accurate work.
3. The fullness of a brush is important too. As you press the bristles against your hand, they should feel full and springy. If the divider

FACTS ABOUT FLOOR FINISHES

Note: The following schedules are for bare floors—either new and sanded, or old with all finish removed and the dust vacuumed. If a stain is used, be sure it is compatible with topcoating. Full drying of finish is important. The time needed varies widely with temperature and humidity. Times given in chart below are approximate.

Preparation	First coat	Wood filler	Second coat	Third coat	Wax
			SHELLAC (3-POUND-CUT)		
See *Note* above; use no oil stain	Brush on uniformly; let dry 2 hours; hand-sand with 2/0 paper; dust	If desired	Let dry 3 hours for recoat, 4 before walking on	Advisable over unfilled woods; sand with 3/0	Apply as directed on container
			LACQUER		
See *Note* above; use no oil stain; apply special primer (optional for oak, required for pine and maple); let dry well	Apply with brush or mohair roller; work fast to avoid lap marks; dry 1 hour; hand-sand with 2/0 paper; dust	No filler required unless pores are very large	Let dry overnight if final coat; for 3rd coat, sand after 3 hours and dust	Reduce: 3 parts lacquer to 1 part thinner	Not essential until wear begins to roughen surface

			PENETRATING WOOD FINISH*		
See *Note* above	Brush, roll, or swab it on; let penetrate 20 to 30 minutes; wipe off excess; let dry, following directions on label	If desired; usually not used	Same as first coat; let dry according to label directions	Not needed	If desired
			VARNISH		
See *Note* above	Use 1 part thinner to 8 parts varnish; brush or roll on; let dry; hand-sand with 2/0 paper; dust	Use if smoothest surface is desired	Apply full strength; let dry 24 hours; for 3rd coat, hand-sand and dust	Apply full strength if desired; let dry 24 hours	Immediately, or delay until wear begins to dull surface
			POLYURETHANE VARNISH**		
See *Note* above	Apply with brush or roller; let dry 6–8 hours; sand with 3/0 paper; use clear to build finish	Use no filler	Use clear for glossy look or to build finish; dry and sand as before	If satin finish is desired, use it for final coat only	Optional

* One-coat method: Swab material on rapidly; keep surface wet for 30 to 60 minutes by adding more material as dry spots appear, then wipe clean and dry. Commercial method: Contractors buff penetrating sealer into the wood with #2 steel wool on a machine, instead of wiping. *Important:* Spread wiping rags to dry outdoors. They're a fire hazard.

** Be sure to read labels of all "plastic" varnishes carefully. Some recommend special fillers. Some have instructions not common to all brands.

(continued)

FACTS ABOUT FLOOR FINISHES *(Continued)*

Note: The following schedules are for bare floors—either new and sanded, or old with all finish removed and the dust vacuumed. If a stain is used, be sure it is compatible with topcoating. Full drying of finish is important. The time needed varies widely with temperature and humidity. Times given in chart below are approximate.

Preparation	First coat	Wood filler	Second coat	Third coat	Wax
GYM-TYPE FINISH					
See *Note* above; seal wood with 3-pound shellac; dry 2 hours; sand and dust	Brush on in a smooth even coating	If desired	Apply after 2 hours and before 6 hours; if latter is impossible, wait 48 hours	Not needed	Optional
TWO-COMPONENT VARNISH					
See *Note* above; use no oil stain	Brush on full strength (for maple, reduce 1 to 4); let dry 3 hours; hand-sand with 2/0 paper; dust	See manufacturer's instructions	Brush on; let dry 4–6 hours; sand and dust before 3rd coat	Required for pine; let final coat dry 48 hours before waxing (cure takes 2 weeks)	As directed on container

* One-coat method: Swab material on rapidly; keep surface wet for 30 to 60 minutes by adding more material as dry spots appear, then wipe clean and dry. Commercial method: Contractors buff penetrating sealer into the wood with #2 steel wool on a machine, instead of wiping. *Important:* Spread wiping rags to dry outdoors. They're a fire hazard.

** Be sure to read labels of all "plastic" varnishes carefully. Some recommend special fillers. Some have instructions not common to all brands.

in the brush setting is too large, the bristles will feel skimpy, and there will be a large hollow space in the center of the brush.

4. Bristle length should vary. As you run your hand over the bristles, some shorter ones should pop up first, indicating a variety of bristle lengths for better paint loading and smoother release.
5. A strong setting is important for bristle retention and maximum brush life. Bristles should be firmly bonded into the setting with epoxy glue, and nails should be used only to hold the ferrule to the handle. Brush size and shape are also important. The choice of a brush width is determined by the amount of open or flat area to be painted. The accompanying table may be used as a guide but should not be considered a limiting factor when selecting a brush.

PAINT BRUSH SIZES

Size (inches)	Application
1 to 1½	Touch-up and little jobs, such as toys, tools, furniture legs, and hard-to-reach corners
2 to 3	Trim work such as sashes, frames, molding, or other flat surfaces; an angular-cut brush helps do clean neat sash or narrow trim work and makes edge cutting easier
3½ to 4	Larger flat surfaces, such as floors, walls, or ceilings
4½ to 6	Large flat areas, particularly masonry surfaces, barns, or board fences

BRUSHING TECHNIQUE. Hold the brush by gripping the wide part of the handle between your fingertips near the metal ferrule. The rest of the handle should be held between your thumb and forefinger, as you would grip a pencil. This is the best way to hold the brush except when working overhead. In this case, wrap your hand around the handle with the thumb resting against the handle's inside curve. Use long, steady strokes and moderate, even pressure; excessive pressure or "stuffing" the brush into corners and cracks may damage the bristles.

Always work toward the "wet edge," the previously painted area, making sure not to try to cover too large a surface with each brush load. When loading the brush with paint, do not dip more than half the bristle length into the paint. Tap the bristle tips lightly against the inside rim of the can to remove excess. Never wipe the brush edgewise against the rim. This removes more paint than necessary, causes the brush to separate or finger, and causes tiny bubbles that make it hard to get a smooth job.

BRUSH CARE. A good brush is an expensive tool, and it pays to invest the necessary time and effort to take care of it properly. Clean brushes immediately after use with a thinner or special brush cleaner recommended by your paint or hardware store. Use turpentine or mineral spirits to remove oil-base paints, enamels, and varnish; alcohol to remove shellac; and special solvents to remove lacquer. Remove latex paints promptly from brushes with soap and water. If any type of paint is allowed to dry on a brush, a paint remover or brush-cleaning solvent will be needed. Use the following procedure to clean paint brushes:

1. After removing excess paint with a scraper, soak the brush in the proper thinner, working it against the bottom of the container.
2. To loosen paint in the center of the brush, squeeze the bristles between thumb and forefinger, then rinse the brush again in thinner. If necessary, work the brush in mild soap suds, and rinse in clear water.
3. Press out the water with a stick.
4. Twirl the brush in a container so you will not get splashed.
5. Comb the bristles carefully, including those below the surface. Allow the brush to dry by suspending it from the handle or by laying it flat on a clean surface. Then wrap the dry brush in the original wrapper or in heavy paper to keep the bristles straight. Store the brush suspended by its handle or lying flat.

TSP PAINT BRUSH CLEANER. A strong solution of trisodium phosphate makes an excellent cleaner for old brushes so hardened with paint they are no longer usable. The water should be hot and contain 4 ounces of TSP per quart (*Caution:* Wear rubber gloves and don't spatter the solution on surroundings.) A squat 1-pound coffee can makes a good working container.

Start by pressing the bristles against the bottom of the can to work the cleaner up into the heel of the brush. Separate the bristles with a comb or the edge of a putty knife as the paint softens. Keep dunking the brush and combing it until all the paint has been removed. When the brush is clean, rinse it thoroughly in plain water to remove all the solution. Squeeze out excess water and smooth the bristles to their proper shape. Let dry thoroughly before wrapping for storage.

Paint Rollers

Paint rollers are faster than brushes when working on large, flat surfaces. It has been estimated that rollers are now being used to apply over 75 percent of all interior wall and ceiling paint, and they are also being used in an impressive share of outdoor painting tasks as well.

SELECTING A ROLLER. It is important to choose the proper type of roller for the particular job to be done. Modern paint rollers are available in various sizes and with handles of different lengths. Many are built so that extensions can be screwed into their handles. This makes it possible to paint ceilings or stairwells as high as 12 feet while standing on the floor, or to paint the floor without stooping. You can enamel a baseboard much faster with a roller than a brush and thus will have to spend less time in an uncomfortable position.

Paint rollers are available in many different shapes, sizes, and "nap" lengths. Some of them are intended for working into corners, some for delicate trim work. There's even one designed specifically for painting posts and columns. Look them over; you can usually tell whether a non-standard roller would be useful by visualizing its performance.

The standard rollers come in a universal core diameter, to fit any roller handle. They come in two lengths—7 and 9 inches. There is a wide range of thickness of the roller pile or nap—actually its length. If you are going to paint a rough surface such as the basement wall, a long nap will work paint into the pores and crevices. But if the job is a smooth wall in the living area, a shorter nap will produce the best results.

ROLLER TECHNIQUE. Before applying the paint with a roller, first cut in the edges of the wall and hard-to-reach areas with a brush or with an edging roller, taking care not to get paint on the ceiling or the adjacent wall.

Some roller models have a roll that may be filled with paint, which soaks through a perforated backing into the pile cover. However, most rollers used by amateurs are manually loaded from a tilted tray, which usually has a corrugated bottom. Before paint is poured into the roller tray, it should be thoroughly mixed in the can to assure even pigment distribution. The tray should be propped so that about two-thirds of the bottom is covered with paint.

Dip the roller into the tray. Drip it into the edge of the paint, rolling the tool back and forth over the slanting corrugated section of the tray to distribute the paint evenly over the entire surface of the roller and to remove excess paint. If the roller drips when lifted from the tray, it is overloaded. The excess should be wiped off on the dry side of the tilted tray before you begin your stroke.

Apply even pressure when rolling paint on a surface. Even if the general direction of the painting may be downward, make your first stroke upward to avoid dripping. Work up and down first, doing about three strips, then work the roller horizontally to assure even coverage. As you progress, always start in a dry area and roll toward one just painted, blending in the laps.

ROLLER CARE. Rollers should be thoroughly cleaned after each use. You should use the same cleaning liquids as those recommended for brushes for the various types of coatings. Pour the liquid into a shallow pan and roll the tool back and forth in it. Then roll out the paint and thinner on newspaper. The roller cover can also be cleaned by putting it into a large-mouth jar filled with thinner for water (if you are using a water-thinned paint), and then shaking the jar.

The paint tray should also be cleaned after each use. If you line it with newspaper held in place with masking tape, before use, your cleaning will be much easier. Tin or aluminum foil serves better with water-base paints, since newspapers may disintegrate when wet with water. After the roller has been washed, wipe with a clean dry cloth and wrap in aluminum foil. This will keep it soft until the next time it is used.

DAUBERS. The first time anyone looks at one of the paint daubers now on the market, he snickers. But after he tries one he is ready to apologize. There are innumerable types of daubers in any good paint store. They are tiny—intended for painting delicate trim and windows. They are gross—intended for painting siding in a single stroke.

Basically, a dauber is a piece of napped fabric fastened to a flat surface, with a handle. The pile or nap is not unlike that on a paint roller. But in operation the dauber slides along the surface, forming a sort of vacuum because of the movement and friction. Like magic, the paint is pulled from the nap, and spread smoothly and uniformly on the surface.

Where does the dauber fit into the world of painting? In the hands of a novice, who finds smooth brush application difficult. And in the hands of any pro who discovers how daubers often do the job more efficiently in many situations, on many surfaces.

Paint Sprayers

Paint sprayers are particularly useful for large areas. Spraying is much faster than brushing or rolling and, although some paint will likely be wasted through overspraying, the savings in time and effort may more than compensate for any additional paint cost. Once you have perfected your spraying technique, you can produce a coating with excellent uniformity in thickness and appearance. In many localities, paint sprayers may be rented on a daily or weekly basis from paint dealers or tool-rental shops.

Surface areas accessible only with difficulty to the brush or roller can readily be covered by the sprayer. All coats can be applied satisfactorily by the spray technique except for the primer coats. Spraying should be done only on a clean surface since the paint may not adhere well if a dust film is present.

Prepreparation of the paint is of critical importance when a sprayer is to be used. Stir or strain the paint to remove any lumps, and thin it carefully. If the paint is lumpy or too thick, it may clog the spray valve; if it is too thin, the paint may sag or run after it is applied. Follow the manufacturer's instructions on the paint label for the type and amount of thinner to be used.

SPRAYER TECHNIQUE. Before you begin, ask your paint dealer to show you exactly how the sprayer works, and to give you pointers on how to use it to best advantage. For best results:

1. Adjust the width of the spray fan to the size of the surface to be coated. A narrow fan is best for spraying small or narrow surfaces; a wider fan should be used to spray table tops or walls.
2. Before spraying any surface, test the thickness of the paint, the size of the fan, and the motion of the spray gun. Excessive thickness can cause rippling of the wet film or lead to blistering later.
3. Hold the nozzle about 8 inches from the surface to be painted.
4. Start the stroke or motion of the hand holding the sprayer while the spray is pointed slightly beyond the surface to be painted. This assures a smooth, even flow when you reach the surface to be coated.
5. Move the sprayer parallel to the surface, moving back and forth across the area with an even stroke. Spray corners and edges first.
6. Use a respirator to avoid inhaling vapors.
7. Cover everything close to the work area with drop cloths, tarps, or newspapers. The "bounce-back" from a sprayer may extend several feet from the work surface.

CARE OF SPRAYING EQUIPMENT. Paint-spraying equipment should be cleaned before the paint sets because otherwise it may be difficult or even impossible to remove the hardened paint from the operating mechanisms. With accelerated or catalyst-set types of paint (such as epoxy) now being used, cleaning must usually be done within a matter of minutes. If paints of the latter type are allowed to harden in the operating mechanism, they cannot be removed and valuable parts may have to be discarded.

When spray equipment is to be taken out of service, clean the paint pot thoroughly with an appropriate solvent and wipe it out. Then place clean solvent in the pot and force it through the gun until all paint has been removed.

The nozzles of small pressurized paint containers may be cleaned by turning the can upside down and pressing the valve until only propellant gas comes through the nozzle.

PAINT REMOVERS

Removing Hard Paint and Varnish with Lye

Many homeowners and do-it-yourself enthusiasts have discovered what professional painters and furniture refinishers have known for a long time—that the fastest and cheapest way to remove old, hard, and many-layered coatings of paint and varnish is with a strong solution of everyday household lye. The method can be used successfully on woodwork, metals (except aluminum), and old furniture. In many cases, a lye solution will do a stripping job as well as, or better than, a solvent-type cleaner costing ten to fifteen times as much.

Don't try lye, however, unless you can meet the following conditions:

1. Lye and the softened paint must be flushed off finally with a garden hose or buckets (literally) of water. This means that it must be used over an unpainted concrete floor (say in a garage or a basement) provided with a drain, or outdoors over concrete or dirt where the runoff will not damage grass or plants.
2. Because lye solution works too slowly when cold, it must be used where the air temperature is at least 70° F.
3. As with other strong paint removers, you must wear rubber gloves (the best for this and similar uses are workmen's gauntlet-type canvas gloves coated with neoprene, a synthetic rubber that resists acids, alkalies, and solvent), and protect from spatter any of the surroundings that might be damaged by it.

If you can meet these conditions, here is what you do: Measure 1 quart of cold water into an earthenware crock or an enamel or stainless steel utensil. Do not use aluminum. Dissolve 1 can of household lye in the water, pouring it in slowly and stirring with a stick as you pour.

Next, measure 2 quarts of water into another container of similar material and stir in 4 heaping tablespoons of ordinary cornstarch. Then pour the lye solution into the cornstarch solution, stirring as you do so. The resulting mixture is of a jellylike consistency that helps hold the lye against upright surfaces.

To remove paint or varnish, merely apply the solution to the surface with a scrubbing brush (remember the rubber gloves!). Let stand a few minutes, then flush off with water. If more paint remains, repeat the procedure. When all has been removed, flush off thoroughly with the hose.

When dry, metal surfaces are ready for repainting without further treatment. After thorough rinsing, wood surfaces should be dried with old rags or paper towels and then rinsed with a solution of 1 part vinegar to 1 part water, followed by a final rinse with plain water.

Lye solution will generally darken wood. If this is objectionable, you can lighten it again by applying a household liquid chlorine bleach (Clorox, Rose-X, Purex, etc.) as a neutralizer instead of the vinegar. Rinse finally, as in the other case.

If you prefer a straight liquid to a pasty remover, you can use the lye solution described above all by itself. You can apply it with a wad of cotton waste or cloth tied to the end of a stick. Keep mopping on the solution, as the paint softens, until you are down to the bare wood.

Lye Paste Paint Remover

Except on flat, horizontal surfaces, the paste form of paint remover adheres better and is easier to apply. Here is another type of lye remover, containing soft soap and whiting to lend body and pumice powder to help final removal of the paint:

	Parts
Sodium hydroxide (lye)	10
Soft soap	30
Whiting	20
Pumice powder	10
Water	30

Put the water in an earthenware, enamel, or stainless steel vessel. Dissolve the lye in the water, pouring it in slowly and stirring with a stick. (*Caution:* Observe all the conditions in handling lye mentioned in the preceding section.) Next stir in soft soap. Mix the whiting and the pumice powder thoroughly, and then stir this into the lye and soap mixture until it is uniformly distributed.

Apply thickly with a fiber-bristled brush (lye eats hair!). Let remain until paint has softened down to the wood, then scrape off. Finally wash the surface thoroughly with plain water, and dry with rags or else with a dry mop.

Universal Paint Remover

The following preparation will remove most finishes, including paint, varnish, lacquer, and shellac:

Toluol	1 quart
Paraffin wax	4 ounces
Acetone	1 pint
Denatured alcohol	1 pint

Warm the toluol slightly by placing a pan of it in another pan of warm water. (*Caution:* All the ingredients in this mixture are flammable, so do not mix or use near any open flame. Also mix and use in a well-ventilated room, as the vapors are somewhat toxic.) Melt the wax separately in a double boiler and pour it, stirring, into the warm toluol. Then add the acetone and alcohol and stir until all are combined. Store it in a tightly capped metal or glass container.

To use, shake well and then flow on in a thick coat on the surface to be treated. Do not brush out. Leave undisturbed for about 30 minutes, then test by pressing down one finger into it, using a small rotary motion. If by this test your finger touches bare wood, the remover has done its job; if not, apply more remover and wait until the test is positive. Then remove the softened finish with a putty knife. Before refinishing, wash off any remaining wax with paint thinner or turpentine.

TSP as a Paint Remover

Used in a much higher concentration than for cleaning paint, trisodium phosphate makes an excellent paint remover—one that is easier to handle than lye, yet is cheap and effective if the paint coating is not too thick. Use it in the same proportion as for the cleaning of paint brushes—1 pound of TSP per gallon of hot water. Mop or brush on the solution and let it remain for about 30 minutes, then remove the softened paint with a dull scraper or putty knife. Rinse the clean surface well with plain water, and dry it with rags or a dry mop to prevent excessive raising of the wood grain. (*Caution:* Wear rubber gloves when handling hot concentrated TSP solution, and do not spill it on surfaces from which you do not wish to remove paint.)

TSP Paint Remover for Walls

This paint remover for vertical surfaces is not quite as caustic as one made with lye, but be sure to wash it off with plain water immediately if you get any on yourself or your surroundings.

Trisodium phosphate	1 part
Whiting	2 parts
Water	

Mix the TSP thoroughly with the whiting and add enough water to make a thick paste. Apply with a trowel or putty knife to a thickness of about ⅜ inch. Allow to remain about 30 minutes. Then scrape it off, with the finish beneath it. Rinse with plain water.

Varnish Remover Procedure

1. Apply paint and varnish remover freely with one-way strokes only. Leave until the old surface softens, wrinkles, or becomes blistered.
2. Peel off the material with a flexible putty knife. Wipe the knife on squares of newspaper. Burn all waste promptly, to reduce fire hazard, or keep it in tightly covered metal containers until this can be done.
3. Recoat the surface as often as may be needed.
4. Use No. 2 steel wool and denatured alcohol for the final cleanup.
5. Wash thoroughly with alcohol and burlap or bagging. Wipe dry with clean rags. Use a wooden picking stick on all panel lines and moldings.
6. Carefully use a scratch brush or a fiber brush to clean any carvings that may be present.

Finishing, Plating, and Working Metals

HOW TO BUFF METALWARE

Few workshop operations are as satisfying as buffing. With little effort, dramatic changes take place right before your eyes.

Almost any metal object that was shiny once will respond. Wall-switch plates, decorative copper pots, silverware, door knobs and knockers, andirons, and golf clubs can all be restored to their original brilliant finish.

The process of buffing involves three operations. The first is *polishing*, which, surprisingly, is the term for a coarse preliminary operation done with a specially prepared polishing wheel. This removes the pits and scratches and prepares the surface for the next operation, *cutting down*. This is actually buffing with sharp buffing compounds that remove the smaller imperfections and leave the metal bright. *Coloring* is the final buffing, done with soft compounds, to bring out the natural color and luster of the metal.

TYPES OF BUFFS AND COMPOUNDS FOR VARIOUS MATERIALS

MATERIAL	FOR CUTTING		FOR COLORING	
	Wheel	Compound	Wheel	Compound
Iron, steel, other hard metals	spiral sewed	emery or stainless	cushion	stainless
Brass, copper, aluminum, soft metals	spiral sewed	tripoli	cushion or loose	stainless or rouge
Brass or copper plate	Do not cut.		loose, cushion, or flannel	tripoli or rouge
Solid and plated gold or silver	Do not cut.		flannel	natural rouge or jewelers' rouge
Nickel or chrome plate	spiral sewed	stainless	cushion or loose	stainless

Selecting Wheels

Buffing wheels are made in various types for different operations. Before buying, consult the table shown on page 111 to determine the wheel diameter and thickness best suited to the horsepower and speed of your motor.

Spiral-sewed wheels are stitched in a continuous circle from center to face, making them hard and well suited to cutting down. Cushion-sewed wheels have only two or three rows of stitching to provide a resilient, cushioning effect. Softest are the loose wheels, which are joined by a single circle of stitching around the arbor hole. Loose wheels are also made in flannel.

Preparing and Using a Polishing Wheel

Mount several spiral-sewed wheels on a dowel and roll them in liquid glue poured on waxed paper. Smooth out blobs of glue with fingers and hang wheel to dry for 24 hours. Then sand smooth to remove loose or projecting threads.

To apply powdered grit, roll wheel again through abrasive, such as

No. 280 grit silicon carbide. Roll wheel back and forth without pressing until entire surface is coated. For fast work, make a second wheel using a coarser grit, such as No. 120.

When glue dries, scrape off loose abrasive and tap face of wheel with ball end of ball peen hammer to produce hundreds of tiny cracks, making the wheel flexible enough to follow contours. Ink an arrow on one side of the wheel so you can always mount it to turn in the same direction. Also mark on it the grit size. Properly made, an abrasive wheel will give long service.

This wheel cuts fast. Rust disappears almost immediately; pits and scratches take a little longer. After a good working over with abrasive wheel, metal is bright and smooth and ready for cutting down and coloring.

Cutting-down and coloring wheels are made by applying stick buffing compounds to uncoated wheels. Mark wheels with the compound used on them and use them only with that compound.

BUFFING AND POLISHING SCHEDULES

Material	Method of working (Note: s.f.p.m. means surface feet per minute)
Aluminum	Polish at 5,500 s.f.p.m. using Nos. 80, 120, and 180 grits. All wheels over 120 grit should be well greased. Buff at 7,500 s.f.p.m., using tripoli for the first buffing and finishing with red rouge.
Brass	Polish at 6,000 s.f.p.m. using Nos. 80, 120, and 180 grits. The 80 grit is necessary only for rough coatings. Buff with tripoli or emery at a speed of about 5,500 s.f.p.m.
Cast iron	Use grits 120, 150, and 180. The two coarser grits can be run dry. Buff at 7,500 s.f.p.m. Buff with 220 to 240 grit silicon carbide applied to a greased rag wheel.
Copper	Same schedule as brass. Fine-grit wheels should be greased. Avoid heavy pressure since copper heats quickly and holds heat longer than other metals.
Lacquered surfaces	Use a lacquer suitable for buffing. Buff at 6,000 s.f.p.m., using any reliable brand of lacquer buffing compound.
Nickeled surfaces	Buff at 7,500 s.f.p.m. using tripoli and lime. A perfect finish is necessary if the work is to be chromium plated.
Plastic	Polish with 200 grit silicon carbide. Buff with 400 and 500 grit silicon carbide on greased wheels. Finish with red or green rouge.
Steel	Polish at 7,500 s.f.p.m., using aluminum oxide grits Nos. 90 and 120 dry and No. 180 greased. Buff with tripoli or a very fine grit aluminum oxide. For a mirror finish, buff with green rouge. For satin finish, buff with pumice on a Tampico brush.

Buffing Techniques

Knowing what wheel to use with what compound on what material is only half of your buffing education. The other, equally important, half is knowing how to use your equipment. Here are some tips:

1. Protect your eyes with safety goggles or a face shield.
2. Leave your necktie in the closet; it is dangerous around a buffing wheel.
3. Wear gloves unless the work is so small or delicate that gloves are impractical. Much heat is generated when buffing and the work often becomes uncomfortably hot.
4. Wear a shop coat and hat to catch the dust that will settle on you.
5. Hold work firmly against the buffing wheel slightly below the spindle center and move it up and down—up to get the maximum cut, and down to blend the cuts together.
6. Never take your eyes off the work, not even for a moment. The fast-moving wheel can snatch the work away from you, especially when it strikes an edge.
7. Inspect the work frequently while cutting. When the many fine lines and scratches are blended out, you are ready for coloring.

BUFFING WHEEL SELECTION TABLE FOR VARIOUS SIZE MOTORS

	RECOMMENDED WHEEL THICKNESS			
Motor size	4-inch diameter	6-inch diameter	8-inch diameter	10-inch diameter
1/6–1/8 hp	1	1/2		
1/4 hp	1 1/2	1	1/2	
1/3 hp	2 1/2	2	1 1/2	1/2
1/2 hp	3	2 1/2	2	2

FORMULA FOR CALCULATING SURFACE FEET PER MINUTE (S.F.P.M.)

(Ideal buffing speed is 5,000 s.f.p.m.)

$$\frac{\text{diameter of wheel in inches}}{4} \times \text{r.p.m. of spindle} = \text{s.f.p.m.}$$

Example:

$$\frac{\text{6-inch diameter wheel}}{4} \times 3{,}450 \text{ r.p.m.} = 5{,}175 \text{ s.f.p.m.}$$

COLORING METALS WITH CHEMICALS

The chemical coloring of metals ought to be more popular in home workshops than it is. In most cases the process is simple, and the results range from pleasing to spectacular.

Before applying any of the following formulas, be sure the metal to be treated is absolutely clean. If lacquered, remove this finish with a lacquer solvent or a heavy-cutting buffing compound. Unlacquered brass, copper, and aluminum can be cleaned by rubbing with a good metal polish. Wash in hot water with a strong detergent and follow with a hot-water rinse.

Many of the processes are simply artificially induced corrosion. Others etch the metal bare. To prevent continued action, rinse them in very hot water. Brass, copper, and aluminum objects can then be waxed or coated with a clear metal lacquer. Colored steel tools and hardware should be coated with oil.

Caution: When using the processes described below, you may be working with acids, lye, or other caustic materials. Protect your skin against spills or splashes with rubber gloves, longs sleeves, and an apron. Wear shop eye goggles. Since heat is required in many cases, you may have to work in the kitchen. In this case, keep chemicals away from food, utensils, and countertops. A final safety note: *Always add acid to water, not the reverse.*

Black on Brass

Dissolve 1 ounce of copper nitrate in 6 ounces of water and apply to the brass. Then heat the brass to change the copper nitrate to copper oxide, which produces a permanent black finish.

Instead of heating, you may apply this solution over the copper nitrate coating.

Sodium sulfide	1 ounce
Hydrochloric acid, concentrated *(Caution:* caustic)	½ ounce
Water	10 ounces

This changes the coating to black copper sulfide.

Dull Black on Brass

Dissolve copper scraps in concentrated nitric acid diluted with an equal amount of water in a glass container. (*Caution:* Nitric acid is extremely caustic.) Immerse brass object in solution until desired depth of black has been produced. Remove and wash well with water. If desired, the coating can be given a sheen by rubbing with linseed oil.

Golden Matte on Brass

Immerse in a solution of 1 part concentrated nitric acid (remember that nitric acid is caustic) in 3 parts water in a glass container. Rock the solution gently. Wipe the object clean under running tap. When dry, protect the surface with wax or lacquer.

Antique-Green Patina on Brass

Potassium bitartrate (cream of tartar)	3 ounces
Ammonium chloride	1 ounce
Copper nitrate	7½ ounces
Sodium chloride (table salt)	3 ounces
Water, boiling	13 ounces

Dissolve the salts in the boiling water and apply the hot solution to the brass with a piece of sponge or rag mounted on a stick. When the desired effect has been attained, wash and dry.

As another method, paint the object daily for 3 or 4 days with this solution:

Copper carbonate	3 ounces
Ammonium chloride	1 ounce
Copper acetate	1 ounce
Potassium bitartrate	1 ounce
Strong vinegar	8 ounces

Yellow-Orange, Blue, Red-Brown on Brass

You can get yellow through bluish tones by immersing the object in the following solution. Increase the concentration for bluish tone.

Sodium hydroxide (lye, *caustic*)	½ ounce
Copper carbonate	1 ounce

Hot water	24 ounces

Get red-brown shades by brief dip in this solution:

Copper carbonate	¼ ounce
Household ammonia	7½ ounces
Sodium carbonate (Washing soda)	¼ ounce
Water, near boiling	48 ounces

Cold-rinse the object and dip for a moment in dilute sulfuric acid (*caution:* caustic). Experiment for different shades.

Black on Copper

Potassium or sodium sulfide	¼ ounce
Household ammonia	1½ ounces
Water	32 ounces

Do not heat this solution, as heat will drive off the ammonia gas.

Light Matte on Copper

Use same treatment as for golden matte on brass, above.

Antique-Green Patina on Copper

Use same treatment as for similar finish on brass, above.

Yellow-Green Patina on Copper

Swab the object for a few days with a mixture of equal parts of sugar, salt, and strong vinegar. Don't immerse the metal. Crush the salt and sugar to a fine powder before mixing the solution.

Bright Blue on Copper

Lead acetate *(Caution:* poison)	½ ounce
Sodium thiosulfate (hypo)	1 ounce
Water	32 ounces

Immerse the object in this solution for about 15 seconds.

Bronze on Copper

Ferric nitrate	1½ ounces
Potassium thiocyanate	½ ounce
Water	32 ounces

Use this solution hot. Heat the metal object by first immersing it in hot water. Then dip in the hot chemical solution until the color is satisfactory. Rinse in running water and dry in breeze of a fan.

Red-Bronze to Brown on Copper

Sulfurated potassium (liver of sulfur)	½ ounce
Sodium hydroxide (lye)	¾ ounce
Water	32 ounces

Use this solution hot and dip the object in it.

Concentration and temperature of the solution, metals alloyed with the copper, and time of immersion will cause differences of color.

Steel-Gray on Aluminum

Zinc chloride	8 ounces
Copper sulfate	1 ounce
Water, boiling	32 ounces

Immerse the objects until desired tone is obtained. Rinse in a 2-percent solution of lye *(Caution)* in water, then thoroughly in clear water.

Near-White and Matte Colors on Aluminum

A soft-etched, imitation anodized finish may be produced on aluminum by dipping it in a solution of 1 tablespoon or more of lye to a pint of water. To color the aluminum, then dip it in a solution of household dye. (*Caution:* Be careful with the lye—caustic.)

Black on Iron and Steel

Heat red-hot and dip in heavy engine or linseed oil. Most cast irons, etched or blasted, will become bluish-brownish or blackish if soaked or painted with a solution of 6 tablespoons of tannic acid in 1 pint of water.

This formula is also good:

Copper sulfate	2 ounces
Concentrated nitric acid	4 ounces
Denatured alcohol	10 ounces
Water	24 ounces

Dissolve the copper sulfate completely in the water. Then stir in the nitric acid (*caution:* corrosive) and the alcohol. Apply this solution uniformly to the metal and allow to air dry. If not black enough, apply again. When dry, rub on a coat of linseed oil.

Brown on Iron and Steel

The following is an old formula for coloring the outside of gun barrels. It is especially popular because the ingredients can usually be obtained at the drugstore.

Copper sulfate	¾ ounce
Mercuric chloride	1 ounce
Concentrated nitric acid	½ ounce
Denatured alcohol	1 ounce
Tincture ferric chloride	1 ounce
Tincture ethyl nitrate (sweet spirits of nitre)	1 ounce
Water	25 ounces

Dissolve the copper sulfate and the mercuric chloride in the water, then stir in the other ingredients in the order named. Apply the solution uniformly with a pad of glass wool and expose to the air for 24 hours. Then wash in hot water, dry in air, and wipe with linseed oil. (*Caution:* nitric acid, caustic; mercuric chloride, poison.)

Blue on Iron and Steel

Ferric chloride	2 ounces
Antimony chloride	2 ounces

Gallic acid	1 ounce
Water	5 ounces

Dissolve in the order given, and apply the same as the last formula. (*Caution:* Antimony chloride, poison.)

Antiquing Copper

When the natural color of copper or a highly polished finish is inappropriate, it is a simple matter to give it a more subdued "antique" or French finish.

Dissolve about 1 cubic inch of potassium sulfide (liver of sulfur) in 1 pint of water. Add 6 drops of household ammonia. Clean the copper thoroughly to remove all dirt and grease, and rapidly swab on the solution. The metal will gradually darken to black. With a cloth or toothbrush and clear water, rub off the outer black deposit immediately. If the metal is not then a deep brown-black, clean thoroughly and repeat the process. Wash well and dry with a cloth.

With a very fine steel wool, rub to bring out the tone desired. The less rubbing, the deeper the tone. Excessive rubbing will restore the copper to its natural color. It is at this point that recessed parts can be left dark, while high parts are brightened to the amount desired. A smooth surface can be given an attractive mottled appearance by judicious use of steel wool, some spots being left darker than others.

The finish should be protected either with clear metal lacquer or by several coats of good-quality wax, each left to harden and then polished.

Apart from embossing, peening, crimping, and other worked effects that are set off by the treatment, considerable variation on a smooth surface is possible by scratch-brushing, sandpapering, or rubbing with coarse steel wool before treatment. The deeper the scratches, the more dark tones will remain, and the more "grain" and the deeper the tone the finish will have.

ANNEALING AND PICKLING COPPER AND ITS ALLOYS

When being shaped, copper, brass, and other alloys of copper become work-hardened and must be softened by annealing. They also become dirty and covered with an oxide, and must be cleaned, or "pickled," in an acid bath. During forming, annealing and pickling may be done in a single operation. When forming is completed, only pickling is necessary.

Annealing

Heat piece to dull red over a Bunsen burner, gas stove, or with torch. Move the piece in the flame to bring it slowly and evenly up to annealing temperature. Holding it with copper tongs or tweezers, slide it gently into pickling solution, avoiding splash. The solution will anneal (by quickly cooling it) and clean the metal at the same time. Remove the piece with tongs and rinse it under warm water.

Pickling Solution

To make pickling solution for copper and alloys, mix 1 part concentrated sulfuric acid with 9 parts water. (*Caution:* Always pour the acid into the water, and not vice versa. Do not spill on skin or clothing, as acid is extremely caustic.) Mix and use in a glass or earthenware container. Cover when not in use and keep in a well-ventilated place, as concentrated fumes from it may rust nearby articles of iron and steel.

When object is completely formed, and does not have to be softened again, place in solution without heating. Let remain 5 to 10 minutes, then remove with tongs, rinse, and dry with paper towels.

CLEANING METAL FOR PLATING

Before metals can be plated, all grease, corrosion, and scale must be removed so the plating solution can make perfect contact with the bare solid metal. Grease can be removed by organic solvents, such as a combination of 1 part trichloroethylene and 1 part naphtha, or by washing in a hot solution of washing soda or trisodium phosphate. (*Careful:* Avoid breathing fumes; wear rubber gloves.) After degreasing, you can remove corrosion and scale from silver, copper, and copper compounds by dipping the objects in the pickling solution described above. From iron and other base metals, you can do so by using a weaker solution: ½ part sulfuric acid to 9½ parts water (mixing and using, of course, with the same precautions).

PLATING WITHOUT ELECTRIC CURRENT

Thin films of nickel or silver can readily be plated on copper or brass without the use of an external source of current, simply by local chemical or electrolytic action. These films are not as durable as those made by regular electroplating, but they may serve on objects that will not be subjected to hard use.

Plating with Nickel

When moistened with water, the following mixture will cause a plating of nickel to be formed on copper or brass:

Nickel ammonium sulfate	60 parts
Powdered chalk	35 parts
Powdered magnesium metal	4 parts

Mix the powders thoroughly, and apply to the previously cleaned metal with a cloth pad kept wet with water. Zinc dust may be substituted for the magnesium powder if a little tartaric acid is added to the mixture.

Plating with Silver

Silver may similarly be plated on copper or brass with the help of one of the following formulas:

FORMULA 1

Silver nitrate	1 part
Salt (not iodized)	1 part
Potassium bitartrate (cream of tartar)	14 parts

Mix these ingredients thoroughly in a glass or ceramic vessel. Apply to the cleaned metal with a damp cloth pad. Keep the powder dry until immediately before use, as moisture causes it to decompose in the presence of light. (*Caution:* Silver nitrate is poisonous and corrosive and produces an indelible stain on the skin, cloth, and other materials. So be careful not to spill it; also wear rubber gloves when applying it.)

FORMULA 2

Salt (not iodized)	12 parts
Potassium bitartrate (cream of tartar)	7 parts
Powdered chalk	10 parts
Silver nitrate	4 parts

Mix salt, potassium bitartrate, and chalk thoroughly, and then mix in the powdered silver nitrate. Apply as in Formula 1, being sure to observe the precautions, and store the remaining powder in well-stoppered bottles.

FORMULA 3

This formula is a solution, in which small objects can be immersed:

Silver nitrate	15 parts
Potassium hydroxide	15 parts
Water	50 parts

Dissolve the silver nitrate in half the water and the potassium hydroxide in the other. Use glass vessels for mixing and do not spatter either solution on yourself or your surroundings, as both are poisonous and caustic. Until ready to use, keep both solutions in opaque glass or plastic bottles with corrosion-resistant stoppers (do not use rubber stoppers on the silver nitrate bottle).

When ready to use, mix the solutions in equal quantity in a glass or plastic container, and immerse the well-cleaned object to be plated in the resulting combination, using a slight motion to remove air bubbles. Leave it for several minutes. Then remove, wash, dry, and buff lightly.

ELECTROPLATING

The plating of copper, chromium, silver, gold, or other superior metals on baser metals by means of an electric current can make a fascinating hobby, or even a profitable small business. To do a first-rate plating job with different metals on different sizes and types of objects requires special equipment, plus a knowledge of techniques and of handling extremely corrosive and poisonous chemicals that cannot be adequately described in a few pages. If you would like to investigate further, consult a book on electroplating, or write to a manufacturer or dealer in electroplating supplies, several of which are listed in the Appendix.

To Copper Plate Nonmetallic Objects

You can do this in a simple acid bath. The process is relatively safe and uncomplicated. By means of this process, you can encase small objects of wood, plaster, plastics, ceramics—or even baby shoes—in a novel and permanent sheath of metal.

First of all, you will need a source of regulated direct current—one that will deliver up to about 6 volts at up to 5, 10, or more amperes, depending upon the size of the object to be plated. This can be a storage battery, a battery charger, or a transformer-rectifier low-voltage power supply such as is used in radios. In any case, a rheostat must be connected in series with the output of the power supply and the tank electrodes to regulate the voltage. To check the current and voltage, an ammeter must be connected in series with the rheostat and a voltmeter connected in parallel with the tank terminals.

The plating tank should be large enough to handle your work. Allow at least 6 inches from the object to be plated to the anode plates, and at least 1 inch from the anodes to the tank sides. You can make it yourself from wood lined with sheet lead or sheet rubber, or you might use a one-piece rectangular glass fish tank or a container made of polyethylene.

Be sure that the finish on the object to be plated is as perfect as you can make it, as any flaws in the surface will be more conspicuous in the final metal coating.

To make the surface conductive you can coat it with copper bronzing powder held in place with thinned-down lacquer. Mix about 1 ounce of this powder with ¾ ounce of clear lacquer thinned with about 6½ ounces of lacquer thinner. Before applying this, test it on a piece of material similar to that of the object. When dry, a finger touched to the surface should show some of the copper powder. If it doesn't, add more thinner and test again.

Good electrical contact with the surface can be ensured by drilling several tiny holes in inconspicuous spots in the work and wedging in them one end of the copper wires from which the object will be suspended, afterwards touching these spots with a brush dipped in the bronzing mixture. Then spray the mixture over the whole surface.

Make the plating solution, or electrolyte, by dissolving 27 ounces of copper sulfate crystals in enough warm water to make a gallon, using a glass or plastic stirrer. Then gradually and carefully stir in 6½ ounces by weight (about 3½ fluid ounces, by measure) of concentrated sulfuric acid. (*Caution:* Always add acid to the water, and not vice versa. Do not spill on skin or surroundings as it is extremely corrosive.) Increase or decrease the quantities proportionately to make enough solution to fill your tank.

With the tank filled, place two copper or brass rods across the top, about 1 inch away from the sides. Hang from these rods (by copper wires, or by bending one end and hooking it over the rods) strips of copper sheet having an immersed area at least equal to the area to be plated. These are the anodes and should be connected to the positive lead from the current source. Connect the negative lead to a "buffer," consisting of a small piece of copper or brass, suspended from a wooden bar across the center of the tank. Turn on the current and adjust the rheostat until the voltage is between 0.75 and 2 volts. Then connect the wires attached to your object to the negative lead and suspend it also from the center bar.

If plating is taking place properly, the lacquered surface will take on a pinkish glow. The buffer sheet may be removed as soon as this happens. After 15 minutes, remove the work and inspect it carefully. Color should be a light shade of pink. If it is darkish pink, the plate is "burning." In this case, the burned areas must be removed and the object recoated with the conductive coating. You must reduce the voltage and begin again. If the color is right, continue plating until about 1/32 inch of metal (determined by caliper comparison) has been deposited.

For best plating, keep the temperature of the solution from about 77° to 80° F and agitate the object frequently. Professional platers generally keep the solution moving about the objects being plated by connecting a mechanical agitator to the rod on which they are hung or by bubbling air through the solution.

After plating, the work can be finished by very light and careful filing, buffing, and polishing. If desired, it may then be lacquered.

Note: Baby shoes can be electroplated by the same method. Begin by removing wax and polish from the shoes and treating them with lacquer to stiffen them and prevent the absorption of moisture. How to do this is explained in the article "To Metallize Baby Shoes Without Electroplating," Chapter 10. Instead of the last coat of lacquer, however, apply the bronzing mixture, suspend the shoes in the center of the tank by means of copper wires, and plate as described above.

ALLOYS THAT MELT AT LOW TEMPERATURES

Certain alloys of lead, tin, and bismuth have a lower melting point than that of any one of these metals. This curious fact was discovered by the famous Isaac Newton more than 250 years ago. Not long after that, a German chemist, Valentin Rose, and a French physicist, Jean Darcet, produced combinations of the same metals that have still lower melting points.

These and similar alloys are used today to make fusible links in automatic sprinklers, safety plugs for steam boilers, special electrical fuses, and other heat-triggered safety devices. They are also used for making molds and casts of wooden or other objects that might be damaged by molten metals of higher temperature.

Their low melting temperature makes such alloys especially useful to the home mechanic who would like to cast small metal objects but has no blast furnace. Because they have the unusual property of expanding when they cool, they make particularly sharp impressions. If he is a practical joker, the home mechanic can use them, too, to make fusible parts in spoons or other tableware. These parts will melt away when an unsuspecting friend tries to stir coffee or other hot liquid with the trick implements.

Here are the approximate formulas and melting points for the original alloys, all parts being measured by weight:

Alloy	Bismuth	Lead	Tin	Melting point, °F
Newton's	5	3	2	201
Rose's	8	5	3	200
Darcet's	2	1	1	199

As Darcet's alloy contains equal parts of lead and tin, you can make it rather easily by melting regular half-and-half solder, and mixing into this melt an equal weight of bismuth.

More recent investigators have found that by substituting cadmium for part of the tin, the melting point of low-melting alloys can be lowered still further. The following are two common examples:

Alloy	Bismuth	Lead	Tin	Cadmium	Melting point, °F
Wood's	4	2	1	1	149
Lipowitz's	15	8	4	3	154

In making fusible alloys, the lead and bismuth are generally melted together first. Then the tin is added and stirred until melted and mixed. Cadmium, which comes in sticks, may catch fire if heated too hot in the open air. So add this metal by holding a stick of it in tongs and stirring it into the other molten metals that are kept just hot enough to melt the cadmium.

Alloy for Making Exact Castings

Most metals shrink when they solidify from a melted state; bismuth, contrariwise, expands. By combining bismuth in different combinations with tin and lead, low-melting alloys that shrink, expand, or do neither, on cooling can therefore be produced.

An alloy that melts at 248° F and maintains its same dimensions when cold can be made by combining 57 percent bismuth with 43 percent tin. This alloy is used in making master patterns in foundry work and for soldering lead, tin, and zinc foils.

SOLDERS AND SOLDERING

The term "soldering" generally means "soft soldering," a method of joining two metals together with an alloy of relatively low melting point, usually composed of tin and lead.

Types of Solder

Common soft solder comes in bar, ribbon, and wire form. Wire solder may be solid or it may be tubular with a core of either acid or rosin soldering flux. Bar solder is used with heavy irons and blow torches on plumbing and large sheet-metal work, while ribbon and wire solder are used with light irons on electrical wiring and other small jobs.

When solder is designated by numbers, the first number represents the proportion of tin, the second of lead. A 40–60 solder, for instance, means a solder with 40 percent by weight of tin and 60 percent by weight of lead. One of the commonest solders for all-round use is 50–50, or "half-and-half." Soft solders for gold and silver and for copper and brass sheet generally contain more tin and melt at a lower temperature. Solders containing more lead are better for lead plumbing, but require more heat. Pewter is soldered with a special alloy to which bismuth has been added to lower the temperature below that of lead and tin alone.

So-called "liquid solders" or "cold solders," which are recommended by their manufacturers for joining all types of materials, are usually not really solders at all, but are cements or glues fortified with aluminum or other metallic powder. Although such preparations may be useful for sealing off small holes to stop leaks and for other minor patching jobs, they should not be used where real solder is required. They do not make a metal-to-metal bond, they are not electrically conductive, and they may disintegrate in the presence of organic solvents or at temperatures considerably below the softening point of lead–tin solders.

Need for Fluxes

For the solder to adhere firmly to the metals to be joined, the surfaces must be completely free of oxide. Because oxides form on most metals at room temperatures, and almost immediately when heated by a soldering iron, a coating material must be used that will remove the film already present and protect both solder and metal from further oxidation. Such a material is called a soldering "flux," from a Latin word meaning "to flow."

Except for electrical work, the fluxes most commonly used for soft soldering are solutions or pastes that contain zinc chloride or a mixture of zinc and ammonium chlorides. The heat of the soldering operation evaporates the medium containing the chloride flux. The flux then melts and partially decomposes with the liberation of hydrochloric acid, which dissolves the oxides from the metal surfaces. The fused flux also forms a protective film that prevents further oxidation.

Acid Fluxes

The fluxes just mentioned, called "acid fluxes," come in both liquid and paste form, and as the core in acid-core wire solders. Zinc chloride and ammonium chloride (sal ammoniac) are also used dry, in the form of cake or powder.

A good liquid zinc-chloride flux can be made simply by adding scraps of zinc to hydrochloric acid until no more zinc dissolves. The resulting solution should be diluted with an equal amount of water before using.

A liquid flux that combines both chemicals can be made by dissolving 2½ ounces of zinc chloride and 1 ounce of ammonium chloride in 6 ounces of water.

To make a paste-type flux, dissolve 1 teaspoon of zinc chloride and 1 teaspoon of ammonium chloride in 4 teaspoons of hot water. Then stir in thoroughly 3 ounces of petroleum jelly, heating the combination until it boils. Let cool before use.

A small stiff brush is useful in applying either liquid or paste. When the liquid flux is applied, the soldering operation should follow immediately. The paste-type flux can remain on the work for as long as an hour before soldering, owing to its lesser activity at room temperature. At soldering temperatures, however, one type is as active as the other, and once heat has been applied, soldering should be continued without delay. Otherwise, salt deposits will be formed, which will make subsequent soldering difficult.

After soldering, excess flux should be removed immediately by using a large swab and hot water.

Rosin Fluxes

Because acid fluxes do have a corrosive action, they should not be used in soldering electrical connections or on other types of work where the last traces of flux cannot be removed after the job has been completed. For such jobs, a noncorrosive flux is necessary. Rosin is the most commonly used flux of this type, and is the only flux known to be noncorrosive in all soldering applications. Rosin may be mixed with alcohol in varying proportions to obtain any desired consistency. Paste rosin flux also can be made by using petroleum jelly as a base.

Other Fluxes

Palm oil, olive oil, or rosin, or mixtures of these, have been recommended as suitable fluxes for pewter. Tallow is often used by plumbers in wiping lead joints. These mild fluxes are not corrosive, but for the sake of cleanliness and appearance are generally removed with naphtha or other organic solvent after soldering.

Soldering Irons

Soft soldering is generally done with a copper-headed tool called an "iron." Nonelectric soldering irons that must be heated by a torch or other means come in sizes from ¼ pound to 5 pounds. Electric irons are more popular today and are generally used wherever an electric circuit is available. They range from 25 to 300 watts.

In wiring radio or other electronic kits, the 25-watt size is the largest recommended for making connections to printed circuit boards, while the 50-watt size may be the largest ever needed for making chassis connections. A 150- to 200-watt iron will do for most home sheet-metal work, with the 300-watt size being required for only the heaviest jobs.

Soldering guns, which heat up almost instantly on the pull of a trigger, are used widely in electrical work; but many consider them too heavy and less convenient than a small regular iron for extensive kit wiring. Some soldering guns are available that are cordless; that is, they don't need to be plugged into an electrical outlet for operation.

Tinning the Iron

Before a soldering iron can be used, one or more faces of its tip must be filed smooth and coated with solder, or "tinned." For most work, the iron should be tinned on all four faces. For work where the iron is held under the object to be soldered, only one face should be tinned—the face to be held against the object. If all four sides were tinned in this case, solder from the top of the iron would flow down the sides and drip off the bottom. Untinned sides will prevent this flow.

To tin an iron, follow these steps:

1. File the tip faces bright while the iron is cold.
2. Plug iron into outlet (or heat over a burner, if nonelectric). As the iron heats, rub flux-core solder (or flux followed by solder) over the tip faces every 15 or 20 seconds. As soon as the iron is hot enough, the solder will spread smoothly and evenly over the faces. The purpose of this caution is to coat the copper before it gets hot enough to oxidize.

3. As soon as the tinning is completed, wipe the tip with a rag or a paper towel while the solder is still molten. This will expose a mirrorlike layer of solder on the tip faces.

Soldering a Joint

First of all, the area to be soldered must be absolutely clean. If it is dirty or greasy, clean it with a solvent cleaner. If it is heavily oxidized, clean the surface with abrasive cloth until it is bright. Make sure the parts to be soldered are rigidly supported, so they won't move while the solder is setting.

Apply the proper flux to the entire surface to which the solder is to adhere. Too much flux, however, will interfere with soldering.

Heat the soldering iron to the proper temperature. Test this by touching solder to the tip: if it melts quickly, the iron is nearly hot enough. Then heat the metal to be joined hot enough with the iron so that solder touched to it will flow into the joint. If the metal is not hot enough to vaporize the rosin and to cause the solder to take its place, the result will be a "cold-soldered" joint held together feebly and nonconductively by rosin, rather than strongly by solder.

Hard Soldering

Hard solders are distinguished from soft solders in that they have much higher melting points and form joints of much higher strength. They are used for joining such metals as copper, silver, and gold, and alloys such as brass, German silver, and so on, which require a strong joint and often solder of a color near that of the metal to be joined. When used to join common metals, hard soldering is generally called "brazing," and the lower-melting alloys are known as "spelter."

There are three general types of hard solders: precious-metal alloy solders or "silver solders," common brazing solders, and aluminum brazing solders. Because of their high melting points, hard solders cannot be applied with a soldering iron, but require the use of torches, furnaces, or dipping tanks.

PRECIOUS-METAL SOLDERS. Silver solders for use with a torch are supplied in the form of wire and powder. They consist of alloys of silver, copper, and zinc, and have melting points ranging from about 1,200° to 1,600° F. Solders containing gold are used primarily for joining gold and gold alloys, and usually are alloys of gold with copper, silver, and zinc. Gold solders are generally designated by karat numbers to indicate the fineness, or karat number of the alloy with which they should be used. Soldered joints in platinum or platinum alloys may be made with fine gold or the higher karat gold alloys.

COMMON BRAZING SOLDERS. These are generally supplied in granular, lump, rod, or wire form. They are made from different combinations of copper, zinc, and tin, and have melting points from about 1,400° to 1,980° F.

ALUMINUM BRAZING SOLDERS. These are used almost exclusively by industry. They consist of special, and usually proprietary, alloys of aluminum and must be obtained from manufacturers of aluminum alloys.

FLUXES FOR HARD SOLDERING. For most purposes, borax, or mixtures of borax with boric acid, is a good flux for the precious metal and ordinary brazing solders. The chloride fluxes used for soft soldering would vaporize immediately under the high temperatures of hard soldering, and so cannot be used here.

PROPANE TORCHES

Propane torches operate on a simple principle. The torch tank is filled with propane, a liquified petroleum gas. The propane remains in a liquid state because it is under pressure. When the valve on the burner assembly is opened, propane is released through the fuel orifice. With reduced pressure, the propane converts to a gas, which burns readily when mixed with air.

The burner assembly unit screws onto the top of the propane tank. It can be tightened by hand; a wrench should not be used. The unit is produced under rigid quality-control standards and is thoroughly flame-tested at the factory. Caution should be exercised to prevent dropping material particles down into the center-inlet valve area. Such particles could wedge the valve pin into the open position preventing normal cylinder-valve closure upon separation of the cylinder and appliance.

Lighting the Torch

If using a match, light the match and twirl or rotate it approximately 180 degrees to create a full flame. Turn the valve-control knob to the ON position as far as it will go. Hold the match to the burner at the top of and slightly behind the tip. Never hold the match directly in front of the burner tip. The force of the escaping propane will usually blow out

SOLDERING TABLE

This table will help you determine what kind of solder to use and when to apply it. For the metals listed along the top of the table, you can use the solders and fluxes shown in the left-hand column and noted for use by Xs.

	Aluminum	Chrome plate	Copper or bronze	Galvanized iron or steel	Silver and silver plate	Stainless steel	Steel
Stainless steel solder and flux (solder flows freely on contact with heated metal)		X			X	X	X
General-purpose acid-core solder (flows freely on contact with heated metal)			X	X			
All-purpose resin-core electrical solder (solder flows freely on contact with heated metal)			X				
Aluminum brazing alloy and flux (flux becomes a clear liquid)	X						
Silver solder and flux (flux becomes a thin, clear liquid and forms dull red)					X	X	X

Note: Metals with Xs in the same horizontal column can be joined.

the match. When the torch is lit, use the control knob to adjust the desired flame.

To light the torch with the sparklighter, place the cup of the sparklighter against the end of the burner. Incline the sparklighter about 30 degrees. Turn the valve-control knob to the ON position as far as it will go. Actuate the sparklighter. Use the control knob to adjust to the desired flame. Always allow the torch to warm up before using it in an inverted or upside down position.

PROPANE-TORCH BURNER TIPS AND USES

Job	Precision-burner tip	Pencil-point burner tip	Brush-flame burner tip	Flame spreader	Chisel-point soldering tip
Soldering small fittings or connections		X			
Soldering jewelry or very tiny wires	X				
Soldering electrical connections					X
Soldering flat surfaces					X
Soldering over large areas			X		
Soldering gutters		X			X
Starting threaded pipe joints		X			
Thawing pipes		X	X		
Sealing soil pipes		X			
Removing paint			X	X	
Removing putty		X			
Bending metal		X	X		
Metal sculpturing		X			
Laying asphalt tile			X	X	
Thawing frozen locks		X			
Loosening screws, nuts, bolts		X			
Lighting charcoal		X	X		
Auto body leading		X			
Removing brake linings			X	X	
Separating exhaust pipes, auto body springs		X			
Plywood sculpturing					X
Glass working		X	X		
Antiquing wood			X	X	

Soldering with a Propane Torch

You can use a propane torch to solder by the direct (open) flame method or the indirect (enclosed) flame method. The latter is usually preferable, where practical.

When using the direct method, select the burner tip best suited to the size of the job. The standard pencil-point tip, for example, is excellent for small fittings and connections. When larger areas are involved, the brush-flame tip is more efficient.

To solder by the indirect method, attach the chisel-point soldering tip to the standard pencil-point burner. Before using the chisel point, the copper tip must be tinned with solder. If the tip is not tinned, oxides will form on it and interfere with the transfer of heat to the workpiece.

When using the chisel point, press one of the flat surfaces against the work and move the tip along as the solder flows onto the workpiece.

Always use a small flame when soldering with the chisel-point tip. A large flame shortens the life of the tip and often makes it necessary to retin the soldering copper frequently.

After lighting the torch, wait about 30 seconds, until the tip hisses when it comes in contact with the flux.

To tin the copper tip, file while cool, and sandpaper or steel wool each flat side of the tip until it presents a metallic sheen. Heat the tip until the soldering copper begins to darken. Rub either solder covered with flux or flux-core solder over each flat side of the tip. Remove excess solder with steel wool or by flicking off excess solder onto a noncombustible surface. (Be careful . . . it's hot!)

Don't dip the soldering tip into the flux. Instead, use a small brush to dab the flux directly onto the part you are soldering. Apply the torch to the area to be soldered. Hold solder to area being joined and wait until temperature of material is hot enough to melt solder. It should flow smoothly over surface. End of solder flow should blend into material with a feathered edge. It should not be abrupt or "puddled" or with cleavage on the interface.

SOLDERING COPPER TUBING AND PIPE FITTINGS. A variety of plumbing jobs can be accomplished quickly and easily with a propane torch and burner attachments. Soldering or "sweating" copper tubing and fittings is a simple task with a Turner Torch. You can install water lines and repair appliances, such as washers, dryers, refrigerators, and hot water heaters, avoiding costly service charges.

"Sweat"-type fittings are widely used when making joints and connections in copper tubing. They are a quick, inexpensive, and sure means of making a joint.

First, cut the tube to the desired length with a hacksaw (32 teeth to the inch) or a disc cutter. Be sure the ends of the tube are cut square and excessive burrs are removed. Wirebrush or sandpaper the end of the tube and the inside of the fitting. Apply flux liberally to both cleaned areas and fit the tube into the joint. Apply an open flame evenly around the circumference of the fitting. As the fitting heats, be sure to move the flame back and forth to prevent overheating. When the fitting is hot enough to melt solder, remove the flame and apply solder to the edge of the fitting where it meets the tube. Continue heating until solder flows completely around the joint. Don't apply torch flame directly to solder joint. Allow heat to move from surrounding area to area being soldered, indirectly.

Wipe off excess solder and flux. Slightly reheat the connection in order to help the solder permeate the metal. Remove the flame and continue to feed solder to make certain the joint is filled. Allow the connection to cool for a moment, then remove surplus solder from around the edges with a wire brush or metal scraper.

When soldering small fittings, use the standard pencil-point burner tip. For larger fittings, use the brush flame and be especially careful to heat the entire circumference of the fitting. The flame will envelop the area to be worked.

SAFETY TIPS. Like many other tools, propane torches are safe when used properly. If abused, they can be dangerous. Follow these simple precautions for safe torch storage and operation:

1. Do not let unignited propane escape from the torch near any possible source of ignition.
2. Never store propane tanks in a confined, unventilated space, such as a closet, or any area where the temperature may exceed 120° F. Do not store in a room for habitation.
3. Never use a flame to test for propane leaks.
4. Never use a tank with a leaking valve or other fitting. If in doubt, test by brushing a generous amount of liquid detergent over the suspected area and check for bubble formations.
5. Never lay a torch down unless the gas flow has been shut off. If maintaining a pilot flame during work pauses, use a rack or stand for the torch and keep it away from combustible materials.
6. Don't start fires. Be very careful when working near combustible materials and use asbestos shields when necessary.
7. Never solder a container that holds or has held flammable fluids or gases unless the container has been totally purged of these mate-

rials. If in doubt as to the previous contents of a container, thoroughly purge it. Be sure any container you work on is well vented.

8. Propane consumes oxygen and generates toxic fumes; therefore, use torch only in a well-ventilated area.
9. Avoid breathing vapors and fumes generated during torch usage. Provide ventilation that will move vapors away from work area.

MAPP GAS TORCHES

While it looks a great deal like the propane torch, the MAPP gas torch designed for home use is not an ordinary outfit. The gas in the cylinder is called MAPP (a trademark of Airco, Inc.), and the regulator and burner heads are different to suit the new compound.

MAPP gas gets hotter than propane, and thus makes metal brazing possible. The flame temperature of MAPP will be about 3200° F, depending on the particular torch used. This is up to 500° F or so hotter than most propane torch units. Even if you use MAPP only for propane torch jobs, you can probably save money because you heat more rapidly.

While the MAPP gas torch is designed as a heating torch that produces the higher temperatures needed for brazing and aluminum welding, the torch can be used for such jobs as flame hardening, melting, burning off paint, removing old putty, softening brittle tile, replacing damaged tile, leveling tile, etc.

Brazing or hard soldering, silver soldering, and aluminum welding, because of the structural superiority of the joints they produce, make the MAPP gas torch a useful home-repair tool. Garden tools, lawnmowers, toys, fences, metal furniture, and many more items can be given new life with brazing repair.

Brazing

Brazing is a process in which metals are joined with metal with the use of a wirelike rod. The brazing rod may be stainless steel, aluminum alloy, nickel silver, or a bronze alloy, and may be bare or coated with flux. The material and type depend on the materials to be brazed. When the metals to be joined are heated (generally to cherry red) and the brazing rod applied, the rod material melts and flows into the joint to make a strong weldlike bond.

A WORD OF CAUTION: If you are not familiar with brazing procedures, study the manual that comes with the torch. Practice the

SOLDERING AND BRAZING RODS FOR MAPP GAS TORCHES

	Aluminum	Chrome plate	Copper	Copper or bronze	Galvanized iron or steel	Silver and silver plate	Stainless steel	Steel
Stainless steel and flux (solder flows freely on contact with heated metal)		X				X	X	X
General-purpose acid-core solder (solder flows freely in contact with heated metal)				X	X			
All-purpose resin-core electrical solder (solder flows freely on contact with heated metal)			X					
Aluminum brazing alloy and flux (flux becomes a clear liquid)	X							
Silver solder and flux (flux becomes a thin, clear liquid and forms dull red)					X	X	X	X
Aluminum bare brazing rod (brazing rod puddles on contact with heated metal)	X				X			

Flux-coated nickel-silver brazing rod (brazing rod flows freely on contact with heated metal)		X		X	X		X	X
Flux-coated bronze brazing rod (brazing rod flows freely on contact with heated metal)		X		X	X		X	X
Copper-phosphorous brazing rod (brazing rod flows freely on contact with heated metal)				X				

Note: Metals with Xs in the same horizontal column can be joined.

USES FOR SOLDER OR BRAZING RODS:

Aluminum: for strength in joining sheets, sections, etc.

Chrome plate: for trim when on steel, brass, copper or nickel alloys (not on die castings)

Copper: for electrical equipment

Copper or bronze: for fittings, tubing, utensils, etc.

Galvanized iron or steel: for cans, buckets, tanks, eavestroughs, etc.

Silver and silver plate: for jewelry, flatware, etc.

Stainless steel: for appliances, kitchen equipment, or wherever strength is needed

Steel: for utensils, pipes, sheets, tool sheets, motors, etc.

procedures, and always make absolutely sure the bond is sound before you put into use any device where the repair, if poorly made, could result in a safety hazard.

SAFETY TIPS. Since a MAPP gas torch produces more heat and will be used for a greater variety of jobs than a propane torch, safety precautions beyond those for propane—such as not refilling or incinerating the empty cylinders, not working around flammable or explosive materials, and not working in poorly ventilated areas—are necessary.

1. Wear protective glasses to protect eyes from sparks or metal splatters.
2. Do not use a MAPP gas cylinder with conventional propane torch regulators and burner heads.
3. Some MAPP torch units require special handling to use in a tipped position. Be sure to check instructions for the particular unit.
4. Never use a flame to check for torch leaks. Periodic leak checks should be made with soapy water. Bubbles indicate a gas leak.
5. Respect hot metal. Handle heated parts with clamps or pliers.

WHICH METAL GAUGE MEASURES WHAT?

This is a question that can sometimes baffle experts as well as laymen. When the wire and sheet-metal industries were young, systems of thickness gauging were devised by, and often named after, individual manufacturers. In an attempt to establish greater uniformity, the United States and the British governments, late in the last century, established national standards. Because even these did not fit all the conditions in the manufacturing of iron and steel sheets, manufacturers jointly set industrial standards for such sheets. To complicate things still further, the dozen or so different metal-thickness gauges that were developed during this time have been variously assigned several times that many names and abbreviations.

To help you find your way through this maze, upcoming pages provide the names and abbreviations for the most commonly used gauges, indicate what the gauges are used for, and list the thicknesses associated with the gauge numbers. A separate table giving additional information on copper wire can be found on pages 596 and 597.

AMERICAN WIRE GAUGE (AWG), or
BROWN AND SHARPE (B&S). This should cause you little trouble. It is the gauge commonly used in the United States for copper, aluminum, and resistance wires; also for copper, aluminum, and brass sheets.

BIRMINGHAM WIRE GAUGE (BWG), or
STUBS' IRON WIRE GAUGE. An old gauge still used in the United States for brass wire, and used to a limited extent in Great Britain.

STEEL WIRE GAUGE (SWG, StlWG, A [steel]WG), or
WASHBURN AND MOEN (W&M), or
AMERICAN STEEL AND WIRE CO'S GAUGE, or
ROEBLING GAUGE. The gauge usually used in the United States for iron and steel wire. Watch out for the abbreviation SWG, as that is also one of the abbreviations for the British standard wire gauge.

BRITISH STANDARD WIRE GAUGE, or
STANDARD WIRE GAUGE (SWG), or
NEW BRITISH STANDARD (NBS), or
ENGLISH LEGAL STANDARD, or
IMPERIAL WIRE GAUGE. Since 1883 this has been the legal standard of Great Britain for wires of all metals. It is a modification of the Birmingham wire gauge.

United States Standard Gauge (US)

This gauge for sheet iron and steel was adopted in 1893 by an Act of Congress, and was formerly the legal standard for duties. It is a weight gauge based on the density of wrought iron at 480 pounds per cubic foot. As originally interpreted, a gauge number in this system represented a fixed weight per unit area. Steel, however, weighs about 9½ pounds more per cubic foot than wrought iron, and so a steel sheet would have a smaller thickness under this system than a wrought iron sheet of the same gauge number. In the face of this discrepancy, some manufacturers make sheets according to weight, others according to thickness, while still others settle on a compromise thickness of their own. In any case, however, thicknesses will not vary greatly from those shown in the table on pages 138 and 139. If you are in doubt about gauge number, order your sheet metal by actual thickness.

COMPARISON OF SHEET-METAL AND WIRE GAUGES

Dimensions are expressed in approximate decimals of an inch.

Gauge	AWG B&S	Birmingham or Stubs BWG	Steel wire gauge	British Imperial NBS SWG	United States Standard US
0000000	—	—	0.4900	0.500	0.5000
000000	0.5800	—	0.4615	0.464	0.4688
00000	0.5165	0.500	0.4305	0.432	0.4375
0000	0.4600	0.454	0.3938	0.400	0.4063
000	0.4096	0.425	0.3625	0.372	0.3750
00	0.3648	0.380	0.3310	0.348	0.3438
0	0.3249	0.340	0.3065	0.324	0.3215
1	0.2893	0.300	0.2830	0.300	0.2813
2	0.2576	0.284	0.2625	0.276	0.2656
3	0.2294	0.259	0.2437	0.252	0.2500
4	0.2043	0.238	0.2253	0.232	0.2344
5	0.1819	0.220	0.2070	0.212	0.2188
6	0.1620	0.203	0.1920	0.192	0.2031
7	0.1443	0.180	0.1770	0.176	0.1875
8	0.1285	0.165	0.1620	0.160	0.1719
9	0.1144	0.148	0.1483	0.144	0.1563
10	0.1019	0.134	0.1350	0.128	0.1406
11	0.0907	0.120	0.1205	0.116	0.1250
12	0.0808	0.109	0.1055	0.104	0.1094
13	0.0720	0.095	0.0915	0.092	0.0938
14	0.0641	0.083	0.0800	0.080	0.0781
15	0.0570	0.072	0.0720	0.072	0.0703
16	0.0508	0.065	0.0625	0.064	0.0625
17	0.0453	0.058	0.0540	0.056	0.0563
18	0.0403	0.049	0.0475	0.048	0.0500
19	0.0359	0.042	0.0410	0.040	0.0438
20	0.0320	0.035	0.0348	0.036	0.0375
21	0.0285	0.032	0.0318	0.032	0.0344
22	0.0254	0.028	0.0286	0.028	0.0313
23	0.0226	0.025	0.0258	0.024	0.0281
24	0.0201	0.022	0.0230	0.022	0.0250
25	0.0179	0.020	0.0204	0.020	0.0219
26	0.0159	0.018	0.0181	0.018	0.0188
27	0.0142	0.016	0.0173	0.0164	0.0172
28	0.0126	0.014	0.0162	0.0148	0.0156

COMPARISON OF SHEET-METAL AND WIRE GAUGES *(continued)*

Dimensions are expressed in approximate decimals of an inch.

Gauge	AWG B&S	Birmingham or Stubs BWG	Steel wire gauge	British Imperial NBS SWG	United States Standard US
29	0.0113	0.013	0.0150	0.0136	0.0141
30	0.0100	0.012	0.0140	0.0124	0.0125
31	0.0089	0.010	0.0132	0.0116	0.0109
32	0.0080	0.009	0.0128	0.0108	0.0102
33	0.0071	0.008	0.0118	0.0100	0.0094
34	0.0063	0.007	0.0104	0.0092	0.0086
35	0.0056	0.005	0.0095	0.0084	0.0078
36	0.0050	0.004	0.0090	0.0076	0.0070
37	0.0045	—	0.0085	0.0068	0.0066
38	0.0040	—	0.0080	0.0060	0.0063
39	0.0035	—	0.0075	0.0052	—
40	0.0031	—	0.0070	0.0048	—

TWIST DRILL SIZES

Above ½ inch, drills are available in fractional sizes only. Three sets of drills are commonly used for smaller sizes. One set is based on wire-gauge sizes—ranging from 80, the smallest, to 1, the largest. Letter sizes begin where wire-gauge sizes end. Fractional-size drills range from 1/64 inch to ½ inch, increasing by steps of 1/64 inch. The table on page 142 includes all three sets. Notice that every drill is of a different size except the E and the ¼-inch drills.

CUTTING SPEEDS FOR DRILLS

The most efficient cutting speed for drills varies with the material being worked, the rate of feed, and the cutting fluid used. Carbon-steel drills lose their temper at about one third to one half the temperature of high-speed drills, and so must be run slower. If they are used within their heat range, however, they will cut just about as well and last just about as long as their high-speed relatives. The table at the top of page 141 suggests conservative speeds for both types of drills under highly controlled industrial use and in ordinary hand use in the home shop. In hand work, the operator must be governed, of course, by the immediate action of the drill and be ready to adjust the speed accordingly.

HOW SHEET METALS ARE MEASURED AND PURCHASED

Sheet metals are measured and sold in the United States in the following manner:

Metal	How measured	How purchased	Characteristics
Aluminum	decimal thickness	24 × 72-inch sheet or 12 or 18 inches by linear foot	pure metal, or stronger and more ductile alloys
Copper	gauge number (Brown & Sharpe or American Wire Gauge) or by weight per square foot	24 × 96-inch sheet or 12 or 18 inches by linear foot	pure metal
Brass	gauge number (B & S or AWG)	24 × 76-inch sheet or 12 or 18 inches by linear foot	copper and zinc alloy
Cold-rolled steel sheet	gauge number (US Standard)	24 × 96-inch sheet	oxide removed and cold rolled to final thickness
Black annealed steel sheet	gauge number (US Standard)	24 × 96-inch sheet	hot-rolled mild steel with oxide coating left on
Galvanized steel	gauge number (US Standard)	24 × 96-inch sheet	mild steel plated with zinc
Tin plate	gauge number (US Standard)	20 × 28-inch sheet 56 or 112 to a package	mild steel plated with tin
Expanded steel	gauge number (US Standard)	36 × 96-inch sheet	Metal is pierced and stretched to produce diamond-shape openings.
Perforated steel	gauge number (US Standard)	30 × 36-inch sheet 36 × 48-inch sheet	Here design is cut in sheet and many designs are available.

Note: The actual thickness of steel sheet may be a shade less than that indicated by the United States Standard Gauge number, but it is close enough for most practical purposes. The reason for this difference is given in the following discussion of wire and sheet-metal gauges.

SAFE DRILLING SPEEDS FOR MILD STEEL (RPM)

Drill size (in inches)	Industrial use (with machine feed and copious lubrication)		Home-shop use (with hand feed and intermittent or no lubrication)	
	Carbon	*High-Speed*	*Carbon*	*High-Speed*
1/16	1830	6110	920	3060
3/32	1220	4075	610	2050
1/8	920	3060	460	1530
3/16	610	2040	310	1020
1/4	460	1530	230	760
5/16	370	1220	180	610
3/8	310	1020	150	510
1/2	230	764	115	380

SAFE DRILLING SPEEDS FOR OTHER METALS

To find the safe drilling speed for any of the following metals, just multiply the number of rpm in the table above by the number given after the metal below. For example, to find the safe drilling speed for aluminum, under home-workshop conditions and using a ¼-inch high-speed drill:

$$760 \text{ rpm} \times 2.5 = 1900 \text{ rpm}$$

Die castings (zinc base)	3.5
Aluminum	2.5
Brass and bronze	2.0
Cast iron, soft	1.15
Malleable iron	.85
Cast iron, hard	.80
Tool steel	.60
Stainless steel, hard	.30
Chilled cast iron	.20
Manganese steel	.15

NUMBER, LETTER, AND FRACTIONAL DRILL SIZES

Diameter	Decimal equivalent	Diameter	Decimal equivalent	Diameter	Decimal equivalent	Diameter	Decimal equivalent
80	0.0135	49	0.073	20	0.161	I	0.272
79	0.0145	48	0.076	19	0.166	J	0.277
1/64	0.0156	5/64	0.0781	18	0.1695	9/32	0.2813
78	0.016	47	0.0785	11/64	0.1719	K	0.281
77	0.018	46	0.081	17	0.173	L	0.290
76	0.02	45	0.082	16	0.177	M	0.295
75	0.021	44	0.086	15	0.18	19/64	0.2969
74	0.0225	43	0.089	14	0.182	N	0.302
73	0.024	42	0.0935	13	0.185	5/16	0.3125
72	0.025	3/32	0.0938	3/16	0.1875	O	0.316
71	0.026	41	0.096	12	0.189	P	0.323
70	0.028	40	0.098	11	0.191	21/64	0.328
69	0.0292	39	0.0995	10	0.1935	Q	0.332
68	0.031	38	0.1015	9	0.196	R	0.339
1/32	0.0313	37	0.104	8	0.199	11/32	0.34375
67	0.032	36	0.1065	7	0.201	S	0.348
66	0.033	7/64	0.1094	13/64	0.203	T	0.358
65	0.035	35	0.11	6	0.204	23/64	0.359
64	0.036	34	0.111	5	0.2055	U	0.368
63	0.037	33	0.113	4	0.209	3/8	0.375
62	0.038	32	0.116	3	0.213	V	0.377
61	0.039	31	0.12	7/32	0.21875	W	0.386
60	0.04	1/8	0.125	2	0.221	25/64	0.3906
59	0.041	30	0.1285	1	0.228	X	0.397
58	0.042	29	0.136	A	0.234	Y	0.404
57	0.043	9/64	0.1406	15/64	0.2344	13/32	0.4063
56	0.0465	28	0.1405	B	0.238	Z	0.413
3/64	0.0469	27	0.144	C	0.242		
55	0.052	26	0.147	D	0.246		
54	0.055	25	0.1495	1/4	0.250		
53	0.0595	24	0.152	E	0.250		
1/16	0.0625	23	0.154	F	0.257		
52	0.0635	5/32	0.15625	G	0.261		
51	0.067	22	0.157	17/64	0.2656		
50	0.07	21	0.159	H	0.266		

TAP DRILL SIZES (Fractional)

Nominal size	Commercial tap drill	Nominal size	Commercial tap drill	Nominal size	Commercial tap drill
1/16—64	3/64	24	Q	27	27/32
72	3/64	27	R	15/16—9	53/64
5/64—60	1/16	7/16—14	U	12	55/64
72	52	20	25/64	1—8	7/8
3/32—48	49	24	X	12	59/64
50	49	27	Y	14	15/16
7/64—48	43	1/2—12	27/64	27	31/32
1/8—32	3/32	13	27/64	1 1/8—7	63/64
40	38	20	29/64	12	1 3/64
9/16—40	32	24	29/64	1 1/4—7	1 7/64
5/32—32	1/8	27	15/32	12	1 11/64
36	30	9/16—12	31/64	1 3/8—6	1 7/32
11/64—32	9/64	18	33/64	12	1 19/64
3/16—24	26	27	17/32	1 1/2—6	1 11/32
32	22	5/8—11	17/32	12	1 27/64
13/64—24	20	5/8—12	35/64	1 5/8—5 1/2	1 29/64
7/32—24	16	18	37/64	1 3/4—5	1 9/16
32	12	27	19/32	10	1 21/32
15/64—24	10	11/16—11	19/32	1 7/8—5	1 11/16
1/4—20	7	12	19/32	2—4 1/2	1 25/32
24	4	16	5/8	3—3 1/2	2 23/32
27	3	3/4—10	21/32	10	1 29/32
28	3	12	43/64	2 1/8—4 1/2	1 29/32
32	7/32	16	11/16	2 1/4—4 1/2	2 1/32
5/16—18	F	27	23/32	8	2 1/8
20	17/64	13/16—10	23/32	2 3/8—4	2 1/8
24	I	12	23/32	2 1/2—4	2 1/4
27	J	7/8—9	49/64	8	2 3/8
32	9/32	12	51/64	2 3/4—4	2 1/2
3/8—16	5/16	14	13/16	8	2 5/8
20	21/64	18	53/64	8	2 7/8

TAP DRILL SIZES (Machine Screw)

Nominal size	Commercial tap drill	Nominal size	Commercial tap drill	Nominal size	Commercial tap drill
0—80	3/64″	44	37	10—24	25
1—56	54	6—32	36	28	23
64	53	36	34	30	22
72	53	40	33	32	21
2—56	50	7/30	31	12—24	16
64	50	32	31	28	14
3—48	47	36	1/8″	32	13
56	45	8—30	30	14—20	10
4—32	45	32	29	24	7
36	44	36	29	16—18	3
40	43	40	28	20	7/32″
48	42	9—24	29	22	2
5—36	40	30	27	18—18	B
40	38	32	26	20	D

Note: The tap drills listed will produce approximately 75-percent full thread. The sizes given are National Form. National Fine (N.F.) comprises a series formerly designated as A.S.M.E. pitches and S.A.E. sizes and pitches. National Coarse (N.C.) comprises a series of former A.S.M.E. pitches and U.S. Standard sizes and pitches.

CUTTING FLUIDS FOR DRILLING AND COUNTERSINKING

Cutting fluids applied at the point of contact between a drill or other cutting tool and the work perform several jobs at once. They reduce heat that would otherwise soften and ruin the cutting edge of a tool by direct cooling and by reducing friction. In this way they permit faster cutting speeds. They also help prevent the sticking of chips to tool or work.

Unfortunately there is no ideal cutting fluid that will serve all purposes. Many of the best cutting lubricants are not good coolants. On the other hand, water is probably the best coolant there is, yet on most materials it has almost no lubricating action.

The table on the next page shows recommended cutting fluids for use with specific materials.

CUTTING-FLUIDS GUIDE

Material	Type of cutting fluid
Aluminum and its alloys	Kerosene, kerosene and lard oil, or soluble oil
Brass and bronze	None
for deep holes	Kerosene and mineral oil, lard oil, or soluble oil
Copper	Mineral-lard oil and kerosene, soluble oil, or none
Monel metal	Mineral-lard oil or soluble oil
Mild steel	Mineral-lard oil or soluble oil
Tool steel or forgings	Sulfurized oil, mineral-lard oil, or kerosene
Cast steel	Soluble oil or sulfurized oil
Cast iron	None
Wrought iron	Soluble oil
Malleable iron	Soluble oil or none
Stainless steel	Soluble oil or sulfurized oil
Manganese steel	None
Titanium alloys	Soluble oil or sulfurized oil

Soda-Soap Cutting Fluid

One of the cheapest lubricant-coolants used for turning and milling steel is a soda-soap mixture you can make yourself. Here are the ingredients:

Sal soda (washing soda)	1½ ounces
Lard oil	3 fluid ounces
Soft soap	3 fluid ounces
Water, enough to make	1 gallon

Dissolve the sal soda in the water, which should be warm to make solution easier. Then stir in the soft soap and finally the lard oil. Boil slowly for about ½ hour, with occasional stirring. If the solution smells bad, you can correct this by stirring in about 3 ounces of unslaked lime.

CUTTING SPEEDS AND RPM FOR METALS ON A LATHE

Cutting speed is the distance the piece you are working on moves past the cutting point in 1 minute, as measured around the circumference of the piece.

		Diameter and RPMs			
Metal	**Cutting speed** (surface feet per minute)	*½inch*	*1 inch*	*1½ inches*	*2 inches*
Tool steel	50	400	200	133	100
Cast iron	75	600	300	200	150
Low-carbon steel	100	800	400	266	200
Brass	200	1600	800	533	400
Aluminum	300	2400	1200	800	600

HOW TO CLEAN FILES

Immerse the files for several minutes in a dilute solution of sulfuric acid made by adding about 1 ounce of the concentrated acid to 4 ounces of water. (To prevent violent spattering, be sure to add the acid to the water and not vice versa. Wear rubber gloves and use a glass dish or pan.) This treatment will etch the embedded iron and steel particles so they may be removed by a stiff wire brush. Next wash the files well in plain water and then coat them slightly with machine oil or penetrating oil diluted slightly with gasoline. Wipe off the excess.

Lead and brass filings lodged in the teeth can best be removed with a stiff brush.

Aluminum filings can be removed quite easily by soaking the files in a warm lye solution. The aluminum is eaten away by this, while the hydrogen gas generated in the process helps to throw out the metal particles. When using lye, again wear rubber gloves and do not spill any on your clothes or surroundings as this chemical and its solution are very caustic. After treatment, wash the files well and oil as before.

SELECTION OF GRINDING WHEELS

ABRASIVE. Fused alumina for materials of high tensile strength; silicon carbide for those of low tensile strength.

GRAIN SIZE. Fine grain for hard and brittle materials, small area of contact, and fine finish; coarse grain for soft, ductile materials, large areas of contact, and fast cutting. The number that designates grain size represents the number of openings per linear inch in the screen used to size the grain—8 to 10 is very coarse; 12 to 14, coarse; 30 to 60, medium; 70 to 120, fine; 150 to 240, very fine; 280 to 600, flour sizes.

GRADE. Hard wheels for soft materials; soft wheels for hard materials. The smaller the area of contact, the harder the wheel should be. Grade is often designated by letters: E to G, very soft; H to K, soft; L to O, medium; P to S, hard; T to Z, very hard.

GRINDING WHEEL SELECTION

Work	Abrasive	Grit	Grade	Bond
Aluminum (surfacing)	aluminum oxide (white)	46	soft	vitrified
Aluminum (cutting-off)	aluminum oxide	24	hard	resinoid
Brass (surfacing)	silicon carbide	36	medium	vitrified
Brass (cutting-off)	aluminum oxide	30	very hard	resinoid
Chisels (woodworking)	aluminum oxide	60	medium	vitrified
Coat Iron	silicon carbide	46	soft	vitrified
Copper (surfacing)	silicon carbide	60	medium	vitrified
Copper (cutting-off)	silicon carbide	36	hard	rubber
Cork	aluminum oxide (white)	60	soft	vitrified
Cutters (moulding)	aluminum oxide	60	medium	vitrified
Drills (sharpening)	aluminum oxide (white)	60	medium	vitrified
Glass (grinding)	silicon carbide (green)	150	hard	vitrified
Glass (cutting-off)	silicon carbide (green)	90	hard	rubber
Glass (cutting-off)	diamond	60	medium	copper
Leather	silicon carbide	46	soft	vitrified
Plastic	silicon carbide	60	medium	rubber
Rubber (hard)	silicon carbide	46	medium	resinoid
Saws (gumming)	aluminum oxide	60	medium	vitrified
Steel (soft)	aluminum oxide	60	medium	vitrified
Steel (high speed)	aluminum oxide (white)	60	soft	vitrified
Tile (cutting-off)	silicon carbide	30	hard	resinoid
Tubes (steel)	aluminum oxide	60	hard	rubber
Welds (smoothing)	aluminum oxide	36	hard	vitrified
Wood (hard)	silicon carbide	30	soft	vitrified

GRINDING WHEEL SPEED

Type	Surface feet per minute
Chisel grinding	5,000 to 6,000
Cutlery wheels	4,000 to 5,000
Cut-off wheels	6,000 to 8,000
Cut-off wheels (rubber, shellac, resinoid)	9,000 to 16,000
Cylindrical grinding	5,500 to 6,500
General grinding	5,000 to 6,500
Hemming cylinders	2,100 to 5,000
Internal grinding	2,000 to 6,000
Knife grinding	3,500 to 4,500
Snagging, off-hand grinding (vitrified wheels)	5,000 to 6,000
Snagging (rubber and resinoid wheels)	7,000 to 9,500
Surface grinding	4,000 to 6,000
Tool and cutter grinding	4,500 to 6,000
Wet tool grinding	5,000 to 6,000

Note: To determine the number of revolutions per minute required, divide the surface speed in feet per minute by the circumference of the wheel you are using (measured in feet or fractions of a foot). You can find the circumference directly with a cloth tape, or calculate it by multiplying the diameter (also measured in feet or fractions of a foot) by 3.1416.

STRUCTURE. Close grain spacing for hard and brittle, for small area of contact, and for fine finish; wide grain spacing for soft, ductile materials, for large area of contact, and for rapid removal of stock. Numerals are sometimes used to indicate spacing: 0 to 3, close; 4 to 6, medium; 7 to 12, wide.

BOND. Resinoid, rubber, and shellac wheels are best for a high finish. Vitrified can be used for speeds up to 6,500 surface feet per minute; rubber, shellac, or resinoid for speeds above that.

SPARK TEST FOR METALS

Metal particles thrown off by the grinding wheel appear as dull red streaks until combined with oxygen to form a spark. The sparks caused by different metals vary, and afford a useful index in distinguishing the metal. Three things should be observed in testing metals in this manner:

GRINDING WHEEL SPEEDS IN RPM

	RPM FOR STATED SURFACE FEET PER MINUTE (SFPM)							
Diameter of wheel	4000 sfpm	4500 sfpm	5000 sfpm	5500 sfpm	6000 sfpm	6500 sfpm	7000 sfpm	7500 sfpm
1	15,279	17,189	19,098	21,008	22,918	24,828	26,737	28,647
2	7,639	8,594	9,549	10,504	11,459	12,414	13,368	14,328
3	5,093	5,729	6,366	7,003	7,639	8,276	8,913	9,549
4	3,820	4,297	4,775	5,252	5,729	6,207	6,685	7,162
5	3,056	3,438	3,820	4,202	4,584	4,966	5,348	5,730
6	2,546	2,865	3,183	3,501	3,820	4,138	4,456	4,775
7	2,183	2,455	2,728	3,001	3,274	3,547	3,820	4,092
8	1,910	2,148	2,387	2,626	2,885	3,103	3,342	3,580
10	1,528	1,719	1,910	2,101	2,292	2,483	2,674	2,865

1. The color of the spark, both as it leaves the wheel and as it explodes.
2. The shape of the explosion as the metal particle ignites.
3. The distance from the wheel at which the explosion occurs.

The diagram on page 150 shows the general spark effect obtained with different metals, but it is best to get a first-hand impression by testing known pieces of metal.

HACKSAWS—HAND AND POWER

The hand hacksaw is a cutting tool essential in metal work. Satisfactory results require care and intelligence in blade selection and use, the same as with other tools. Hand hacksaw blades come in 10- and 12-inch lengths and are held in frames having the required tensioning adjustment.

The blade should be taut but not overstrained. A properly strained blade when "thumbed" gives a clear humming note that, once heard, is readily remembered. After a few cuts with a new blade, the tension should be checked and slightly increased. Rigidity of the work is equally important. If possible, the work should be locked securely in a vise and positioned to engage the maximum number of saw teeth during the cut. In cutting sheet metal, for example, it is preferable to saw along the flat surface.

Use a coarse tooth blade (14 or 18 teeth per inch) to cut thick work;

SPARK TEST FOR METALS

Length and thickness of spark streams depend on variables such as the metal, grinding pressure, and hardness and condition of wheel. Grind at point on wheel that allows long spark stream for comparison of colors near wheel and at stream end. "Forked" spurts branch only once from single spark. "Repeating" sparks branch and rebranch. Sparks from manganese and carbon steel are hard to tell apart. Some cast iron produces smaller stream than shown, with fewer spurts. Tungsten carbide creates small stream, orange to light orange, with no spurts. (For practice, grind known test samples.)

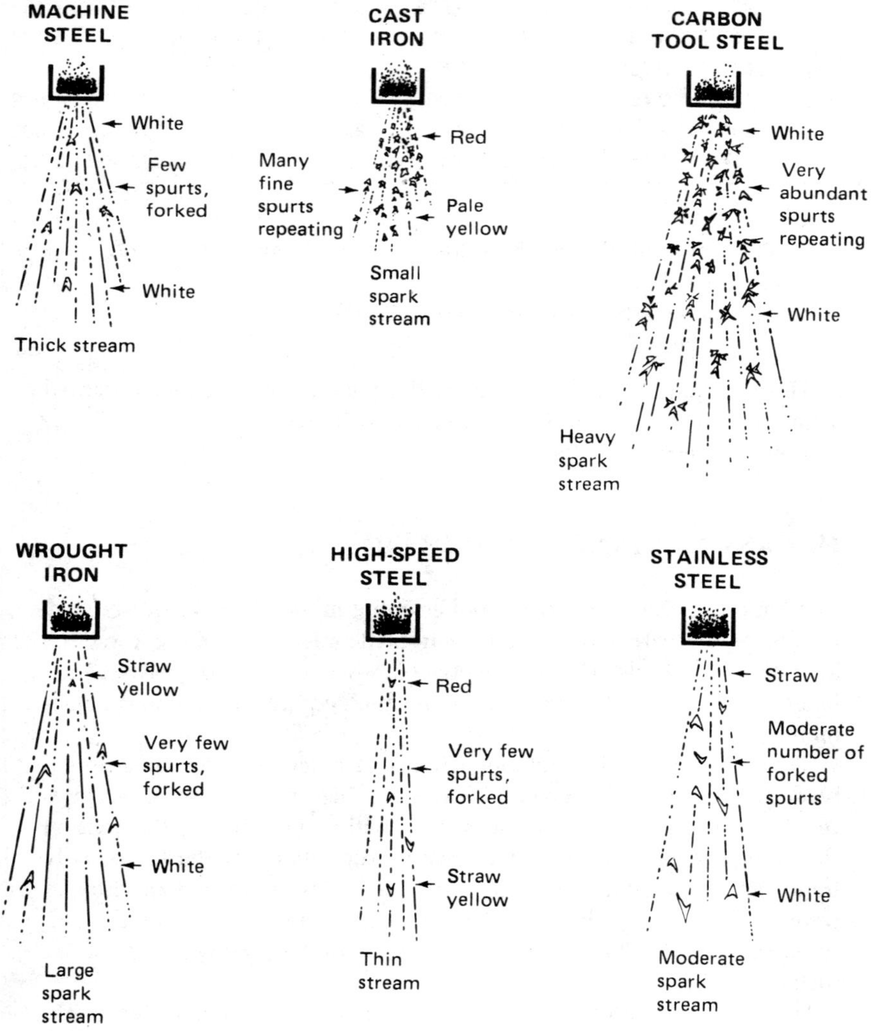

this increases cutting efficiency and chips are removed more effectively. Use a fine tooth blade (24 or 32 teeth per inch) to cut work of thin section; this reduces risk of teeth straddling the work, striping, or breaking the blade.

Teeth should point away from the handle so that the blade will cut on the forward stroke. The cutting stroke, using the same motion as in filing, should be long, steady, and sufficiently firm to assure a cut rather than a slide. The pressure should always be lifted on the return stroke to

MATERIAL CUTTING TABLE FOR HAND HACKSAW BLADES

Material	Type	Teeth per inch
Aluminum	solids	14
Angles	heavy	18
Angles	light	24
Babbitt	heavy	14
Brass	solids up to 1 inch	18
Brass pipe	heavy	24
Brass tubing	light	24
Bronze	solids up to 1 inch	18
BX cable	heavy	24
BX cable	light	32
Cable	heavy	18
Cast iron	up to 1 inch	18
Channel	heavy	18
Channel	light	24
Copper	solids up to 1 inch	14
Drill rod	over ¼ inch	18
Drill rod	No. 30 to ¼ inch	24
Drill rod	No. 30 and smaller	32
General-purpose cutting	heavy	18
Iron pipe	heavy	24
Metal conduit	light	24
Sheet metal	over 18 gauge	24
Sheet metal	under 18 gauge	32
Steels	¼ to 1 inch	18
Steels	¼ inch and under	24
Tubing	over 18 gauge	24
Tubing	under 18 gauge	32

prevent dulling the teeth. Forty to fifty strokes a minute should be the maximum.

It should be kept in mind that there is a great variety of blades for every kind of material and service.

Like hand hacksaw blades, power hacksaw blades are used for cutoff work. They are thicker, wider, and longer to fit various machines, and they cut off stock on a fast, production basis.

Power blades are held in heavy-duty, mechanically driven machine frames. They are fed into the work by mechanical or hydraulic means. Correct blade tension is obtained by using a torque wrench. The tension

MATERIAL CUTTING TABLE FOR POWER HACKSAW BLADES

Material	Teeth per inch	Strokes per minute	Feed pressure
Aluminum alloy	4–6	150	light
Aluminum, pure	4–6	150	light
Brass castings, hard	6–10	135	light
Brass castings, soft	6–10	150	light
Bronze castings	6–10	135	medium
Cast iron	6–10	135	medium
*Carbon tool steel	6–10	90	medium
*Cold-rolled steel	4–6	135	heavy
Copper, drawn	6–10	135	medium
*Drill rod	10	90	medium
*High-speed steel	6–10	90	medium
*Machinery steel	4–6	135	heavy
*Malleable iron	6–10	90	medium
Manganese bronze	6–10	90	light
*Nickel silver	6–10	60	heavy
*Nickel steel	6–10	90	heavy
Pipe, iron	10–14	135	medium
Slate	6–10	90	medium
*Structural steel	6–10	135	medium
Tubing, brass	14	135	light
*Tubing, steel	14	135	light

*Use cutting compounds or coolant.

should be checked after one or two cuts and the blade tightened slightly as it stabilizes in position on the machine mounting pins.

Successful power hacksawing depends on choosing the right type of blade for the material to be cut, plus the right combination of teeth per inch, speed in strokes per minute, and feed in square inches per minute. The figures in the table on page 152 are offered as starting suggestions and may be altered as specific materials and operating conditions require.

CUTTING METAL WITH A SABER SAW

Because of the high speeds, cutting metal or abrasive materials with a wood-cutting saber saw blade will almost instantly dull it. Good metal-cutting blades are made of high-speed steel (HSS). They work best in a

METAL-CUTTING SABER SAW BLADE-SELECTOR TABLE

Teeth per inch	Material to be cut	Comments
6 (HSS)*	aluminum, copper, brass, laminates, compositions	heavy cutting in plate or tubing; sample maximum cut: ½ inch in aluminum plate
10 (HSS)	same as above	general cutting with smoother finish than above
14 (HSS)	aluminum, brass, bronze, copper, laminates, hardboard, mild steel, pipe	general cutting with smooth finish; maximum in steel: ¼–½ inch depending on manufacturers' specifications
18 (HSS)	same as above	for lighter materials: maximum cuts about ⅛ inch
24 (HSS)	sheet metal, light-gauge steel, thinwall tubing, Bakelite, tile, etc.	finest-tooth blade offered by some makers
32 (HSS)	thin-gauge sheet metals, thinwall tubing, metal trim	wave-set blade cuts fine kerf; maximum in steel: 1/16 inch for typical hacksaw jobs

*High-speed steel

saber saw with a variable-speed or two-speed feature, where you can run at a slower speed. Refer to the table on page 153 for the right tooth-per-inch blade to use for common metal-cutting and abrasive-material-cutting projects with a saber saw.

Tungsten carbide, one of the hardest materials known, is now used to make saw blades that are long lasting and that will easily cut materials that other blades won't, including things like files, glass bottles, ceramic tile, etc. The cut-anything blades are made by bonding hundreds of tiny carbide particles on the cutting edge of the blades.

The "carbide grit" blades are available two ways for hacksaws: a regular-style blade with carbide on the edge, and a "rod saw" blade, which is a wire coated with carbide all around. Eyes at the end of the coated wire are used to fasten it in the blade frame. This type cuts in any direction.

Carbide grit blades for saber saws come in fine, medium, and coarse grit. Refer to the table below for suggestions on selection for typical tough cutting jobs.

CARBIDE GRIT SABER SAW BLADE-SELECTOR TABLE

Material to be cut	Fine grit	Medium grit	Coarse grit
Fiberglass, reinforced plastics	good	good	best
Ceramic tile, slate, cast stone	best	good	—
Asbestos cement, nail-emnail-em bedded wood, plaster with nails	—	—	best
Chalkboard, clay pipe, brick	good	best	—
Stainless steel, trim, sheet metal to 18 gauge, ducting counter top materials, tempered hardboard	best	—	—

TEMPERING TEMPERATURES FOR STEEL

After hardening, steel is given a heat treatment that increases its toughness without reducing its hardness. As the steel heats up a film of oxide forms on its surface. The color of this oxide is an indication of the steel's temperature. This table gives the temperatures judged by color and colors for tempering:

Degrees centigrade	Degrees Fahrenheit	High temperatures, judged by color	Degrees centigrade	Degrees Fahrenheit	Colors for tempering (color of oxide film)
400	752	red heat, visible in the dark	221.1	430	very pale yellow
474	885	red heat, visible in twilight	226.7	440	light yellow
525	975	red heat, visible in daylight	232.2	450	pale straw-yellow
581	1075	red heat, visible in sunlight	237.8	460	straw-yellow
700	1292	dark red	243.3	470	deep straw-yellow
800	1472	dull cherry red	248.9	480	dark yellow
900	1652	cherry red	254.4	490	yellow-brown
1000	1832	bright cherry red	260.0	500	brown-yellow
1100	2012	orange-red	265.6	510	spotted red-brown
1200	2192	orange-yellow	271.1	520	brown-purple
1300	2372	yellow-white	276.7	530	light purple
1400	2552	white welding heat	282.2	540	full purple
1500	2732	brilliant white	287.8	550	dark purple
1600	2912	dazzling white (bluish white)	293.3	560	full blue
			298.9	570	dark blue

4

Masonry, Plastering, Roofing, Paneling, and Flooring

HOW TO MIX CONCRETE FOR DIFFERENT JOBS

Properly made concrete is a strong and versatile building material made by combining portland cement and sand with pebbles, crushed stone, or other aggregate, and enough water to cause the cement to set and to bind the whole mass solidly together.

In mixing concrete the most important proportion to remember is that between cement and water. As long as a mix is workable, the amount of aggregate may be varied considerably. For a given strength of concrete, the ratio between cement and water, however, is fixed. The relationship between strength of concrete and the relative quantities of water and cement is expressed more definitely by concrete experts:

For given materials and conditions of handling, the strength of the concrete is determined primarily by the ratio of the volume of the mixing water to the volume of cement as long as the mixture is plastic and workable.

In other words, if 6 gallons of water are used for each sack of cement in a mixture, the strength of the concrete at a certain age is already determined. The only extra provision is that the mixture is plastic and workable and the aggregates are strong, clean, and made up of sound particles. More water will mean less strength and less water greater strength.

Following this principle, the modern practice is to state the amount of mixing water for each sack of cement to produce "pastes" of different strengths. Common combinations are 5-gallon paste, 6-gallon paste, and 7-gallon paste, to be selected according to the type of work to be done.

To help choose pastes and make trial mixes for different types of jobs, the table on page 158 shows proportions recommended by the Portland Cement Association.

Choosing Materials

Portland cement is sold in sacks of 94 pounds each, or 1 cubic foot in volume. It should be free from all lumps when used. If it contains lumps that cannot be pulverized between thumb and finger, don't use it.

Water should be clean and free of oil, acid, or alkali. As a general rule, you can use any water that is fit to drink.

Aggregates are classified as fine or coarse. Fine aggregate consists of sand or other solid and fine material including rock screenings. Suitable sand will contain particles ranging uniformly in size from very fine up to ¼ inch.

Coarse aggregate consists of gravel, crushed stone, or other materials up to about 1½ inches in size. Material that is sound, hard, durable, and free from foreign matter is best for making concrete.

The maximum size of coarse aggregate depends on the kind of work for which the concrete is to be used. Aggregate up to 1½ inches, for example, may be used in thick foundation walls or heavy footing. In ordinary walls, the largest pieces should never be more than one fifth the thickness of the finished wall section. For slabs the maximum size should be approximately one third the thickness of the slab. Coarse aggregate is well graded when particles range uniformly from ¼ inch up to the largest that may be used on the kind of work to be done.

ALLOWANCE FOR MOISTURE IN THE AGGREGATES. Most sand or fine aggregates contain some water. Allowance must therefore be made for this moisture in determining the amount of water to be added to the mix. You can easily determine whether sand is damp, wet, or very wet by pressing some together in your hand. If the sand falls apart after your hand is opened, it is damp; if it forms a ball that holds its shape, it is wet; if the sand sparkles and wets your hand, it is very wet. If the sand is bone dry—an unusual condition—you should use the full 5, 6, or 7 gallons of water called for in the table.

HOW TO SELECT PROPER CONCRETE MIX

KINDS OF WORK	ADD U.S. GALLONS OF WATER TO EACH SACK BATCH IF SAND IS			SUGGESTED MIXTURE FOR TRIAL BATCH*			MATERIALS PER CU. YD. OF CONCRETE*		
	Very wet	Wet (average sand)	Damp	Cement, sacks	Aggregates Fine cu. ft.	Aggregates Coarse cu. ft.	Cement, sacks	Aggregates Fine cu. ft.	Aggregates Coarse cu. ft.
5-Gallon paste for concrete subjected to severe wear, weather or weak acid and alkali solutions									
					Maximum size aggregate ¾ in.				
One-course industrial, creamery and dairy plant floors, etc.	3½	4	4½	1	2	2¼	7¾	15½	17½
6-Gallon paste for concrete to be watertight or subjected to moderate wear and weather									
					Maximum size aggregate 1½ in.				
Watertight floors, such as industrial plant, basement, dairy barn; watertight foundations; driveways, walks, tennis courts, swimming and wading pools, septic tanks, storage tanks, structural beams, columns, slabs, residence floors, etc.	4¼	5	5½	1	2½	3½	6	15	21
7-Gallon paste for concrete not subjected to wear, weather or water									
					Maximum size aggregate 1½ in.				
Foundation walls, footings, mass concrete, etc., for use where watertightness and abrasion resistance are not important.	4¾	5½	6¼	1	3	4	5	15	20

* Mixes and quantities are based on wet (average) aggregates and medium consistencies. Actual quantities will vary according to the grading of aggregate and the workability that is desired for each job.

Measuring Materials

All materials, including water, should be measured accurately. For measuring water, a pail marked on the inside to indicate quarts and gallons will prove handy. On small jobs a pail may also be used for measuring cement, sand, and pebbles. In mixing 1-sack batches merely remember that 1 sack holds exactly 1 cubic foot. Sand and pebbles are then conveniently measured in bottomless boxes made to hold exactly 1 cubic foot or other volumes desired.

If you can buy concrete aggregates in your community by weight, you may assume, for purpose of estimating, that a ton contains approximately 22 cubic feet of sand, or about 20 cubic feet of gravel. For closer estimates on local aggregates, consult your building material dealer.

How to Obtain a Workable Mixture

A workable mixture is one of such wetness and plasticity that it can be placed in the forms readily, and with light spading and tamping will result in a dense concrete. There should be enough portland cement mortar to give good dense surfaces, free from rough spots, and to hold pieces of coarse aggregate into the mass so that they will not separate out in handling. In other words, the cement-fine aggregate mortar should completely fill the spaces between the coarse aggregate and ensure a smooth, plastic mix. Mixtures lacking sufficient mortar will be hard to work and difficult to finish. Too much fine aggregate increases porosity and reduces the amount of concrete obtainable from a sack of cement.

A workable mix for one type of work may be too stiff for another. Concrete that is placed in thin sections must be more plastic than for massive construction.

Mixing and Placing the Concrete

Mixing should continue until every piece of coarse aggregate is completely coated with a thoroughly mixed mortar of cement and fine aggregate. Machine mixing is preferable, if you have the equipment available, and should continue for at least 1 minute after all the materials have been placed in the mixer.

The concrete should be placed in the forms within 45 to 60 minutes after mixing. It should be tamped or spaded as it goes into the form. This forces the coarse aggregate back from the face or surface, making a dense concrete surface.

How to Estimate Materials Required

The accompanying table will give you the approximate quantities required for 100 square feet of concrete of a given thickness. Actual quantities used may vary 10 percent, depending upon the aggregate used. It is good practice to provide 10 percent more fine and coarse aggregates than estimated, to allow for waste.

ESTIMATING MATERIALS FOR CONCRETE

Thickness of concrete, in.	Amount of concrete, cu. yd.	PROPORTIONS: 1:2:2¼ mix Cement, sacks	1:2:2¼ mix Aggregate Fine, cu. ft.	1:2:2¼ mix Aggregate Coarse, cu. ft.	1:2½:3½ mix Cement, sacks	1:2½:3½ mix Aggregate Fine, cu. ft.	1:2½:3½ mix Aggregate Coarse, cu. ft.	1:3:4 mix Cement, sacks	1:3:4 mix Aggregate Fine, cu. ft.	1:3:4 mix Aggregate Coarse, cu. ft.
3	0.92	7.1	14.3	16.1	5.5	13.8	19.3	4.6	13.8	18.4
4	1.24	9.6	19.2	21.7	7.4	18.6	26.0	6.2	18.6	24.8
5	1.56	12.1	24.2	27.3	9.4	23.4	32.8	7.8	23.4	31.2
6	1.85	14.3	28.7	32.4	11.1	27.8	38.9	9.3	27.8	37.0
8	2.46	19.1	38.1	43.0	14.8	36.9	51.7	12.3	36.9	49.3
10	3.08	23.9	47.7	53.9	18.5	46.2	64.7	15.4	46.2	61.6
12	3.70	28.7	57.3	64.7	22.2	55.5	77.7	18.5	55.5	74.0

ESTIMATING TRANSIT-MIX NEEDS. When estimating the amount of transit-mix concrete needed for a given project, multiply the length and width in feet by the thickness in inches and divide by 12 to get the cubic footage. You'll need a yard of concrete for each 27 cubic feet.

It may pay you to figure your job so you use enough concrete to get the best price. In some areas, 2 yards bought separately cost more than 3 yards taken at one crack, which works out to an appealing 33 percent discount on the latter.

How to Prevent Concrete from Sticking to Forms

To prevent concrete from sticking to wooden forms, the forms must be treated with a suitable oil, varnish, or other coating material. This oil should also prevent absorption of water from the concrete.

Almost any light-bodied petroleum oil will do. Fuel oil is satisfactory for use with normal gray concrete except in very warm weather, when it should be thickened with 1 part petroleum grease to each 2 parts oil.

When making pastel-colored concrete or concrete using white portland cement, use white mineral oil to prevent staining.

Before applying oil, be sure the form is clean and smooth. Rough wood surfaces may cause the concrete to stick. Apply the oil evenly with a brush, spray, or swab. Wipe off excess so it does not soften or discolor the concrete.

Several coats of shellac applied first to plywood is better than oil alone in preventing moisture from raising the grain and so marring the finished surface of the concrete. Forms that are to be used repeatedly should be coated with asphalt paint, varnish, or several coats of boiled linseed oil rubbed in and allowed to dry. Forms so coated may be used just as they are, or oiled as usual for extra ease in removal.

If oil is not available, wetting the forms with plain water just before placing the concrete may help prevent absorption and sticking, but this method is not so effective and should be used only in an emergency.

FINISHING CONCRETE

Concrete can be finished in many ways, depending on the effect desired. Walks and floors may require screeding only to proper contour and height. In other cases you may wish to give surfaces a broomed finish or trowel them smooth. Here are the basic operations in finishing horizontal slabs:

Screeding

The term "screed" comes from an old Anglo-Saxon word meaning "strip" or "band." To the cement mason, screeds are the side strips of a concrete form that mark the height at which the concrete is to be leveled off. Screeding, then, is simply leveling off the concrete by drawing along it a straight-edged or contoured board whose ends ride on the screeds.

Screeding should be done just as soon as possible after the concrete has been dumped and spread—before free water in the concrete has had time to rise to the surface, or "bleed." This is one of the most important rules of successful concrete finishing. *Screeding or any other operation performed on a concrete surface when bled water is present may result in subsequent severe scaling, dusting, or crazing.*

Do your screeding with a "strikeboard," which can be simply a 2×4 or 2×6, a foot or so longer than the width of the form. The working edge should be straight, unless you are making a walk or other surface that you want higher in the middle to provide better drainage. In the latter case, contour the edge as desired.

Move the strikeboard back and forth across the concrete with a sawing motion, advancing it a short distance along the length of the slab with each motion. Keep a surplus of concrete against the front face of the strikeboard as a supply to fill depressions as the board is moved forward.

Floating

If you want a smoother surface than that obtained by screeding, the surface should be worked sparingly with a "float." This can be a flat rectangle of wood, 12 to 18 inches long and 3½ to 4½ inches wide, provided with a handle on its upper face. Use the float to remove high or low spots or ridges left by the strikeboard, also to embed the coarse aggregate so the surface is smooth enough for subsequent troweling. This operation must be done immediately after screeding, being careful not to overdo it and so bring an excess of water and mortar to the surface. Concrete is often floated a second time, after the surface water has disappeared and just before troweling.

Troweling

If a dense, smooth finish is desired, floating must be followed by steel troweling at a time after surface water has disappeared and the concrete has hardened enough so that no fine material and new water will be worked to the top. This step should be delayed as long as possible, but not so long that the surface is too hard to finish properly. Troweling should leave the surface smooth, even, and free of marks and ripples. If there are wet spots on the surface, do not trowel these spots until the water has been absorbed, has evaporated, or has been mopped up. Never sprinkle dry cement on such spots to take up the water; this will only produce a surface that will later scale off.

Brooming

A nonskid surface can be produced by brushing or brooming. The brushed surface is made by drawing a soft-bristled push broom over the slab just after it has been steel-troweled. For coarser textures, a stiffer bristled broom may be used.

CURING CONCRETE

The first requirement for strong, high-quality concrete is the proper proportion between water and cement; the second, and more often neglected, requirement is proper curing.

Concrete hardens because of a chemical reaction between cement and water. This reaction starts as soon as they are mixed and causes the concrete to set solid in a matter of hours. Hardening, however, does not stop with this setting. If you do not let the concrete dry out, it will continue to harden for about a month. Tests have shown that if you keep concrete warm and moist during a curing period as long as 28 days, it will be more than twice as strong as it would have been if you had kept

EFFECT OF WATER AND CURING TIME ON CONCRETE

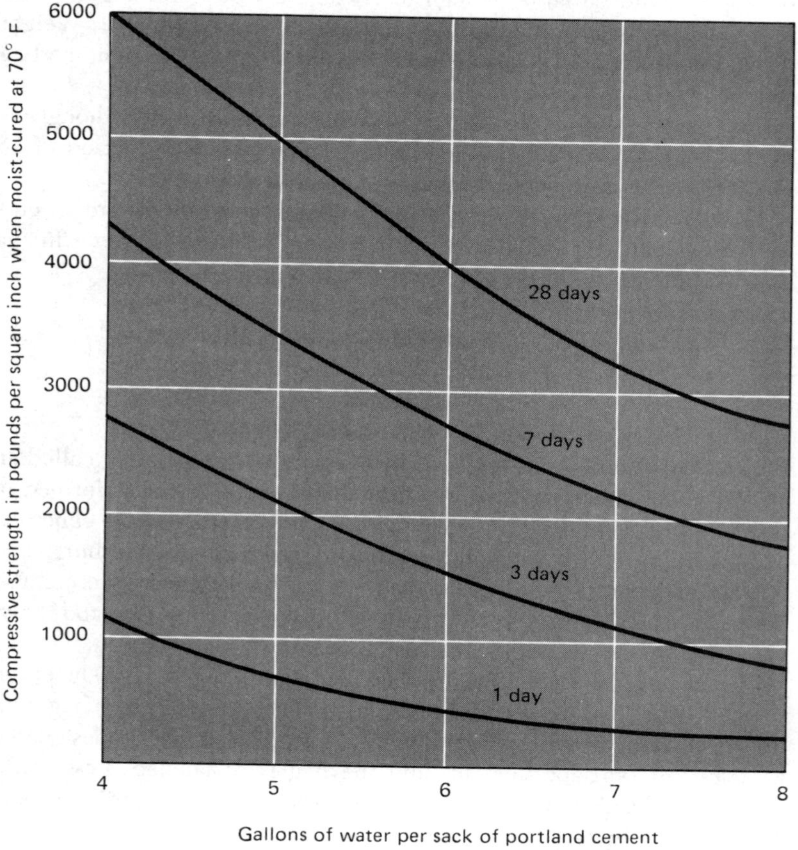

it that way only 3 days. Concrete that is allowed to dry before it is fully cured is relatively soft, porous, and of poor appearance.

For concrete to cure thoroughly, it must be protected so that little or no moisture is lost during the curing or hardening period. Newly placed concrete must not be allowed to dry out too fast and so must be protected from the sun and from drying winds. This may be done in the beginning with burlap or canvas coverings kept constantly wet.

One method of moist curing that is applicable to horizontal surfaces after the concrete has become surface hard is called "ponding." This is accomplished by building an earth dike around the edges of the concrete slab and keeping the slab covered with an inch or so of water. Another method that may be used under the same conditions is to first wet the surface thoroughly with a fine spray of water and then keep it covered during the entire curing time with a sheet of plastic film. The plastic sheet should be large enough to cover the width and edges of the slab. If several sheets must be used, lap them at least 12 inches. Weight down the joints and edges to keep the sheets moisture-tight and in place.

The barest minimum of curing time should be 3 days, although 14 days would make the concrete much stronger. A curing period of 28 days at 70° F is considered standard for greatest strength.

How the proportion of water to cement and the length of proper curing both affect the strength of the resulting concrete is shown in the graph on the preceding page.

CONCRETES FOR SPECIAL PURPOSES

Air-Entrained Concrete

By adding to the concrete mix a small amount of a chemical called an air-entraining agent, billions of microscopic air bubbles are formed in the resulting concrete. These change the basic structure of the concrete, making it more workable during mixing, laying, and finishing, and stronger and more durable after it has set. Air-entrained concrete also has superior resistance to scaling caused by alternate freezing and thawing as well as that caused by salts used to melt snow and ice.

You can buy ready-mixed air-entrained concrete from producers in the colder parts of the country. Or you can buy cement by the bag with the air-entrained chemical already incorporated in it. This is designated as Type 1A portland cement, and the bag is so labeled. Less water should be mixed with air-entrained concrete than with ordinary concrete for an otherwise similar mix.

Lightweight Concrete

Normal portland cement concrete weighs about 145 pounds per cubic foot. By using special lightweight aggregates, concrete can be made weighing only 40 to 110 pounds per cubic foot. Such concretes are used for concrete blocks, for filler material where high strength is not necessary, for fireproofing steel, and for concrete that can be nailed. Lightweight concretes possess good insulating properties and they also have good fire-resistance, especially those made from burned clay or shale.

Aggregates for lightweight concrete are produced by crushing pumice, infusorial earth, lava, or tufa, a porous rock formed as a deposit from springs or streams. Others are made from cinders, by burning clay and shale, and by expanding molten slag with steam.

Because lightweight aggregates vary in their uses and mixing proportions, buy them only from reliable dealers who understand their characteristics and can give you definite instructions for making concrete with them.

Another type of lightweight concrete can be made by adding a chemical compound to standard concrete. This compound causes a gas to form in the mix, expanding it and thus reducing its weight.

Porous Concrete

This concrete, through which water can easily pass, can be made by omitting sand and using coarse aggregate only. Such concrete is frequently used for drain tile, in which the mix proportions are 5 parts pea gravel by weight to 1 part cement. The maximum-size particle in the pea gravel should be ⅜ inch and the smallest ³⁄₁₆ inch. Porous concrete is put in place without much tamping, since tamping tends to overconsolidate it and so reduces its porosity. If cured for about 7 days under conditions recommended for standard portland cement concrete, the compressive strength of porous concrete should be at least 1,000 pounds per square inch.

Grout

This is a special sand-cement mortar made for such uses as sealing cracks, sealing the joints of precast pipe, and filling the space between the bed plates of machinery and foundations. The primary requirement of grout is that it should not shrink. To meet this requirement, mortar used for grouting should be as dry as possible. Shrinkage can also be reduced by prolonged mixing and by the addition of a small amount of aluminum powder.

Aluminum powder mixed in concrete causes the concrete to swell. Thus, by blending in just the right amount, the natural shrinkage of a mortar can be balanced. Only extremely small amounts of aluminum are needed; one teaspoon per sack of cement has been found satisfactory in many cases. The aluminum powder should be mixed thoroughly with fine sand first, because unmixed powder tends to float. One pound of sand–aluminum powder mixture should contain enough aluminum for a batch of mortar that you can place completely within 45 minutes after mixing.

Watertight Concrete

This must be as dense as possible and moist-cured for a longer period than would be necessary if watertightness was not important. Here are the main requirements:

1. Do not use more than 6 gallons of water per sack of cement.
2. Use aggregates that are sound and of low porosity.
3. Place the concrete properly and compact it thoroughly.
4. Keep the concrete moist and at a temperature of more than 50° F for at least 7 days.

The most effective way to prevent the passage of water through concrete is to sandwich a membrane of waterproof material between two concrete layers. On horizontal surfaces the method ordinarily used is to first coat the surface to be waterproofed with hot roofing asphalt. This can be applied with a mop as soon as the concrete surface is dry enough to allow the hot asphalt to stick. One layer of roofing felt is placed on this coating while it is still hot. The felt is then mopped with hot asphalt and a second layer of felt is applied, which is then also coated with asphalt.

On vertical surfaces a thick coat of fibrous tar or asphalt cement is troweled on, and a layer of flexible tar or asphalt-treated burlap is embedded in this coat.

On both horizontal and vertical surfaces, the membrane should be protected with an outer coating of 3 inches of concrete or 1 course of brick.

Waterproofing compounds are sometimes added to the concrete mix or applied as a surface wash to the finished concrete. As they do not affect the strength, setting, or curing of new concrete, and may also be applied to old concrete, the washes are generally preferable. These include tar coatings, asphalt emulsions, and special portland cement paints. For best results, surface washes should be applied on the surface where the water enters. Because they vary so in nature, they should be applied according to the manufacturer's specifications.

HOT-WEATHER CONCRETING

Making concrete in hot weather poses special problems, among which are reduction in strength and the cracking of flat surfaces due to rapid drying. Concrete also may harden before it can be consolidated because of rapid setting of the cement and excessive absorption of mixing water. This makes it difficult to finish flat surfaces.

The most important considerations in hot-weather concreting are to keep materials and mixed concrete cooler than 90° F, prevent absorption, protect against too rapid evaporation, place the concrete without delay, and begin curing immediately. Here are a few specific suggestions:

1. During extremely hot weather, start jobs in the late afternoon.
2. Sprinkle stockpiles of coarse aggregate with water to cool the material by evaporation. Chill the mixing water by refrigeration or with ice—making sure that the ice has all melted before placing the concrete.
3. To prevent absorption of water from the mix, sprinkle the wood forms and the surface on which the concrete is to be placed with water just before the concrete is laid. Sprinkle coarse aggregates just before they are added to the batch.
4. Erect windbreaks of canvas or polyethylene sheet to prevent strong, hot winds from drying exposed surfaces while they are being finished.
5. Place concrete as soon after mixing as possible. Level it immediately. Then cover it with a temporary cover of burlap kept continuously wet. When hard enough for final finishing, uncover and finish only a small area at a time, protecting it again after finishing by replacing the wet cover.
6. Start curing as soon as the surface is hard enough to resist marring. In extremely hot weather use the "ponding" method described under "Curing" for at least the first 12 hours. After that, keep the concrete *continuously* wet to avoid alternate wetting and drying. Cure for at least 7 days.

COLD-WEATHER CONCRETING

Concrete may be placed in winter provided it is protected against freezing. A single cycle of freezing and thawing during the first few days may not lower the eventual strength of the concrete, but it will decrease its watertightness and reduce its resistance to weathering. Several such cycles at an early age, however, will permanently affect its strength, water resistance, and wearing qualities. This is the reason why walks and driveways placed late in the fall often deteriorate within a few years. Below are some of the steps to follow to avoid cold-weather problems:

1. When the air temperature is very low, you must heat the materials. The temperature of the concrete as it is placed in the forms should be between 50° and 70° F. If the air temperature is between 30° and 40° F, heat the mixing water. If the temperature is below 30° F, heat the sand also, and sometimes the coarse aggregate. Be sure no lumps of frozen aggregate are in the concrete when it is placed. To prevent flash setting of the concrete do not overheat the materials. Water temperature should be kept below 140° F. Do not place concrete on frozen ground. Thawing will produce unequal settling.
2. Accelerators to speed the setting of the concrete may be used with care. About 1 pound of calcium chloride per sack of cement will hasten hardening safely. Add it in the form of a solution, considered as part of the mixing water. Never use more than 2 pounds per sack because of the danger of flash set. Never use antifreeze compounds or other materials to lower the freezing point of concrete. The amounts required will seriously reduce the strength and wearing qualities of the concrete.
3. When using normal portland cement, keep the temperature at 70° F for the first 3 days, or 50° F for 5 days. Do not let concrete freeze for the next 4 days. Then let concrete cool gradually at the rate of 1 to 2 degrees per hour until it reaches the outside temperature.
4. In many cases a thick blanket of straw or other insulating material is sufficient protection during curing for slabs on the ground. At very low temperatures, however, housings of wood, insulation board, waterproofed paper or tarpaulins over wood frames, plus artificial heat, may be necessary. Moist, warm air should be circulated between slab and housing. If the concrete is indoors, and heating units are used, be sure to keep the concrete moist by sprinkling it or evaporating water into the air.

PREVENTING SURFACE DEFECTS

Many defects that soon develop on the surface of new concrete are caused by improper construction techniques, or by these combined with unsuitable weather. Here are some of the most common defects, with suggestions on how to prevent them:

SCALING

In this the surface of a hardened slab breaks away in scales up to about 3/16 inch thick.

Causes	Preventive measures
Cycles of freezing and thawing right after concrete has been placed.	Keep the temperature of newly placed concrete above 50° F for at least 5 days when using normal portland cement.
Later cycles of freezing and thawing in normal portland cement concrete, also the use of deicing salts in connection with them.	Coat cured concrete with linseed oil mixture described later in this chapter, or use air-entrained concrete in place of regular concrete.
Performing any of the finishing operations—such as screeding, floating, or troweling—while free water is on the surface. By mixing this water into the top of the slab, these operations will bring to the surface a layer of cement that is not bonded to the concrete under it. This layer will scale off after the concrete sets.	Don't perform any finishing operation while free water is present. First let the water evaporate from the surface, or remove the water by dragging a rubber garden hose over it.

CRAZING

Crazing is the formation of an overall pattern of fine cracks on newly hardened concrete due to surface shrinkage.

Causes	Preventive measures
Rapid drying of the slab surface generally caused by hot sun, high air temperature, drying winds, or any combination of these.	Cover with burlap or canvas immediately after screeding or leveling the surface of the newly placed concrete. Keep this cloth damp until ready for floating and troweling. Begin the moist cure of the concrete as soon as possible without marring the surface.
Second floating and troweling while there is too much moisture on the surface or while the concrete is still too plastic. Doing this will bring too much water and fine materials to the surface. If the surface water then evaporates too fast, the result may be shrinking and crazing.	Don't start second floating and troweling until excess moisture has evaporated, and the concrete has begun to set. To avoid excess moisture, increase the amount of fine and coarse aggregate in the mix or use air-entrained concrete.

(Continued)

PREVENTING SURFACE DEFECTS *(continued)*

Many defects that soon develop on the surface of new concrete are caused by improper construction techniques, or by these combined with unsuitable weather. Here are some of the most common defects, with suggestions on how to prevent them:

DUSTING

This is the appearance of a powdery coating on the surface of newly hardened concrete.

Causes	Preventive measures
Too much clay or silt in the concrete. These harmful materials degrade the cement at the surface, causing it to dust off later.	Use only clean and well-graded coarse and fine aggregate.
Second floating and troweling while there is still excess surface water on the concrete slab.	Delay these operations until all free water has disappeared from the surface and the concrete has started its initial set.
Dry heat from winter-protection heaters may lower the relative humidity around the concrete excessively, causing the concrete to dry out too fast. This will produce weak concrete as well as dusting by preventing proper hydration of the cement.	Place water jackets on the heaters to increase the relative humidity, and employ any of the previously described methods for moist curing. Move the heaters periodically so that no area will become overheated.
No curing or insufficient curing.	Proper curing for sufficient time is necessary. Uncured concrete will be weak and its surface easily worn off by foot traffic.

COLD-WEATHER TREATMENT FOR CONCRETE

Winter damage to driveways, sidewalks, steps, patios, and other structures of exposed concrete is caused by repeated cycles of freezing and thawing of water entrapped in the pores of the concrete. It takes the form of scaling and pitting known to the cement trade as "spalling." The process is aggravated by the use of salt and other deicing chemicals.

You can prevent spalling by the application of an inexpensive compound you can make from linseed oil and mineral spirits. This compound has been endorsed by the Bureau of Public Roads of the U.S. Department of Commerce and has been used successfully for some years on highways, bridge decks, parking lots, and other outdoor concrete installations throughout the country.

To make it, simply mix together equal quantities of mineral spirits (obtainable in paint and hardware stores under this name or as "turpentine substitute" or "paint thinner") and boiled linseed oil. The linseed oil reacts with oxygen in the air to form a tough film through which moisture and destructive salt solutions cannot penetrate. The mineral spirits makes the oil easier to spread and enables it to penetrate deeper into the concrete.

The compound is most effective if applied to new concrete at the end of the curing period, which is about 28 days. It has been successfully applied, however, after 7 to 10 days' curing. It will also inhibit damage to old concrete where spalling has already begun.

The compound dries and cures best if the atmospheric temperature is 70° F or above, although it has been successfully applied at temperatures as low as 35° F. The surface to be treated should be dry and free from dirt and debris.

On highways and other large areas the compound is generally applied by spraying. The best means of application for the small user is a cheap short-nap paint roller that can be thrown away after use. A long handle will make the work easier. A brush is not recommended, except to touch up edges, because with a brush the rate of application is hard to control and too much compound is left on the surface.

Two coats should be applied—the first at the rate of about 40 square yards per gallon; the second at about 67 square yards per gallon. The first coat should be completely dry before applying the second. At 70° F or above, drying should be complete within a few hours.

Under moderate weather conditions and ordinary usage, the first application may last up to 3 years. Under severe conditions, reapplication may be required each year for the first 3 or 4 years. After that, every third or fourth year should suffice.

The treatment leaves no greasy residue after drying. At first the concrete may be slightly darkened, but this tends to bleach out and become unnoticeable with time.

HOW TO COLOR CONCRETE

By adding color to concrete you may be able to create many pleasing decorative effects around your home and garden. Stepping stones, patios, swimming pool decks, floors, walks, and driveways, and so on, may all be livened by this means.

To color concrete you have four methods to choose from: (1) mix dry color through the whole material; (2) place a foundation layer in the usual way, and then top this with a layer of colored concrete; (3)

sprinkle the concrete before it hardens with a special "dry-shake" mixture of pigment, cement, and sand; (4) color a finished slab with stain, dye, or paint. The first three methods are outlined below, the fourth is described in Chapter 2.

Pigments for Concrete

Only commercially pure mineral pigments should be used, as other pigments are apt to fade or to reduce the strength and wearing qualities of the stucco, mortar, or concrete in which they are used. You may buy them as "cement colors" or "limeproof colors" under brand names, or you may get them under their chemical names as listed here:

Blues	Cobalt oxide
Browns	Brown iron oxide
Buffs	Synthetic yellow iron oxide
Greens	Chromium oxide green
Reds	Red iron oxide
Grays or Slate effects	Black iron oxide or carbon black; common lampblack should not be used

These pigments may be blended to get intermediate colors or tones. Red, yellow, and brown dry pigments are the least expensive; blues and greens may cost up to three times as much. Use the smallest amount of pigment necessary to get the tint or shade required. Always weigh the amount you use, so you can duplicate or alter a future mix. Never, however, add more than 10 percent of the weight of the cement.

CONCRETE COLORED ALL THE WAY THROUGH. This costs the most for pigment but is the easiest to make. Full-strength pigments will usually produce a deep color when 7 pounds are mixed with 1 bag of cement. Extra deep shades may take 10 pounds, while 5 pounds will do for medium shades, 3 pounds for light shades, and 1½ pounds for a pleasing pastel tint. For cleaner, brighter colors use white portland cement instead of the normal gray type and also white sand. Regular cement will do for black or dark grays. To prevent streaking, blend the dry cement thoroughly with the pigment before adding to the mix. Mix longer than usual to further distribute the color, then place, finish, and cure as you would ordinary concrete.

COLORED TOP-LAYER CONCRETE. Begin by placing a base layer of uncolored concrete in the usual manner. As soon as this layer has stiffened and the surface water has disappeared, place on top of it ½ to 1 inch of colored concrete, made as described above. This method requires a little more labor, but there may be a considerable saving in the cost of materials.

THE DRY-SHAKE METHOD. This is the least expensive, but it is the most difficult to carry out satisfactorily. If you want to risk it, you'd better buy a ready-made dry-shake mix of mineral oxide, white portland cement, and special fine aggregate. The manufacturer will specify the area a given amount should cover.

After the concrete has been placed and screeded, and the surface water has evaporated, work over the surface with a magnesium or aluminum float. This will remove any ridges or depressions that might cause variations in color intensity, and also bring to the surface sufficient moisture to combine with the dry coloring material. Then immediately shake about two-thirds of the mixture as evenly as you can over the surface.

In a few minutes the powder will appear moist. It should then be worked into the surface with the float. As soon as this floating is finished, distribute the remainder of the dry-shake material evenly over the surface. Work this also in with the float. If you want the surface to be smoother, now go over it with a trowel.

CURING COLORED CONCRETE. This must be cured as thoroughly as ordinary concrete. During drying and curing, take care to avoid any staining by dirt or foot traffic. After curing, give interior surfaces at least two coats of concrete floor wax containing the same mineral-oxide pigment used in or on the concrete.

HOW TO CLEAN CONCRETE

If concrete floors, walls, or walks become discolored beyond the capabilities of ordinary methods to clean them, here are several more drastic ones that should do the job:

Cleaning with Mortar

Repair all defects in the surface, and let the repair material set. Then make a cleaning mortar of 1 part portland cement and 1¼ parts fine sand, mixed with enough water to make a thick paste. If a light-colored surface is desired, use white portland cement. Apply the mortar to the surface with a brush, and immediately after scour the surface with a wood float such as is used in making concrete. After an hour or two, remove excess mortar from the surface with a trowel, leaving that which sticks in the pores. After the surface has dried, rub it with dry burlap to remove all visible remaining mortar. Complete each section without stopping. Mortar left on the surface overnight is very difficult to remove.

Rubbing with Burlap

Another mortar-cleaning method consists in rubbing the mortar over the surface with clean burlap. The mortar in this case should have the consistency of thick cream, and the surface should appear almost dry. Wait long enough to prevent smearing, but not long enough for the mortar to harden, and then wipe off the excess with clean burlap. Let the remainder set for 2 hours, after which keep it damp to cure it for the next 2 days. Then let it dry and sand it vigorously with No. 2 sandpaper. This removes all excess mortar not removed by the sand rubbing and leaves a surface of uniform appearance. For best results, mortar cleaning should be done in the shade on a cool, damp day.

Acid Cleaning

You can wash a concrete surface with acid if the staining is not too severe. First wet the surface and, while it is still damp, scrub it thoroughly with a 10-percent solution of hydrochloric acid. (The "muriatic" acid sold in paint and hardware stores is generally a 20-percent solution of hydrochloric acid. If you use this, just dilute it with an equal amount of water.) Then rinse off the acid with plain water. (*Caution:* Wear rubber gloves, a rubber or plastic apron or jacket, and protective goggles when scrubbing with hydrochloric acid. It is harmful to skin and clothing.)

PREPARING CONCRETE FLOORS FOR PAINTING

Because most concrete floors are below ground level, moisture may creep to the surface from the underside in sufficient quantity to cause the paint film to peel. Unless they have aged at least 6 months, there also may be free alkali on the surface that will attack the paint.

To neutralize the alkalinity and also to provide a slightly rougher surface for better adhesion, all concrete floors should be acid etched before painting.

To do this, scrub the surface with a solution of 1 part concentrated muriatic acid in 3 parts water, using a stiff fiber brush. (*Caution:* Muriatic acid is corrosive. Mix in a glass or polyethylene container, wear rubber gloves when applying it, and don't spatter on clothes or furniture.)

Allow about 1 gallon of solution to each 100 square feet of surface. Let it remain until all bubbling stops and then flush it off thoroughly with plain water. If the surface has not dried uniformly within a few hours, some of the acid still remains, so flush it again.

Depending upon the porosity of the surface, the floor will dry in several hours or it may take a day or more. As soon as it is completely dry, it may be painted.

If the finish on an old floor is poor, it should be removed before etching. Rubber-base paints require special solvents, but most other paints may be removed with a solution of 1 pound of lye in 5 pints of water (or 1 13-ounce can to 2 quarts). (*Caution:* Handle lye with care, as it is poisonous and caustic. Never mix it in hot water or in an aluminum container. Wear rubber gloves while handling it.)

After the paint has softened, remove it with steel wool or a scraper. Flush the surface with plain water to remove remaining paint and lye. Then etch with the muriatic solution mentioned above, applied at a rate of about 75 square feet to the gallon.

HARDENERS FOR CONCRETE FLOORS

Concrete floors that are not to be painted can be hardened, and so given longer life and freedom from "dusting," by treating with a diluted solution of sodium silicate prepared as follows:

Sodium silicate solution (commercial grade, 40° Baumé)	1 gallon
Water	3 gallons

Mix thoroughly and apply three coats, letting each dry a day or more before putting on the next. Succeeding coats will penetrate better if you scrub preceding coat with a stiff fiber brush and water.

Another hardener for concrete floors is a solution of zinc sulfate. This darkens the concrete somewhat, but produces a hard, uniform surface.

Here is a formula recommended by the Portland Cement Association:

Sulfuric acid, concentrated	¼ ounce
Water	2 gallons
Zinc sulfate	3 pounds

Stir the sulfuric acid into the water and then stir in the zinc sulfate until thoroughly dissolved. (*Careful:* The acid is extremely corrosive; if you spatter any on yourself or surroundings, flush off immediately with plenty of plain cold water.) Apply two coats—the second, 4 hours after the first. Before applying the second coat, scrub the surface with hot water and mop it dry.

REINFORCING CONCRETE

Here is a trick that makes reinforcing rods or mesh do the best possible job of internal bracing. Remember that concrete has great compressive strength, but much weaker tensile strength. Therefore place the rods where the concrete has the most tendency to pull apart under the load. In other words, if a slab is to be supported under its middle, with its ends unsupported, place the reinforcing rods near the top of the slab. On the other hand, if the slab is to be supported at its ends, embed the rods near the bottom. In either case, however, be sure that the rods are far enough from any surface so they are strongly keyed in the concrete.

REPAIRING CRACKS IN CONCRETE

For this purpose, use regular cement mortar, made by mixing 1 part portland cement with 3 parts fine sand and adding enough water to make a puttylike consistency. Before packing in the mortar, widen the crack, dust it out, and wet it with water.

PATCHING A CONCRETE FLOOR OR SIDEWALK

A sidewalk that has settled, a crack in the basement floor, or other damaged concrete can often be restored by timely patching. Here are the steps that ensure a good job:

1. Thoroughly clean the areas to be patched and roughen them with a chisel. Then go over the surface with a wire brush and wash away all dust and loose particles with clean water.

2. Dampen the surface that is to be patched, but leave no excess water on the surface.
3. Make a thick, creamy mixture of portland cement and water and brush it on the prepared surface. The patch should be applied before this creamy mixture dries.
4. Make a stiff mix of 1 part portland cement, 2 parts sand, and 2 parts pea gravel. Tamp this mixture firmly into the cavity and smooth off lightly with a wood float. After the concrete begins to stiffen, finish with a steel trowel or wood float. For narrow cracks where pea gravel cannot be used, use mortar made of 1 part portland cement and 3 parts sand.
5. Keep the freshly patched place damp for a minimum of 5 days.

WORKING WITH MORTAR

Mortar for Concrete Masonry

Good mortar for bonding together concrete blocks must have sufficient strength, good workability, and a property called *water retentivity,* which resists rapid loss of water to blocks that may be highly absorptive. The latter is very important, because concrete blocks, unlike some types of brick, should never be wetted to control suction before the application of mortar. The accompanying table shows formulas for mixes to be used under ordinary and under unusually severe conditions.

MORTAR MIXES FOR CONCRETE BLOCKS

(Proportions by volume)

Type of service	Portland cement	Hydrated lime	Mortar sand (in damp, loose condition)
For ordinary service	1	½ to 1¼	4½ to 6
To withstand unusually heavy loads, violent winds, or severe frost conditions	1	0 to ¼	2¼ to 3

Use clean sharp sand of a type suitable for making concrete, but with all grits and pebbles larger than ¼ inch screened out. Mix the dry ingredients first with a hoe or a shovel until no variations in color are visible. Then form in a ring, add a little water at a time to the center of this ring, and hoe the mixture into the water until the combination forms a smooth and plastic paste. If the paste is too stiff, add water sparingly.

Mortar for Brick Masonry

Unless properly mixed and applied, mortar will be the weakest part of brick masonry. Both the strength and the watertightness of brick walls depend largely on the strength of the mortar bond.

The general instructions described earlier for mixing mortar for cementing concrete blocks apply also to mixing mortar for bricks. There is one exception, however, in the application. Porous or high-suction brick, if laid dry, will absorb enough water from the mortar to prevent the cement from properly setting. Therefore, such brick must be drenched with a hose and then allowed to surface dry before they are laid. A rough way to tell if a brick should be wet before laying is to sprinkle a few drops of water on one of its sides. If these drops sink in completely in less than 1 minute, the brick should be wet before laying it.

One of the types of mortar in the table below should suit almost any kind of brick-construction job.

MORTAR MIXES FOR BRICK MASONRY

(Proportions by volume)

Type of service	Portland cement	Hydrated lime	Mortar sand, in damp, loose condition
For general use in work below ground level and in contact with earth, such as walks, foundations, and retaining walls	1	¼	3
For general use, especially where high lateral strength is needed	1	½	4½
This is the commonest and most economical mortar for general use, and is suitable for most exterior walls above ground	1	1	6
Still less expensive, this mortar will do for solid load-bearing walls where compressive forces do not exceed 100 pounds per square inch and which will not be exposed to freezing and thawing in the presence of great moisture	1	2	9

Retempering Mortar

Mortar that has become too stiff on the mortar board to work with properly because of evaporation may be restored to workability by thorough remixing and the addition of sufficient water. Mortar that has stiffened because it has started to set, however, cannot be thus retempered and should be discarded. If you can't determine the cause of stiffening, make it a rule to discard mortar that is more than 2½ hours old when the air temperature is 80° F or higher, or more than 3½ hours old at lower temperatures.

Speeding the Setting of Mortar

By adding up to 2 percent of calcium chloride to the weight of the cement, you can hasten the setting of mortar and cause it to gain full strength earlier. Dissolve the calcium chloride in a small amount of water and add this solution with the mixing water. A trial mix will give you an idea of the proper amount of the chemical to produce the desired rate of hardening.

Antifreeze Chemicals

The use of calcium chloride or other chemicals to lower the freezing point of mortars during winter construction should be avoided. The amount of such chemicals required for any appreciable effect would ruin the strength and other desirable qualities of the mortar.

Estimating the Number of Concrete Blocks Needed

If you are using the standard 8×8×16-inch blocks—they are really 7⅝×7⅝×15⅝—multiply the wall height by the length. Multiply the result by 1.2. Your answer is the number of blocks required. For example, to find out how many blocks to buy for a wall 16 feet long by 8 feet high: 16×8×1.2 gives 154 blocks, approximately.

Size	*Mortar needed for 100 square feet of wall area*	*Per 100 blocks*
4 inches high	13½ cubic feet	6 cubic feet
8 inches high	8½ cubic feet	7½ cubic feet

BRICK SIZES AND TYPES

Standard bricks made in the United States are 2¼ by 3¾ by 8 inches. English bricks are 3 by 4½ by 9 inches. Roman bricks are 1½ by 4 by 12 inches. The actual dimensions of brick may vary a little because of shrinkage during burning. Here are some common types of brick:

1. *Building brick* formerly called common brick, is made of ordinary clays or shales and is burned in kilns. It is used generally where it can't be seen, as in the backing courses in solid or cavity brick walls.
2. *Face brick* has better durability and is better looking than backup or building brick, and so is used in the exposed face of a wall. It is produced in various shades of brown, red, gray, yellow, and white.
3. *Pressed brick* is made by a dry press process and has regular smooth faces, sharp edges, and perfectly square corners. Ordinarily it is used entirely as face brick.
4. *Glazed brick* has one surface of each brick glazed in white or some color. This glasslike coating makes such brick particularly suited for walls in hospitals, dairies, laboratories, or other buildings where cleanliness and ease of cleaning are necessary.
5. *Cored brick* is made with two rows of holes extending through its beds to reduce weight. It is just about as strong and as moisture-resistant as solid brick, and may be used to replace the solid type wherever lighter weight is desired.
6. *Fire brick* is made of a special type of fire clay that will stand the heat of fireplaces, furnaces, and other locations of intense heat without cracking or otherwise deteriorating. It is usually larger than regular brick and is often molded by hand.

PLASTERING

Plastering whole walls and ceilings is not a job for the novice do-it-yourselfer. To produce finished plaster work over large surfaces requires long experience. In case you would like to experiment on a modest scale, however, here is the general procedure.

A professional plaster job usually consists of three coats—a rough or "scratch" coat is applied directly to the wood or metal lath; a "brown" coat is applied over this; and a thin, smooth finishing coat is finally skimmed over the brown coat, which has been roughened to make it hold. The first two coats are made of gypsum or hydrated lime plaster mixed with sand and with cattle or goat hair (or in cheaper jobs, jute,

QUANTITIES OF MATERIAL REQUIRED FOR BRICK WALLS*

Wall area (square feet)	WALL THICKNESS							
	4 inches		8 inches		12 inches		16 inches	
	Number of bricks	Cubic feet of mortar	Number of bricks	Cubic feet of mortar	Number of bricks	Cubic feet of mortar	Number of bricks	Cubic feet of mortar
1	6.17	0.08	12.33	0.2	18.49	0.32	24.65	0.44
10	61.7	0.8	123.3	2	184.9	3.2	246.5	4.4
100	617	8	1,233	20	1,849	32	2,465	44
200	1,234	16	2,466	40	3,698	64	4,930	88
300	1,851	24	3,699	60	5,547	96	7,395	132
400	2,468	32	4,932	80	7,396	128	9,860	176
500	3,085	40	6,165	100	9,245	160	12,325	220
600	3,712	48	7,398	120	11,094	192	14,790	264
700	4,319	56	8,631	140	12,943	224	17,253	308
800	4,936	64	9,864	160	14,792	256	19,720	352
900	5,553	72	10,970	180	16,641	288	22,185	396
1,000	6,170	80	12,330	200	18,490	320	24,650	440

* Quantities are based on ½-inch-thick mortar joint. For ⅜-inch-thick joint, use 80 percent of these quantities. For ⅝-inch-thick joint, use 120 percent.

wood fiber, or asbestos) to give the plaster greater strength. The finishing coat usually consists of plaster of Paris mixed with hydrated lime.

A typical formula for the scratch coat might be: 25 pounds of hydrated lime, 100 pounds of dry plastering sand, and 1/4 pound of hair or fiber. These ingredients are mixed with water to produce a workable paste stiff enough to cling to the lath and not drop off. The plaster is applied with enough force to cause it to penetrate the openings between the lath and so anchor it firmly. The batch mentioned should cover about 2 1/4 square yards on wood lath to a thickness of 1/4 inch.

The scratch coat is roughened with a comb before it sets hard, to give "teeth" to hold firmly the brown coat, which is applied after the scratch coat has dried. The brown coat usually has a smaller proportion of lime and hair than the scratch coat—say, 12 pounds of hydrated lime, 60 pounds of sand, and 1 ounce of hair, for a batch that would cover the same area to the same thickness. This coat should be applied as straight and as evenly as possible, and within about 1/8 inch of the final finished surface desired.

For a white smooth finish, mix 10 pounds of hydrated lime with 2 1/2 pounds of plaster of Paris. Water is then added to this mixture to form a thick paste, which is applied to the brown coat in two or three very thin layers, one after the other. The brown coat should be thoroughly dry. To make the surface still smoother, go over it as soon as it has initially set with a brush wet with plain water, followed by a steel trowel. Dampen the surface only enough to soften it slightly, then buff it with the trowel.

REPAIRING PLASTER

Cracks, holes, and other surface imperfections on plaster walls can be repaired easily. If the ingredients are at hand, you can make up your own patching plaster or crack filler from one of the following formulas. If they are not, you can buy excellent and inexpensive ready-made preparations at your local paint or hardware store. If a hole is deep, the filling should be built up in two or three layers, letting one set before applying the next. For repairing very thin surface imperfections better use a ready-made spackling compound, which contains a glue as well as plaster for better adhesion.

Filling Cracks in Plaster Walls

Cracked plaster walls can be repaired with plaster of Paris combined with a small amount of slaked lime and mixed with thin glue size. Mix only enough for about 15 minutes' work at a time, as this crack filler hardens quickly.

If plaster walls are to be painted with oil paints, the cracks may be filled with thick white lead paste to which either whiting or plaster of Paris has been added. If the walls have already been painted, the crack filler may be colored with oil pigment to match.

Patching Plaster or Crack Filler

An inexpensive patching plaster or crack filler can be made as follows:

Plaster of Paris	1 pound
Casein glue or yellow dextrin	2 ounces
Whiting	2 ounces

Dental plaster of Paris, if available, is better than the ordinary grade because it does not shrink so much. Mix thoroughly. Stir the mixture into water to make a thick paste, mixing only as much as you can use immediately. Apply to dents or bruises with a flexible putty knife, let dry hard, and sand clean. Apply more after drying, if not puttied up to level the first time.

To prepare a crack filler or cold-water putty, the following may also be used:

Dental plaster of Paris	12 ounces
Yellow dextrin	3 ounces
French ochre or other dry color	1 ounce

Mix thoroughly, then work up only enough with water for immediate use.

Corrective for Soft Plaster

This final coat of plaster sometimes develops soft, chalky areas in dry weather due to too rapid drying. These may be hardened by moistening with this solution:

Zinc sulfate	¼ ounce
Alum	¼ ounce
Water	32 fluid ounces

Plaster Stipple Coat

A stipple coat for use on interior walls or craftwork projects to which you wish to give a stippled and glazed finish can be mixed as follows:

Soft white lead paste	5 pounds
Plaster of Paris	10 pounds

Use flatting oil to make as thin or heavy a consistency as required. For most wall work, thin to a very soft paste that can be brushed on from 1⁄16 to 1⁄8 inch thick. Then stipple the coating with a floor-scrubbing brush dipped in water, a wad of crumpled paper, or the cut face of a sponge, according to the texture desired. Do not coat too much wall surface before stippling, and avoid any regular pattern effects. Let dry overnight before painting or other finishing.

ROOFING

Nowadays eight of ten homes are roofed with asphalt-strip shingles. Wood shingles, cedar shakes, and asbestos cement roofs comprise the balance. Let's quickly survey these more common roofing materials.

Asphalt Shingles

Today you have a wider choice of asphalt shingles than in former years. When asphalt shingles are manufactured, a felt or fiberglass base is saturated with oily asphalt (not natural asphalt, but the residue left after the fractional distillation of crude oil), and then the top surface is coated with a filled asphalt formulated for best weather resistance. Rock or colored ceramic granules are impressed into this top coating. The heavier the shingle, generally speaking, the better the quality. Since World War II, three-tab asphalt strip shingles weighing 235 pounds per square (100 square feet), which ordinarily last some twenty years before the asphalt dries out and the shingles curl, have been used to roof nearly all moderately priced housing. These shingles are serviceable, inexpensive, and easy to lay—but they look commonplace, and for this reason other roofing materials often were used on more expensive homes.

Then in 1970 one manufacturer, Bird & Sons, Inc., introduced a much heavier two-layer asphalt shingle, a shingle having a cut-out top layer that gave the roofing a texture similar to that of random-laid wood shingles. Style-conscious architects welcomed the idea.

Now every major asphalt shingle manufacturer has a similar two-layered textured asphalt shingle on the market. One manufacturer calls his product Shake-Shingles; another calls his Shangles. Some are random-laid, and some are laid in patterns. These two-layer shingles weigh from 350 to 400 pounds per square, cost roughly twice as much as single-layer 235 pound shingles, and all last 25 years plus.

All asphalt shingles with a rock- or ceramic-granule surface are fire-retardant and most carry an Underwriters' Lab "C" rating. Asphalt shingles with a fiberglass base are even more fire-resistant and are available with an "A" rating. A-rated roofing is required by local codes on homes in some high fire-risk areas, and in many areas it is required on commercial buildings. In most parts of the country, however, using an A-rated rather than a C-rated roofing material on your house will not reduce your fire insurance premium. Nearly all better quality asphalt shingles now are self-sealing for wind resistance. Spots of heat-softening asphalt cement automatically seal down the overlaying shingle when hot summer sunshine warms the roof.

Essentially the same materials used in the manufacture of asphalt-strip shingles can also be used on the job to lay built-up roofing, which is laid by laminating layers of asphalt-saturated felt in mopped asphalt and surfaced with crushed gravel. Ordinarily a built-up roof is the most satisfactory roofing available for flat or very low-pitched roofs.

Cedar Shingles

In years past, cedar shingles were widely used because they were cheap. They're no longer cheap and, moreover, laying wood shingles is slower work requiring more skill than is needed to lay asphalt shingles. A skilled workman can lay over 100 square feet (1 square) of wood shingles per day. Because of the high cost of application, roofers always use best-quality vertical-grain No. 1 Blue Label shingles on roofs. A wood-shingled roof will last some thirty years. Some circumstances (when the attic under the roof lacks ventilation, for example) justify treating the shingles before they are laid with preservative to extend their life. Some mills supply shingles factory-stained in attractive colors.

Shingles are sawed. Shakes are split. Cedar shakes have a rough, rustic look that no other roofing really matches. They have excellent thermal characteristics, and they are not difficult to lay. Like wood shingles, shakes can be applied over either spaced or solid roof sheathing.

Asbestos Cement Shingles

These have obvious advantages: They are completely fireproof and nearly everlasting, but they also have two drawbacks—they're much more expensive than other roofing materials, and they are considerably heavier. Manufacturers' literature gives application instructions. A special cutter, which can be rented, is needed to install them. Roof valleys generally are flashed with sheet stainless steel, and the shingles are fastened with stainless steel nails. Before selecting asbestos cement shingles for your roof, be sure that the roof framing will support their weight.

There are other roofing materials that you may want to consider—roll roofing, metal shingles, slates and tiles—but these are less commonly used.

Estimating Your Needs

When you've selected a roofing material, the next problem will be to figure out how much of it you'll need. To calculate the area of your roof, first figure the ground area of your house, including eave and cornice overhang in square feet, multiplying length by width. Next determine the roof's pitch, or degree of slope, sighting over a protractor to find the angle of the roof above horizontal. Then, using this angle, make a drawing using a carpenter's square and measure the "rise" in inches per foot of "run," and add a percentage as below to ground area of the house.

3-inch rise per foot add 3 percent

4-inch rise per foot add 5½ percent

5-inch rise per foot add 8½ percent

6-inch rise per foot add 12 percent

8-inch rise per foot add 20 percent

12-inch rise per foot add 42 percent

18-inch rise per foot add 80 percent

Dividing the total by 100 will give you the number of squares of roof area. Then add one square of roofing for each 100 lineal feet of valley to determine the total number of squares of roofing needed.

From the roof's area in squares you can also figure the number of rolls of 15-pound felt underlayer you'll need. This special asphalt-saturated roofer's felt is recommended for use under all asphalt or asbestos cement shingles. It minimizes condensation problems. Do not use heavier vapor-barrier material in place of roofer's felt. The underlayer not only protects the roof deck from any wind-driven rain that might work in under the shingles, but it also protects the shingles from contact with resinous spots in the deck, which because of chemical incompatibility might damage the shingles. A standard roll of 36-inch-wide 15-pound felt underlayer covers four squares of roof deck.

Other Roofing Materials

The quantity of other materials you'll need will depend upon the roof and the roofing applied. Usually metal or vinyl drip strips should be used along the roof's eaves, and also, unless the roof has wood drip strips, along the rakes to cover the edges of the sheathing. Along the eaves, install the drip strip under the underlayer. Along the rake, nail it over the underlayer. Measure the number of lineal feet of roof edge to figure the number of lengths needed.

The material needed for valley linings will depend upon the valley treatment used. Use the valley treatment the roofing manufacturer recommends unless you're an experienced roofer. Most manufacturers of asphalt-strip shingles now recommend "closed" valleys, with the courses of shingles laid right across the valley on a 90-pound roll-roofing lining. A woven valley offers the advantage of adding extra thicknesses of roofing in the valley, which is the roof's most vulnerable point. But these extra layers of roofing form noticeable humps along the valley, which some roofers find objectionable, and those who do still prefer traditional open valleys—open-valley flashing can be either doubled 90-pound roll roofing, painted galvanized sheet metal, or sheet copper.

Most asphalt-shingle manufacturers make special shingles for capping hips and ridges that match their standard shingles. The hot-dip galvanized roofing nails used should be long enough to penetrate the deck's sheathing. You'll need about 2½ pounds of 1½-inch nails per square of roofing, together with a few pounds of 1-inch nails for the 15-pound felt underlayer.

WALL PANELING

There are various wall paneling materials on the market—plywood, fiberboard, gypsum board, and hardboard being the most popular. These drywall materials are easy to install because they are available in 4×8-foot panels and vary in thickness from ¼ to ⅝ inch thick depending on the material. They may be fastened to the walls with nails or contact cement. (For details on the latter, see Chapter 6.)

To estimate the number of panels required, measure the perimeter of the room. This is merely the total of the widths of each wall in the room. Then divide the perimeter by 4 to determine the number of 4×8-foot panels needed.

For example, if the walls of a room measure 14 feet + 14 feet + 16 feet + 16 feet, this would equal 60 feet, which divided by 4 gives 15 panels required. To allow for areas such as windows, doors, fireplaces, etc., use the following deductions:

Door	½ panel
Window	¼ panel
Fireplace	½ panel

Since this room has a fireplace, two doors, and two windows, the actual number of panels needed for the room would be 13 pieces (15 pieces minus 2 total deductions). If the perimeter of the room falls in between the figures in table, use the next highest number to determine panels required. These figures are for rooms with 8-foot ceiling heights or less. For walls over 8 feet high, select a paneling that has V grooves and that will "stack," allowing panel grooves to line up perfectly from floor to ceiling.

WALLCOVERING

Wallcoverings, including wallpapers, are still a popular form of decoration. To estimate the amount of wallcovering required for a job, keep in mind that the roll is a standard unit of measurement in the wallcovering industry. The material may come in double A or triple A roll bolts, but the roll is still the standard unit of measurement, and each roll contains approximately 36 square feet.

However, when hanging the material you will always have a certain amount of waste while trimming and cutting the strips to size, so you will actually obtain approximately 30 square feet of usable material out of each roll.

To figure how many rolls you will need for a given room, first measure the distance around the room. Then multiply this figure by the distance from the baseboard to the ceiling. This will give the number of square feet of wall area. For example:

Your room is 15 by 20 feet and 8 feet high. The distance around the room is 15 + 15 + 20 + 20 = 70 feet. Multiply this by the height of the wall: 70×8=560 square feet of wall area. But there are doors and windows that require no paper, and you must deduct this space. For ex-

ESTIMATING WALLCOVERING

Distance around room (feet)	Single rolls for wall areas at ceiling height of			Number of yards for borders	Single rolls for ceilings
	8 feet	9 feet	10 feet		
28	8	8	10	11	2
30	8	8	10	11	2
32	8	10	10	12	2
34	10	10	12	13	4
36	10	10	12	13	4
38	10	12	12	14	4
40	10	12	12	15	4
42	12	12	14	15	4
44	12	12	14	16	4
46	12	14	14	17	6
48	14	14	16	17	6
50	14	14	16	18	6
52	14	14	16	19	6
54	14	16	18	19	6
56	14	16	18	20	8
58	16	16	18	21	8
60	16	18	20	21	8
62	16	18	20	22	8
64	16	18	20	22	8
66	18	20	20	23	10
68	18	20	22	24	10
70	18	20	22	25	10
72	18	20	22	25	12
74	20	22	22	26	12
76	20	22	24	27	12
78	20	22	24	27	14
80	20	22	26	28	14
82	22	24	26	29	14
84	22	24	26	30	16
86	22	24	26	30	16
88	24	26	28	31	16
90	24	26	28	32	18

Note: This quick-reference chart is based on a single roll covering 30 square feet; deduct one single roll for every two ordinary size doors or windows or every 30 square feet of opening. It is wise to buy one or two extra rolls in case you ruin some of the covering in hanging. Most dealers will take back uncut rolls. You may wish to keep some covering for patching.

ample, your room contains one door, 7 feet by 4 feet, and two windows, each one 5 feet by 3 feet. Multiply height by width to get the square feet in each.

$$7 \times 4 \times 1 = 28 \text{ square feet of door space}$$

$$5 \times 3 \times 2 = 30 \text{ square feet of window space}$$

Add these to get the total amount of space you will deduct from the room size:

$$28 + 30 = 58 \text{ square feet}$$

Subtract this from the total:

560 square feet — 58 square feet =
502 square feet of wall area to be papered.

Now divide this figure by 30; this room would require approximately 17 rolls of wallcovering. Estimate the number of rolls of ceiling covering needed in the same way, multiplying the length of the ceiling by the width to get the square feet.

For a quick reference aid in estimating the amount of coverage needed, use the table on page 189.

RESILIENT FLOORING

Practicality, convenience, ease of application, and long wear are a few of the reasons why resilient flooring continues to be one of the most popular choices of homeowners everywhere. With the tremendous variety of materials, designs, and colors available, it is possible to create just about any floor scheme that strikes your fancy. For example, you can install a floor of one color, or you can combine different colors into a custom-floor design that matches room requirements and individual taste. If you prefer the natural look, you will find countless resilient materials that closely resemble the appearance of slate, brick, wood, terrazzo, marble, and stone. Many of these floors feature an embossed surface texture that adds a striking note to the design.

Types of Resilient Floors

Resilient floors are manufactured in two basic types: sheet materials and tiles. The latter are cemented in place to serve as a permanent floor.

Sheet materials are also cemented in place, but in some cases can be installed loosely like rugs. Tiles generally come in 9- or 12-inch squares; sheet materials are available in continuous rolls up to 12 feet wide.

Estimating Number of Tiles Needed

The accompanying table will aid you in figuring the number of tiles to complete an installation job. For instance, if you are working with a floor area that is 280 square feet (a 14×20-foot family room), and you want to use 9×9-inch tiles, the table indicates 356 tiles for 200 square feet and 143 tiles for 80 square feet, a total number of 499 tiles.

When ordering tiles, it is most important to consider the waste factors. In our example, the allowance for waste is 7 percent of the total number of tiles, or an extra 35 tiles. This would make a grand total of 534 tiles. Since tiles are usually boxed 80 to a carton, this would mean that we need over 6¾ cartons. Even if the dealer is willing to split a carton, it would be wise to take the seven full cartons. This assures an adequate supply of tiles from the same lot and also allows for replacement if any should be needed.

ESTIMATING TILE QUANTITIES

Square feet	Number of tiles needed (inches)			Square feet	Number of tiles needed (inches)		
	9×9	12×12	9×18		9×9	12×12	9×18
1	2	1	1	60	107	60	54
2	4	2	2	70	125	70	63
3	6	3	3	80	143	80	72
4	8	4	4	90	160	90	80
5	9	5	5	100	178	100	90
6	11	6	6	200	356	200	178
7	13	7	7	300	534	300	267
8	15	8	8	400	712	400	356
9	16	9	8	500	890	500	445
10	18	10	9	600	1,068	600	534
20	36	20	18	700	1,246	700	623
30	54	30	27	800	1,424	800	712
40	72	40	36	900	1,602	900	801
50	89	50	45	1,000	1,780	1,000	890

GUIDE TO RESILIENT FLOORING

Material	Backing	How installed	Where to install	Ease of installation	Ease of maintenance	Resilience and durability	Quiet
TILE MATERIALS							
Asphalt	none	adhesive	anywhere	fair	difficult	poor	very poor
Vinyl	none	adhesive	anywhere	easy	very easy	excellent	poor
Asbestos vinyl	none	adhesive	anywhere	easy	easy	good–excellent	fair
Rubber	none	adhesive	anywhere	fair	easy	good	good
Cork	none	adhesive	on or above grade	fair	fair (with vinyl, good)	good	excellent
SHEET MATERIALS							
Inlaid vinyl	felt	adhesive	above grade	fair	easy	good	fair
	foam and felt	adhesive	above grade	difficult	easy	good	good
	asbestos	adhesive	anywhere	very difficult	easy	excellent	fair
	foam	adhesive	anywhere	very difficult	easy	excellent	good
Printed vinyl	felt	loose-lay	above grade	easy	fair	poor	poor
	felt	adhesive	above grade	fair	easy	fair	poor
	foam and felt	loose-lay	above grade	easy	easy	fair	good
	asbestos and foam	adhesive or loose-lay	anywhere	fair–easy	easy	good	good
	foam	loose-lay	anywhere	easy	easy	good	good

ALLOWANCE FOR WASTE

1–50 square feet	14 percent
50–100 square feet	10 percent
100–200 square feet	8 percent
200–300 square feet	7 percent
300–1,000 square feet	5 percent
Over 1,000 square feet	3 percent

5

Heating and Cooling Know-How

HOME INSULATION

Most homes, built in the days when energy was plentiful and cheap, don't have enough insulation, but insulation can be added to any house, even if some already exists. Insulating an attic floor, where savings generally will be greatest, usually can be done by the home owner himself.

Other home improvements that will save energy are to insulate sidewalls, add storm windows and doors, install weatherstripping, and caulk around window and door frames.

In the heating season alone, adequate insulation in the attic floor generally will save up to 30 percent on fuel bills, sometimes even more. In an air-conditioned home, summer savings will add to the total. Insulation works year-round.

In your case, the percentage of savings will depend on these factors:

- How much insulation you had in the first place
- The attic area of your house in relation to wall area
- The number and size of windows and doors
- Whether you have storm windows and doors and good weatherstripping
- The amount of insulation you install
- The climate in which you live.

Insulation Efficiency Ratings

In R-numbers, "R" stands for resistance to winter heat loss and summer heat gain. R-numbers are more accurate than inches as a means of designating insulation performance. One type or brand of insulation might be slightly thicker or thinner than another, but if they're rated at the same R-number they'll perform about the same.

R-numbers should be plainly marked on all packages of all types of insulation. If they are not, don't buy that product or allow a contractor to install it.

Recommended R-values for maximum savings rise every time fuel prices rise. Current standards are shown in the accompanying map of R-values. You can exceed these values if you choose, but don't go with less. Otherwise, you'll only lose money and waste fuel in the long run.

"WHICH R-VALUES GO WHERE?"

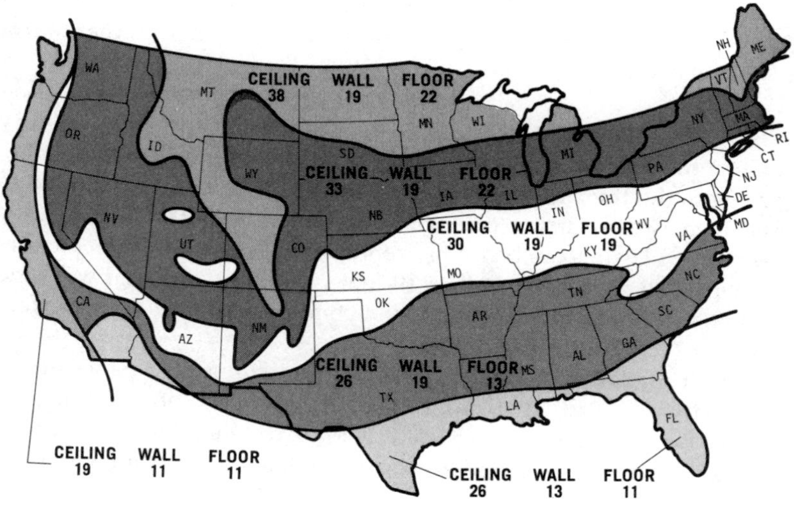

Types of Insulation

There are a lot of different materials, types, and sizes of insulation used in residential work. Which type to select depends on the area of the house that is to be insulated and often on whether it is a new or an existing dwelling. It also depends very much on what is locally available, for local building-supply houses usually stock only those materials in demand by local contractors and builders. You should check on the cost of various materials locally.

MINERAL WOOL. This is probably the most common kind of insulation on the market. It is made of rock, slag, or glass fibers and comes in three basic forms: batts, blankets (rolls), and loose fill (also called "blow-in").

BATTS. These are in short lengths—usually about 48 inches long—and in widths to fit between standard 16- and 24-inch on-center framing. The two most common are the 3⅝-inch (R-13) and the 6-inch (R-19). Batts come with or without a vapor barrier and are used primarily to insulate an attic floor where joists are exposed and there is a ceiling below to support the batts. Unfaced batts are excellent to use for adding insulation to an attic floor. You can cut them to size with a sharp knife or heavy scissors after first compressing the material along the line to be cut with a piece of scrap lumber. Batts can also be used to insulate between wall framing, but blanket insulation is more commonly used on this job because it offers an uninterrupted vapor barrier on the "warm side" of the insulation.

BLANKETS. These are similar in composition to batts, but they come in rolls rather than in short lengths. The length of a roll varies according to the thickness of the material. The 1⅛-inch insulation used to insulate between furring comes in 100-foot rolls but is seldom used these days. Plastic foam board has replaced it. The 6- or 6½-inch material with an R-22 value comes in 10-foot rolls. For residential work the R-19 and R-11 are most common and come inrolls from 24 to 56 feet long.

Blanket insulation comes either unfaced or with a kraft paper or foil vapor barrier. Usually there are stapling flanges. The unfaced type goes in place between the studding and is held by friction. You cover it over with a vapor barrier after an entire section of the wall has been insulated.

Blanket insulation works on walls, floors, ceilings, and roofs. It goes up quickly on walls and is easily handled by one person. For ceilings and roofs, it is handy to have a helper.

LOOSE FILL. This consists of nodules of rock or slag mineral wool. This is the type of insulation used by contractors to blow into walls and ceilings of existing houses. It is also a handy material to use for adding to the thickness of insulation in an attic where the joists are exposed.

Loose fill comes in a bag and the R-value depends on how thickly the material is applied.

Vermiculite is made of expanded mica and was once quite popular for use in attic floors before other kinds of loose fill insulation became available. It is relatively expensive, but it is handy to fill areas that can't be reached by other types of insulation because it pours and flows easily.

Another form of loose fill is cellulose. This material is relatively cheap and offers slightly more R-value per inch than mineral wool. It is made by chopping up waste paper and then treating it with fire retardant chemicals. If you buy this type of insulation, make absolutely sure it has been fire rated by the Underwriters Labs. Look for the UL rating on the insulation packaging. If there is no rating, do not buy. The fire retardant treatment may not be up to standards, and the insulation could present a serious fire hazard.

PLASTIC FOAM BOARDS. These are usually made of polystyrene or polyurethane foam. They range in thickness from ½ inch to over 4 inches, but the most common are the 1- and 2-inch thick boards. A 2-inch thick polyurethane board has slightly over an R-16 value. These boards come with square or tongue-and-groove edges, and you can cut and work them with ordinary woodworking tools, applying them most efficiently with a mastic. Because of the composition of these boards, many types can be used under normal conditions without the need of a vapor barrier.

Foam boards are commonly used for perimeter insulation, but they are gaining acceptance for general-purpose insulation work. They are very convenient for insulating the inside surfaces of a basement or below-grade masonry wall. And they make a suitable base for gypsum wallboard. Some manufacturers recommend mastic for installing both the foam board and gypsum board. These boards are frequently used under decks and on roofs where exposed rafters prevent the use of other kinds of insulation. In some situations they provide both sheathing and insulation in one operation. They are very light and easy to handle, but can present a fire hazard. Most building codes require foam to be covered with a fire-resistant material. Check your local code.

SPRAYED FOAM. This is a method of insulating just coming into use in residential work. It is applied by an applicator and goes on fast. Two trained men can completely insulate a 2000-square-foot house in a couple of days. The great advantage to this type of insulation is that every square inch, crack, and crevice in the house can be covered, and the R-values for plastic foams are very high.

HOW THICK SHOULD YOUR INSULATION BE?

	BATTS OR BLANKETS		LOOSE FILL (POURED IN)			RIGID PLASTIC FOAMS		
	Glass fiber	Rock wool	Glass fiber	Rock wool	Cellulosic fiber	Urethane	U-F	Styrene
R-11	3½″–4″	3″	5″	4″	3″	1½″	2″	2¼″
R-19	6″–6½″	5¼″	8″–9″	6″–7″	5″	2¾″	3¾″	4¼″
R-22	6½″	6″	10″	7″–8″	6″	3″	4″	4½″
R-30	9½″–10½″	9″	13″–14″	10″–11″	8″	4½″	5¾″	6½″
R-38	12″–13″	10½″	17″–18″	13″–14″	10″–11″	5½″	7½″	8½″

Sprayable rigid urethane foam is now approved by building codes as a structural insulation for walls, eliminating the need for sheathing in many cases. For this type of application, the depth of the foam four feet from each corner is equal to the depth of the studding. The rest of the wall requires only a thickness to produce the required R-value. Foam does not require a vapor barrier, but it must be covered either with gypsum board, plaster, etc., or a fire retardant.

Plastic foams such as urethane and U-F can also be shot into the hollow wall spaces of existing homes. These treatments give very good R-values, but there are problems. U-F must be mixed to exacting standards or it may give off formaldehyde odors and make your house unliveable. It may also shrink after a time, losing some of its original insulating value. Ask any firm you may hire to install gunned-in foam to provide you with references or even some sort of guarantee in writing. Make sure they weigh a sample of the foam to check it for proper mix before they begin gunning.

FOIL OR REFLECTIVE. This type of insulation is made of aluminum foil or heavy paper backed with aluminum foil or aluminum paint. Unlike other kinds of insulation, it does not depend on trapped particles of air to reduce heat transmission, but rather on the bright surface that reflects heat back to its source. In cold weather it reflects heat back into the house and in hot weather it reflects it back outdoors. Foil or reflective insulation is not used by itself much today. To be effective, it must be installed so that there is an air space on both sides. Thus the installation must be done with great care. More important, it would require about six layers of foil to obtain an R-13 value. But foil or reflective insulation can be used with good effect *along with other kinds of insulation.* It not only makes an excellent vapor barrier but also reduces heat loss through a wall from radiation. One excellent way to accomplish these two important jobs is to use a foil-backed gypsum board for interior walls or ceilings or to cover the insulation after it is in place with foil—or use insulation with a foil rather than paper vapor barrier.

Other factors—in addition to cost—to be considered in selecting an insulation are fire resistance, moisture resistance, rot resistance, and attractiveness to vermin. The table on page 200 will be of help.

Types and Use of Vapor Barriers

Many materials used as interior coverings for exposed walls and ceilings permit water vapor to pass slowly through them during cold weather. Temperatures of the sheathing or siding on the outside of the wall are often low enough to cause condensation of water vapor within the cavities of a framed wall. When the humidity at the surface of an unprotected wall is greater than that within the wall, water vapor will migrate through the finish into the stud space and condense.

Vapor barriers, properly installed, will resist this water vapor or moisture movement. These barriers are used on the warm side of all exposed walls, ceilings, floors, under concrete slabs, and to cover crawl spaces.

Vapor barriers can be part of the insulation or a separate film. Commonly used materials are (a) asphalt-coated or laminated papers, (b) kraft-backed aluminum foil, and (c) plastic films such as polyethylene. Foil-backed gypsum board and various coatings also serve as vapor barriers.

A good general rule to follow when installing vapor barriers is to place them as close as possible to the interior or warm surface of all exposed walls, ceilings and floors. This usually involves placing the barrier on the inside edge of the studs just under the rock lath or dry wall finish, also on the underside of the ceiling joists of a one-story house or the second floor ceiling joists of a two-story house, as well as between the subfloor and finish floor, or just under the subfloor if you have an unheated crawl space. The insulation, of course, is normally placed between studs or other frame members on the outside of the vapor barrier. The exception is the insulation used in concrete floor slabs, where a barrier is used *under* the insulation to protect it from ground moisture.

What about the situation in which insulation material is blown into an existing wall and no form of sheet material can be applied? Fortunately, a couple of coats of aluminum oil-base paint on the interior wall surfaces will do the job.

TYPES OF INSULATION AND THEIR CHARACTERISTICS

CHARACTERISTICS	MINERAL				PLASTIC (RIGID)		RESIN	REFLECTIVE FOIL	
	Vermiculite	Perlite	Fiberglass	Rockwool	Styrofoam	Urethane	Urea foam	Batt board	Multifoil
Fire resistant	yes	yes	yes	yes	no	no	yes	no	no
Moisture resistant	no* yes	no* yes	no* yes	no	yes	yes	yes	no	no
Vermin proof	yes	yes	yes	yes	yes	yes	yes	no	yes
Rot proof	yes	yes	yes	yes	yes	yes	yes	no	no
Vapor barrier	no* yes	no* yes	no* yes	no	yes	yes	no	yes	could be

*Characteristics with both "no" and "yes" apply to insulation types for which there are options.

Figuring How Much Insulation You Will Need

First, to calculate the overall area to be covered, multiply the length by the width. Then adjust this number to allow for the area taken up by joists or studs. If joists or studs are 16 inches apart, multiply by .90. If they are 24 inches apart, multiply by .94. The answer is the number of square feet of insulation you'll need.

Mineral blankets and batts are usually available to fit 16-, 24- and sometimes, 20-inch, joist and stud spacing.

If you're going to use loose insulation in an attic floor, a label on the mineral wool bag will tell you how many square feet the bag will cover for a desired R-number. Divide that number into the total number of square feet you want to insulate, and you'll know how many bags to buy.

Where to Insulate

Two important questions that must be answered are:

1. Is there enough insulation to meet today's standards?
2. Are all the areas insulated that are recognized today as essential even though they may not have been properly handled in an old-fashioned insulating job?

ATTIC INSULATION. The place to begin an inspection of existing insulation is your attic or attic crawl space. To insulate an attic floor where there is no insulation, lay batts between the joists. They do not need to be stapled. The vapor barrier must face down. *Note:* When working with mineral wool, wear gloves, long sleeves, eye protection, and a dust mask. This will protect you from minute particles of wool fibers in the air.

If some insulation already exists, add a layer of batts or blankets on top of the old. It is important that the new insulation *not* have an effective vapor barrier. Preferably, the new insulation should be unfaced—that is, have no vapor barrier. If unfaced material isn't available, use the vapor-barrier type, but remove the vapor barrier or slash it freely with a knife. Then install the insulation with the slashed surface down.

Loose-fill insulation also can be used to insulate an attic floor. The insulation is simply poured out of a bag, then leveled with a rake or a short piece of board.

If the attic has a floor—usually rough boards in older homes—you'll have to rip up a few boards to check the insulation. If it turns out that you need more, the inexpensive way to get it is to rip up the floor yourself and add the new material. Or you can hire an insulation contractor to blow more insulation into the spaces between the floor joists.

Even when there is an adequate amount of insulation in the attic floor, there are often spots where it has not been applied. Among these are at the ends of the joists where they butt against the siding or outside wall, cracks around framing and an inside chimney, and seams where plumbing vent stacks come through the attic floor. These areas should all be packed with insulation. Despite their seeming insignificance, these places permit an expensive—and preventable—heat loss.

The access door to the attic should be insulated; this can be most easily done with a sheet of 2-inch rigid foam fastened in place with a mastic.

WALL INSULATION. To insulate a wall, fit the end of a blanket snugly against the top piece of framing. Working down, staple the flanges to the sides or the faces of the studs. (With foil-faced blankets, staple to the sides to create an air space, which is necessary for the heat-reflective value of the foil to be achieved.) Space the staples about 8 inches apart. Fit blankets tightly against the framing at the bottom. If more than one piece of blanket is used in the same stud space, butt the ends tightly together. The vapor barrier must face the side of the wall that is heated in winter.

To insulate stud spaces that are narrower than normal, cut the insulation about 1 inch wider than the space to be filled. Staple the remaining flange, then staple the cut edge of the vapor barrier to its stud.

Walls can be insulated with unfaced blankets and a separate vapor barrier—either 2-mil-or-thicker polyethylene sheeting or foil-backed gypsum board. Keep polyethylene taut as you apply it. Staple it in place to the faces of the studs.

Install insulation behind pipes and ducts (to keep them warm) and behind electrical boxes. Spaces of this sort also may be hand-packed with loose fill insulation. To get loose fill, pull pieces from a blanket. Cracks and very narrow spaces, such as those around window framing, should be stuffed by hand with loose fill insulation and covered with a vapor barrier.

On finished exterior walls, there is no easy way to measure the thickness of the insulation without damaging the wall, assuming there is any at all. You can, however, get an idea of conditions by holding your hand on the inside surface of the wall in cold weather. If the inside surface feels cold, chances are there is little if any insulation. Another way to check the walls is to place one thermometer in the center of the room and attach a second one to the inside surface of the wall with masking tape. After about four hours, check the results. If the one set against the wall measures five degrees or more lower than the one at the center of the room, the wall is probably not properly insulated.

One way to put insulation in a finished exterior wall, of course, is to blow it in—a job for an insulation contractor. This treatment produces good results unless there are too many obstructions between the studs—firestops, wiring, etc.—so that the insulation cannot fill the space completely. If the house happens to be going through extensive restoration, the logical approach is to rip off the existing wall material and insulate with batts or blankets.

Another modern-material idea is to apply 1- or 2-inch rigid foam over the existing wall; then cover the foam with gypsum board.

Some homeowners have insulated outside walls themselves by cutting holes through the interior wall material and pouring vermiculite into the wall cavity. Vemiculite pours easily, requiring only small holes between the studs. Put the hole at the top of the wall, just below the plate. When the level of the vermiculite comes up to the hole, stuff the remaining space with loose-fill mineral wool.

Any wall between heated and unheated areas should be insulated. This would include the wall between the house and an unheated attached garage or unheated summer room or enclosed porch.

Masonry walls, basement walls and the like, are insulated by first fastening furring strips in place vertically. They should be placed 16 or 24 inches from the center of one strip to the center of the next.

Then insulation blankets or rigid foam sheets are applied as between regular wall studs.

FLOOR INSULATION. To insulate floors above cold spaces, push the batts or blankets between the floor joists from below, vapor barriers up. To support the insulation, lace wire back and forth among nails spaced about 2 feet apart in the bottoms of the joists. Or staple chicken wire to the joists. Pieces of blanket cut to size should be fitted, vapor barriers in, along the sill at the outside of the floor area. Rigid foam can also be used to insulate such floors.

An area in the basement that is often not insulated is along the sill where the floor joists butt the header. Cut pieces of rigid foam and put them in place with mastic. Strips of mineral wool work also.

If a heated area of the house has a concrete slab on grade, the perimeter of the slab should be insulated. It is easy to tell if this has been done in areas where it snows. If there is no insulation, the snow around the foundations of the house will melt faster than the surrounding snow. And in the spring, the grass around the foundations will be the first to turn green.

There is only one effective way to deal with heat loss at the perimeter. This involves digging a narrow trench about 2 feet or so in depth so that sheets of rigid foam or rigid fiberglass can be attached to the exposed surfaces of the concrete slab.

Do's and Don'ts of Insulating

The following do's and don'ts must be kept in mind when installing insulation:

1. DO put the vapor barrier side of insulation blankets and batts down in the ceiling—even if, when adding new insulation on top of old, you've slashed the barrier to let moisture vapor pass through.
2. DO insulate under unheated attic walkways, pulling or pushing the insulation as needed. If much of the area is covered with flooring, you might need to remove some boards for access to the space.
3. DO work from the outer edge of the attic space toward the center. You'll be able to do whatever cutting and fitting is necessary at the center of the attic rather than near the eaves, where there's little headroom.
4. DO insulate the top of the attic scuttle panel. Staple directly through the edges of the insulation into the panel board.
5. DO hand-pack insulation around pipes and electrical cables that pass through the attic floor. Stuff openings around interior chimneys with mineral wool.
6. DO patch the vapor barrier of wall insulation if it has been torn. Strip a piece of vapor barrier from a scrap section of blanket or use polyethylene, taping the patch to secure it.
7. DO paint interior walls as a substitute vapor barrier if you are having a contractor install blowing mineral insulation. Use at least two coats of paint and brush them in well. (Paints vary widely in the rate at which they allow water vapor to pass through. Ask a paint dealer about the "perm rating"—vapor permeability rating—of the paint he carries. A rating of 1 perm or less for primer and finish coat combined is desirable. If the dealer doesn't know about perm ratings, ask him to check with the manufacturer. Oil paints with aluminum pigments usually have very low ratings.) Once the barrier coats are dry you can go over them with the finish coat of your choice.
8. DON'T insulate on top of recessed lighting fixtures, and other heat-producing equipment that protrudes through the attic floor.

To be in accord with the National Electrical Code, improvise a way of holding insulation 3 inches away from the sides of the protrusion. Here you can make a sheet-metal shield, possibly by cutting the ends off a tin can of suitable size. There should be 24 inches clearance directly above a fixture. The clearances are intended to prevent overheating of the fixture. With cellulose, the clearances also reduce the possibility that lighting heat might ignite improperly treated, or untreated, paper insulation.

9. DON'T cover eave vents with insulation. With batts, just be careful about batt placement. With loose fill insulation, either construct a baffle with boards or lay pieces of thick batts next to the vents; you'll keep the wind from disturbing the loose insulation and you won't inadvertently cover the vents in the first place.
10. DON'T allow vapor barriers to be exposed. Cover them with gypsum board or some other rigid material. Don't allow "breather" paper to be exposed either. Breather paper is the covering around the non-vapor-barrier side (the side without flanges) of some batts. It's intended only to protect the insulation fibers during shipment and installation. If it is exposed, strip it off after the batts are in place.
11. DON'T allow gaps, or "fishmouths," at vapor barrier edges when you are insulating walls. Keep the edges tight against the studs. If fishmouths appear, staple them down tight.

If You Don't Do-It-Yourself

If you prefer to hire an insulation contractor, you can find one by asking your utility company for suggestions, consulting friends and neighbors, or looking in the phone book "yellow pages" under "Insulation Contractors—Cold & Heat" or a similar heading. Remember that a contractor has the special skills needed to insulate sidewalls as well as to do an expert job of insulating the ceiling.

The next step is to call in two or three contractors to give you quotes on the job. You should consider a contractor's reliability as well as his price. Here are some suggestions:

1. Check a contractor with the local Better Business Bureau (also listed in the phone book). Or ask your bank to get a report on his credit rating.
2. Ask a contractor for references, including other homeowners for whom he has done work. Check them out.
3. Give all the contractors exactly the same outline of the job. For

example, say, "I want to add R-19 to my attic floor," then stay with that specification and that way of saying it. Don't be satisfied if a contractor says, "Ok, I'll add 6 inches." Why not be satisfied with 6 inches? Because not all brands of insulation have the same heat-retarding ability. Six inches of one brand might not be the same as 6 inches of another. Stick with R-numbers. If a contractor won't deal with you in R-number language, don't deal with him.

4. If a contractor is going to use blowing wool in your attic floor, how can you tell if you're getting R-38 performance, or R-30 or R-19? Or whatever thermal resistance rating you decide you want? It's easy if you look at the bag label. A U.S. Government specification, HH-1-1030A, requires that each bag of loose-fill mineral wool insulation be labeled as shown in the table below. There is another Government specification for ureaformaldehyde.

   If a contractor uses mineral wool or cellulose insulation packed in bags that aren't labeled, don't hire him; the quality of his material will be unknown.

VALUES FOR LOOSE-FILL MINERAL WOOL

R Value	Minimum thickness (inches)	Maximum net coverage per bag (sq. ft.)
R-38	17½	26
R-30	13¾	33
R-22	10	45
R-19	8¾	51
R-11	5	90

The thicknesses and coverages shown on the bag label, which apply only to attic floor installations, may be different for different manufacturers.

The coverage figure gives you a means of knowing how many bags of insulation the contractor should blow into your attic floor to achieve a particular R-value. Multiply the overall square-foot area of your attic floor by .90 or .94, then divide that number by the "maximum net coverage" listed on the label for the R-number you want.

When you talk to a contractor's salesman, ask him to show you the bag label for his brand of insulation and explain it to you. When the job is being done, stay home and count the number of bags actually used.

5. Ask a contractor how he pays his installers—by the number of

square feet they cover or by the hour. If he pays them by square footage, they might do a hasty job on your house just so they can get on to the next one.

6. Ask a contractor about the insurance he carries. Does he have insurance to protect his own men if they are injured? Are you covered if one of his men damages your house, perhaps by stepping through the ceiling?

In regard to contractor installation of blown insulation in sidewalls, the weight per cubic foot of the material after it has been installed is a critical factor. In practice, if sidewalls are insulated by a competent contractor, the R-value achieved will be about R-12 or R-14 with either mineral wool or cellulose.

VENTILATING ATTICS AND CRAWL SPACES

Attics

Ventilation above insulation in an attic floor is necessary both winter and summer. In summer, heat often builds up in attic spaces to 135°F, and it may even reach 150°F when the sun beats down on the roof. This superheated air soon penetrates through ceilings (even if insulated) into the living area below. Thus, if you and your house are to live comfortably together, you need a proper ventilation system. Proper ventilation will substantially reduce air conditioning costs. And in houses without air conditioning, the living area will be kept at a more comfortable temperature level.

In winter, open attic vents let moisture vapor escape. This vapor is caused by the use of various household appliances, such as dishwashers, dryers, and humidifiers. As well, daily use of the shower and tub, and cooking vapors all contribute to excessive moisture within your home. When moisture-laden air from the living area rises to the attic, problems will result. This condensed moisture can soak insulation, impairing its efficiency. It can stain or crumble ceilings, and blister exterior paint. Frozen and thawed, it can damage roof boards and shingles.

VENTILATION SYSTEMS. There are two types of ventilation systems: natural (or static) ventilation and power ventilation.

An important aspect, common to both the natural and power ventilation systems, is the need for a fresh air intake ventilator and a hot or moist air outlet ventilator. The system best suited for your house will depend on the type of roof construction and whether you are planning to ventilate an existing home or a home under construction.

Natural ventilation systems. These employ fixed or non-mechanical devices usually referred to as ventilators. These ventilators are installed in openings in an attic space and must be properly positioned to take advantage of the natural flow of air.

There are five basic types of attic ventilators: ridge, roof, undereaves, gable end-rectangular and triangular. These will do a satisfactory job with most roof designs. Also they will blend with any style of architecture.

Ridge ventilators with undereaves strip ventilators are regarded as the best natural ventilation system. Ridge vents are designed to provide a continuous opening along the entire ridge line of a pitched roof. These vents are formed to prevent rain and snow from entering the attic, but the openings allow a full flow of air to be ventilated from the attic. The intake ventilator, to complete this effective system, is the undereaves strip vent. It is recommended that these intake vents be installed into the roof overhang on both sides of the house. Since the installation of ridge vents is a fairly big job, most homeowners select this system when building a new home, thus allowing the vents to be installed at the time the roof is being constructed.

Optional systems classified as natural ventilation are also available. Roof vents with undereaves vents provide a good ventilation system for a hip style roof, while gable end roofs may be equipped with either a rectangular or triangular gable end vent mounted in the high-point of the gable. In all cases, intake undereaves ventilators complete the system.

Power ventilation systems. These offer a mechanical device to control the air change in an attic space. Power ventilators are usually equipped with automatic thermostats which activate the unit at a preselected temperature, and shut the unit off when the attic temperature is sufficiently reduced. In this way, power ventilation provides positive air removal. It removes the excess summer heat on hot days and on cold days the optional humidistat will actuate the unit to remove excess winter moisture. That is, the power ventilator moves more air and with better control than methods which depend on the natural flow of air or inconstant winds.

Power ventilators with an undereaves vent as an intake provide an extremely effective attic venting system. This system is recommended for existing structures because of its ease of installation, although it is not limited to this application and is found in new home construction as well. The power ventilator typically is placed on the rear slope of the roof, near the peak and centered, with air intakes at the eaves. This reaches all attic space efficiently. If roof location is not practical or desirable, a power gable ventilator may be installed vertically on the gable sidewall.

A power ventilator automatically keeps homes cooler and reduces the high cost of air conditioning. Obviously, lifting such a summer heat load with a unit that uses only about the energy of a 75-watt light bulb (part time) saves significant electrical energy. Exactly how much depends on various factors of individual housing and living characteristics, but direct field results conducted by the National Bureau of Standards indicate 10- to 30-percent reduction in air conditioning load. When installing an air conditioner, initial savings resulting from purchase of a smaller capacity unit are often possible when an automatic power ventilation system exists. And some homeowners, especially in the North, require only the use of a power ventilator system for summer comfort.

HOW MUCH VENTILATION IS NEEDED? To tell exactly how much ventilation is needed for your home with either the natural or power system, it is necessary to determine the square feet of your attic floor and relate that to the *free area* of the ventilation system you have selected. Free area is the approximate clear or free opening of the ventilator through which air may move.

The net free area of the ventilators required for a house employing a natural system of ventilation is normally based on a ratio of the attic floor space. That is, the space ventilated should have a net free ventilated area of 1/150. This means that for each 150 square feet of attic area, 1 square foot of free area is required. If certain conditions prevail, this ratio can be reduced to 1/300, or 1 square foot of free area to every 300 square feet of attic floor space. These conditions include:

1. A vapor barrier, such as a polyethylene sheet or insulation batts, with a low moisture transmission rate, is installed on the warm side of the ceiling.
2. At least 50 percent of the required ventilating area is provided by ventilators located in the upper portion of the space to be ventilated (at least 3 ft. above the undereaves vents) with the remainder of the required ventilation provided by undereaves vents.

To find the exact free area needed to properly ventilate your home by natural means, find the length of the area to be ventilated in the vertical column of the natural-ventilation table on pages 212 and 213, by the U.S. Department of Housing and Urban Development (HUD). Then find the width of the area in the horizontal column. The total net free area required is shown where these two columns intersect. This free area is expressed in *square inches*. (The table utilizes a 1/300 ratio.) For example, let us suppose the total area to be ventilated is 1200 square feet, such as a house 30×40 feet. By looking at the table we find that we would need a total of 576 square inches. If roof or gable end and undereaves vents are used, 50 percent of the 576 square inches, or 288 square inches are required for the roof or gable end vents and the same amount would be required for the undereaves. This satisfies the requirement for a ratio of 1/300. If undereaves vents are not used, the above total free area requirement must be doubled. This is equivalent to 1/150 ratio.

Even if your attic area is presently vented, it should be carefully checked to determine whether or not the present vent arrangement is adequate to provide proper ventilation.

The Home Ventilating Institute (HVI), a recognized control agency, certifies air delivery of power attic space ventilators in cubic feet per minute (CFM). HVI standards recommend a minimum of 0.7 CFM per square foot of attic floor space, plus 15 percent for dark roofs.

In order to determine what size power ventilator is needed to cool your attic efficiently, find the length of the area to be ventilated in the vertical column of the powered-ventilation table on pages 214 and 215, by HVI. Then find the width in the horizontal column. The total CFM required is shown where these two columns intersect. For example, in our 30×40 foot house, the power vent unit should be capable of at least 840 CFM.

Crawl Spaces

At least two vents, opposite each other, should be provided in an unheated crawl space. Basic minimum opening size, with moisture seal (4-mil-or-thicker polyethylene sheeting or 55-pound asphalt roll roofing, lapped at least 3 inches) on the ground: 1 square foot of vent for each 1,500 square feet of crawl space area. Basic minimum opening size without moisture seal: 1 square foot for each 150 square feet of area. Four vents, one on each of the four sides, are recommended. If crawl space vents are protected by screening or rain louvers, the basic opening size should be increased as shown in the table on page 211.

Solving Condensation Problems

High moisture content of the air inside your home is the cause of condensation. Building materials such as glass, varnish, paint, tile, plastic wallcovering and vapor-seal insulation all contribute to trapping moist air inside your house and preventing drier outside air from entering.

The visible result of condensation, which is simply excess moisture, is window fogging. However, there can be more problems including

CRAWL SPACE VENTILATION

Type of covering	Size of opening
¼-inch hardware cloth	1 × net vent area
¼-inch hardware cloth and rain louvers	2 × net vent area
8-mesh screen	1¼ × net vent area
8-mesh screen and rain louvers	2¼ × net vent area
16-mesh screen	2 × net vent area
16-mesh screen and rain louvers	3 × net vent area

ruined window sills, and in severe cases, damaged wallpaper or plaster. Condensation which lasts a long time and covers large corners of your window can be potentially more troublesome than you realize. And it is in the less visible, not-so-obvious places where condensation is a real troublemaker. It may collect and freeze in the insulation in your attic or ceiling, and when the weather warms, melt on ceiling plaster. Or it may, through vapor pressure—moisture migrating toward dryer areas—escape to the outside even passing through wood, plaster, stucco and brick to blister any paint or stain finish you may have.

Condensation problems can be eliminated by specifying proper construction details during planning of the house. Correct placement of vapor barriers, adequate insulation, the use of attic ventilation, and other good practices can be incorporated at this time. However, when one or more of these details have not been included in an existing house and condensation problems occur, they are often more difficult to solve. Nevertheless, there are methods which can be used to minimize such condensation problems after the house has been constructed.

VISIBLE CONDENSATION. The following are the points to check and take care of to reduce visible condensation:

Glass surfaces. Visible surface condensation on the interior glass surfaces of windows can be minimized by the use of storm windows or by replacing single glass with insulated glass. However, when this doesn't prevent condensation on the surface, the relative humidity in the room must be reduced. Drapes or curtains across the windows hinder rather than help. Not only do they increase surface condensation because of colder glass surfaces, but they also prevent the air movement that would warm the glass surface and aid in dispersing some of the moisture.

NATURAL VENTILATION (prepared by HUD)

	Width (in feet)															
	20	**22**	**24**	**26**	**28**	**30**	**32**	**34**	**36**	**38**	**40**	**42**	**44**	**46**	**48**	**50**
20	192	211	230	250	269	288	307	326	346	365	384	403	422	441	461	480
22	211	232	253	275	296	317	338	359	380	401	422	444	465	485	506	528
24	230	253	276	300	323	346	369	392	415	438	461	484	507	530	553	576
26	250	275	300	324	349	374	399	424	449	474	499	524	549	574	599	624
28	269	296	323	349	376	403	430	457	484	511	538	564	591	618	645	662
30	288	317	346	374	403	432	461	490	518	547	576	605	634	662	691	720
32	307	338	369	399	430	461	492	522	553	584	614	645	675	706	737	768
34	326	359	392	424	457	490	522	555	588	620	653	685	717	750	782	815
36	346	380	415	449	484	518	553	588	622	657	691	726	760	795	829	864
38	365	401	438	474	511	547	584	620	657	693	730	766	803	839	876	912
40	384	422	461	499	538	576	614	653	691	730	768	806	845	883	922	960
42	403	444	484	524	564	605	645	685	726	766	806	847	887	927	968	1008
44	422	465	507	549	591	634	676	718	760	803	845	887	929	971	1013	1056
46	442	486	530	574	618	662	707	751	795	839	883	927	972	1016	1060	1104
48	461	507	553	599	645	691	737	783	829	876	922	968	1014	1060	1106	1152

	Width (in feet)															
50	480	528	576	624	672	720	768	816	864	912	960	1008	1056	1104	1152	1200
52	499	549	599	649	699	749	799	848	898	948	998	1048	1098	1148	1198	1248
54	518	570	622	674	726	778	830	881	933	985	1087	1089	1141	1192	1244	1296
56	538	591	645	699	753	807	860	914	967	1021	1075	1130	1184	1237	1291	1345
58	557	612	668	724	780	835	891	946	1002	1058	1113	1170	1226	1282	1337	1392
60	576	634	691	749	807	864	922	979	1037	1094	1152	1210	1267	1324	1382	1440
62	595	655	714	774	834	893	953	1012	1071	1131	1190	1250	1309	1369	1428	1488
64	614	676	737	799	861	922	983	1045	1106	1168	1229	1291	1352	1413	1475	1536
66	634	697	760	824	888	950	1014	1077	1140	1204	1268	1331	1394	1458	1522	1585
68	653	718	783	849	914	979	1045	1110	1175	1240	1306	1371	1436	1501	1567	1632
70	672	739	806	874	941	1008	1075	1142	1210	1276	1344	1411	1478	1545	1613	1680

POWERED VENTILATION (prepared by HVI)

	Width (in feet)															
	20	**22**	**24**	**26**	**28**	**30**	**32**	**34**	**36**	**38**	**40**	**42**	**44**	**46**	**48**	**50**
20	280	308	336	364	392	420	448	476	504	532	560	588	616	644	672	700
22	308	339	370	400	431	462	493	524	554	585	616	647	678	708	739	770
24	336	370	403	437	470	504	538	571	605	638	672	706	739	773	806	840
26	364	400	437	473	510	546	582	619	655	692	728	764	801	837	874	910
28	392	431	470	510	549	588	627	666	706	745	784	823	862	902	941	980
30	420	462	504	546	588	630	672	714	756	798	840	882	924	966	1008	1050
32	443	493	538	582	627	672	717	761	806	851	896	941	986	1030	1075	1120
34	476	524	571	619	666	714	762	809	857	904	952	1000	1047	1095	1142	1190
36	504	554	604	655	706	756	806	857	907	958	1008	1058	1109	1159	1210	1260
38	532	585	638	692	745	798	851	904	958	1011	1064	1117	1170	1224	1277	1330
40	560	616	672	728	784	840	896	952	1008	1064	1120	1176	1232	1288	1344	1400
42	588	647	706	764	823	882	941	1000	1058	1117	1176	1234	1294	1352	1411	1470
44	616	678	739	801	862	924	986	1047	1109	1170	1232	1294	1355	1417	1478	1540
46	644	708	773	837	902	966	1030	1095	1159	1224	1288	1352	1417	1481	1546	1610

	Width (in feet)															
48	672	739	806	874	941	1008	1075	1142	1210	1277	1344	1411	1478	1546	1613	1680
50	700	770	840	910	980	1050	1120	1190	1260	1330	1400	1470	1540	1610	1680	1750
52	728	801	874	946	1019	1092	1165	1238	1310	1383	1456	1529	1602	1674	1747	1820
54	756	832	907	983	1058	1134	1210	1285	1361	1436	1512	1588	1663	1739	1814	1890
56	784	862	941	1019	1098	1176	1254	1333	1411	1490	1568	1646	1725	1803	1882	1960
58	812	893	974	1056	1137	1218	1299	1380	1462	1543	1624	1705	1786	1868	1949	2030
60	840	924	1008	1092	1176	1260	1344	1428	1512	1596	1680	1764	1848	1932	2016	2100
62	868	955	1042	1128	1215	1302	1389	1476	1562	1649	1736	1823	1910	1996	2083	2170
64	896	986	1075	1165	1254	1344	1434	1523	1613	1702	1792	1882	1971	2061	2150	2240
66	924	1016	1108	1201	1294	1386	1478	1571	1663	1756	1848	1940	2033	2125	2218	2310
68	952	1047	1142	1238	1333	1428	1523	1618	1714	1809	1904	1999	2094	2190	2285	2380
70	980	1078	1176	1274	1372	1470	1568	1666	1764	1862	1960	2058	2156	2254	2352	2450

Attic areas. Condensation or frost on protruding nails, on the surfaces of roof sheathing, or other members in attic areas normally indicates the escape of excessive amounts of water vapor from the heated rooms below. If a vapor barrier is not already present, place one between joists under the insulation. Make sure the vapor barrier fits tightly around ceiling lights and exhaust fans, caulking if necessary. In addition, increase both inlet and outlet ventilation to conform to the minimum recommendations a few pages earlier. Decreasing the amount of water vapor produced in the living areas is also helpful. Use of kitchen, laundry and bathroom ventilating fans will help to some degree to accomplish this. But to save heat, use these fans only when necessary.

Crawl spaces. Surface condensation in unheated crawl spaces is usually caused by excessive moisture from the soil or from warm humid air entering from outside the house. To eliminate this problem, place a vapor barrier over the soil; if necessary, use the proper amount of ventilation as recommended earlier.

Concrete slabs. Concrete slabs without radiant heat are sometimes subjected to surface condensation in late spring when warm humid air enters the house. Because the temperature of some areas of the concrete slab or its covering is below the dewpoint, surface condensation can occur. Keeping the windows closed during the day, using a dehumidifier, and raising the inside temperature aid in minimizing this problem. When the concrete slab reaches normal room temperatures, this inconvenience is eliminated.

Concealed condensation. Concealed condensation is condensation that takes place out of sight within a component such as a wall cavity. In cold weather, condensation often forms as frost. Such conditions can cause staining of siding and peeling of the paint and possibly decay in severe and sustained conditions. These problems are usually not detected until spring after the heating season has ended. Solve these problems before repainting or residing. Several methods might be used to correct this problem.

1. Reduce or control the relative humidity within the house.
2. Add a vapor-resistant paint coating such as aluminum paint to the interior of walls and ceilings.
3. Improve the vapor resistance of the ceiling by adding a vapor barrier between ceiling joists.
4. Improve attic ventilation.
5. Install paint breather vents or miniature circular louvered vents.

These vents are easily installed between the stud spaces by simply drilling a hole the diameter of the vent and tapping the vent into place. Installation of vents near the lower and upper part of the outside wall provides an intake and an outlet ventilation system.

REDUCING RELATIVE HUMIDITY. Reducing high relative humidities within the house to permissible levels is often necessary to minimize condensation problems. Discontinuing the use of room-size humidifiers or reducing the output of automatic humidifiers until conditions are improved is helpful. The use of exhaust fans and dehumidifiers can also be of value in eliminating high relative humidities within the house. When possible, decreasing the activities which produce excessive moisture, as discussed in a previous section, is sometimes necessary. This is especially important for homes with electric heat.

Measuring relative humidity. When we complain about the "humidity," we generally mean the high relative humidity often suffered in hot summer weather. Relative humidity is simply the relationship between the amount of moisture in the air to the amount it can hold. Since hot air can hold more moisture than cold air, one way to reduce the relative humidity is to pass it through the cooling system of an air conditioner or a dehumidifier.

For the sake of health and comfort, however, it is often necessary to *add* moisture to hot indoor air in winter. For cold outdoor air, even when saturated, becomes drier than the air over the Sahara when brought indoors and heated to 70 or 80° F.

For greatest comfort at ordinary indoor temperatures, the relative humidity should be kept somewhere between about 30 and 45 percent.

The most reliable indicator of relative humidity for home use is the wet-and-dry-bulb thermometer. (The dial-type humidity indicator that comes with thermometer and barometer sets is usually notoriously inaccurate.) The wet-and-dry-bulb indicator consists simply of a pair of thermometers, mounted vertically side by side, one of which has a piece of wet cloth wrapped around its bulb. When fanned strongly, either by hand or by an electric fan, evaporation of moisture from the cloth on the wet bulb causes the temperature on that thermometer to read lower than that on the dry-bulb thermometer. To find the relative humidity from these readings, merely subtract the wet-bulb temperature from the dry-bulb temperature and refer to the table on page 218.

Or if you don't have a ready-made wet-and-dry-bulb thermometer, you can improvise one from any two household or chemical thermometers, one of which has an uncovered bulb. Wet a small square of muslin thoroughly with water and wrap it about one and a half times around this bulb, tying it in place at top and bottom with thread. Place both thermometers in the breeze of a fan and read both after a minute or so. Then find the relative humidity as described in the preceding paragraph.

Temperature-Humidity Index (THI). With a ready-made or home-made wet-and-dry-bulb thermometer, you can also determine the THI or temperature-humidity index. The purpose of the THI is to measure or predict human discomfort in the summertime resulting from the combined effects of temperature and humidity. To calculate the THI, add wet-bulb and dry-bulb thermometer readings, multiply the sum by 0.4 and add 15. The theory behind this measurement is that more than half the people will be uncomfortable when the THI passes 75. Practically everybody will be uncomfortable when it reaches 80 or above.

HOW TO MEASURE RELATIVE HUMIDITY

Dry-bulb temp. °F	DEPRESSION OF THE WET BULB, °F									
	2	4	6	8	10	12	14	16	20	24
	Relative humidity (percent)									
60	89	78	68	58	48	39	30	21	5	
62	89	79	69	59	50	41	32	24	8	
64	90	79	70	60	51	43	34	26	11	
66	90	80	71	61	53	44	36	29	14	
68	90	80	71	62	54	46	38	31	16	3
70	90	81	72	64	55	48	40	33	19	6
72	91	82	73	65	57	49	42	33	21	9
74	91	82	74	65	58	50	43	36	23	11
76	91	82	74	66	59	51	44	38	25	13
78	91	83	75	67	60	53	46	39	27	16
80	91	83	75	68	61	54	47	41	29	18
82	92	84	76	69	61	55	48	42	30	20
84	92	84	76	69	62	56	49	43	32	21
86	92	84	77	70	63	57	50	44	33	23
88	92	85	77	70	64	57	51	46	35	25
90	92	85	78	71	65	58	52	47	36	26
92	92	85	78	72	65	59	53	48	37	28
94	93	85	79	72	66	60	54	49	38	29
96	93	86	79	73	66	61	55	50	39	30
98	93	86	79	73	67	61	56	50	40	32
100	93	86	80	73	68	62	56	51	41	33

Ice Dams

Ice dams form during the winter when heat escaping through the roof melts snow. Water runs down the roof until it reaches that part of the roof that overhangs the house. Since the roof there is much colder, the water freezes, creating a dam that backs up more runoff. Eventually a small reservoir of water trapped behind the dam may result. It can then back under shingles and leak into the house, causing severe damage.

Several methods can be used to minimize this problem. Reducing the attic temperatures in the winter so that they are only slightly above outdoor temperatures, is the best approach. This can be accomplished in the following manner:

1. Add insulation to the ceiling area in the attic to reduce heat loss from living areas below. This added insulation coupled with ventilation will also be helpful by reducing summer temperatures in the living areas below.
2. Provide additional inlet ventilation in the soffit area of the cornice as well as better outlet ventilation near the ridge.
3. When reroofing, use a flashing strip of 36-inch-wide roll roofing paper of 45-pound weight along the eave line before reshingling. While this doesn't prevent ice dams, it is a worthwhile precaution, preventing backed-up water from entering the house.
4. Under severe conditions, or when only some portions of a roof produce ice dams (such as at valleys), the use of electric-thermal wire laid in a zig-zag pattern and in gutters may prove effective. The wire is connected and heated during periods of snowfall and at other times as needed to maintain channels for drainage.

OTHER ENERGY-SAVING TIPS

Storm Windows and Doors

Windows and doors can be big energy-wasters. There are three reasons:

1. Glass is a highly heat-conductive material.
2. Doors and windows that open (all except "fixed sash" or picture windows) necessarily have cracks all around them.
3. Air can pass through the joints around window and door frames if they aren't tightly sealed.

Storm windows and storm doors cut heat loss (or heat gain) at these points about in half. Insulating glass (two panes of glass sealed together at the edges) has approximately the same effect. Triple glazing (insulating glass plus a storm window) is even more effective and often is used in extremely cold climates.

According to the National Bureau of Standards, an investment in storm windows will pay for itself in a decade where the average winter temperature is similar to that of Washington, D.C. In regions of the country where snow lies on the ground all winter, payback will occur in less than seven years, the NBS says.

Storm windows and doors can be installed by a contractor or a skilled home handyman. Using prehung doors, which are already assembled to frames, makes the job easier.

Plastic sheeting, available in hardware stores, makes effective storm sash. It should be taped or tacked to the inside of windows and glass portions of doors. An inexpensive material, it is often used by people who rent their homes. Other types of plastic storm windows also are made for do-it-yourself installation.

Weatherstripping

Weatherstripping comes in various forms—rigid and flexible. Materials include felt strips, foam rubber, flexible vinyl, spring bronze, and interlocking metal. These are designed for different applications to the interior side of windows and the exterior side of doors. The advice of a knowledgeable hardware store salesman will help in making a choice. Instruction sheets generally are included in the package.

Window sash and doors should be weatherstripped on all sides and tops and bottoms. Don't overlook the meeting rail where the top and bottom sash of double-hung windows come together.

Entrance doors should be weatherstripped—as should attic doors, inside and outside basement doors, and any other doors between a heated space and an unheated one.

Caulking

Here are places where a house needs to be caulked:

1. Between window drip caps (tops of windows) and siding.
2. Between door drip caps and siding.
3. At joints between window frames and siding.
4. At joints between door frames and siding.
5. Between window sills and siding.
6. At corners formed by siding.
7. At sills where the wood structure meets the foundation.
8. At outside water faucets or other special breaks in the outside house surface.
9. Where pipes and wires penetrate the ceiling below an unheated attic.
10. Between porches and the main body of the house.

11. Where chimney or masonry meets siding.
12. Where storm windows meet the window frames, except for drain holes at the window sill.
13. And, *if you have a heated attic,* where the wall meets the eave at the gable ends.

Caulking compound is available in these basic types:

OIL OR RESIN BASE CAULK: readily available and will bond to most surfaces, including wood, masonry and metal; not very durable but least expensive for initial cost. Unfortunately, this tends to dry out and crack after a time, requiring repeated applications over the years.

LATEX, BUTYL OR POLYVINYL BASED CAULK: all readily available and will bond to most surfaces; more durable but more expensive than oil or resin based caulk for initial cost.

ELASTOMERIC CAULKS: most durable and most expensive; includes silicones, polysulfides and polyurethanes; follow instructions on the labels.

Estimating the required number of cartridges of caulking compound is difficult since the number will vary according to the sizes of cracks to be filled. Rough estimates are:

½ cartridge per window or door
4 cartridges for the foundation sill
2 cartridges for a two-story, outside wall chimney

Here are some points to remember when caulking:

1. Before applying caulking compound, clean the area of paint buildup, dirt, or deteriorated caulk with solvent and putty knife or a large screwdriver.
2. Drawing a good bead of caulk will take a little practice. First attempts may be a bit messy. Make sure the bead overlaps both sides for a tight seal.
3. A wide bead may be necessary to make sure caulk adheres to both sides.
4. Fill extra wide cracks like those at the sills (where the house meets the foundation) with materials such as oakum or glass fiber insulation strips.
5. Caulking compound also comes in rope form. Unwind it and force it into cracks with your fingers. You can fill extra long cracks easily this way.

Maintain an Efficient Heating Plant

The burning of fuel often produces deposits of combustion on surfaces of stoves, furnaces, and chimney flues that interfere with good heat transfer. Further, to burn a fuel completely it is usually necessary to provide some excess air for combustion. Too much air, on the other hand, means excess draft that will seriously increase losses of heat up the chimney. For these reasons it is definitely to your best interest to have the heat exchange surfaces of your heating plant cleaned when needed, and to periodically have the combustion air adjustment checked or improved by service professionals. If your heating plant has air filters through which the recirculated house air passes, it is desirable to clean or replace them when they become loaded with dust or lint, something you can readily do.

The use of smaller orifices or jets in your burner, and a proportionate decrease in combustion air, will maximize the benefits that can be attained in reducing your fuel input rate. If your fuel input rate is correct, your burner will operate almost continuously in the coldest weather. Have your serviceman prepare your heating plant for efficient winter operation.

Maintain an Efficient Air-Conditioning System

Most air-conditioning systems are equipped with automatic thermostats that turn the compressor on to bring the room temperature down to the desired level and then turn off, leaving the air-circulating mechanism operating at low level to circulate the cool air throughout the room. The more the compressor runs, the more electricity you use. Insulation, weatherstripping, storm doors and windows, and caulking are all helpful in cutting this electrical cost because they prevent hot air gain. Maintain efficiency by turning the air conditioner on and off only infrequently.

Use the air conditioner when the room becomes warm; then leave it on. Also, have your air-conditioning system checked in early spring. It's important to clean the filter. Follow the manufacturer's directions in your operating manual. Check and recaulk the air conditioner's wall installation to eliminate cracks and resulting air leaks. Always cover the air conditioner during the winter months to prevent drafts and damage from the weather. It pays to pull down shades and close drapes to prevent direct sunlight entering through windows and heating inside temperatures.

More Energy-Saving Ideas

In addition to points already discussed, here are a few other ways to save heating and cooling energy:

1. Keep doors and windows firmly shut and locked to cut down heat loss in winter and heat gain in summer. Check your windows and door latches to see whether they fit tightly and, if necessary, adjust the latches and plug any air leaks. You don't really need to open windows in winter to freshen the air. You usually get enough fresh air just from normal exchanges of air leakage and infiltration even if your house is well caulked and weather-stripped.
2. Use heavy or insulated draperies. Keep them closed at night, and fit them tightly at the top. In the summer and in warm climates, light colored curtains that you can't see through will reflect the sun and help keep your house cool. Don't let drapes or furniture block circulation paths of heating or cooling units.
3. The tightest storm door in the world doesn't work when it's open. Try to cut down the number of times that you and your pets go in and out. Adding a vestibule at your front and back doors will also help to tighten up your house.
4. Use a wood stove instead of the furnace or to supplement it.
5. A good way to keep your house cool in the summer is to shade it from the outside. The south, east, and west sides are where the most heat comes through. If you can shade those exposures, you'll have a lower air-conditioning bill and a cooler home. Any method that stops the sun before it gets through windows is *seven times* as good at keeping you cool as blinds and curtains on the inside. So trees and vines that shade in the summer and lose their leaves for the winter are what you want. They'll let the sun in during the winter months. If you can't shade your house with trees, concentrate on keeping the sun out of your windows. Here awnings or even permanent sunshades will do the job, but only on the south side. They won't work on the east and west.
6. Don't overheat rooms and don't heat or cool rooms you're not using. It's important that no room in your house get more heating than it needs, and that you should be able to turn down the heating or cooling in areas of your home that you don't use. If some of your rooms become too hot before the other rooms are warm enough, you're paying for fuel you don't need, and your system needs *balancing*. In this case, call your serviceman. If your house is "zoned," you've got more than one thermostat and can turn

down heating or cooling in areas where they're not needed. But if your house has only one thermostat, you can't properly adjust the temperature in rooms you're not using, and that wastes energy too. To correct this situation fairly cheaply, try these steps:

- STEAM RADIATORS. Most valves on radiators are all-on or all-off, but you can buy valves that let you set any temperature you like for that radiator.
- FORCED-AIR HEATING OR COOLING. Many registers (the place where the air comes out) are adjustable. If not, get registers that are, so you can balance your system.
- HOT-WATER RADIATORS. If there are valves on your radiators at all, you can use them to adjust the temperature room by room.

7. If you have a kitchen vent or attic cooling fan, make sure the vent is closed when unit is not in use.
8. Turn off lights, TV, radio, and other appliances when they are not needed. Every kilowatt-hour saved saves you money and shows consideration for worldwide energy shortages. Try to avoid prolonged use of major appliances in the early morning and during late afternoon and early evening hours.
9. Plan your lighting sensibly. Reduce lighting where possible, concentrating it in work areas or reading areas where it is really needed. Fluorescent lamps should be used rather than the incandescent kind in many cases. A 25-watt fluorescent bulb gives off as much light as a 100-watt incandescent bulb, but costs one fourth as much to light. Remember, however that constant on/off switching increases a fluorescent lamp's electrical consumption, and also shortens its life. For this reason, fluorescents are better where they will remain on for periods of at least three hours at a time. Decorative gas lanterns should be turned off or converted to electric because electric lamps use much less energy to produce the same amount of light.
10. All of your leaky faucets should be fixed—particularly the hot ones. One leaky faucet can waste up to 6000 gallons of water a year. You can also save by turning the thermostat on your water heater down when you'll be away from home for a weekend or more. Always use full loads in your dishwasher and clothes washer, and use warm wash and cold rinse. Take brief showers

rather than baths because they use less hot water. You should use cold water to run your garbage disposal. In general, you *save* every time you use cold water instead of hot.

11. Water heaters should be well insulated with thermostats set no higher than 140°F. Wrapping additional insulation around the unit saves still more and exposed hot water pipes should be insulated from the tank to points of water use.
12. If your house has been insulated since it was built, then your furnace may be too big for your home. In general that means it's inefficient, and would use less fuel overall if it were smaller. Here's how to tell: Wait for one of the coldest nights of the year, and set your thermostat at 65°F. Once the house temperature reaches 65°F, if the furnace burner runs less than 40 minutes out of the next hour (time it only when it's running), your furnace is too big. A furnace that's too big turns on and off much more than it should, and that results in inefficient heat transfer and wasted energy. Depending on your type of fuel burner, your service company may be able to reduce the size of your burner nozzle without replacing the whole burner.
13. Lower the thermostat setting in your house or apartment for 8 hours per night. Additional savings can be made by turning down the thermostat as low as you can stand it. The map and table on page 226 show the savings you get with this simple step. Clock thermostats are available which will automatically turn your heat down every night and turn it up in the morning. Some will turn the heat down again while you are at work, then raise it about the time you usually get home.
14. A room or home humidifier can help your home feel warmer with less fuel. Humidifiers add moisture to the air. Moist air feels warmer than dry air at the same temperature.
15. As noted earlier, one alternative to energy-consuming air conditioning is the use of an *attic fan* to cool your home. Normally a house holds heat, so that there's a lag between the time the outside air cools after sunset on a summer night and the time that the house cools. The purpose of the attic fan is to speed up the cooling of the house by pulling air in through open windows up through the attic and out. When the fan's on, you can let air through the attic either by opening the attic door partway or by installing a louver that does the same thing automatically. In a part of the country that has hot days and cool nights, using an attic fan in the evenings and closing the windows and curtains during the day can eliminate the need for air conditioning. The size

PERCENT SAVINGS WITH THERMOSTAT TURNDOWN

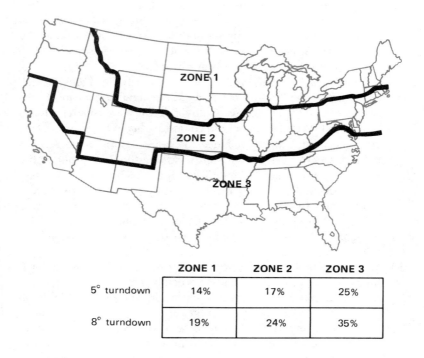

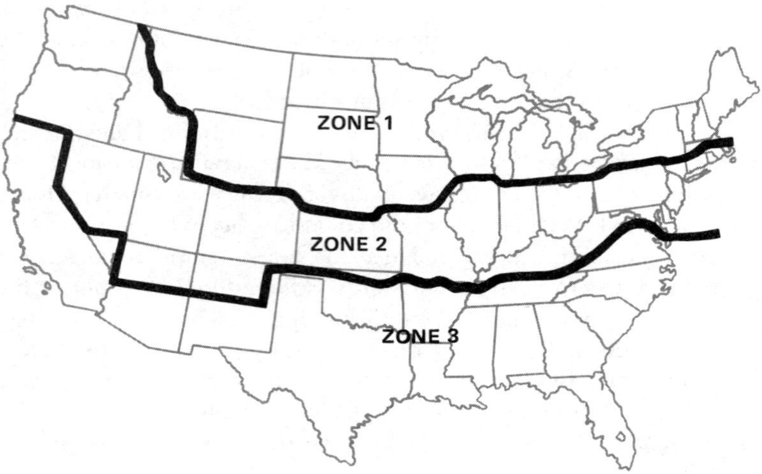

	ZONE 1	ZONE 2	ZONE 3
5° turndown	14%	17%	25%
8° turndown	19%	24%	35%

of the fan you buy should be determined by the amount of space you want to cool. You can figure out the fan size you need by finding the *volume* of your house—rounding off to the nearest foot, multiply by its height (from the ground to just below the attic). This will give you the volume in *cubic feet.* The capacity of all fans is marked on the fan in CFM (*C*ubic *F*eet of air moved per *M*inute). Divide the volume of your house by 10; this will give you the CFM rating of the fan you need to change the air in the house 6 times an hour.

While saving energy today, you may be able to save even more money with federal and state tax benefits that can be claimed for insulating your home and saving energy. Check your local Internal Revenue Service and local government tax offices for the latest allowable deductions.

AIR CONDITIONING

Cooling Capacity of Air Conditioners

The earliest home air conditioners were rated in terms of tons of refrigeration—1 ton of refrigeration being the cooling capacity of 1 ton of ice melting in 24 hours. Today air conditioners are generally rated in terms of British thermal units of heat removed per hour (Btuh or Btu/hr). One ton of refrigeration is equal to 12,000 Btu/hr.

On a clear day at noon, solar energy received by 1 square foot of horizontal area is about 290 Btu/hr.

Figuring Air-Conditioning Needs

There are two basic types of air-conditioning systems used to cool a house: room conditioners and central air conditioners. Let's take a look at both:

SMALL ROOM CONDITIONERS. More houses are cooled with small room conditioners than with any other method. Usually the homeowner starts out with a single unit in the bedroom or living room and adds others as his pocketbook allows. Thus he spreads the cost over a period of years. That's one of the advantages of the multi-small-room-conditioner approach to whole-house cooling, but it's not the only one. You also get maximum cooling effect in each room in which a conditioner is installed. Furthermore, you can cool each room to a different comfort level, and cut off rooms, thus reducing operating cost when they are unoccupied.

If the conditioners you put in are designed to operate on 120 volts and 7½ amps or less, you can plug them directly into existing 120-volt, 15-amp circuits, provided the circuits are not or will not be used to serve lamps and appliances with a total wattage exceeding 860. This obviously cuts the initial cost of the air conditioning; but since it's highly unusual to find more than one underused 120-volt, 15-amp circuit in a house, the odds are that the second, third, and fourth conditioners you put in will require special wiring even though they may be rated at less than 7½ amps.

Another advantage of small conditioners is that you can install them quickly, easily, and at little if any expense. You can do the job yourself. And when you move, you can take the units with you to cool down your new home as rapidly as the old. This, however, presupposes that you install the conditioners in the windows; and therein lies one of their drawbacks; the great majority of models block the view out the window.

Only a handful are designed in a U-shape to fit over the window-sill with only a couple of inches projecting above.

Another disadvantage of putting in several small conditioners is that they raise the noise level in each room in which they're installed. To be sure, all manufacturers are making efforts (successful) to build quieter machines, but these efforts are not confined to small units. Big ones are getting attention, too. So it stands to reason that several small room conditioners are still going to be noisier than one big one.

LARGE ROOM CONDITIONERS. If your house is of average size, installing a single room conditioner with a capacity of roughly 20,000 to 35,000 Btus is a good way to cool it. The purchase price of the unit is less than that of several small room conditioners, although the installation cost may tip the scales the other way since the unit is so large that it should be installed through an outside wall—not in a window—and since you need a 240-volt circuit to serve it. Operating cost, on the other hand, will probably run a little lower.

The efficiency of the system depends on the heating system. If you have hot water, steam, or electric heat, don't expect miracles. When installed in your largest room, the conditioner will move some of the cooled air into the smaller rooms, provided the house is reasonably compact, on one floor, and all doors are left open. But the smaller rooms will never be as cool as the big one.

If you have a warm-air heating system and set it for continuous air circulation, however, you can achieve pretty even comfort throughout the whole house, even if the house is two stories high. The secret is to install the conditioner in a room that has a return duct leading to the furnace. Keep this register open but close the supply registers in the room. You should also seal all other return lines in the house with pieces of hardboard placed behind the grilles. Then turn on the air conditioner and furnace fan, and forget what the weather is like outdoors.

When buying an air conditioner for this kind of system, it's important to calculate the cooling requirements of the house carefully. Let an expert do it or use the "Cooling Load Estimate Form" on pages 230–231. Putting in a slightly smaller unit than is called for is advisable because it runs all the time and thus does a better job of dehumidifying the air. By contrast, on mild days, an oversized unit lowers house temperature rapidly, but may shut off before humidity has been brought down to an appropriate level.

When purchasing a room air conditioner—either large or small—check the EER (Energy Efficiency Ratio). The higher the EER number, the less electricity the unit will use to cool the same amount of air. You should consider your possible fuel savings when deciding how much to spend on your air-conditioning unit. A unit which costs more to begin with may save enough money over the next summer to make it worth it. Typical EER's range from 4 to 12; a unit with an EER of 4 will cost about *3 times as much* to operate as one with an EER of 12.

CENTRAL AIR CONDITIONING. This is the thorough way to cool a house because sooner or later all the air in the house passes over the cooling coil in the air conditioner and is blown back into the house through the supply ducts. Thus, if the system is properly sized and installed, you get balanced comfort everywhere. In addition, you can build into the system an electronic filter that removes almost all pollen, smoke, dust, and other contaminants from the house air. You can even add an odor absorber.

Of course, you pay for what you get. As a rule of thumb, one ton (12,000 Btus) of air conditioning is required for every 500 square feet of floor space. Thus, if the cost in your area ranges around $500 to $700 to install each ton of air conditioning in an existing house, a 1500-square foot house would need a unit costing $1500 to $2100 to cool it. (Central air-conditioning systems are less costly in a home that is being built.)

The perfect setup for central air conditioning is a fairly new house with good insulation, 240-volt wiring, and a modern forced-warm-air heating system. Given this, all you have to do is have a cooling coil installed in the furnace plenum and connected to a condensing unit installed in a shady place outside the house where the noise it makes will not be upsetting. Then have the furnace blower, which is used to circulate the cooled air through the house, set for constant air circulation. This will level out conditions in the house and is likely to reduce the air conditioner's consumption of electricity as well.

In a house with an old forced-air heating system, installation of central air conditioning is somewhat more difficult but not impossible. As a rule, the main problem is that the ducts are too small to carry a proper volume of cold air, but this can usually be corrected by replacing the old fan with a larger one. You probably will also have to replace the registers with new units which can be adjusted to blow cold air upward in summer and warm air downward during the cold winter months.

Central air conditioning can even be installed in a house without a ducted heating system, and the cost need not be as horrendous as you fear. For instance, if you have any kind of an attic in a one-story house, it's a simple matter to install the air conditioner in it and duct the cooled air into the rooms through ceiling registers. Or if you don't have an attic, put the conditioner in the basement or crawl space. Or if you have a two-story house, put in two small central systems: one in the attic to serve the second floor, the other in the basement for the first floor.

COOLING LOAD ESTIMATE FORM

Customer ______________________ Estimate by ______________________ Date ______________________

HEAT GAIN FROM	QUANTITY	FACTORS: NIGHT	FACTORS: DAY — No Shades*	DAY — Inside Shades*	DAY — Outside Awnings*	DAY — (Area x Factor)	Btu/Hr (Quantity x Factor)
1. **WINDOWS:** Heat gain from sun.							
Northeast	____ sq ft	0	60	25	20	____	____
East	____ sq ft	0	80	40	25	____ Use	____
Southeast	____ sq ft	0	75	30	20	____ only	____
South	____ sq ft	0	75	35	20	____ the	____
Southwest	____ sq ft	0	110	45	30	____ largest	____
West	____ sq ft	0	150	65	45	____ load	____
Northwest	____ sq ft	0	120	50	35	____	____
North	____ sq ft	0	0	0	0	____	____
*These factors are for single glass only. For glass block, multiply the above factors by 0.5; for double-glass or storm windows, multiply the above factors by 0.8.							
2. **WINDOWS:** Heat gain by conduction. (Total of all windows.)							
Single glass	____ sq ft	14	14				____
Double glass or glass block	____ sq ft	7	7				____
3. **WALLS:** (Based on linear feet of wall.)			Light Construction	Heavy Construction			
a. Outside walls							
North exposure	____ ft	30	30	20			____
Other than North exposure	____ ft	30	60	30			____
b. Inside Walls (between conditioned and unconditioned spaces only)	____ ft	30	30				____
4. **ROOF OR CEILING:** (Use one only.)							
a. Roof, uninsulated	____ sq ft	5	19				____
b. Roof, 1 inch or more insulation.	____ sq ft	3	8				____
c. Ceiling, occupied space above.	____ sq ft	3	3				____
d. Ceiling, insulated with attic space above	____ sq ft	4	5				____
e. Ceiling, uninsulated, with attic space above	____ sq ft	7	12				____
5. **FLOOR:** (Disregard if floor is directly on ground or over basement.)	____ sq ft	3	3				____
6. **NUMBER OF PEOPLE:**	____	600	600				____
7. **LIGHTS AND ELECTRICAL EQUIPMENT IN USE**	____ watts	3	3				____
8. **DOORS AND ARCHES CONTINUOUSLY OPEN TO UNCONDITIONED SPACE:** (Linear feet of width.)	____ ft	200	300				____
9. **SUB-TOTAL**	x x x x x	x x x x x	x x x x x				

10. **TOTAL COOLING LOAD:** (Btu per hour to be used for selection of room air-conditioner(s).) ____________ (Item 9) X ______________________ (Factor from Map) = ____________

NOTE: See Reverse side for instructions on use of this form.

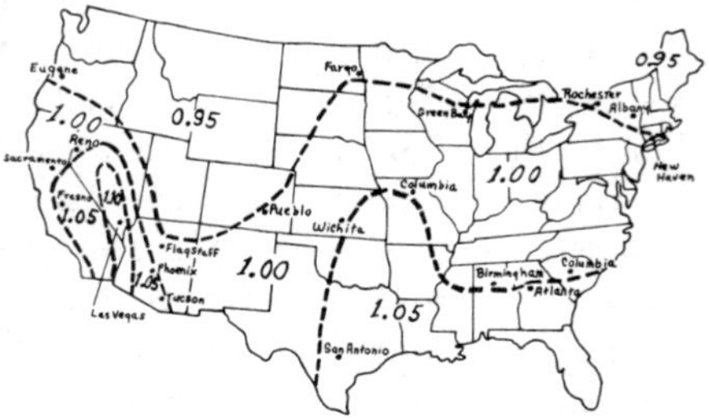

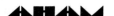

Published and distributed by the

Association of Home Appliance Manufacturers
20 North Wacker Drive Chicago, Illinois 60606
Phone A. C. 312/ 236-2921

INSTRUCTIONS FOR USING COOLING LOAD ESTIMATE FORM FOR ROOM AIR CONDITIONERS

(FROM AHAM STANDARD RAC-1)

A. This cooling load estimate form is suitable for estimating the cooling load for comfort air-conditioning stallations which do not require specific conditions of inside temperature and humidity.

B. The form is based on an outside design temperature of 95 F dry bulb and 75 F wet bulb. It can be used for eas in the continental United States having other outside design temperatures by applying a correction factor for e particular locality as determined from the map.

C. The form includes "day" factors for calculating cooling loads in rooms where daytime comfort is desired such as living rooms, offices, etc.), as well as "night" factors for calculating cooling loads in rooms where nly nighttime comfort is desired (such as bedrooms). "Night" factors should be used only for those applications here comfort air-conditioning is desired during the period from sunset to sunrise.

D. The numbers of the following paragraphs refer to the correspondingly numbered item on the form:

1. Multiply the square feet of window area for each exposure by the applicable factor. The window area is the area of the wall opening in which the window is installed. For windows shaded by inside shades or venetian blinds, use the factor for "Inside Shades." For windows shaded by outside awnings or by both outside awnings and inside shades (or venetian blinds), use the factor for "Outside Awnings." "Single Glass" includes all types of single-thickness windows, and "Double Glass" includes sealed air-space types, storm windows, and glass block. Only one number should be entered in the right-hand column for item 1, and this number should represent ***only the exposure with the largest load.***

2. Multiply the total square feet of *all* windows in the room by the applicable factor.

3a. Multiply the total length (linear feet) of all walls exposed to the outside by the applicable factor. Doors should be considered as being part of the wall. Outside walls facing due north should be calculated separately from outside walls facing other directions. Walls which are permanently shaded by adjacent structures should be considered as being "North Exposure." Do not consider trees and shrubbery as providing permanent shading. An uninsulated frame wall or a masonry wall 8 inches or less in thickness is considered "Light Construction." An insulated frame wall or a masonry wall over 8 inches in thickness is considered "Heavy Construction."

3b. Multiply the total length (linear feet) of all inside walls between the space to be conditioned and any unconditioned spaces by the given factor. Do not include inside walls which separate other air-conditioned rooms.

4. Multiply the total square feet of roof or ceiling area by the factor given for the type of construction most nearly describing the particular application. (Use one line only.)

5. Multiply the total square feet of floor area by the factor given. Disregard this item if the floor is directly on the ground or over a basement.

6. Multiply the number of people who normally occupy the space to be air-conditioned by the factor given. Use a minimum of 2 people.

7. Determine the total number of watts for lights and electrical equipment, except the air conditioner itself, that will be ***in use*** when the room air-conditioning is operating. Multiply the total wattage by the factor given.

8. Multiply the total width (linear feet) of any doors or arches which are continually open to an unconditioned space by the applicable factor.

   NOTE—Where the width of the doors or arches is more than 5 feet, the actual load may exceed the the calculated value. In such cases, both adjoining rooms should be considered as a single large room, and the room air-conditioner unit or units should be selected according to a calculation made on this new basis.

9. Total the loads estimated for the foregoing 8 items.

10. Multiply the sub-total obtained in Item 9 by the proper correction factor, selected from the map, for the particular locality. The result is the total estimated design cooling load in Btu per hour.

E. For best results a room air-conditioner unit or units having a cooling capacity rating (determined in accordance with the AHAM Standards Publication for Room Air Conditioners, RAC-1) as close as possible to he estimated load should be selected. In general, a greatly oversized unit which would operate intermittently vill be much less satisfactory than one which is slightly undersized and which would operate more nearly ontinuously.

F. Intermittent loads such as kitchen and laundry equipment are not included in this form.

RAC-1 Printed in USA

When installing a central air-conditioning system, you may want to look into the *air economizer*, a system which turns off the part of your air conditioner that uses a lot of electricity, and circulates outside air through the house when it's cooler out than it is in. By using the cooler outside air, the system reduces its own job and saves money for you. Ask your air-conditioning dealer if he can install one on your system.

Air-Conditioning Wisdom

The easiest way to save money on air conditioning is simply to avoid waste. Don't use an air conditioner when it isn't really necessary. Set the air conditioner for the warmest comfortable setting. Often this setting rises with outdoor temperature, especially when the outdoor humidity is high. Thus when the temperature outdoors is 80°F, you might set your air conditioner to 75°F. But when it's 95°F outside an air conditioner setting of 80°F might feel perfectly comfortable. *Never make a room so cool that you must wear a sweater to remain comfortable.*

HEAT PUMPS

In summer they cool the house by extracting heat from the inside air and pumping it outdoors. (That's exactly what an ordinary air conditioner does.) In winter, they reverse themselves and extract heat from the outdoor air—even at zero degrees or less—pumping the heat indoors.

Heat pumps today are available as large central units which circulate cooled and heated air through the house via ductwork and as room units which are installed either on a windowsill or through an exterior wall. In an existing house, it doesn't make much sense to install a central heat pump unless you live in a warm climate, need to replace an old heating system, and want air conditioning to boot. In this event, the very low heating cost makes the unit extremely attractive.

The room-conditioner heat pump is another matter, however. You can use it in an old house to supplement the heat in an underheated area and provide cooling as well.

SOLAR HEATING

Until lately, solar energy just wasn't economically practical. True, sunlight is free, but collecting it and putting it to use can cost a lot of money. There are two reasons for this. First, solar energy is plentiful, but it is spread out over an extensive area. To get a useful amount of energy, you need large collectors, which can be costly. Second, solar energy is intermittent. The sun does not shine all the time, but we need energy all the time. To solve that problem, there are storage systems, which can be costly too.

So, until just a few years ago, it was simply cheaper to burn inexpensive fossil fuel in a $1,000 furnace than to collect free sunlight in a $7,000 solar heating system. Now things are changing. Fossil fuels are no longer inexpensive. As their prices rise, it becomes more and more economical to spend the extra money for solar hardware.

What is that hardware? A solar heating system consists of three basic parts: (1) the collectors, (2) the storage system, (3) the distribution system.

The Collector

This is the key to any solar system. It picks up the widely scattered solar energy, transforms it into heat and allows us to carry it away for use. There are many types of solar collectors, but by far the most common is the flat-plate type. This is essentially a flat black metal plate housed in an insulated box with one or more glass covers. The sun shines into the box through the covers and strikes the black plate. There the sun's heat is concentrated. The insulated box keeps the heat from escaping until the heat can be carried off for use.

The average collector is about 55-percent efficient. This means it captures about 55 percent of the solar energy striking it. When you buy a collector, you are not really interested in efficiency per se. What is important is dollar efficiency. How many Btu will the collector produce for every dollar the collector costs? A collector that's only 10-percent efficient, yet costs just $2 a square foot is more economical than one that is 60-percent efficient but costs $20 a foot. All things considered, the amount of energy a collector can produce is directly proportional to its area. Double the area of your collector array, and you get twice as many Btu. In Washington, D.C., for example the average daily solar radiation is about 400 Langley's per day. A Langley is equal to 3.69 Btu per square foot. So Washington gets an average of 1,476 Btu per square foot every day. Thus a collector with an area of 1 square foot and an efficiency of 50 percent would gather about 738 Btu per day. Interestingly, that's about equal to the energy you'd get from burning a cubic foot of natural gas.

Obviously, 1 square foot of collector is not going to provide enough Btu to heat your home. As it turns out, the average solar-heated home needs a collector area equal to about half the home's floor area. Thus a 1,000-square-foot home would need about 500 square feet of collectors.

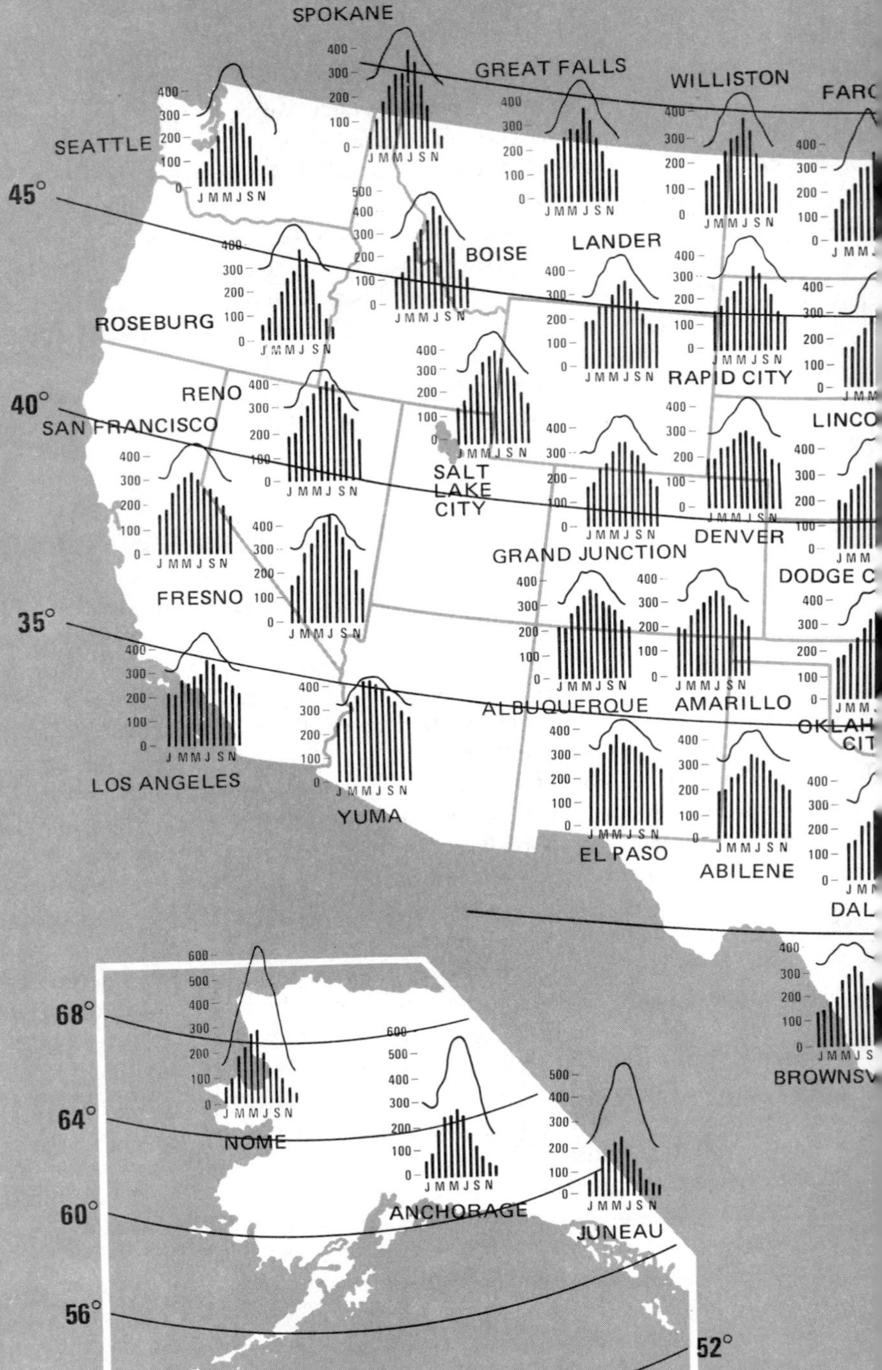

SPOKANE
GREAT FALLS
WILLISTON
SEATTLE
45°
ROSEBURG
BOISE
LANDER
RAPID CITY
RENO
40°
SAN FRANCISCO
SALT LAKE CITY
GRAND JUNCTION
DENVER
FRESNO
35°
LOS ANGELES
YUMA
ALBUQUERQUE
AMARILLO
EL PASO
ABILENE
68°
64°
60°
56°
52°
NOME
ANCHORAGE
JUNEAU
J M M J S N

MEAN MONTHLY TOTAL HOURS OF SUNSHINE

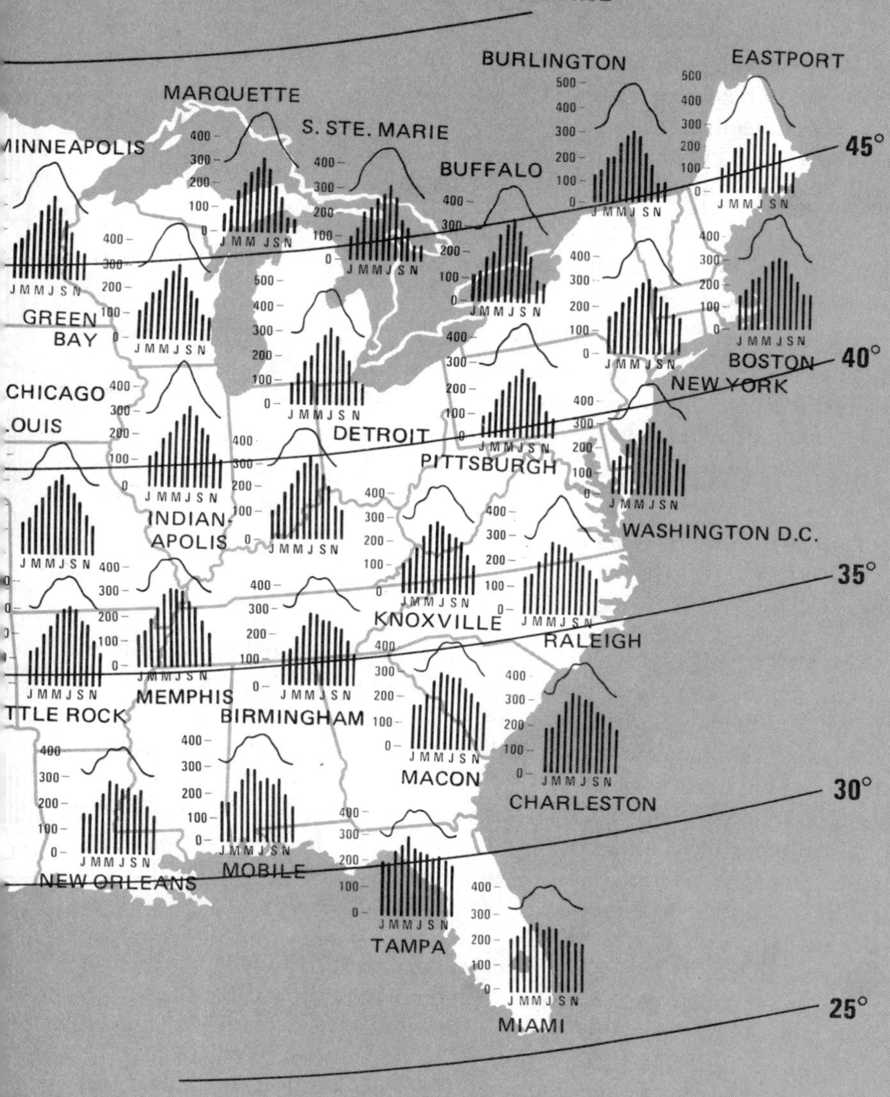

This map shows relative hours of sunshine throughout the U.S. The lines above the graphs indicate possible hours. For space heating, the figures during the heating season are important. For the heating of domestic water, figures throughout the year are helpful. *Note:* These figures are averages over several decades. Actual hours of sunshine in given months or a given year may vary greatly from these averages.

Since most collectors available today cost at least $10 a square foot, a 500-square-foot array would run at least $5,000.

Once the collector has gathered the sunshine and turned it into heat, the heat must be transported for use. There are two ways to do this: with air and with liquid.

AIR-TYPE COLLECTOR. We can blow air through the collector and over the heated plate. As the air passes through the collector, it picks up the heat.

LIQUID-TYPE COLLECTOR. The other way to pick up the heat is to use a liquid such as water, or a water/antifreeze mix. The liquid can trickle over the plate, or run through pipes built into it. Either way, the liquid picks up the heat from the plate.

WHICH TYPE IS BETTER? Neither is a clear-cut winner. The water type is the best for heating domestic water supplies. But the air type may have advantages for space heating.

Storage

Once the heat is picked up at the collectors, it is usually routed into storage, from which heat can be tapped during cloudy periods and at night. (Of course, the heat can also be routed past storage, directly to the home.) If the collectors are of the air type, heat is usually stored in a large bin full of rocks located in the basement. The hot air from the collectors is ducted into this bin—usually about 500 cubic feet—and the fist-size rocks pick up the heat and hold it. The air then returns to the collectors for reheating. This cycle goes on and on as long as the sun shines, with the rocks in storage becoming hotter and hotter and thus storing more and more energy.

If the collectors are of the liquid type, energy is usually stored in a large (1,500 gallon) tank of water. The liquid circulates through the collectors, picks up heat, then goes to the storage tank, then back to the collectors in an endless loop. With each pass through the collectors the temperature of the water rises. Soon the tank is full of hot water, and Btu.

Distribution System

This lets you extract heat from storage and use it to heat your home. If you have a hot-air collection system, you extract the heat simply by blowing house air through the bin of rocks. The air is warmed by the hot rocks, then ducted to the individual rooms of your home.

If you have a hot-water storage system, you extract heat by running the hot water through a series of finned pipes in a heat exchanger. When air is blown over the fins, the air becomes heated and travels through ductwork to your home. Don't make the mistake of trying to use this hot water in a standard hot water baseboard heating system. The solar-heated water will rarely be hot enough to provide much useful heat in such a system.

There's one other way to distribute heat. This involves a heat pump. This is a sort of air conditioner that can run backwards. Using a compressor, refrigerant, and condensor and evaporator, a heat pump picks up heat from one point and delivers it to another. When used in conjunction with a solar system, it picks up heat from storage and delivers it to your home. Heat pumps are relatively expensive to buy, and they cost more to run than a heat exchanger, but they can extract useful heat even from relatively cool storage tanks, which would be too cool to heat your home by any other method. This makes heat pumps useful for solar installations in areas only marginally suited to solar heating.

Backup Systems

In theory at least, a solar heating system can provide your home with 100 percent of its heating needs. Unfortunately, it can't do so economically. Why not? Periodically each winter your home will probably be hit with several days of cloudy weather. This period, during which your system can collect no heat, might even extend a week or more. A solar heating system designed to cope with a situation like this would require a tremendous amount of collector area, and a huge storage tank or bin. This would simply make the system so expensive it could never pay for itself in saved fuel.

To solve this problem, solar heating systems are engineered to provide about 50 to 75 percent of your heating needs. The rest of your heat is provided by conventional means, such as gas, oil, coal or wood, or electricity. Doing this brings the cost of the solar system down to around $6,000. A system designed to provide 100-percent solar heat might cost five or 10 times that amount, yet it would provide only twice as much heat as a solar system designed to provide 50 percent of your needs.

Solar Heat and Your Home

Solar heat isn't for every home. Since solar hardware is expensive, any home to be solar heated should retain as much of the heat collected for as long as feasible. This requires insulation to the maximum R-values as shown on R-values map shown earlier in this chapter. The home should also be well weatherstripped and caulked. All glass areas should be double or triple glazed. And the house should have a minimum amount of surface area in relation to volume.

The home should also be positioned on its site to take maximum advantage of shading and prevailing winds. It should also be oriented with the ridge of the roof running east and west. This lets you place your collectors on the sloping south face of the roof, for maximum exposure to the sun. Ideally, the south face of the roof should be sloped at an angle equal to your geographic latitude plus 10 degrees.

Of course your home needn't fit these requirements perfectly. Roof angles can be off by 30 degrees without great loss. And if the collectors face up to 23 degrees east or west of due south, losses will amount to only about 5 percent. You can even put your collectors vertically on a fence, or flat on their backs on a flat roof if desired. But the closer to the ideal you can come, the cheaper and more effective the system will be. So don't be tempted to skimp in preparing your home for solar heat, especially in insulation, caulking, and weatherstripping. Experts say a dollar spent on insulation is worth more than two dollars spent on solar hardware.

Sizing a Solar System

The object here is to balance the heating needs of your home against the ability of your chosen system to meet those needs.

The easiest way to determine the heating needs of your home is to work from past records of fuel consumption. If you don't keep records, call your fuel company. They usually keep them for each of their customers.

Costs vs. Paybacks

Before you convert to solar energy you should know one thing: How much will it save you? That is, how long until it pays for itself? Because of the variables involved—weather, fuel prices, interest rates, inflation and so on—this is difficult to predict. About the best you can do is amortize the cost of the installation against the estimated savings in fuel per year.

Let's say you presently heat your home for $500 a year. You pay $7,500 for a solar system that is engineered to produce 75 percent of your needs. Thus the system will produce 75 percent of $500 or $375 worth of heat every year. Divide $375 into the cost of the system and you get 20 years for the system to pay for itself. Is that a good deal? No.

You could simply put your $7,500 in the bank, draw from it to pay for fuel and come out ahead. But all this assumes the current price of fuel remains constant for the next 20 years. It won't. It could easily double within a year or two of your installing solar heating. If that happens, payback time is cut to 10 years.

And all these calculations leave out the fact that your solar hardware is worth money sitting there on your house. When you sell, you will get at least some of that money back. Who knows how much. If you sell in 10 years, the value of the heating system could be even more than you paid for it. How? If energy prices rise enough, energy-efficient homes like yours would sell for a premium. In that case your solar hardware will have essentially cost you nothing, yet saved you thousands of dollars. There's no sure way to calculate exactly the economics of a solar installation at this point. But you can make some rough comparisons.

Take a look at the fuel-value table below. Then multiply the value given below (for the fuel you use) by the amount of fuel you use per year. The result is your heating requirement, in Btu per heating season. The chart assumes 75-percent efficiencies for gas, coal, and oil furnaces, and 100-percent efficiencies for electric heat.

HOME HEATING FUEL VALUES

Fuel oil	102,000 Btu per gallon
Gas	750 Btu per cubic foot
Electricity	3,412 Btu per Hwhr
Coal	18,750,000 per ton

Once you know your Btu load for the season, simply compare it to the ability of the collectors you have chosen. Most collector makers can supply you with data on their collectors, telling how many Btu they will deliver in your area. These figures are often given in terms of Btu per each month of the year. So simply add up the Btu the collectors can deliver during those months when your home requires heat. If you match Btu collected against Btu required, and consider payback times, you'll come up with a system that provides about 70 percent of your heating needs.

Today, most experts recommend a system of about 70-percent capacity because it will pay off soonest when balanced against today's costs for heating fuels. But again, as prices for fossil fuels continue to rise, you might consider expanding your collector area to provide closer to 100 percent of your needs.

Solar-Heated Domestic Water

Probably the first step for anyone interested in cutting costs and energy consumption with solar heat is to install a *water* heating system. A solar heater for domestic hot water is an easy first step. Commercial units are relatively inexpensive, and do-it-yourself models are even more reasonable. And time to payback runs an average of about 6 years. A good homemade unit might pay off in 4 years; an expensive commercial unit may take as long as 10, counting installation costs.

One last reason for starting with solar water heaters: Unlike solar space heaters, they are easy to tie into existing homes. No matter how poorly insulated, weatherstripped, caulked, or glazed your home might be, a solar water heater will still do its job. You can't say the same for solar space heaters. And it is important at this point in history to begin the changeover from fossil fuels to solar power as soon as possible.

There are several solar water heaters on the market. But the important thing when purchasing a unit is that it will have to provide trouble-free service for a number of years. Performance and durability are the two most important considerations. When you shop, think performance and durability first, price second. Here are some important steps to consider before buying any solar water heater—or even a solar space heater.

1. Investigate the firm that sells the unit. A quick call to your Better Business Bureau or chamber of commerce might save you years of grief. Before you buy, check over the sales contract and warranty very carefully. Better yet, let your lawyer do the job. Look for a warranty of at least a year on mechanical components such as pumps and controls. You'd be justified in expecting warranties for five years on simple structural parts such as collectors and plumbing.
2. Examine the performance figures for the unit you plan to buy. If you are not sure, take your problem to a consulting engineer. Have him check the system out.
3. Make sure the unit is approved by your local building codes. If it isn't, you may have to rip it out. Check your local tax situation, too. In some localities, energy-saving hardware is not subject to property taxes. And you may qualify for sales and income tax credits as well.
4. Make sure you get a quotation on all costs, including installation. You don't want any surprises when the final bill comes in.
5. Don't be unduly influenced by prices. Sure, it's smart to get the lowest price you can, but don't sacrifice quality and durability just

to save money. Remember, a water heater is an investment. It adds to the value of your home, the same as any other home improvement. When you sell your home, you should be able to get your money back—if the system is still in good shape, still operating as it should.

Solar Information

For a listing of manufacturers and distributors of solar equipment and for the latest listing of homeowner tax incentives for solar installations, contact the national Solar Heating and Cooling Information Center, P.O. Box 1607, Rockville, MD 20850; toll free: (800) 523-2929.

HEATING WITH WOOD

Chances are that you can save money by heating your home with firewood instead of electricity or your present fossil fuel. The economics depend upon a number of variables such as the price you pay for your present fuel, the price you pay for wood, the type of wood you buy, and the appliance you use to burn the wood. Obviously if you live in an area with plentiful supplies of cheap fuel but very little firewood, you won't save money by switching. But there are very few areas of the country where this situation exists. Fossil fuels are becoming scarcer all the time, yet firewood is available to many people. And it is a renewable resource.

Buying Wood

Wood is ordinarily sold by the cord. This is a stack of logs 4×4×8 feet. The amount of energy you can get out of that volume of wood when you burn it is roughly proportional to the weight of that wood when air dried, or seasoned. The heavier the better. For this reason, dense woods such as hickory and oak can give you over twice as much heat as lighter woods such as aspen and most conifers. So when you shop for wood you must take the species of wood into account.

Dryness is very important. When you burn unseasoned, green wood, much of the energy produced by the fire is wasted in boiling off all the excess water in the wood. Most woods will yield about 20 percent more heat when air dried to around 18 percent moisture content than they will when green. Wet wood can also hasten the buildup of chimney deposits called creosote that may fuel a dangerous chimney or stovepipe fire. Since a fire in your chimney can spread to the rest of your house, that's another good reason to burn dry wood. Experts recommend that wood be air dried 6 months to a year before burning. Yet the initial few months of drying—well ventilated and under cover—can improve burning quality dramatically.

The Burning Appliance

Wood heating is most economical if you burn your wood in an efficient wood stove. There are dozens of different stove designs, each design claimed to have amazing efficiency. Two important features include airtightness and an air-flow pattern that promotes a long residence time for exhaust gases that can transfer heat to the stove walls and then to the room. An airtight stove gives you full control over the draft and thus the rate of burn. This lets you admit combustion air at a low steady rate, allowing a slow steady flow of gases out the stove, for best heat transfer. Airtight stoves with good air-flow patterns can deliver efficiencies of around 50 percent and better.

Ordinary wood stoves that aren't built with airtight seams and doors are much less efficient than the airtights. They draw excessive amounts of warm room air and they cause the wood to burn at much faster rates than may be desired.

Most fireplaces are less than 10-percent efficient. This assumes that the fireplace is used almost constantly. A fireplace that is used intermittently may have a negative efficiency. This is for two main reasons. First, the fireplace is inefficient at delivering heat from the fire to your home. Even worse is the fact that an open fireplace allows huge volumes of room air to escape up its chimney, and room air is air you have already paid to heat. An open fireplace can exhaust 200 to 300 cubic feet of warm room air up the flue *per minute.* In effect you wind up reheating that room with fossil fuels to compensate.

As mentioned, fireplaces are at their worst when used intermittently. Unfortunately, that's the way they are most often used. A family lights the fire in the evening and then keeps it burning until bedtime. At this point the damper must be left open or the dying fire will send smoke and poisonous fumes back into the house. So while the family sleeps, warm air slips up the chimney all night, carrying with it more Btu than the fireplace ever delivered while the fire was burning.

Efficient Woodburning

Whether you cut and season your own wood or buy it from a supplier, you should try to avoid burning unseasoned wood. There can be dollar savings in doing all the work yourself, but there are costs of equipment and your labor. If you buy your wood cut to stove length and split, you may be able to get favorable prices by buying unseasoned wood in spring before the peak demand occurs in fall and winter.

To compute the economics of wood heat for your particular situation, take a look at the two tables on page 244. The first lists the heating values of today's common fossil fuels, and those of electricity. Using this table you can easily find how much you pay per Btu of heat actually delivered to your home. Just divide your cost for fuel by its heating value listed in the table.

For example, if you pay four cents a kilowatt hour to heat electrically, your cost per Btu will be $.04 ÷ 3,142 or $.0000127 per Btu. If you pay 50 cents a gallon for fuel oil your cost per Btu will be $.50 ÷ 102,000 or $.0000049 per Btu.

That's how to figure your cost per Btu for your present heating system. To figure your costs for heating with wood, take a look at the table of wood heating values. Simply divide the price per cord by the Btu yield for the wood type in the appliance you will use. For example, if you burn ash in an airtight stove and pay $75 a cord, divide $75 by 10,000,000. Your answer is $.0000075. As you can see, in this example, heating with $75-per-cord ash in an airtight stove would be cheaper than heating with electricity at 4¢ a kwh, but more expensive than heating with oil at 50¢ a gallon.

These same tables can help you determine approximately how much firewood you will need to heat your home for a season. To do this, simply check your records from past years to see how much fossil fuel or electricity you used to heat your home. Multiply that total by the heating value for that particular fuel. This will tell you how many Btu you needed. Divide that number by the Btu per cord available from the wood of your choice in the appliance of your choice and you know roughly how many cords of that wood you will need for an average heating season.

Example: Say you heated your home last year with 1,000 gallons of oil. Each gallon provides you with 102,000 Btu. So multiply 1,000 × 102,000. That gives 102,000,000 Btu required for a season of heating. You could get those same 102,000,000 Btu by burning just a bit over 10 cords of ash in an airtight, 50-percent-efficient stove (102,000,000 ÷ 10,000,000 = 10.2).

Incidentally, 10 cords is more than most homes require. Statistics show that the average home can be heated for a winter on about six cords of wood. Superinsulated northern homes may get by on only a few cords each heating season.

HEATING VALUES OF FOSSIL FUELS AND ELECTRICITY

(Assumes 75-percent efficiency for coal, gas and oil, 100 percent efficiency for electricity)

Fuel	Btu
Coal	18,750,000 per ton
Oil	102,000 per gallon
Natural gas	750 per cubic foot
Electricity	3,412 per kilowatt-hour

HEATING VALUES OF COMMON FIREWOODS

		ACTUAL YIELD (million Btu)		
WOOD	**AVAIL. HEAT PER CORD million Btu**	**Fireplace** (10% eff.)	**Box stove** (25% eff.)	**Airtight** (50% eff.)
Ash	20	2	5	10
Aspen	12.5	1.25	3.13	6.25
Beech	21.8	2.18	5.45	10.9
Birch	21.3	2.13	5.33	10.65
Doug. fir	18	1.8	4.5	9
Elm	17.2	1.72	4.3	8.6
Hickory	24.6	2.46	6.15	12.3
Red maple	18.6	1.86	4.65	9.3
Sugar maple	21.3	2.13	5.33	10.66
Red oak	21.3	2.13	5.33	10.66
White oak	22.7	2.27	5.68	11.35
White pine	12.1	1.21	3.03	6.05
Yellow pine	20.5	2.05	5.13	10.25

Note: Figures assume wood to be air dried. Deduct 20 percent for green wood. A cord is a stack 4 × 4 × 8 feet. Deducting the spaces between logs this comes to about 80 cubic feet of solid wood.

6

Glues, Adhesives, Cements, and Sealing Compounds

Today, there is a seemingly endless variety of glues, adhesives, and cements on the market. To make a proper selection, two factors must be taken into consideration:

TYPE OF MATERIAL. Are you trying to join porous or nonporous material? Wood, paper, and cloth are porous materials that can be bonded by a wide variety of glues. Nonporous materials such as glass, tile, metal, porcelain, and most plastics generally require a different type of glue. If you are trying to join two dissimilar materials such as vinyl and wood, you will need a glue that will do an adequate job on both.

CONDITIONS. Will the joint be exposed to moisture, heat, or cold? Do the parts to be joined fit snugly together, or is a good filler needed? Also, what kind of stress will the joint be subjected to? Some glues are very strong when the joint is subjected to shear forces, but weak when the materials are in tension. Another consideration is the toxic effect of the glue. If you are working in an area with poor ventilation, or repairing a child's toy, a nontoxic glue is essential.

Types of Glues, Adhesives, and Cements

Fortunately, the glues found in retail stores are limited to the five following categories. If you remember them, selecting an adhesive for your needs ceases to be a chore.

CYANOACRYLATE. This adhesive—better known as *super glue* because of its great tensile strength—sets (hardens) as soon as chemicals in the glue combine with moisture in the air. It is the quickest setting glue being sold to consumers. Surfaces bonded together with cyanoacrylate require no clamping and take hold within 30 to 90 seconds. Full strength is attained in 12 to 24 hours.

Cyanoacrylate bonds together practically all solid, nonporous materials, either to themselves or to another nonporous surface. This includes metal, rubber, jewelry, china, glassware, most plastics, most ceramics, and some hardwoods.

The key word here is *nonporous.* Cyanoacrylate should not be used on such porous materials as softwoods. (A few cyanoacrylates will adhere to softwoods; the addition of an ingredient called orthonol is the "secret.") Cyanoacrylate resists water, extreme temperature, and most chemicals. (*Caution:* Cyanoacrylate should not be used with abandon. The glue will bond skin together almost instantaneously, and there have been cases of people having to have surgery to get fingers unglued.) You can tell if the glue is a cyanoacrylate, because the term appears on the package.

It is not economical to use cyanoacrylate if another type of glue can be used instead. Cyanoacrylate is the most expensive adhesive sold.

SOLVENT-TYPE GLUES. Solvent-type glues consist of an adhesive base (vinyl resin or acrylic resin), perhaps fillers and pigments, and a solvent that makes the mixture spreadable. As the solvent evaporates, the adhesive sets. The ingredients in solvent-type adhesive include toluene, methyl ethyl ketone, and acetone. You may see reference to this on the package.

All solvent-type adhesives—or water-type adhesives—are not the same. The degree of adhesion depends on the adhesive base. For example, glues using a *vinyl* resin adhesive base bond wood, metal, glass, concrete, and most plastics to themselves or each other.

Adhesives using an *acrylic* resin adhesive base bond wood, metal, glass, and concrete to themselves or each other, but do not accommodate plastic. However, acrylic resin adhesive does, and in addition, bonds masonry and plaster.

The so-called liquid solder, aluminum and steel mender, plastic solder, and silicone glues are also usually of the solvent-type adhesive. The latter, available in white, black, and clear, are waterproof and withstand a wide temperature range, are flexible and will join fabrics, glass, ceramics, metal, tiles, paper, and leather. Silicone glue is also used as a caulking around showers and tubs. It is a fairly strong adhesive, but do not try to paint over it—paint will not stick to most silicone glues.

Consider, too, so-called contact cements. They do several things, chief among them being that they make plastic laminates adhere to wood—which is something the others will not do—because contact cement has a neoprene rubber base. As its name implies, it bonds on contact. A coat of cement is applied to both surfaces to be joined, the glue is allowed to dry just enough to become tacky, and the surfaces are pressed together. The bond is immediate and the pieces cannot be positioned once stuck together. It is water resistant and strong in shear, but most cements are flammable and the fumes are toxic.

While most so-called panel adhesives are of solvent-base adhesive, a few are water based. Actually, one of the surest ways of determining that you are buying a solvent-type adhesive is a warning on the package that says something like this: "Danger: Extremely flammable. Vapors may cause flash fire. Harmful if swallowed. Vapors harmful, toxic."

Another type of contact cement made by the same company states, "No fire hazard. No sniffing problem." This notice appears on water-type contact cement, which is not flammable or toxic.

Solvent- and water-type adhesives do the same job as long as they have the same adhesive base—acrylic resin, vinyl resin, or neoprene rubber. Because solvent evaporates quicker than water, the only difference is in the length of time it takes for the adhesive to set.

WATER-TYPE GLUES. The composition and action of water-type glues are the same as that of solvent-type glue, except that water is used as a vehicle. Although water-type adhesives work slower than solvent-type glue, they contain no toxic solvents. They are safe to breathe and will not ignite if exposed to flame. Another advantage of water-type glue is that your tools are easily cleaned with soapy water.

White glue is one of the most common and useful household glues because it sets relatively fast, dries almost clear, and works well on wood, leather, cork, and paper. It is strong, but not water resistant, and it softens under heat. A similar type of glue, aliphatic resin, is stronger and more tolerant of high temperatures.

There is also a water-type glue in powdered form. This is a plastic resin glue; it's used for bonding all types of woods. The powder is mixed with water, spread, and clamped. Of course, one of the oldest water-type powdered glue is casein glue. Made from milk protein and mixed with water to form a paste, it has good strength and is water resistant once dry. It works well on wood, and like vegetable glue, it is nontoxic and a good choice for children's toys.

TWO-PART GLUES. In this category are epoxy and resorcinol. One part contains the glue, and the other contains a catalyst or hardener. When the two parts are mixed together in correct proportion, chemical action takes place and the glue sets.

Epoxy is fast-setting, with hardening taking place in from 5 minutes to 1 hour, depending on the formulation. Epoxy is formulated primarily for working with metals.

Resorcinol glue provides complete waterproofing. It is a wood glue that is used primarily for repairing boats, but it can be used also for repairing outdoor furniture and other wooden fixtures that are exposed to water.

There are two drawbacks to two-part adhesives. First, the mixture must be exact. Disproportionate amounts result in a weak repair.

Second, both epoxy and resorcinol have a short pot life. Once the two parts are mixed together, you must work rapidly to complete repairs before the glue begins to harden.

ANIMAL HIDE GLUES. These are among the oldest types of wood glue (if not the oldest), and the source of all the old jokes about broken-down, swaybacked horses and the glue factory. Yes, the glue is made from the hides, bones, sinews, and hide fleshings of animals. Most animal glues come in dry form and are prepared for use by soaking in water and then melting, and are applied hot. Liquid animal glues, ready to use at room temperature, are also available. Animal glues come in different grades, the higher grades being preferable for joint work, and the lower grades for veneering. Hot animal glues develop strength first by cooling and gelling and later by drying, and are often preferred for spreading on irregularly shaped joints and for furniture. The chief disadvantages of these glues are their relatively high cost, the importance of temperature control in their use, and the low moisture resistance of the joints.

MAKING YOUR OWN ADHESIVES AND SEALERS

Hide Glue

Although the ready convenience of liquid, casein, and synthetic resin glues has caused these newer products to largely replace hot hide glue in the home workshop, this versatile and time-tested adhesive is still widely used in commercial wood fabrication and by the meticulous cabinetmaker. It combines qualities obtainable in no other type of adhesive at comparable cost.

Hide or animal glue can be bought by the pound in flake or ground form. If protected from moisture, this dry glue will keep indefinitely. The proper proportion of glue to water must be determined by experiment, if it is not stated on the glue you buy, as this may vary somewhat with a particular glue and job.

As a test, try 1 part glue to 2 parts water, measured by weight. Add the glue to the cold water and stir until the glue is thoroughly wet. Let soak for an hour, or until the glue is thoroughly swollen. Melt the glue by heating the combination to 145° F, either in a regular glue pot or in a Pyrex or stainless steel container heated by hot water. (It will lose strength if overheated.) After stirring into a smooth solution, it is ready to use at 140° to 145° F.

Don't make the glue too thin under the common misconception that it must thoroughly penetrate the wood in order to produce tendrils or hooks that will mechanically attach the glue to the pores of the wood. This can only result in weak and glue-starved joists. Hide glue does not work by hooking on. It apparently bonds a substance to itself because of a true electrochemical attraction between its own molecules and those of the substance. (For example, hide glue will grip smooth, nonporous glass with a bond stronger than the glass.) For maximum strength of adhesion, make the glue just thick enough so it will form a thin but continuous film between the wood surfaces.

Here are the basic rules for making a perfect bond:

1. Apply the glue with a brush in a thin continuous film to one surface only of the matching parts to be joined.
2. Permit the glue film to thicken slightly to a tacky condition before applying pressure.
3. Apply enough pressure to squeeze out the excess glue and to bring perfect contact over the entire assembled area.
4. Maintain this pressure until the initial set of the glue is strong enough to keep the parts from separating.

When held at the recommended temperature of 140° to 145° F, and covered to prevent evaporation, hot animal glue will keep in usable condition for at least 8 hours.

If further mechanical operations are to be done on a glued piece, it is best to wait at least overnight to allow the glue to develop its maximum strength.

OTHER ADHESIVES

Adhesive	Characteristics	Typical uses	What materials
Hot melt	Chalksize polyethylene-base cartridges used in electric glue gun; fast-setting, waterproof	Spot gluing; small-job repairs like broken or loose chair rungs, wood-to-metal joints	Wood, paper, cloth, leather, fiberglass, rough surfaces
Household cement	Crystal clear, waterproof	Mending china and glass	China, glass, metal, leather, canvas, wood
Liquid rubbery	For flexible repairs; caulks, bonds, insulates, rustproofs	Motor belts, weatherstrips, rubber inflatables, tents, tarps	Rubber, fabrics, plastics, glass, metal
Model cement	Colorless, fast-drying	Building and repairing models, toys	Polystyrene, balsa wood
Old-fashioned glue	Liquid hide or fish in bottles or cans	Furniture assembly and repair	Wood, leather, cloth, cardboard, glass, china
Plastic mender	Waterproof, flexible mender for most plastics	Swimming pools, rainwear, inflatables	Vinyl, acrylic, phenolic and styrene plastics; also china, glass, paper, leather, canvas
Vinyl seal	Repairs vinyl plastic without patches	Seals leaks and rips in pools, rafts, shower curtains, raincoats, beach toys, seat covers	Vinyl plastic
Fabric mender	Use instead of sewing	Repairing rips, tears, burns, reinforcing worn spots in fabric	Cotton, wool, canvas, Leatherette, felt
Marine repair	Nonrusting, flexible	Repairing water or gas tanks, anchoring screws, bolts, fittings, filing gouges and dry rot in planking	Wood, fiberglass, metal

OTHER ADHESIVES *(continued)*

Adhesive	Characteristics	Typical uses	What materials
Fixture	Weatherproof, waterproof, fast grab	Mounting house numbers, brackets, electric boxes	Wood, brick, concrete, glass, ceramic tile, metal
Chair fixer	Use with flexible needle for repairing furniture without disassembling	Loose chair rungs, table legs, drawers, etc.	Wood
Rubber cement	Fast drying, noncurling	Graphic art, paper	Paper, cloth, wood, leather, rubber
Mastics	Synthetic latex or rubber-based adhesives that are used in caulking guns or troweled or for floors and walls	Used for ceiling tiles, floor tiles, wall paneling	Wood, ceramic tile, panel boards, ceiling tiles, floor tile of various material

If you use this type of glue in small quantities, it may be more convenient to buy it in combined powder form, ready to mix with water. For large-scale gluing, you may want to mix your own at the place where it is to be used. In this case, do not mix more than you need, or mix it too soon, for it will remain usable in wet form for only 6 or 7 hours.

	Parts by weight
Casein	100
Water	150
Sodium hydroxide	11
Water	50
Hydrated lime	20
Water	50

Mix in glass, enameled, or stainless steel vessels. Soak the casein in the proportion of water indicated for 15 to 30 minutes. Add the solution of sodium hydroxide in water (*Caution:* Be careful with sodium hydroxide; it is caustic to skin and surroundings) and stir thoroughly until the casein is completely dissolved. Then add the lime suspended in its proportion of water and stir until smooth.

A casein glue with better water resistance can be made by omitting the sodium hydroxide and adding sodium silicate and a salt of copper. Here is a formula of this type developed by the Forest Products Laboratory:

	Parts by weight
Casein	100
Water	200
Hydrated lime	25
Water	100
Sodium silicate solution 40° Baumé	70
Cupric chloride or cupric sulfate	2 to 3
Water	30 to 50

Stir the casein in the water, and let soak as in the previous formula. Stir into it the dissolved copper salt. Mix the hydrated lime and water in another container and, while stirring constantly, add it to the casein-water-copper mixture. In about 1 minute after the lime and casein have been united, the glue will thicken a little. Immediately pour in the sodium silicate and continue stirring until the glue is free from lumps.

How to Make Your Own Paste

The word "paste" come from the late Latin word "pasta," which means roughly a thick mixture of flour and water. Down through the ages this useful adhesive, used largely for sticking paper, has been made either from this combination, from water and a derivative of flour such as starch or gluten, or from some admixture of ingredients that looks and acts like its ancestor. Here are a few sample formulas:

FLOUR PASTE. This simple and inexpensive paste is excellent for children's paper work and as a general household paste for emergencies.

Wheat flour	4 tablespoons
Cold water	6 tablespoons
Boiling water	1½ cups

Blend the flour into the cold water to make a smooth paste. Stir this into the boiling water in a saucepan. Boil over very low heat for about 5 minutes, stirring and smoothing constantly to remove lumps. Use when cold.

STARCH PASTE. Here is a thinner paste that is just as easy to make:

Cornstarch	3 tablespoons
Cold water	4 tablespoons
Boiling water	2 cups

Blend the starch into the cold water to make a smooth paste. Stir this into the boiling water. Stir until the opaque white liquid becomes translucent. Use when cold.

HOUSEHOLD PASTE. This paste may be used for making scrapbooks, mounting photographs, preparing paper decorations, and so on:

White dextrin	9 ounces
Water	15 fluid ounces
Sugar	½ ounce
Glycerin	½ fluid ounce
Alum	¼ fluid ounce

Stir the dextrin (which should be the white and not the yellow variety) in 13 ounces of the water and heat to 140° F, with continued stirring, until completely dissolved. Dissolve the sugar, glycerin, and alum in the rest of the water. Add this solution to the first one and heat to 176° F until the combined solution becomes clear.

LIBRARY PASTE. For mounting valuable pictures and clippings on paper, here is the formula for a paste used by a number of important museums and libraries:

Wheat flour	18 ounces
Water	4¾ pints
Alum	¼ ounce
Formaldehyde	¼ fluid ounce

Blend the flour with part of the water to form a thin paste. Heat the rest of the water to a boil and dissolve the alum in it. Then stir the flour paste into the boiling water. Continue to heat, with constant stirring, for another 5 minutes over a very low flame or in the top of a double boiler. Then add formaldehyde to the mixture. The formaldehyde will help to preserve the paste for some time.

WALLPAPER PASTES. Here is a good paste for hanging wall-coverings:

Wheat flour	8 ounces
Water	1 quart
Powdered rosin	⅓ ounce

Blend the flour into 8 ounces of the water to make a smooth paste. Bring the rest of the water to a boil in a saucepan or the top part of a double boiler. Then stir in the flour paste, bring nearly to a boil again, and sprinkle in the rosin. Hold at this temperature for about 5 minutes while stirring and smoothing constantly to remove lumps. If the paste is too thick when cool, stir in a little more hot water.

● Here is another wheat flour paste that uses alum in place of rosin:

Wheat flour	1 pound
Cold water	1 pint
Boiling water	3 pints
Alum	½ ounce
Hot water	2 ounces

Blend the flour into the cold water to make a smooth paste. Stir this into the boiling water, and continue stirring and boiling very gently until the liquid thickens. Dissolve the alum in the small amount of hot water and then stir this into the paste.

- Some paperhangers prefer a paste made from rye flour, which depends more on gluten than on starch for its adhesiveness. Here is a typical formula for rye flour paste:

Rye flour	1 pound
Cold water	1 pint
Boiling water	1½ quarts
Powdered rosin	½ ounce

Blend the rye flour with the cold water to make a smooth paste. Stir this into the boiling water and sprinkle in the rosin. Reheat nearly to boiling and stir for several minutes until the paste is smooth. If the paste is too thick when cool, it may be thinned with a little hot water.

FLEXIBLE PASTE. The glycerin in this paste helps keep it pliant. It is useful for cloth or paper where the joints must be flexed.

Cornstarch	2 ounces
White dextrin	1 ounce
Cold water	4 fluid ounces
Borax	½ ounce
Boiling water	1 quart
Glycerin	2 fluid ounces

Mix the cornstarch and dextrin in the cold water to make a smooth paste. Dissolve the borax in the boiling water, add the glycerin, and then stir the dextrin-starch mixture into this solution. Reheat nearly to the boiling point, and stir for several minutes longer until the paste is smooth.

HOBBY AND CRAFT PASTE. Made from household ingredients, this paste is good for fastening together paper toys and decorations, mounting photos, and so on:

Cornstarch	¼ cup
Water	¾ cup

Corn syrup (Karo), light	2 tablespoons
White vinegar	1 teaspoon

Combine these ingredients in a medium-size saucepan. Cook, stirring constantly, over medium heat until mixture is thick. Remove from heat.

In another vessel, stir together the following until smooth:

Cornstarch	¼ cup
Water	¾ cup

Immediately stir, a little at a time, into the thickened mixture. Stir smooth after each addition. Finally, to act as a preservative, stir in:

Oil of wintergreen	¼ teaspoon

The resulting paste may be used immediately, but will set up to thicker consistency in 24 hours. Stored in a covered container, it will keep about 2 months.

Mucilage

Gum acacia	2 ounces
Cornstarch	2 ounces
Sugar	8 ounces
Benzoic acid	50 grains
Water	20 fluid ounces

Use powdered gum acacia. Soak it in part of the water until it becomes jellylike. Mix the cornstarch and sugar with enough water to make a smooth paste. Combine these mixtures, add the rest of the water in which you have dissolved the benzoic acid, and boil gently until the solution becomes clear.

Another mucilage substitutes glycerin for the starch and sugar:

Gum acacia	2 ounces
Glycerin	2 fluid ounces
Benzoic acid	50 grains
Water	30 fluid ounces

Prepare the gum acacia as in the previous formula. Stir the resulting jelly into the water in which has been dissolved the glycerin and benzoic acid. Boil gently, with stirring, until smooth and clear.

Cement for Porcelain and Earthenware

Porcelain and earthenware articles that are not heated in use can be repaired or cemented together securely with ordinary sealing wax or stick shellac. The trick is to first heat the parts sufficiently so they will melt the shellac or wax. A little of either of these materials is smeared on the edges to be joined and the parts are then held or clamped tightly together until cool. If melted wax or shellac is applied to cold edges, the joint will break apart at the slightest strain.

China Cement

Stir plaster of Paris into a thick solution of gum arabic until it becomes a viscous paste. Apply to broken edges of china and clamp the parts tightly together until the cement has hardened.

Marble Cement

This is a good cement for mending marble or any other kind of stone:

Litharge	20 parts
Quicklime	1 part
Boiled linseed oil	enough to make thick paste

Mix the litharge and lime thoroughly. Then work the linseed oil into this mixture to form a thick paste. It sets in a few hours, having the appearance of light stone.

Another marble cement can be made of the following:

Portland cement	12 parts
Hydrated lime	6 parts
Fine sand	6 parts
Kiselguhr	1 part
Sodium silicate solution	enough to make thick paste

Mix the dry ingredients thoroughly and then mix into a thick paste with the sodium silicate solution. The object to be cemented need not be warmed. The cement will set within 24 hours and be as hard as the original stone.

Aquarium Cement

This term is applied to various waterproof cements used in making tanks constructed of glass panels fitted in metal frames. One of the most reliable aquarium cements is litharge–glycerin cement, described in a separate item below. Here is another:

Litharge	3 parts
Plaster of Paris	3 parts
Fine white sand	3 parts
Powdered rosin	1 part
Boiled linseed oil	enough to make thick putty

Mix the dry ingredients well, and then work in enough of the boiled linseed oil to make a thick putty. Let it stand 4 or 5 hours before using it, kneading it occasionally during this time. Apply it by working it well into all the joints of the tank, then let it set for several days. Finally test for leaks by filling the tank with water. Before putting fish in the tank, wash the tank out several times.

Cement for Roof Flashings

Where sheet metal meets chimneys, or where it is desired to repair open seams in a metal roof without soldering, use white lead and washed and dried sand mixed into a thick paste with boiled linseed oil and a few drops of a drier. If white lead paste is used, only a small amount of linseed oil will be needed. The sand acts as a filler that keeps the joint from opening up.

Skylight Cement

Red lead, powder	8 ounces
Litharge	16 ounces
White lead, dry	24 ounces
Linseed oil	8 fluid ounces
Varnish	8 fluid ounces

If white lead paste is used instead of the dry form, decrease the amount of linseed oil, adding just enough oil to give the desired consistency.

Oil-Proof Cements

A stopper for small leaks in water- and oil-containing vessels, which can be easily removed when a permanent repair is to be made, can be made of the following:

Water	7 parts
Gelatin powder	2 parts
Glycerin	1 part

Put the water in the top part of a double boiler, add the gelatin and let it soak for about an hour. Then heat the water to about 140° F. As soon as the gelatin melts, stir until it is uniformly distributed throughout the water. Finally stir in the glycerin. Apply it warm to the leaks. It will stiffen rapidly.

An emergency stopper for small leaks in oil-containing pipe lines and containers can be made by mixing up a stiff paste of flour and molasses. Work it well into holes or cracks.

Where you can temporarily shut off pressure, a tight seal can be made with a stiff paste of sodium silicate or water glass with whiting or precipitated chalk.

For a permanent seal against oil leaks, as well as water and acid, try litharge–glycerin cement, described below.

The following cement will produce a leakproof barrier between joints on gasoline, water, or oil lines:

Powdered iron	1 part
Portland cement	1 part
Litharge	1 part
Sodium silicate solution	enough to make paste

Mix these powders thoroughly and then stir in enough sodium silicate solution to make a paste of the desired consistency. The cement will harden in about 20 minutes.

Litharge–Glycerin Acid-Resisting Cement

Here is a cement useful for a number of applications for which ordinary cements would be neither practical nor desirable. It will withstand an unusual degree of combined heat and moisture. Its most conspicuous feature, however, is its resistance to practically all acids, provided they are not of full strength. It may be used for making watertight connections between iron pipes and porcelain fittings. It also makes an excellent aquarium cement.

Make it by mixing thoroughly—preferably by grinding in a mortar—enough litharge with 95-percent glycerin to form a paste of the desired consistency.

This combination remains soft for only 10 minutes, then sets in the form of a chemical compound of incredible hardness. The addition of about 10 percent of inert matter such as silex, Fuller's earth, or asbestos flock will delay the setting time considerably and also help prevent cracking.

Other Acid-Resisting Cements

Mix asbestos powder in sodium silicate solution to the consistency of thin paste. If allowed to dry for 24 hours, the resulting cement will resist the strongest acids.

Kaolin or china clay mixed to a thick paste with boiled linseed oil also makes an acid-resisting cement.

Quicklime mixed to a thick paste with boiled linseed oil is a time-tested formula for a cement that will resist both heat and acids.

Iron Cement

Here is a cement that can be used to fill holes and cracks in cast-iron parts, make steam-tight joints, or cement iron parts into stone or cement:

Fine iron filings	40 parts
Flowers of sulfur	10 parts
Sal ammoniac	1 part
Portland cement	20 parts
Water	enough to make thick paste

First mix the dry ingredients thoroughly together. Then blend in the water, after adding a few drops of a wetting agent or a household liquid detergent to help the water wet the sulfur. Mix just before using, as this cement sets quickly.

It works by chemical reaction. Mixed with sulfur in the presence of an electrically conducting solution of sal ammoniac, the iron first rusts and then reverts to iron sulfide. In doing so, the iron expands, cementing the mass solidly together.

Sodium Silicate Cements

When mixed into a thick paste with certain white or colored dry pigments, sodium silicate solution or water glass will harden overnight into a strong and waterproof cement that can be used for mending and filling cracks in ceramics and other materials. Here are some of the colors you can make and the pigments to use to make them:

WHITE: Whiting or precipitated chalk.

GRAY: Zinc dust. This combination will make an exceedingly hard cement, which, on buffing, will exhibit the white and brilliant appearance of metallic zinc. It may be used to mend and fill ornaments and objects of zinc. It will also stick well to metals, stone, and wood.

BRIGHT GREEN: Powdered copper carbonate.

DARK GREEN: Chromium oxide green pigment.

BLUE: Cobalt blue.

ORANGE-RED: Dry red lead.

BRIGHT RED: Vermilion.

Common or Glazier's Putty

This is an inexpensive and good putty for general use:

Whiting	16 ounces
Boiled linseed oil	9 fluid ounces

Mix the whiting into the oil until it becomes of the usual putty consistency. Because of the differences in the fineness of the whiting, the proportions may vary somewhat. If you have time, let the putty stand in a tightly closed glass or plastic container for a week; if it has then become too soft, work some more whiting into it.

White Lead Putty

Professional painters often consider white-lead putty to be the best for all-round use. You can make this by mixing white-lead paste (white lead ground in linseed oil) with whiting. Work in enough of the whiting to make the putty stiff, but still tacky.

Colored Putty

Colored putty to match paint or to lend a touch of contrast can be made by mixing oil paint with the regular putty. Use colors-in-oil or the thick pigment from the bottom of the paint can. To prevent a streaky appearance, work it well into the putty.

For Removing Hardened Putty

Washing soda	10 ounces
Water	16 ounces
Soap flakes	4 ounces
Hydrated lime	12 ounces

Dissolve the washing soda in the water and then stir in the soap flakes and the lime. Apply this solution to the putty. After several hours the putty should be soft enough to be easily removed.

House-Joint Caulking Compounds

Whiting	10 ounces
Boiled linseed oil	10 ounces
Asbestos fiber	4 ounces

Mix about three-quarters of the whiting thoroughly into the oil and then stir the asbestos into this mixture. If the compound is not thick enough, blend in more of the whiting.

A more up-to-date, but more complex, caulking compound can be made as follows:

Drier	2 ounces
Boiled linseed oil	18 fluid ounces
Asbestos fiber	10 ounces
Asbestine	10 ounces
Powdered talc	5 ounces
Kerosene	4 ounces

Because they become finally so thick, mixing this and the preceding compound is quite strenuous work and is best done by a heavy mixing machine.

Mix the drier with the linseed oil. Mix thoroughly together the dry ingredients. Then combine the latter into the oil by rigorous stirring. A heavy mixing machine would help here, but the job can be done by a little strenuous effort and a strong wooden paddle. After the dry materials are blended with the oil, work in the kerosene.

Pipe Joint Sealers

White-lead or red-lead paste, just as it comes from the can, is excellent for making threaded pipe joints gastight, watertight, and airtight. Apply it to the threads before screwing the parts together.

Commercial pipe-joint compounds may consist of the following:

White lead ground in oil	8 ounces
Red lead ground in oil	8 ounces
Linseed oil	4 fluid ounces

Mix the ingredients thoroughly and keep any that is not to be used immediately in an airtight container.

FOR AIR AND GAS PIPE CONNECTIONS. Several coats of shellac make an easy and effective seal for joints in gas and air lines. Just paint it on with a brush. Because a shellac film is brittle, the pipes can be easily taken apart at any time.

FOR STEAM-PIPE JOINTS. To permanently stop leaks in steam pipes where plugging or caulking is not practicable, mix enough powdered manganese dioxide with raw linseed oil to make a thick paste. Apply this to the joint or leak. Take off steam pressure, but keep the pipe warm enough to cause absorption of the oil. This cement should be very hard within 24 hours.

FOR RESISTANCE TO HEAT, ACIDS, AND OIL. Use the litharge–glycerin cement described above, mixing the litharge with about 10 percent of asbestos flock.

Gasket Compounds

Many cements may be used with rings of asbestos and other materials to form gaskets. Asphalt, tar, and pitch are simple ones. Mixtures that will stand heat, steam, and acids can be made by mixing sodium silicate solution with asbestos, with asbestos and slaked lime, with fine sand, or with fireclay, to form a thick liquid. Paint this liquid on the rings, or let them soak in it until they are thoroughly impregnated.

7

Household Cleaning and Polishing

Many of the most popular proprietary soap and scouring powders, wall cleaners, wax and paint removers, paint-brush cleaners, and even denture baths are composed largely, if not entirely, of one or both of two cheap and time-tested household chemicals—sodium carbonate (sal soda or washing soda, or its dry form soda ash) and trisodium phosphate (TSP).

You will, therefore, find these old faithfuls included frequently among the following formulas. For further information on ways in which they may be used by themselves, see Chapter 9.

CLEANING HOUSEHOLD METALS

Although today you can buy a special ready-made cleaner for every type of metal in your home, for centuries housewives kept their metalware shining by the use of common sense backed by kitchen chemicals. Here are a few suggestions of how this can be done:

ALUMINUM. Never leave food in aluminum utensils any longer than necessary. Leaving food in the pan, soaking the pan for a long time, or boiling an alkali in it will cause the metal to become pitted or darkened. Aluminum can be brightened by boiling in it a solution of a weak acid, such as one containing cream of tartar or vinegar, or by cooking rhubarb, tomatoes, tart apples, sour milk, or buttermilk in the utensil.

BRASS. Unlacquered brass can be kept in condition by daily dusting with a soft cloth. Spots on brass should be rubbed with hot vinegar and salt, hot buttermilk, hot sour milk, tomato juice, or rhubarb juice.

BRONZE. Clean with weak soapsuds, hot vinegar, or hot buttermilk. Rinse and dry thoroughly.

CHROMIUM PLATE. If soap and water won't clean it, use a soft abrasive paste such as whiting mixed with water.

COPPER. Keep copper absolutely clean if you use it for food; otherwise it is dangerous. Follow recommendations for brass.

IRON. Wash in hot sudsy water or in hot water containing washing soda. When not in use always keep it thoroughly dry because even slight moisture may cause it to rust. Remove rust with steel wool or scouring powder. If you want to store an iron pan for long, coat it with a saltless fat or oil, wrap it in tissue paper or plastic, and put it in a dry place.

STAINLESS STEEL. Clean off hard-to-remove spots or burned-on food on the inside of the pot with steel wool or a gritless cleaning powder. Clean the polished outside with just soap or detergent in hot water.

TINWARE. Don't try to keep tin shiny. If you do, you will take off the very thin coating of tin and leave the metal underneath open to rust. Remove burnt foods by boiling washing soda and water in the pan for less than 5 minutes.

Polishes and Cleaners for Metal

Metal polishes generally consist of a powdered abrasive suspended in a liquid or semiliquid that lubricates the abrasive and also helps remove soil. To be acceptable, the abrasive must be hard enough to remove oxide and other surface coatings, yet fine enough and soft enough so that it polishes without scratching. The vehicle must not contain any mineral acid or other material that might eat or discolor the metal.

Mild abrasives for tableware and other highly polished surfaces include jewelers' rouge (oxide of iron), powdered talc, and precipitated chalk or whiting (calcium carbonate). Harder ones for kitchenware and similar relatively dull surfaces include silica dust, kieselguhr (diatomaceous or infusorial earth), and tripoli (rottenstone). Vehicles may include thin petroleum products, soap solutions, and emulsions for liquid polishes, and heavier oils, soaps, and waxes for paste polishes.

As a rule, liquid polishes are more efficient where a great deal of tarnish has to be removed.

Equal parts by weight of the heavy, pleasant-smelling solvent, orthodichlorobenzene (technical grade) and whiting make a safe and effective cleaner-polish for highly polished kitchen appliances and auto trim. Apply with a soft cloth, and rinse off thoroughly after application. Orthodichlorobenzene is not considered flammable, though it will burn if deliberately ignited.

COPPER CLEANER. Here is a formula for a good copper cleaner:

Oxalic acid	1 ounce
Rottenstone	6 ounces
Gum acacia	½ ounce
Cooking oil	1 ounce

Mix these ingredients thoroughly and add enough water to make a paste. Apply to a small surface at a time, with rubbing, and then rub dry with a clean soft cloth. (*Caution:* Wash your hands carefully after using oxalic acid. It is poison if swallowed.)

COPPER CLEANER AND POLISH. A nonpoisonous but a little more complicated copper cleaner and polish is composed as follows:

Water	
Shaved soap or soap flakes	16 ounces
Precipitated chalk	2 ounces
Jewelers' rouge	1 ounce
Cream of tartar	1 ounce
Magnesium carbonate	1 ounce

Heat the soap in the top of a double boiler with just enough water to bring it into solution. Add the other ingredients to the solution, with constant stirring, while it is still hot. The mixture will form a paste, which should be put up in widemouthed shallow containers before it is completely cold.

ALUMINUM CLEANER AND POLISH. Aluminum can be cleaned and polished with the following formula:

Trisodium phosphate	1	ounce
Water	48	fluid ounces
Finest tripoli	8	ounces
Water glass	4	fluid ounces

Dissolve the trisodium phosphate in the water, stir in the water glass, and sift in the tripoli. As the tripoli does not dissolve, you must agitate the liquid when bottling it to make sure you distribute the tripoli equally.

Shake the bottle before use. Apply with a soft cloth and only in one direction. Polish with a clean soft cloth.

PEWTER CLEANER. For brilliantly polished pewter use polishing rouge rubbed on with a soft cloth. Then wash with detergent or soap and water and dry thoroughly.

For dull-finish pewter use finest pumice powder and water, rubbed on with a soft cloth.

CHROMIUM CLEANER. Orthodichlorobenzene and whiting, mixed equal parts by weight, make one of the best chromium cleaners. Apply with a soft cloth or soft paper towel, and rub off with a clean cloth or towel.

SILVER POLISH. An excellent and nonscratching silver polish that is also cheap can be made on the spot simply by moistening precipitated chalk or finely powdered whiting with household ammonia. Apply with a soft cloth, rinse, and dry. The tarnish should be gone.

LIQUID SILVER POLISH. If you prefer a liquid polish you can keep on hand, here is a simple one that also includes whiting and ammonia:

Whiting	8	ounces
Soap flakes	4	ounces
Ammonia	½	ounce
Water	32	ounces

(Continued)

Heat the water and dissolve the soap flakes in it, then stir in the whiting. As soon as the mixture is cool, add the ammonia. Keep in tightly stoppered bottles and shake before using.

CLEANING SILVER ELECTRICALLY. Solutions and "magic" plates of aluminum or magnesium that are sold to clean silverware without scouring depend upon the principle of exchange of metals discussed in the chapter on household chemistry. A solution of ordinary baking soda (sodium bicarbonate) or of trisodium phosphate, plus an old aluminum pan, will enable you to work the same magic.

A rectangular cake pan is excellent. Place the silver so that each piece touches the pan. Cover with an almost-boiling solution of 1 teaspoon of trisodium phosphate or of 1 tablespoon of soda in each quart of water. After several minutes, take out the silver, rinse, and dry. The tarnish should be gone.

Touching the aluminum and surrounded by the electrolyte, the silver forms one plate of an electric cell. By action of this cell, the tarnish of silver sulfide is dissolved. Then the sulfur is separated and the silver is redeposited. Actually this method removes less silver than does ordinary polishing. The finish is slightly duller, however; a matter that may be remedied by giving the pieces a light buffing occasionally with regular polish.

Do not use this method on cemented pieces, as the hot solution might loosen the cement. Don't use it on oxidized or "French-finish" silver, either, as it may alter the finish.

SILVER DIP FOR SILVER CLEANING. Instant silver cleaners are old. In the past, they were based on the poisonous chemicals, sodium and potassium cyanide. More recently, however, silver dips have appeared that use materials that are quite safe when in the concentrations required for the product. Here is a typical formula:

Thiourea	8 parts
Hydrochloric acid, 38%	5 parts
Liquid dishwashing detergent	½ part
Water-soluble perfume	⅓ part
Water	86 parts

To use, merely dip the silverware into the undiluted compound. The chemicals dissolve away the tarnish, leaving a surface of clean silver.

Despite its general convenience, the dip method has several limitations. Like the electrolytic method just described, it should not be used on oxidized or "French-finish" silver, and it leaves a slightly dull or hazy surface that must be buffed occasionally to bring back a high shine. It may also stain "stainless" steel knifeblades if left in it too long.

Preventing Tarnish on Silver

Good-grade furniture or floor waxes will give lasting protection against tarnish on ornamental objects of silver. They should not be applied to tableware or other items that come in contact with food. Apply two coats, letting the first coat dry and harden 2 hours before putting on the second. The "no-rubbing" liquid waxes go on easiest. If, after some months, they begin to yellow, they may be removed with soap or detergent in hot water, and new coatings applied.

NONTARNISH STORAGE FOR SILVER. Polyethylene bags, used for wrapping food for storage in home freezers, make excellent nontarnish containers for storing silverware between use. They may be bought from any store selling home-freezer supplies.

NONTARNISH CLOTH FOR SILVER. Soak cotton flannel in a solution made by dissolving 1 ounce of zinc acetate to each pint of water. Squeeze out excess solution and dry the cloth. Make cloth into a bag, or simply wrap silverware in it. Silver completely surrounded by the cloth won't tarnish. After removing the stored silver, wash it before using.

Improvised Metal Polishes

Portland cement mixed with motor oil makes a cheap and effective polish suited to rough work.

Rottenstone, mixed with household mineral oil or any other nonacid oil to a creamy consistency, also makes a good polish. Finish the job with a final rubbing of dry rottenstone or whiting.

There are three methods for cleaning the surface of rugs and carpets at home—the shampoo or suds method, the powder method, and the dry-cleaning fluid method.

THE SHAMPOO OR SUDS METHOD. Vacuum rug or carpet thoroughly. Then, with brush or sponge, rub shampoo suds into area of about 1 square foot at a time. (Some makes of vacuum cleaners have an attachment for shampooing rugs with a foam cleaner.) Finish by stroking nap to lay smooth; let dry undisturbed. Many rug and hardware stores are now renting a rug cleaning machine that combines a foam

CARPET-CLEANING GUIDE

QUALITIES OF RUG AND CARPET MATERIALS

	Wool	Acrylic	Nylon	Polyester	Polypropylene	Cotton
Retains texture	good	good	good	good	excellent	good
Durable	good	good	excellent	good	excellent	fair
Resilience	good	good	good	fair	fair	fair
Crushing recovery	good	fair	good	fair	poor to fair	fair
Fade resistance	fair	good	fair	good	good	fair
Cleaning	excellent	fair	excellent	good	good	excellent
Spot and stain removal	fair	good	fair	good	excellent	good
Static electricity	poor in low humidity	low	high	poor in low humidity	low	low

cleaner and steam. These machines are easy to use and do an effective job. Be sure to follow manufacturer and dealer instructions.

THE RUG-CLEANING POWDER METHOD. Vacuum rug or carpet thoroughly. Sprinkle rug-cleaning powder over a section of the rug about 4 feet square (laying newspaper under edges of rug first is a good idea). With long-handled brush, using crisscross motion, scrub powder into nap of rug. Repeat process on adjoining area; continue until entire rug is covered. Let powder stand a few hours or overnight, then run vacuum cleaner over rug until all traces of powder have disappeared.

This treatment will revive the color of your rugs and the liveliness of the nap; don't expect it to remove heavy, neglected soil or eliminate the eventual need for professional cleaning.

CLEANING FLUID METHOD. Vacuum rug or carpet thoroughly. Dip long-handled rug eraser into pan of cleaning fluid; shake to remove surplus. Then rub eraser over rug, one section at a time, following direction of weave. (If rug underlay is foam rubber, make sure cleaning fluid does not come in contact with it.)

CLEANERS AND POLISHES FOR SPECIAL PROBLEMS

REMOVING SCORCH FROM GLASS OR ENAMELWARE. Make a solution of 1 part household liquid chlorine bleach to 4 parts

METHODS FOR CLEANING RUG AND CARPET MATERIALS

Types of rugs and carpets	Cleaning	Spotting
Wool	Vacuum thoroughly from week to week and clean periodically with a rug powder or shampoo. Send rug out for professional cleaning once a year.	Wool rugs are easiest of all to spot-clean. Try detergent suds first. Let dry. If spot remains, sponge with grease-dissolving solvent.
Synthetics and blends	Clean same as wool rugs; however, synthetic rugs may need more frequent periodic cleaning. Because of special treatment, newer synthetic yarns have greatly increased soil resistance.	Spot-clean same as wool rugs.
Cotton	Tank or canister-type vacuum is best for looped or tufted cotton rugs. To keep colors clean, wash frequently. Wash small sizes in home washer; send large rugs to commercial laundry or rug-cleaning establishment. Do not dry clean rubber-backed rugs.	Do not try to spot-clean long-looped cotton-pile rugs. Short-pile or woven cotton rugs can often be spot-cleaned with detergent suds or a rug shampoo.
Wall-to-wall carpets	Clean same as wool rugs, but yearly cleaning will be more troublesome. Carpeting must either be cleaned on the floor by a reliable professional, or it must be taken up in order to be sent out.	Wall-to-wall carpets of cotton usually have a short pile, and if so can be spot-cleaned like wool rugs.
Oriental rugs	Vacuum regularly, and send out for professional cleaning when necessary. Some Orientals have a high luster because of their finish. After washing, water-soluble finishes must be replaced with a sheen-producing resin.	Spot-clean same as for wool rugs, but spot-cleaned area may be dulled by treatment with suds if the rug has a high luster.
Fiber rugs	Vacuum regularly, and shampoo periodically.	Spot-clean same as wool rugs, but the smooth, hard surface of fiber rugs is more difficult to spot-clean.

water. Cover burned areas with it and bring solution slowly to a boil, or soak overnight. Rinse. (Do not use this bleach on *chipped* enamelware. It will react with the bare metal.)

REMOVING INK SPOTS FROM WOOD. Ink spots can usually be removed from woodwork with a strong solution of oxalic acid. Prepare the solution by dissolving oxalic acid crystals in a small amount of water until no more will dissolve. If several applications do not cause the spots to disappear, apply the acid once more and immediately flush with sodium hypochlorite laundry bleach. Be sure to remove all traces of the chemicals from the surface with water, and allow the wood to dry thoroughly before attempting to refinish it. (*Caution:* Oxalic acid is poison. Wash your hands thoroughly after using it.)

RUST-REMOVER POWDER. Rust remover in powder form can be made by mixing thoroughly 2 ounces of potassium bitartrate (cream of tartar) with 1 ounce of oxalic acid.

To use this, moisten the spot and place some of the powder on it for about 10 minutes. Then wash thoroughly in plain water.

PORCELAIN CLEANER. Toilet bowls and the smooth, glazed finish in sinks, bathtubs, and wash bowls are made of porcelain, which is a type of glass. Care must be taken therefore to avoid scratching and chipping. Although harsh scouring powders effectively remove soil, they also damage the surface, making it harder to clean thereafter.

To clean these surfaces, wash them with detergent and water, and then rinse and dry them. If an abrasive is needed, use the finest powdered whiting, or, if preferred, a paste of soap and whiting made as follows:

Soap flakes	¼ cup
Boiling water	1 cup
Fine whiting	1 cup

Dissolve the soapflakes in the water and pour into a widemouthed glass jar. When cooled and jelled, add the whiting and mix thoroughly. To use, apply with a soft cloth and rub lightly.

CLEANING WINDOWS. For normally soiled windows, any dishwashing detergent in warm water will do a good job. Ordinary soap is apt to streak.

For very soiled windows, wipe off some of the loose dirt with a damp cloth or crumpled paper. Then wash with a mixture of 1 quart of warm water with *one* of the following:

1 tablespoon household ammonia

½ tablespoon kerosene

3 tablespoons denatured alcohol

Use a soft cloth, a clean damp chamois, or a squeegee to polish. Do not work in direct sunlight since the liquids may dry too quickly and so show streaks.

WINDOW-CLEANING PREPARATIONS. A paste of powdered whiting and water can also be used to clean windows. Apply paste to glass, let it dry slightly, then remove with a soft lintless cloth or paper towel.

The following may do a better job, but is a little more complicated to prepare:

Powdered whiting	1	ounce
Denatured alcohol	1	fluid ounce
Household ammonia	1	fluid ounce
Water	1	pint

Mix, shake before using, and apply to the window with a soft cloth or a spray bottle. After the surface has dried, wipe off any remaining film with another soft cloth.

Here is a somewhat similar formula that does not contain water:

Denatured alcohol	8	fluid ounces
Household ammonia	8	fluid ounces
Powdered talc	1	ounce

Mix and apply as with the previous formula.

WALLPAPER CLEANERS. A moderate amount of soil may be removed from wallpaper by rubbing it with a slice of rye bread. This does not seem so strange when we remember that many regular wallpaper-cleaning preparations are made largely from rye flour. It's the gluten in rye flour that does the trick. In fact, the basic ingredient of many wallpaper cleaners is gluten, which may be supplied satisfactorily by the use of rye or wheat flour. The flour is made up into a dough with plain water or with water containing about 25-percent common salt. Preservatives may be added, such as sodium salicylate, sodium benzoate, or borax.

Here is a good cleaner if the paper is extremely soiled:

Water	1 quart
Salt	1¼ pounds
Aluminum sulfate	1 ounce
Kerosene	1 fluid ounce
Flour	2½ pounds

Dissolve the salt and aluminum sulfate in the water, and heat the solution to a temperature of 180° F. Remove from the source of heat and stir in the kerosene. Then slowly sift in the flour, stirring constantly to prevent lumps. Finally knead into a dough with which you can rub off the soil.

DISHWASHING POWDER. This can be used for washing dishes and for cleaning porcelain and glass. Mix thoroughly by shaking together in a box or bag for several minutes:

Trisodium phosphate	24 ounces
Borax	2½ ounces
Powdered soap	1 ounce

To use, just add a little of the powder to the dishwater.

DUSTLESS DUST CLOTHS. Cloths that will pick up dust without scattering it can be made by saturating clean rags or cotton flannel with kerosene, hanging them up to allow the more volatile parts to evaporate, and then rubbing the oiled cloth on a wooden surface until it no longer streaks.

Other dustless cloths can be made by saturating similar materials with a mixture of 1 part mineral spirits or benzine with 2 parts mineral oil, linseed oil, cottonseed oil, or corn oil. Wring out the cloths and dry them at room temperature. (If one of the vegetable oils is used, be sure to dry the cloths in a cool place with a good circulation of air to avoid the danger of spontaneous combustion.) For a typical cleaning odor, add a little cedar oil or lemon oil to any of the above preparations.

A solution for coating a dusting cloth more heavily can be made without using a solvent. The following mixture is a sample:

Light mineral oil	12 ounces

Corn oil	4 ounces
Cedar or lemon oil	½ teaspoon

Saturate cloths with this, wring them out, and hang them to dry in a well-ventilated place.

DUSTLESS MOP OIL. The preparations just mentioned for dustless cloths can also be used for making or retreating dustless mops. Here is the formula for an effective mop oil that has even the expected aroma:

Mineral oil	2 parts
Turpentine	1 part
Cedar oil	as desired

ABRASIVES FOR CLEANING AND SCOURING POWDERS

For general use, such an abrasive should be of 200-mesh or finer. It should be hard enough to do its job efficiently, but not so hard that it will scratch the surface to be cleaned. Porcelain enamel, wall tile, and painted woodwork require the softest abrasives, such as talc, whiting, or diatomaceous earth. (Coarser abrasives used in some proprietary cleaners may take off the dirt faster at first, but they also roughen polished or soft surfaces, making subsequent cleaning more difficult.) Concrete or stone floors, bare wood, unpolished metalware, and other rougher or tougher surfaces may be cleaned safely and more efficiently with the harder abrasives.

Here is a list of the common abrasives used in cleaning powders—the softest ones first:

TALC. A natural hydrous magnesium silicate. Very soft; suited for scouring powders for porcelain enamel and tile, but not for a general household powder.

DIATOMACEOUS EARTH (also called tripolite, kieselguhr, infusorial earth, etc.). A soft earthy material made up of the siliceous skeletons of small aquatic plants called diatoms. Although safe for all surfaces, it is too expensive for general household cleaning.

WHITING. A special finely powdered form of calcium carbonate. Originally powdered crude chalk (such as came from the chalk cliffs of

England, Belgium, and France), it is now produced chemically. Cheap, and good for tile cleaners, but too soft for general cleaning.

VOLCANIC ASH. Material made up of volcanic dust, ash, and cinders. Cheap and of medium hardness, and good for general household cleaners.

PUMICE. A relative of volcanic ash, but slightly harder. May be used for the same purpose.

FELDSPAR. A mixture of various aluminum silicates. About as hard as volcanic ash but usually whiter. This is a favorite when it can be obtained.

QUARTZ. Natural, crystallized silicon dioxide. Quite hard and apt to scratch softer metals such as copper and aluminum, though sometimes useful for very rough scouring.

SAND. Grains of disintegrated siliceous rock. It is mostly quartz, and just about as hard.

GENERAL-PURPOSE SCOURING POWDER. Here is a good general-purpose scouring powder:

Soda ash	12 parts
Powdered soap	7 parts
Abrasive powder	81 parts

Soda ash is a crude and dry form of sodium carbonate. Be sure to use powdered soap and not soap powder; the latter is a combination of soap with fillers and other ingredients. For the abrasive, use feldspar, pumice, or volcanic ash. Mix thoroughly by stirring and passing through a sieve several times.

SCOURING POWDER FOR TILE OR TERRAZZO FLOORS. This scouring powder can be used on ceramic and terrazzo floors:

Soda ash	5 parts
Powdered soap	8 parts
Feldspar, pumice, or volcanic ash	87 parts

Mix as in previous formula.

SCOURING POWDER FOR FINE MARBLE FLOORS. For marble floors, the following scouring powder can be used:

Soda ash	4 parts
Powdered soap	3 parts
Feldspar, pumice, or volcanic ash	93 parts

Mix as in last two formulas. So that it does not scratch the marble, 95 percent of the abrasive should be able to go through a 200-mesh sieve, and all must go through a 100-mesh sieve.

SCOURING POWDER FOR KITCHEN UTENSILS. To clean kitchen utensils, you can use this scouring powder:

Powdered soap	20 parts
Powdered borax	5 parts
Soda ash	5 parts
Fine pumice	35 parts

Mix thoroughly by stirring and sieving as in the other formulas. To clean with it, shake this powder onto dampened utensils. Rub with a damp cloth and then rinse. Do not use on highly polished ware.

NONSCRATCHING SCOURING POWDER. Measure out 9 parts of whiting or precipitated chalk and 1 part of trisodium phosphate. Mix thoroughly by shaking together in a box or bag for several minutes. The combination makes an inexpensive, nonscratching, and effective compound for cleaning porcelain, brass, copper, nickel, and stainless steel. To use, just dampen with water and rub with a cloth.

SOAP-TYPE ABRASIVE CLEANING COMPOUND. This is suitable for porcelain enamel, tile, painted surfaces, and other surfaces that might be scratched by harsher compounds.

Transparent soft soap	100 parts
Fine talc or whiting	30 parts
Soda ash	1½ parts

Mix these ingredients thoroughly in a solution of 2 parts of sodium silicate of 38° Baumé dissolved in 25 parts of water. When thoroughly mixed, stir into combination 20 parts of a 5-percent solution of starch in water. Apply the resulting paste with a soft damp cloth.

Cleaning Marble

For routine cleaning of polished marble, use plain warm water applied with a soft clean cloth. If the marble has become soiled by ordinary use or exposure, try a solution of general household detergent in warm water. Ingrained dirt on unpolished marble may generally be removed by scrubbing with a fiber brush. In either case, rinse with plenty of plain water and immediately wipe dry with a cloth or chamois to prevent streaks or water spots.

Stains are easiest to remove if you can wipe them up as soon as they occur, thus preventing penetration into the pores of the stone. If this is impossible, you will get best results if you can first determine the general type of stain and treat it accordingly.

If you have trouble in getting marble-cleaning and polishing materials, or prefer prepackaged kits for marble care, try "Marble dealers" listed in the Yellow Pages of your telephone directory.

POULTICE METHOD. If the marble is really grimy, the application of a detergent poultice may be better than scrubbing. Make a thick paste of household detergent and water. Apply with your hand, a putty knife, or a trowel in a layer at least ¼-inch thick over the whole area to be cleaned. Then cover with plastic sheeting or a damp cloth (which should be kept damp) for 24 hours. After that, let the poultice dry in place for another 24 hours. Finally remove the poultice, flush the marble with clean water, and dry with a cloth or chamois.

OIL AND GREASE STAINS. These are generally more or less circular spots, darkest toward the center. If you wet the area with water, the spot will repel the water and so appear lighter than its surroundings. Such spots are often the most difficult to remove. The poultice method, however, will generally do the trick. In this case make your poultice by mixing powdered talc or whiting (for small jobs, ordinary talcum powder or precipitated chalk will do just as well) with V.M.&P. naphtha or a combination of equal parts of acetone and amyl acetate, to make a thick paste. As all three of these solvents are highly flammable, use them only outdoors or in a well-ventilated room and away from all fire. Apply the poultice over the spot in a thick layer and leave in place until dry. If the spot is not then completely gone, try again. Any remaining greasless stain may usually be removed by bleaching, as described below. When stain is gone, wash the spot with detergent solution, rinse, and dry.

TEA, COFFEE, SOFT DRINK, WINE, TOBACCO, AND MANY STAINS PRODUCED BY INKS AND DYES. These usually respond readily to bleaching. First wash the area with warm water, and dry. If the piece is horizontal, pour on a little household liquid chlorine bleach (Clorox, Rose-X, Purex, etc.) or a 6-percent (hair-bleach concentration) solution of hydrogen peroxide. If you use the latter, after pouring activate it with a few drops of household ammonia. If the stained area is vertical, apply a heavy poultice made up of a thick paste of whiting or talc mixed with either bleach. Let dry. Remove, rinse marble, and dry.

IRON AND RUST STAINS. Those that are fresh can usually be wiped off or washed off with household-detergent solution. More stubborn fresh stains may be removed with fine pumice powder or mild scouring powder and water. If the stain has gone deeper, sprinkle with sodium hydrosulfite powder (the dye-remover chemical sold with some packaged household dyes), dampen the powder, and leave for not more than half an hour. Follow right away with a solution of sodium citrate. Repeat the sequence, if necessary. Finally wash with water and dry. This treatment works by changing colored insoluble salts into colorless soluble ones that can be washed away. It may, however, dull polished surfaces somewhat, possibly necessitating repolishing.

COPPER AND BRONZE STAINS. Coming from oxidized fittings or plaques, these are usually muddy brown or green. They can often be removed by applying a poultice of 1 part ammonium chloride (sal ammoniac) and 4 parts whiting made into a paste with household ammonia. Apply over stain and leave to dry. Repeat if necessary. Finally rinse and dry.

SUPERFICIAL SMOKE STAINS. These can usually be removed by thoroughly washing and scrubbing with an abrasive cleaner. On fire stains from creosote that have penetrated deeply, try alternately the bleach- and the oil-stain-removing methods.

PAINT. On marble, it should be removed as soon as possible to eliminate the absorption and spreading of the oil. First carefully scrape off the surface paint with a razor blade or knife. Then apply liquid or paste varnish and paint remover over the stained area. Remove with cloths after a short time and scrub with a fiber brush and a solution of household detergent. Bleach any color that remains with a poultice of hydrogen peroxide or liquid chlorine bleach as described above under tea and coffee stains.

STAINS THAT ARE NOT STAINS. What is often mistaken for a stain may be just a dull spot in the polish of the marble caused by the etching action of acid-containing liquids or foods. You can determine this by comparing the gloss on the spot with that of the surrounding area. Repolishing large dull spots or pitted or scratched areas requires the equipment and experience of the professional marble worker. Faint rings and small spots slightly rough to the touch, however, can be restored to a fine finish with a little patience and elbow grease. The polishing material universally used is tin dioxide, known in the stone trade as "putty powder" or "polishing powder." Buy the smallest amount you can from a marble dealer, monument maker, or chemical supply house.

TO POLISH AWAY DULL SPOTS. Just sprinkle the powder lightly on the surface of the marble and buff steadily and persistently with a pad made of medium-hard felt (such as a piece cut from an old hat), short-nap wool carpeting, or chamois, dampened with water. Add a few drops of water whenever additional lubricant seems necessary. Also add powder occasionally, so that a thin, dry slurry remains on the marble surface. Rub straight back and forth, not in circles. After long rubbing, the amount of time depending on the depth of the etch, the surface will take on the characteristic shine of polished marble. Continue rubbing until this shine is uniform. Then rinse the surface and dry thoroughly with a soft cloth.

Toilet Bowl Cleaners

Chemicals for toilet bowl cleaning usually consist of sodium hydroxide (lye), sodium carbonate (washing soda) combined with sodium hydroxide, or sodium bisulfate, a by-product in the manufacture of nitric and hydrochloric acids.

LYE. The oldest and cheapest cleaner, lye alone works as well as any. To use it, flush the bowl and as soon as it fills again slowly shake about 2 tablespoons of lye into the bowl. Allow it to dissolve, then stir and rub the lye solution over the entire interior with a long-handled brush or swab. Flush again. (*Caution:* Because lye is a very caustic poison, be careful in handling it. If you spill any on your skin or surrounding objects, wash immediately with plenty of cold water.)

WASHING SODA AND LYE. This is milder than plain lye and so takes longer to work, but is just as effective. Make it by shaking together in a covered and partly filled glass jar or tin can (don't use aluminum, as lye attacks this metal) 1 pound of washing soda with 3 tablespoons of lye (careful with the lye!). Flush the bowl and let it fill again. Sprinkle into it about 4 tablespoons of the mixture, letting some coat the porcelain above the water line. Stir with a stick to mix, let stand about 15 minutes, then rub the whole interior with a long-handled brush or swab, as above, and flush again.

SODIUM BISULFATE. This is the chief or sole ingredient of many proprietary bowl cleaners. It depends for its action on the formation of sulfuric acid on contact with water. For this reason, sodium bisulfate cleaners should be used only on solid porcelain bowls. They should not be used on bathtubs, washstands, sinks, or other metal or enameled fixtures. They are harmless, however, to plumbing and septic tanks.

Only the crude grade is needed for toilet cleaning. You should be able to get this considerably cheaper under its own name, or simply as "toilet bowl cleaner," from a supplier of institutional or industrial cleaning materials than under a brand name at the supermarket. Use it according to the directions for the cleaner above. (*Caution:* Handle sodium bisulfate as carefully as you would lye. If you spill any, flood the spot immediately with cold water.)

Drainpipe Cleaners

The basic ingredient of most drainpipe cleaners is again sodium hydroxide in the form of lye. This is used either alone or mixed with aluminum turnings or chips that are sometimes zinc coated. In the latter case the lye reacts with the aluminum to produce bubbles of hydrogen gas, which helps the cleaning action by producing a physical turbulence.

Drain sluggishness is usually caused by a buildup of hardened grease, hair, and lint. Lye does its job by combining with the grease to form a soluble soap, and by dissolving the hair and lint.

The best way to prevent the clogging of drains is to give them a mild treatment with either lye or washing soda every week or so. If you use washing soda, pour 3 tablespoonfuls into the drain or drain basket and run very hot water slowly through the drain until the granules are completely dissolved. If you use lye, put 1 tablespoonful in the drain sieve and flush into the pipe with 1 cup of hot water. Allow to remain 5 minutes, then flush with more water. (Be sure to rinse spoon thoroughly!)

To open a badly clogged drain, remove all the water possible from the inlet of drain. Then slowly dissolve a 13-ounce can of lye in 2 quarts of cold water. Use only a pyrex, enameled, iron, or stainless steel utensil—never aluminum. Stir with a stick or a plastic or stainless steel spoon. Then pour the solution (which will have been heated by the lye) slowly and carefully down the drain. In 10 minutes flush with water. (*Caution:* Lye is caustic poison. If you spill any on your skin or surrounding objects, wash immediately with cold water.)

Car-Cooling System Cleaners

For many years nearly all automobile radiator cleaners were alkaline cleaners, consisting usually of washing soda, trisodium phosphate, a silicate of sodium, or of combinations of these chemicals. Sometimes a corrosion inhibitor such as sodium, potassium, or zinc chromate was added.

Although alkaline cleaners have no ability to dissolve rust or remove hard caked-on scale, they do cut through grease and flush out loose rust and dirt. They are cheap, easy to obtain and use, and satisfactory for most ordinary cleaning jobs.

The general procedure in using them follows the pattern for most types of radiator cleaners. Drain the cooling system, add the cleaner, and fill the system with water. Then run the engine at fast idling speed for about 20 to 30 minutes. Cover the radiator, if necessary, to build up and maintain a temperature of between 180° and 200° F, so that the thermostat valve remains open and the flow of cleaning solution is continuous.

At the end of this period, stop the engine and drain out the cleaning solution along with the dissolved and loosened scale, grease, and dirt. Then thoroughly flush the system with clean water.

The simplest and cheapest alkaline cleaner can be made by dissolving about 1 pound of washing soda or 10 ounces of trisodium phosphaste in 3½ quarts of water in a 1-gallon bottle. Washing soda will dissolve more easily if you use warm water.

An alkaline cleaner that will inhibit further corrosion in the cooling system can be made by dissolving about ⅓ ounce of sodium chromate in the trisodium phosphate solution just mentioned.

In pouring the alkaline cleaners, be careful not to spill any of the solution on the car's aluminum, decorative metal, or paint. If you should do so accidentally, wash it off immediately with plain water.

Cleaning Leather

Once used chiefly for cleaning saddles and harness, saddle soap is now used for cleaning all kinds of leather equipment. Any neutral soap may be used for cleaning leather, though preparations most used generally contain oils and waxes to lubricate the leather and to leave a preservative film. Here are two sample formulas:

Soap powder	7½ ounces
Water	36 ounces
Neat's-foot oil	2½ ounces
Beeswax	4 ounces

Dissolve the soap in hot water. Heat the neat's-foot oil and wax together until the wax is melted. Pour the hot mixture into the hot soap solution, then stir until thickening begins and put into containers.

Palm oil	3¾ ounces
Coconut oil	3¾ ounces
Glycerin	1½ ounces
Powdered rosin	½ ounce
Flake lye	1½ ounces
Water	17½ ounces
Powdered whiting	½ ounce

Put first four items in the top of a double boiler and heat to 167° F, stirring until the rosin is melted and thoroughly mixed in. Dissolve lye in water and heat the solution also to 167° F. Then add slowly to first mixture, stirring until the two are completely emulsified. Finally stir in the whiting. (*Caution:* Do not spill lye on skin or surroundings; it is extremely caustic.)

Leather Polish

Montan wax	8 ounces
Paraffin wax	6½ ounces
Stearic acid	1 ounce
Oil-soluble dye	⅓ ounce
Turpentine	24 fluid ounces

Melt the montan wax, paraffin wax, and stearic acid over low heat in separate containers. Remove the montan wax from the heat, and stir in slowly the paraffin wax, then, also slowly, the melted stearic acid. Next stir in dye of desired color, or leave the polish colorless if preferred. When the mixture cools enough, it begins to solidify. At this point add it slowly to the turpentine, stirring constantly. (*Caution:* Keep the turpentine away from all open flames.)

Preserving Leather

The most common cause for the cracking and peeling of the leather in luggage, upholstery, straps, and bookbindings is the gradual destruction of the oil in the leather. Prevention should start when the articles are new and should then be repeated every year or two.

For leather in good condition, the simplest dressing is neat's-foot oil, or neat's-foot oil mixed with an equal quantity of castor oil. These, or any other dressing, will darken leather slightly, but will greatly prolong its life.

Apply either the plain oil or the combination with a small swab of soft cloth. With a firm, rapid stroke spread the dressing in a thin film uniformly over as much of the leather at one time as is feasible. Rub the dressing into the leather until it is completely absorbed. After several hours, repeat the application.

To preserve the leather on new books and to restore that on old ones, one large library uses the following formula:

Neat's-foot oil	25 parts
Lanolin, anhydrous	17½ parts
Japan wax	10 parts
Sodium stearate, powdered	2½ parts
Distilled water	45 parts

In a double boiler melt together the first three ingredients. In another pan mix the sodium stearate and water. Cover this pan and heat gently until the stearate is dissolved. Pour the resulting solution in a thin stream into the melted grease, stirring vigorously as you pour. Allow to cool. Stir the cold mixture until it becomes a smooth ointmentlike emulsion. Then transfer it to screwcap jars.

The library applies this dressing with a flat varnish brush and the book is then set aside for a few hours. The binding is finally polished with a soft cloth. The same method may be used on other leather goods.

A large law library has preserved its sheepskin-bound books for more than 40 years by a similar application of medicinal-grade white petroleum jelly.

Do not apply any dressing directly on gold lettering or decorations. This might loosen or remove the gold.

Bleaching Ivory Objects

Discolored ivory may be restored to its original condition by several methods. In one, immerse the ivory objects in a solution of 1 part household hydrogen peroxide in 2 parts water for 30 to 60 minutes, or until the ivory is sufficiently bleached. Then polish the ivory by rubbing briskly with a woolen cloth.

If the ivory has become yellow through handling or contact with dishwater, it is advisable to first immerse it in denatured alcohol or paint store naphtha. After drying, rub vigorously with a cloth dipped in household hydrogen peroxide or a 10-percent solution of citric acid in water. After bleaching, rinse the ivory with clean water and wipe it dry.

If ivory forms the handles of tableware, care should be taken to protect the metal parts by first coating them with petroleum jelly and then wrapping them with paper to prevent the grease from spreading. If necessary, the process may be repeated.

Cleaning Concrete Floors

To clean an unpainted concrete floor, first wet the surface with clear water and then apply a solution of about 2 to 2½ ounces of washing soda to a gallon of hot water. Sprinkle a good scouring powder uniformly over this. Brush the surface, and then rinse with clear water. Do not use straight soap on unpainted concrete because this often forms a scum of lime soap.

To clean painted concrete floors, wash or mop with plain water. Water containing a small amount of soap or detergent may be used on very dirty floors. Rinse with clear water.

Cleaning Resilient Flooring

Keeping a resilient floor clean and presentable involves three phases of care: preventive care to avoid dirt buildup and wear; damp-mopping for getting up more widespread dirt; and washing to be sure the floor is "really clean."

The steps of *preventive care* are as follows:

1. If the floor is near doors from the outside, put mats or throw rugs at the entrances to keep dirt and moisture from being tracked in. They should not be rubber or foam backed, since these materials may cause the floor to become discolored.
2. Sweep, dust-mop, or vacuum the floor frequently to remove loose dirt before it can scratch or be ground into the floor's surface.
3. Use floor protectors on the legs of furniture to minimize scratches and indentations.
4. To avoid scratching and gouging when moving heavy furniture or appliances, slip a scrap of carpet face down under each leg, and slide the furniture carefully.

5. Wipe up spills as soon as possible before they get sticky or dry.
6. Remove dried spills with a damp cloth or mop.
7. If a spot or stain sets, check the Stain Removal table a bit later in this chapter for the right procedure.

When light soiling is widespread and spot-cleaning is impractical, use this *damp-mopping procedure:*

1. Sweep or vacuum floor thoroughly.
2. Damp-mop with warm water. Dip a sponge mop into a bucket of warm water, wring it out well, and push the sponge across the floor—pressing enough to loosen the surface dirt. Damp-mop a small area at a time, wringing the sponge out frequently to make sure you're picking up the dirt and not just redistributing it. When damp-mopping a large floor, the water should be changed several times so that the dirt doesn't get redeposited on the floor.

If the floor looks dull and scuffed with dirt buildup that can't be removed by damp-mopping, it's time to *wash.*

1. Sweep or vacuum the floor thoroughly.
2. Prepare a cleaning solution with warm water and a general-purpose liquid detergent. (Do not use soap-based products, which can leave a dulling film.) The dilution level on the detergent label generally applies for use on floors with smooth surfaces. For a textured surface, use a stronger solution. To find the dilution level that works best, test it on a small area of the floor until satisfactory results are obtained.
3. Dip a sponge mop into the cleaning solution and, without wringing it out, spread it on a small area of the floor (about 3 × 3 feet). Wait a minute and let the cleaning solution do the work. The detergent action will loosen a lot of the dirt and bring it up into the liquid, keeping it suspended for pick up.
4. Go over the area again with the sponge mop, scrubbing hard enough to loosen the remaining dirt. Hard-to-remove marks can be removed with the nylon pad.
5. Wring out the sponge thoroughly, and take up the cleaning solution left on the floor.
6. Use a second bucket of clean warm water with a "rinse-only" mop, and thoroughly rinse the area. Apply the water, wring out the sponge, and then try to soak up as much of the liquid as possible. Rinsing is the most important step in washing the floor. Often general-purpose detergent directions will say rinsing is not necessary. While this may be true on other surfaces, any detergent film left on a floor will hold tracked-in dirt. Ideally, use one

sponge mop and bucket to wash the floor and another mop and bucket for rinsing. A good sponge mop for washing is the type available with a nylon scrubbing pad attached to the front edge. This pad is similar to those recommended for use on Teflon pans.

7. Repeat this procedure of washing and rinsing one area at a time until the whole floor is clean. Change rinse water often to make sure dirt or detergent is not redeposited.
8. If a protective floor polish is to be applied on the same day, let the floor dry completely before applying the polish. When applying polish, be sure to follow manufacturer's instructions to the letter.

SPOT AND STAIN REMOVAL. In general, the key to avoiding floor stains is to attend to spills as soon as possible after they occur. One important advantage of these floors is that spilled liquids do not readily soak in. On the other hand, certain substances can create a stain if allowed to remain on the floor for an extended period of time. In these cases special methods are required to remove or minimize the stain.

The accompanying table lists those situations that require special treatment. The numbers at the right refer to the instructions. Then locate the applicable instructions in the text that follows. Follow each step in the sequence given.

Staining substance	**Removal procedure**
Writing ink	1, 2, 3, 8
Lipstick	1, 2, 6, 8
Mustard	1, 2, 8
Iodine	1, 2, 3, 8
Mercurochrome	1, 2, 3, 8
Merthiolate	1, 2, 3, 8
Paint (oil-base), varnish	1, 2, 4, 8
Nail polish	1, 2, 5, 8
Tar, asphalt	1, 2, 6, 8
Rust	2, 7, 8

1. Take up freshly spilled materials with a clean white cloth, using a pickup motion toward the center of the spill to avoid spreading. If the spill has dried, remove excess with a plastic spatula or other tool that will not scratch the floor.

2. Wet a clean white cloth with a detergent floor cleaner, and wipe over the stained area. For heavy residue, use a nylon pad (recommended for nonstick pans) dipped in the detergent. If a stain still shows, proceed to the next instruction indicated.
3. Wet a clean white cloth with rubbing alcohol*, and wipe over the stained area, turning the cloth frequently. Don't walk on the treated area for 30 minutes. If a stain still shows, repeat the procedure, using a liquid chlorine bleach.
4. Wet a clean white cloth with turpentine*, and wipe over the stained area, turning the cloth frequently. Don't walk on the treated area for 30 minutes.
5. Wet a clean white cloth with nail polish remover*, and wipe over the stained area, turning the cloth frequently. Don't walk on the treated area for 30 minutes.
6. Wet a clean white cloth with lighter fluid*, and wipe over the stained area, turning the cloth frequently. Don't walk on the treated area for 30 minutes.
7. Apply New Beginning full strength to the area, and allow to stand for 5 to 10 minutes; then scrub vigorously with a stiff bristle brush, rinse, and dry. If traces of rust still remain, they may be removed by rubbing with a nylon pad (recommended for nonstick pans) dipped in a solution of oxalic acid diluted in water. (*Note:* Oxalic acid is a toxic chemical, and all precautions should be followed to prevent its ingestion, inhalation, or contact with the skin in either the solid or solution form.)
8. Rinse with water, and let dry. Reapply floor finish if normally used.

Maintenance of Shellac Finishes

Shellac coatings may be cleaned with a damp rag or, where stubborn stains are involved, mild soap and water. Wood floors should never be flooded. Water gets in between cracks and causes the floor to swell or buckle.

Like lacquer, shellac will spot when exposed to standing water. Ordinarily this can be cured by rubbing with an alcohol-dampened rag. Where the damage is too severe for this remedy, or where a spot has been damaged by a burning cigarette or is otherwise marred, remove the old film, in the damaged area only, by sanding. Then apply two or more thin coats of 2-pound shellac to the area. Allow to dry. Finally buff with 2/0 steel wool until the new finish blends with the old.

**Caution:* These solvents are highly flammable, so exercise proper care.

Maintaining Wood Floors

UNWAXED VARNISHED AND SHELLACKED FLOORS. Dust these with a soft brush or dry mop. Rub the floor with an oiled mop or a cloth lightly moistened with turpentine, floor oil, or furniture polish. In general, avoid using water, but if surfaces are badly soiled, wipe with a mop or cloth dampened with warm slightly soapy water, and then with a cloth moistened with clear water. Wipe the surface dry at once and polish with an oiled mop or cloth. Apply wax to worn varnish surfaces.

OILED AND PAINTED FLOORS. Use a soft brush to sweep oiled and painted wood floors, and then rub them with an oiled mop or cloth. Occasionally they may be washed with slightly soapy water and rinsed with a wet cloth or mop, then wiped dry and polished with an oiled cloth or mop.

To reoil a wood floor, apply one coat of oil made by mixing equal volumes of boiled linseed oil and mineral spirits. Mop the oil on the floor and rub it in across the grain with a stiff brush. Remove excess with a clean dry cloth or mop and allow 24 hours for the oil to penetrate and dry.

WAXED FLOORS. Clean these with a soft brush or mop. Do not use oil, since oil softens wax. To remove dirt and wax film that darkens the surface, use a cloth moistened with warm soapy water. Turpentine works better, but if you use it have plenty of ventilation and be sure there are no open flames in the room. If water-cleaning has whitened a waxed floor, restore its luster and color by rubbing with a woolen cloth or a weighted brush, applying a little wax if needed. Remove spots by rubbing with a little turpentine and refinishing with a thin coat of wax.

Polishes

CAR CLEANER AND POLISH. This liquid combination cleaner and polish contains a mild abrasive to help remove surface dirt, an oil that leaves a slight surface sheen, and a gum to emulsify the water and oil and to help keep the abrasive suspended.

Gum acacia	1	part
Water	145	parts
Light mineral oil	22	parts
Kieselguhr	26	parts
Glycerin	6	parts

(Continued)

The gum acacia should be in powdered form. To dissolve it readily, put it in a bowl and add a considerable part of the water all at once, then stir well until combined. Add the rest of the water and the other ingredients, stir well or shake together to produce an emulsion and put in bottles. Shake well before each use.

INSTANT FURNITURE POLISH. Many commercial furniture polishes of the straight-oil type consist of light mineral oil alone, or mineral oil scented with a small amount of pine or cedar oil. To save money and get the same results, use any light medicinal or mineral lubricating oil, scenting it similarly if you desire. Apply with a soft cloth, and polish with another clean one.

FURNITURE WAX FOR OLD FURNITURE. This old-time and easy-to-make wax works well on any furniture, but is especially good for old furniture. Just melt 1 pound of pure beeswax in a vessel placed in hot water. (Do not heat over an open flame.) Then add 1 pint of gum turpentine, remove from the hot water, and stir constantly while the mixture cools. Package in a widemouthed container before it really hardens.

Apply with a soft cloth. Let stand until solvent evaporates, and then polish with a clean cloth.

EMULSION-TYPE FURNITURE POLISH. This is an easy-to-make emulsion-type furniture polish that will give a smooth, soft sheen:

Soap flakes	1 ounce
Potassium carbonate	½ ounce
Water	1 quart
Beeswax	4 ounces

Dissolve the soap and potassium carbonate in hot water. Add the beeswax and continue to heat gently until the beeswax is melted. Then remove from heat and stir thoroughly to produce an emulsion. Bottle, and shake before using.

WATER-FREE FLOOR POLISH. Here is an interesting water-free floor polish:

Carnauba wax	6 parts
Paraffin (melting point 48° to 50° C)	12 parts

Beeswax	12 parts
Gum turpentine	70 parts

Melt together waxes in double boiler (never over an open fire) at about 90° C. Remove from fire and add turpentine in a thin stream with constant stirring. Pour into widemouthed containers when cooled to about 40° to 45° C.

WAX AUTOMOBILE POLISH. Paste polishes are applied to a car finish after it has been thoroughly washed or cleaned by other means. They require more labor in application than do liquid polishes, but the tough, durable film they produce is worth the extra effort. This relatively simple paste wax is a basic type:

Carnauba wax	2 parts
Ceresin	2 parts
Turpentine	3 parts
Mineral spirits or V.M.&P. naphtha	3 parts

Melt the waxes in a vessel placed in hot water (never over an open fire). Add the turpentine and mineral spirits or naphtha rapidly in a thin stream, with constant stirring. Then cool the mixture as rapidly as possible, while stirring vigorously to produce a smooth creamy consistency.

This formula may be modified, as determined by experiment, by mixing other waxes with the carnauba wax base. Candelilla or montan waxes are suggested. By increasing the amounts of turpentine and mineral spirits or naphtha, liquid wax may be made.

8

Laundering and Stain Removing

DETERGENTS FOR LAUNDERING

To clean a fabric it is essential to wet the material and the dirt in order to remove the dirt from the fabric and to hold the removed dirt in suspension—that is, to keep it from redepositing or settling back on the fabric before it is rinsed away.

Water alone has little cleaning ability. The addition of a soap or other detergent to water increases enormously both its wetting and its suspending ability. When soiled fabric is agitated during the washing process, oily dirt is broken up into small particles, each of which is surrounded by a film of the detergent solution. As the dirt is lifted off the fabric, the detergent suspends it in the solution so that it does not settle back to coat the cloth with a gray film.

Soaps

The oldest and most familiar laundry detergent is soap, made since ancient times from fat and lye. For removing dirt from heavily soiled fabrics, a combination of soap and alkali is still probably the most effective. Although the newer synthetic detergents wet fabrics more thoroughly, they are not the match for soap and alkali in prying loose and suspending the dirt.

Laundry soap comes in two general types—"unbuilt" and "built." Unbuilt soap products consist generally of from 93- to 97-percent pure soap, with the remaining fraction made up of water, sodium chloride, and perhaps a colorless fluorescent dye. The latter becomes fixed on the fabrics during washing and glows with a pale blue fluorescence under daylight to make the fabrics appear a brighter and bluer white.

Unbuilt soaps are intended for laundering fine fabrics and lightly soiled garments. They are recommended for cotton, linen, and man-made fibers. They are relatively safe for most dyes and are mild on hands.

Examples of unbuilt soaps are Chiffon Flakes, Instant Fels, Ivory Flakes, Ivory Snow, Kirkman Flakes, and Lux Flakes.

Built soaps contain at least 50-percent soap and varying amounts of alkaline chemicals. The chemicals, or "builders," increase sudsing, improve the cleaning action of the soap, and help to soften hard water so that less soap scum forms. Builders include sodium carbonate (washing soda), borax, sodium silicate, trisodium phosphate, and various other phosphates.

Common brands of built soap contain from 55- to 80-percent soap, from 10- to 30-percent builder, about 5-percent moisture, and usually a fluorescent-dye brightener.

Built soaps are general-purpose soaps for the family wash and for laundering heavily soiled cloth—rugs, grimy play clothes, and greasy jeans and coveralls. They are harder on hands and on some dyes than the unbuilt soaps, and because of their increased alkalinity they are not recommended for silk or wool.

Examples of built soaps are American Family Flakes, Duz, Fels Naphtha, Instant Fels, Rinso, and White King.

Soap powders, or washing powders, contain only 10- to 15-percent soap, with the rest builders or inert fillers. These should not be confused with powdered soaps, which are true soaps in powdered form instead of bar, chip, flake, or bead. Soap powders are sometimes used for laundering but more often for dishwashing.

Synthetic Detergents

Synthetic detergents began their meteoric rise during the war years of 1939–1945 when fats became scarce. Since then their use in laundering has overtaken and passed that of soap. They are complex compounds having as their base ingredient a chemically synthesized by-product of petroleum or other nonfatty-based raw material. This base ingredient, known technically as a surface active agent, gives the synthetic detergent its principal cleaning power. The synthetic detergents are neutral in solution, and they do not depend on alkalinity for their cleaning ability.

Synthetic detergents dissolve readily, do not form scum in hard water, and have a pronounced ability to emulsify oil and grease. In hand laundering, however, the latter ability may be a disadvantage as it tends to remove oil from the skin and thus may be drying or even irritating to the hands.

Some synthetic detergents form suds readily, whereas others clean with little or no suds. Like soaps, they come in two types—unbuilt (light-duty) and built (heavy-duty)—and in liquid, powder, and tablet forms.

Unbuilt synthetic detergent products may contain only 30- to 40-percent detergent. The remainder in powdered products may be from 50- to 60-percent neutral salts, such as sodium chloride (common salt) or sodium sulfate (Glauber's salt); in liquids, 50 percent may be water. Both contain a fluorescent brightener. The neutral diluents contribute little or no cleaning power but are added chiefly to give greater bulk. This enables a detergent to be measured in amounts comparable with a less powerful product and to be competitive in price.

Unbuilt synthetic detergents may be used for the same purposes as unbuilt soap. Because they are nonalkaline in solution, they are safe for dyed fabrics and for wool and silk, which an alkali might harm.

Examples of unbuilt synthetic detergents are: GRANULAR: Dreft, Gentle Fels, Swerl, Trend, and Vel. LIQUID: Chiffon, Dawn, Dove, Ivory, Joy, Lux, Octagon, Palmolive, Trill, Trend, Vel, and White Magic.

Built synthetic detergent, like built soaps, contain alkaline salts and phosphates that increase their cleaning ability. These salts and phosphates make the products alkaline in solution. In addition, they may contain any or all of the following: fluorescent dyes; carboxymethylcellulose (CMC) to help prevent loosened soil from redepositing on clothes; silicates to prevent corrosion in the washing machine; bleach to aid in stain removal; water softener to help combat hardness; bacteriostatic agents to help retard bacteria growth.

Manufacturers recommend built synthetics as general-purpose detergents for washing heavily soiled clothes. Both high-sudsing and low-sudsing products are available. The latter are made for use in certain types of automatic washing machines where high suds interfere with mechanical action. Examples of phosphate type of detergents follow on page 295.

	HIGH SUDSING	
Granular		
Ajax	Grain	Silver Dust
Breeze	Oxydol	Speedup
Cheer	Rinso	Super Suds
Duz	Sail	Surf
Fab	Salvo	Tide
Liquid		
Dynamo	Fels	Wisk
	LOW SUDSING	
Granular		
All	Cold Power	Control Suds
Amway	Cold Water Surf	Dash
Bold		
Liquid		
All	Cold Water All	Wisk
Tablets		
Quick Solv Vim		

Nonphosphate Washing Products

As already mentioned, during World War II washing products that used a combination of phosphate builders with synthetic detergents in place of soap were introduced. These products were especially beneficial for washing in hard water. Hardness minerals in water (mainly calcium) react with soap to form insoluble curds or film that build up on fabrics to make them dull and dingy. Phosphates, however, tie up hardness minerals so they do not curd, and a better wash results.

Recently phosphates have been accused by various groups of being a major factor in excessive growth of algae in lakes and streams. As a result, the sale of detergents containing phosphates has been banned in various towns, counties, and even whole states. This has led to the introduction of nonphosphate washing products that can provide poorer washing results and cause other problems.

Nonphosphate products have thus far relied mainly on replacement of phosphate with carbonate (washing soda), which ties up calcium by precipitating it out of the washing solution. Unfortunately the calcium carbonate (limestone) deposits on, and is firmly bound to, textiles, machine parts, and anything else contacted.

This is a minor problem in areas with soft water because hardness minerals come into the wash water as part of the soil on textiles. However, the problem grows increasingly serious the harder the fresh water is because the deposits of calcium carbonate will become excessive. If you want to or must use a nonphosphate washing product, ask your water company how hard your water is (or have your water tested), and then take appropriate steps to get the best washing results you can.

If your water is very hard—more than 21 grains per gallon or 360 parts per million (ppm)—you should soften the water used for laundering, even if you use a phosphate-based detergent. If you use soap or a carbonate-based, nonphosphate washing product, you should soften the laundry water if it is other than soft (maximum of 3.5 grains per gallon or 66 ppm).

One consequence of calcium carbonate deposits is more frequent washing machine service calls. Deposits on the inside of tubs and outside of agitators do not interfere with the basic operation of most washers, but they mystify the owners and may cause other problems. Variable blade agitators sometimes become locked due to limestone buildup in the vane-control mechanism. Excessive buildup on perforated tubs has occurred to the extent that 80 to 90 percent of the holes are plugged, so that drainage of wash water and subsequent rinsing are incomplete and overall laundry results are poor.

A washer pump is analogous to a human heart and the hoses, etc., are like veins and arteries through which blood flows. Therefore it is not surprising that chunks or accumulations of limestone in the water-circulation system of a washer have led to machine failure, just as deposits in blood-circulation systems have led to heart failure and other problems in humans.

Massive accumulations have also been observed in sewer pipes that receive the wash water. If the slope of a pipe is very slight, the waste water moves so slowly that calcium carbonate tends to deposit. Sewer lines as large as 6 inches in diameter have been partially or completely plugged. This requires major repair if the plugged sewer line is under a concrete floor such as in a basement.

While deposits on tub and agitator may not interfere with your washer's operation, the deposits do present a rough surface to the textiles being laundered. The result is excessive abrasion of the textiles and consequent shorter useful life for them. This is a problem particularly with textiles that are normally subject to abrasive effects.

Deposits occur on cotton more rapidly than on manmade fibers. Towels become scratchy, colored items appear to lose color as the deposits build up, and some items give off the deposits as dust when shaken. In addition, some durable-press items require more touchup ironing when washed with carbonate-based products.

Manufacturers of nonphosphate washing products frequently use the same names for their phosphate types except that they note the difference on the containers. Others have produced new products. Here are some of the more popular nonphosphate detergents.

NONPHOSPHATE DETERGENTS

Granular		
Ajax	Cheer	Miracle White
All	Cold Power	Pure Water
Amway No-phosphate	Drive	Purex
Arm & Hammer	Ecolo-G	Speedup-No Phosphate
Bio B	Fab	Tide XK
Bravo	Ivory Snow Detergent	
Liquid		
Dynamo	ERA	Wisk

Suiting the Detergent to the Water

The type of detergent to use depends in part on whether the water for washing is soft or hard. In soft or softened water, soap is economical to use and does an excellent job of cleaning. Hard water, however, is an extravagant waster of soap. The soap combines with the minerals in it to form an insoluble scum that sticks to tub and washer parts and settles on clothes as gray specks that are almost impossible to remove. Hard water wastes synthetic detergents, too. These do not form a scum, but more of them are required to do a good job.

If hard water causes a laundering problem, you may either choose a synthetic detergent or soften the water and use soap. In the latter case, it pays to soften both the wash water and the water for the first rinse. A water-softening system installed in the water-supply line is a great convenience. Or you can use a water-softening chemical, as described later in this section under Hard and Soft Water.

Suiting the Detergent to the Fabric

What the cloth is made of and the type of dye used also influence the choice of a detergent.

Wool and silk are damaged by alkali. To prolong the life of these fabrics, wash them with a mild neutral soap or an unbuilt synthetic detergent. The shrinkage of wool fabrics from laundering depends more on the agitation during the washing process than on the type of detergent used. Agitation, squeezing, or other manipulation of wool should be kept to a minimum.

Cotton, linen, and synthetic fibers (acetate, Acrilan, Dacron, Dynel, nylon, Orlon, and rayon) resist alkalies better than wool and silk. So for these, the amount of soil and the type of dye are more important in choosing a detergent than the fabric itself.

For white cloth, be governed by the amount of soil. If light, use unbuilt detergent. For the regular wash and for heavy soil, use built products.

Fabrics with colorfast dyes may be treated the same way. If you are not sure about the dye, however, it is safest to use an unbuilt synthetic detergent.

In tests made by textile chemists of the U.S. Department of Agriculture, it was found that cottons washed in soft-water solutions of both unbuilt and built soaps came slightly cleaner than those washed in similar solutions of unbuilt synthetic detergents. Some of the high-sudsing built synthetics, however, removed as much soil as the soaps. In hard water, both unbuilt and built synthetics were more effective than the soaps.

Similar tests with man-made fibers came out about the same. All the detergents removed more soil from the acetate and nylon samples than from the others. Laundering fabrics of all the man-made fibers 75 times caused only slight loss in strength and little change in whiteness.

Suiting the Detergent to the Washer

In machine washing, the kind of detergent to use depends somewhat on the kind of washer. Because of their washing action, some machines work better with low-sudsing than with high-sudsing detergent. If this is so, the instructions should say so.

Soaps depend on suds for keeping removed dirt suspended; therefore enough should be used to maintain good suds. The cooler the water and the dirtier the clothes, the more soap will be needed.

Synthetic detergents suspend dirt in a different way, so the volume of suds is not necessarily an indication of the amount of detergent to use. Some detergents clean with little or no suds, while others produce a great volume of suds even when used in quantities too small to clean well. Follow the directions on the package.

Tips on Using Detergents

1. *For laundering lightly soiled fine fabrics,* use unbuilt soaps or unbuilt synthetic detergents.
2. *For general laundering and for heavily soiled fabrics,* use built soaps or built synthetic detergents.
3. *For fabrics of cotton, linen, and manmade fibers,* if white or colorfast, use soaps or synthetic detergents—unbuilt for lightly soiled materials, built for those more heavily soiled. If not colorfast, use unbuilt synthetic detergents.
4. *For wool and silk, and for blends of these with other fibers,* use unbuilt synthetic detergents.
5. *In soft water,* both soaps and synthetic detergents, built or unbuilt, are suitable.
6. *In hard water,* built synthetics are the most efficient; or soften the water and use soap.
7. *If fabrics and color will stand it,* wash in hot water instead of warm, since detergents are generally more efficient at high temperatures. Remove stains first, however, for some are set by hot water.
8. *When using soaps,* maintain good suds.
9. *When using synthetic detergents,* use the amount recommended by the manufacturer. Some synthetics are high-sudsing; others clean with little suds. The low-sudsing types are especially suited to certain designs of washing machines.

BLEACHING AGENTS

Bleaching does not remove ordinary dirt and is not a substitute for good washing methods. But it is helpful in removing problem stains, in reducing the natural yellowing of age in fabrics, and in some cases as a sanitizing agent.

Most bleaching agents are chemicals that oxidize the colored compounds in stains to colorless ones. If bleaching is necessary, choose a type of bleach to suit the fabric. For household use, there are two general types, chlorine and peroxygen. Following are suggestions for the use of these bleaches in general laundering; for their use in removing specific stains, see the article on stain removal that appears later in this chapter.

Chlorine bleach, the more powerful of the two, is the most effective in removing difficult stains and the yellow of old age from the bulk of the family wash. In its liquid form it comes as a 5- to 6-percent solution of sodium hypochlorite (Clorox, Rose-X, Purex, etc.) and must be used carefully and sparingly to prevent fabric damage. The usual dilution is 1 tablespoon per gallon of water (about 1 cup for top-loading washers, and ½ cup for the front-loading type). Either mix it thoroughly with the wash water before adding the clothes, or blend dosage with at least 1 quart of warm water before adding to the wash cycle. *Never pour it directly over the clothes.* Except for a variation of less than 1 percent in strength, there is no essential difference between brands of liquid chlorine bleach. It pays, therefore, to buy the least expensive.

Granular chlorine bleach (Action, Linco, Stardust, etc.) is initially safer to handle than the liquid, because its chlorine is not released until the granules begin to dissolve. It is better to dissolve it completely before adding the clothes, as partially dissolved particles trapped in the folds of the fabric might cause damage. If your washer has a bleach dispenser, follow the washer instructions.

Chlorine bleach should never be used on fabrics containing silk, wool, or spandex fibers, or on "wash-and-wear" materials with a chlorine-retentive resin finish. Such fabrics are marked "Do not use a chlorine bleach" either on the label or on attached washing instructions. The use of chlorine bleach on these fabrics usually results in yellowing rather than bleaching and may seriously damage them.

Do not use too much chlorine bleach or use it too often. Rinse it out thoroughly after use. Bleach carryover will damage fabrics. *Note:* Never mix chlorine bleach with ammonia; poisonous gases will result.

Peroxygen bleaches, generally called oxygen bleaches, come in powder form and may contain either sodium perborate (Dexol, Lestare, Snowy) or potassium monopersulfate (Beads O' Bleach, Dri Brite, Glo). Though less effective than the chlorine type, the peroxygen bleaches are safe on all washable fabrics—natural and synthetic—and for resin-finished cottons. The sodium perborate bleach is totally effective only in water of about 160° F, a temperature seldom reached in home washing machines. According to the manufacturer, the monopersulfate type is effective in water of all temperatures.

Bleaching by Sunlight

An age-old method of bleaching is to spread wet fabrics in the sun. Some fibers are weakened by sunlight, however. So keep sun treatments brief and infrequent.

HARD AND SOFT WATER

The water you use for drinking, cooking, and washing may contain the dissolved salts of calcium, magnesium, and other elements. If it reaches you with less than 5.8 grains per gallon or 100 parts per million (ppm) of such salts, water is said to be "soft." If it contains more, it is called "hard."

Hard water can be expensive in two ways: it wastes soap and synthetic detergent, and it forms scale inside pipes and boilers, which may cause them to corrode, crack, or get stopped up.

Temporary Hard Water

Water containing dissolved calcium bicarbonate and occasionally smaller amounts of the bicarbonates of magnesium and iron is sometimes called "temporary" hard water. When such hard water is boiled, the bicarbonates are decomposed into insoluble compounds that settle out and leave the water soft.

Permanent Hard Water

This usually contains the sulfates, nitrates, or chlorides of calcium or magnesium, which must be removed by treatment with other chemicals or by distillation.

How to Soften Water

If you don't have a water-softening system, you can easily soften water for washing by adding one or another of common household chemicals. Washing soda and trisodium phosphate are the least expensive. These will settle or precipitate the water-hardness minerals. Sodium hexametaphosphate, sold under the trade name of Calgon, costs a little more and works in a different way. Instead of precipitating the minerals, it holds them in suspension in such form that they cannot produce soap scum. In either case, it is best to add the water softener to the warm or hot water at least 1 minute before you add the soap or detergent.

AMOUNT OF SOFTENER TO USE. To find out how much of a particular softener is needed with your own hard water and a particular kind of powdered or flake soap, make the following test:

1. Dissolve ½ teaspoon of softener in 1 gallon of water at about 140° F.
2. Half fill a quart jar with this water. Add ½ teaspoon of soap, cap the jar, and shake vigorously for 10 seconds. If good suds form and hold for 5 minutes, the water is softened. Try again, using less softener, to find out if a smaller amount would do to make good suds.

3. If the ½ teaspoon of softener does not make good suds with the soap, repeat the test with fresh water, using 1 teaspoon of softener to 1 gallon of water.
4. Continue until the minimum amount is found that will make and sustain good suds.

Repeat this test, and make a record of your findings, for each combination of softener and soap that you use.

If you know the hardness of your local water in terms of grains per gallon or parts per million, you can soften it with washing soda according to the following table. Amounts needed are based on concentrated or partially dehydrated soda such as Con-Sal or Arm & Hammer. If you use the ordinary crystalline kind, use twice as much.

To be fully effective as a water softener, the washing soda should be put in the water and given time to dissolve before you add soap or detergent.

SOFTENING WATER WITH WASHING SODA

WATER HARDNESS		WASHING SODA NEEDED TO SOFTEN 10 GALLONS
Parts per million	Grains per gallon	
50	2.9	.1 ounce
100	5.8	.2 ounce
150	8.7	.3 ounce
200	11.7	.4 ounce
300	17.5	.6 ounce
400	23.3	.8 ounce
600	35.0	1.2 ounces

Washing Soda Soap

One of the most commonly used "builders" in built or heavy-duty soap and synthetic detergent products is sodium carbonate. It is included to help cut grease and to make the soap or synthetic more effective by softening the water. Because sodium carbonate (in the form of "sal soda" or "washing soda") is considerably cheaper than the combination product, you can get the same results more economically by buying it separately and adding it together with unbuilt soap or detergent to each wash. For fabrics with average soil, just add 4 heaping tablespoons of sal soda to your washer or tub and less soap or detergent than you normally would. Use more if the wash is heavily soiled. To prevent the sal soda from caking, be sure the water is warm. Dissolve the granules thoroughly by stirring the water, and let the solution stand at least 1 minute before adding the soap or detergent. Do not use sodium carbonate for washing silk or wool, materials with which you should not use *any* built soap or detergent.

Trisodium Phosphate in Laundering

Trisodium phosphate (TSP) may be used in laundering in the same manner as washing soda. Because it is stronger, use only about half as much. For very dirty fabrics of cotton or linen, presoaking loosens the dirt so it can more readily be washed out. Soak for half an hour or more in a solution of 1 tablespoon of TSP to about 10 gallons of lukewarm water. Don't use hot water for soaking. Hot water coagulates starch and albuminous matter, making them stick more tenaciously to the clothes.

For washing cotton curtains, lingerie, and other delicate fabrics without soap, use 1 tablespoon of TSP to 3 gallons of water. Let soak for an hour, wash gently by hand, rinse thoroughly and dry.

For further uses of TSP, see Chapter 9.

Uses for Sodium Hexametaphosphate

Don't let the name of this chemical frighten you. It is a common product obtainable in any supermarket under the name of Calgon. The great usefulness of Calgon in laundering is twofold: It can prevent hard water from forming a dingy and insoluble scum on fabrics, and it can remove this scum once it has formed. Either results in a brighter wash. Unlike other water-softening chemicals, Calgon is nearly neutral rather than alkaline in reaction, and so can be used safely on all fabrics.

You can find out if Calgon will benefit your regular washing procedure by making this simple test:

1. Fill washing machine with warm water or hot water of the temperature you would normally use.
2. Add 1 cup of Calgon and a load of soiled clothes. Do not add soap, synthetic detergent, or any other washing ingredient.
3. Run clothes through wash and rinse cycles.

If suds appear during any of this operation, they are from soap or synthetic detergent that has been trapped in the fabric from previous washings and just released by Calgon. (Calgon itself does not form suds.) This means you have not been using enough soap, synthetic detergent, or water softener to prevent hard-water scum. If no suds appear, your normal washing procedure is adequate.

Calgon can be used to correct the first condition in either, or both, of two ways. First, you can use it in the wash water in place of a more conventional water softener. In this case, instead of precipitating the hardness minerals, it holds them to itself so they can't join with the soap or synthetic detergent to coat the fabric with a gray film. Second, you can use it in the rinse water to detach any film that may have formed. Or, for more complete guarantee against film formation, you can do both.

Dissolve the Calgon completely before adding soap or synthetic detergent. For more information about the nature and uses of this chemical, see Chapter 9.

WATER SOFTENER GUIDELINES

Here are suggested amounts of the compound to use for different degrees of water hardness and washers of different capacity.

Washer tank capacity (gallons)	**Soft water** (up to 5 grains per gallon)	**Medium water** (5 to 10 grains per gallon)	**Hard water** (10 to 15 grains per gallon)	**Very hard water** (over 15 grains per gallon)
5	⅛ cup	¼ cup	⅓ cup	½ cup
10	¼ cup	½ cup	⅔ cup	1 cup
15	⅓ cup	⅔ cup	1 cup	1½ cups
20	½ cup	1 cup	1½ cups	2 cups

SANITATION IN HOME LAUNDERING

In the days when housewives boiled their clothes in laundering them, there was little chance for bacteria to survive. With today's relatively low wash-water temperatures, however, bacteria usually thrive. In tests made in the Clothing and Texiles Laboratory of the U.S. Department of Agriculture, the wash of nine families was laundered regularly for several months. An automatic household washer and typical home-laundry methods were used. Examination of the laundry at the end of the test showed that thirty kinds of bacteria were still alive.

According to the experts' findings, neither the water temperatures nor the detergents ordinarily used in today's automatic washers can be relied on to reduce the number of bacteria in fabrics to a safe level. Even at the hot-water setting, 12 gallons of wash water may contain as many as 1,536,000,000 bacteria!

Home-equipment specialists, for instance, recommend a temperature of 140° F for hot-water laundering. At that temperature, it takes 20 minutes to kill *Staphylococcus aureus*, a type of bacterium that can cause boils and carbuncles, as well as skin, respiratory, kidney, and other types of infections. However, the average hot-water temperature in home washers is not 140°F but 125° to 130°F, while the average washing cycle is only from 5 to 10 minutes. Besides, in an attempt to spare fabrics, much laundry is now washed in cold or lukewarm water.

Most bacteria, luckily, are harmless. Occasionally, however, a dangerous strain will spread stubborn infections from one member of a family to another through contact in the home washer, or from one family to another family through a public washing machine.

Can These Bacteria Be Controlled?

USDA experts say they can be through the use of suitable disinfectants. The following were chosen as being lethal to most bacteria, harmless to fabrics and dyes, harmless to humans at the end of the wash cycle, compatible with detergents, readily available, and reasonable in cost. In using any of them, be sure to read the label and follow all directions and precautions carefully.

LIQUID CHLORINE BLEACH. The type containing 5- to 6-percent sodium hypochlorite (Clorox, Rose-X, Purex, etc.) is probably the most familiar. This household chemical is an effective and inexpensive bacteria killer as well as a fabric whitener when used in quantities recommended on the bottle for regular bleaching. Usually 1 cup should be added to a top-loading machine or ½ cup to a front-loading machine. It should not, of course, be used on wool, silk, or spandex, or on dyes or other finishes where chlorine bleach would not normally be used.

QUATERNARY DISINFECTANTS. These are sometimes known as "quats," and work well when added to the wash water at the beginning of the rinse cycle. One brand, co-op Sanitizer, is available in certain supermarkets; another, Roccal, is available from janitors', dairy, and poultry supply houses. Use the amount recommended on the label, or add ½ cup to rinse water in a top-loading machine or 8 tablespoons to rinse water in a front-loading machine.

PINE OIL DISINFECTANTS. Available in grocery stores under such names as Fyne Pyne, Fyne Tex, King Pine, Pine-o-Pine, and White Cap, these should contain at least 80 percent of pine oil. Add them at the beginning of the wash cycle—if possible, mixing them with the water before placing clothes in the machine. Use ¾ cup for a top-loading machine or ½ cup for a front-loading machine.

PHENOLIC DISINFECTANTS. These may be added either to wash or rinse water. Examples are Pine-Sol and Al Pine, available at grocery stores, and which contain approximately 3 percent of active ingredient. At this concentration, use 1 cup for a top-loading machine or 10 tablespoons (5 fluid ounces) for a front-loading machine.

Besides sanitizing the clothes, sanitize the washing machine occasionally to kill bacteria that may abide on its inner surfaces. Pour a disinfectant into the empty machine and then complete a 15-minute cycle at the hot-water setting.

How Hot Should the Wash Water Be?

This depends on the amount of soil, the type of fabric, and whether you depend on the temperature of the water to provide sanitizing. The hotter the water, the better it penetrates fabrics and liquifies grease so that it may be more easily removed. If the temperature is above 140° F, it also kills germs. On the other hand, water that is too hot can damage silk, cause wool to shrink, make colors run, and weaken and wrinkle modern synthetic materials.

To help you get the cleanest wash with the least damage to materials, here are some general suggestions:

HOT. This includes temperatures from 140° to 160° F, provided only from the "hot" line of the water heater and with temperature control on washer set for "hot." Although higher temperatures may get out more dirt, to prevent shortening of life of pipes and heater and also accidental scalding, it is better not to set the thermostat of the water heater much above 140°F. If you want the water very hot, and have an ample supply, you can preheat the washer with hot water, then empty the washer and refill it.

Water in this temperature range provides the most soil removal and sanitizing. It is ideal for white cottons and linens, and for heavily soiled articles of these materials in washfast colors. It also softens and reduces the resilience of synthetic and resin-treated fibers, causing wrinkles and preventing them from returning to their original shape. It also may cause some colors to run.

MEDIUM. By mixing cold water with the hot, water of about 120° F is produced by automatic washers on the "medium" setting. This is good for lightly soiled clothes, also for washing many bright or dark colors that do not actually run in the wash but may fade in time from washing in hot water. It provides no sanitizing, but is somewhat superior to warm water in removing dirt.

WARM. The "warm" setting of an automatic washer usually regulates temperature at about 100° F. This is suitable for silk and washable woolens, and is comfortable for hand washing. It protects colors from running and wrinkles synthetic fibers less than hot water. Most automatic washers rinse at this temperature.

COLD. Water of 80° F or less from unheated supply is recommended only for lightly soiled laundry or laundry pretreated by working concentrated detergent thoroughly into the heavily soiled areas. Use in it plenty of liquid detergent, a cold-water detergent, or a granular detergent that has been dissolved in hot water before adding. Cold water adds the fewest new wrinkles to synthetic or coated "wash-and-wear" fabrics, but on the other hand it may not remove those that are already there.

Care for Modern Fabrics

The new man-made fabrics do not absorb water readily, so they dry quickly, shrink less, and are more wrinkle-resistant. Because of their thermoplastic finish, some are less tolerant of high heats in washing and drying. Whenever you wash a synthetic, be sure to use the correct wash cycles and water-temperature selections. To care for your fabrics safely, first consult the general washing guide on pages 308 and 309. For more information, consult the instructions included with your washer and dryer. When there are no instructions included, dry-clean any garments you question. Dry-clean lined or bonded garments and any items containing over 50-percent acetate, rayon, or silk. Dry-clean wool unless indicated washable. Dry-clean any knits, lace, or cotton that is not preshrunk.

WASH-DAY PREPARATIONS

SOAK HEAVILY SOILED CLOTHES FIRST: Presoak them until dirt and grease are loosened (15 to 30 minutes). Use the water temperature best for each kind of soil and fabric.

GREASE: Soak in warm-water solution of detergent and 1 cup ammonia or ¼ cup washing soda.

CARE OF MODERN FABRICS

Generic name	Trade names	End uses	Care
Rayon	Bemberg, Celanese, Colorspun, Cupioni, Topei, Coloray, Corval	Outerwear and underwear, household items	Wash in warm or cold water; dryer dry on delicate setting; press on warm iron setting
Acetate	Arnel, Colorspun, Chromspun, Acele, Avisco	Woven and knitted wear, lingerie, household items	Wash in warm or cold water; dryer dry on delicate setting; press on low setting
Nylon	Chemstrand, Enka, DuPont	Very sheer fabrics, lingerie; may be permanently pleated, blended for suitings and skirts	Wash in cold or warm water; dryer dry on delicate setting
Acrylic	Acrilan, Orlon, Zefran, Creslan	Sweaters, knitted garments, skirts, slacks, suits	Wash in warm or cold water; dryer dry on delicate setting; press on low setting
Mod acrylic	Dynel, Verel	Fur-type fabrics, scatter rugs, bath mats, robes, coats, children's apparel	Wash in warm water; dryer dry on delicate setting; dry clean deep-pile garments
Polyesters	Dacron, Vycron, Kodel, Teron	Suits, dresses, blouses shirts—also in many blends	Wash in warm or cold water; dryer dry on permanent press setting

Generic name	Trade names	End uses	Care
Glass	Fiberglass, Aerocor, Unifab, Vitren	Curtains and draperies	Follow manufacturer's instructions for washing and drying
Spandex	Lycra, Vyrene	Foundation garments and swimsuits	Wash in hot or warm water; dryer dry on delicate setting
Rubber	Lestex	Usually covered by fabric—foundation garments and swimsuits	Wash in warm or cold water; air dry only
Metallics	Melton, Lame, Mylar	Decorative trims and yarns	Wash in warm or cold water; air dry only
Cotton	Natural fiber	Outerwear and underwear, household items	Wash in hot water unless fabric is not colorfast; dryer dry on regular setting
Wool	Natural fiber	Winter garments, coats, sweaters, woven and knitted wear	Dry-clean unless tag indicates washable—hand wash knits in cold water, dry flat; consult manufacturer's care instructions for machine washables

Note: Garments made of blends should be laundered as though they were made entirely of the predominant fiber. Follow manufacturer's care instructions if available.

DIRT: Soak in detergent solution.

DIAPERS: Soak in cold water with 2 tablespoons of borax or ¼ cup of bleach and detergent.

Removing Stains from Textiles

Stains should be removed before washing, but complicated by the endless variety of dyes, synthetic textiles, blends, and surface finishes in use today, successful stain removal has become an art that requires a combination of considerable skill with a fair knowledge of chemistry.

Before you begin you must select a method best suited to stain, dye, and fabric. To make sure that it does not cause fading or running of the dye, change of surface of the textile, or the removal of a nonpermanent finish, first test the treatment on some hidden part of the article.

If you are in doubt, or an article is of great value, don't attempt to remove the stain yourself but take the article to a professional cleaner. But even a professional may not be able to remove it. There are some types of stain on some materials that cannot be removed by *any* treatment without damaging the material.

Following is a description of materials used in stain removal, methods for removing stains of general types, and finally methods for removing specific stains.

Solvents for Nongreasy Stains

WATER. Or water with a detergent will remove many nongreasy stains.

ACETONE. This will dissolve such stains as fingernail polish, lacquer, and ballpoint ink. It should not be used on acetate, Arnel, Dynel, or Verel. Flammable. Poison if swallowed.

AMYL ACETATE. This can be used for some stains on fabrics that would be damaged by acetone. Use the chemically pure grade. Flammable. Poison if swallowed.

ALCOHOL (denatured ethyl alcohol, or ethyl or isopropyl rubbing alcohol). This may be used for a number of stains if it is safe for the dye on the fabric. Flammable. *Caution:* Poison if swallowed.

Solvents for Greasy Stains

Use these with care. Some are flammable, and all can cause serious illness or death from swallowing the liquids or from breathing too much of the vapors. If used away from flame, with good ventilation, and only in the small quantities needed for spot removal, however, they can be safe and effective.

NONFLAMMABLE. Perchloroethylene, trichloroethane, and trichloroethylene are nonflammable grease solvents. (The latter should not be used on Arnel or Kodel fabrics.) They are sold under these names and under various trade names. Carbon tetrachloride, once very popular as a household cleaning solvent, is now banned and is considered a hazardous substance.

FLAMMABLE. These are less expensive than the nonflammable solvents and are usually distillation products of petroleum. Two suitable types are Stoddard solvent, a petroleum naphtha of high flash point made especially for dry cleaning (and sold also under various other trade names), and V.M. & P. (Varnish Maker's and Painters') naphtha, available in grocery, drug, hardware, and paint stores.

Never use these near an open flame. Don't put them in a washing machine or put articles that have been cleaned with them in a dryer.

MIXTURES. Many spot removers sold in grocery and drugstores under various brand names are mixtures of flammable solvents with enough of the nonflammable type to keep them from burning.

Bleaches for Removing Stains

Bleaches are the most widely used of the chemical stain removers and the ones most likely to damage fibers and fade dyes if directions are not carefully followed.

Three kinds of bleaches are recommended for home use—chlorine bleaches, peroxygen bleaches, and color removers. The first two may generally be used interchangeably. Color removers are used where the bleaches are not effective.

CHLORINE BLEACHES. Never use these on fabrics that contain silk, wool, or spandex fibers, polyurethane foams, or on fabric with a special finish unless the manufacturer states on the label that chlorine bleach is safe.

The commonest bleach of this type is a solution of sodium hypochlorite, sold under such names as Clorox, Purex, and Rose-X. For treatment on washable articles, mix 2 tablespoons of liquid bleach with 1 quart of cool water. Apply to small stains with a medicine dropper; soak large stains in the solution. Leave for 5 to 15 minutes. Rinse well with water. Repeat if necessary.

For stubborn stains mix equal parts of bleach with water. Apply as above, but rinse immediately. Repeat if necessary. Be sure all bleach is finally rinsed out.

On nonwashable articles, use solution of 1 teaspoon of liquid bleach with 1 cup of cool water. Apply with medicine dropper and leave for 5 to 15 minutes. Rinse well and repeat if necessary. (*Note:* Never mix chlorine bleach with ammonia; poisonous gases will result.)

PEROXYGEN BLEACHES. Also called oxygen bleaches, these may contain sodium perborate or potassium monopersulfate, which are powders also sold under various trade names.

For washable articles mix 1 to 2 tablespoons of either chemical with 1 pint of lukewarm water for wool, silk, or Dynel, or 1 pint of hot water for other fabrics. (Hot water shrinks Dynel and is not safe for silk and wool.) Mix just before using, as the solution loses strength on standing.

Cover stained area with solution or soak entire article. Soak until stain is removed. This may take several hours or overnight. Rinse well.

If wool or silk is yellowed by the solution, sponge with 10-percent acetic acid or vinegar, then rinse.

For a stronger treatment, sprinkle sodium perborate or potassium monopersulfate powder directly on stain. Dip stain into very hot or boiling water (do not use this treatment on wool, silk, or Dynel). Stains should vanish in a few minutes. Rinse well. Repeat if necessary.

For nonwashable articles, sprinkle either powder on stain. Cover with a pad of cotton, dampened with lukewarm water for wool, silk, and Dynel, and hot water for other fabrics. Keep damp until stain is removed, which may take hours. Rinse well. To remove yellowing caused by bleach, treat with acetic acid or vinegar as mentioned above.

For strong treatment, dampen stain with cool water. Sprinkle on powdered bleach. With spoon or medicine dropper apply small amount of boiling water to stain. Use a sponge or other absorbent pad under stain to absorb the water. Repeat if necessary.

STAIN REMOVAL

While more information on general stain removal is given later in this chapter, the following instructions can be used for specific kinds of stains.

Stain	Man-made fabrics, washable silk, wool and noncolorfast cottons	Colorfast cottons and linens
Airplane glue	Sponge with fingernail polish remover to dissolve glue, wash in warm water; for acetate, do not use fingernail polish remover containing acetone as it will dissolve the fabric	Same procedure; use hot water
Alcoholic beverages	Sponge immediately with cold water, wash in warm water; remove old stains with peroxygen bleach	Same procedure; use chlorine bleach, wash in hot water
Blood	Soak or sponge with cold water or soak in warm water with a detergent	Soak in cold water; if stains are old, soak in lukewarm ammonia water (3 tablespoons ammonia per gallon of water); wash in hot water; bleach
Candle wax	Remove excess wax; press between blotters with moderately hot iron; sponge with cleaning fluid; bleach remaining stain with oxygen bleach	Same procedure except use chlorine bleach
Chewing gum	Chill and remove excess; sponge with cleaning fluid; wash in hot water	Same procedure
Chlorine bleach	Soak in 2 tablespoons sodium hyposulfite to 1 quart water; or remove yellow with commercial color remover; rinse, then wash in hot water	Same procedure
Chocolate	Soak in warm water with detergent; wash in lukewarm detergent solution; use solvent to remove any grease spots	Soak in warm water with detergent; wash in hot detergent solution; bleach remaining stains
Coffee	Soak in cool water; wash; bleach remaining stain with oxygen bleach	Same procedure; use chlorine bleach
Cosmetic stains	Pretreat before washing; if greasy, treat with a grease solvent; wash in warm water with plenty of detergent; bleach remaining stain with oxygen bleach	Same procedure; use chlorine bleach and hot-water wash

(Continued)

* Permanent-press garments or fabrics containing polyester fibers (Dacron, Fortrel, Kodel, Vycron) should not be rubbed with fat or grease. Use cleaning fluid only.

STAIN REMOVAL *(continued)*

While more information on general stain removal is given later in this chapter, the following instructions can be used for specific kinds of stains.

Stain	Man-made fabrics, washable silk, wool and noncolorfast cottons	Colorfast cottons and linens
Cream, ice cream	Soak in cold water; wash; if grease spot remains, sponge with cleaning fluid	Same procedure
Deodorant	Sponge with white vinegar; for stubborn stains, saturate cotton with denatured alcohol; wash	Same procedure
Dye stain	Wash; bleach remaining stain with oxygen bleach	Wash; bleach remaining stain
Fresh fruit	Sponge with warm water; wash; bleach remaining stain with oxygen bleach	Pour boiling water through stain; wash; bleach remaining stain
Grass	Soak in warm detergent water; wash; bleach remaining stain with oxygen bleach	Soak in warm detergent water; wash; bleach remaining stain
Grease and tar	Use a spotting fluid such as Energine; wash in hot water with detergent	Same procedure
Ink	Washable ink—rub in detergent or glycerine, then wash in warm detergent water and bleach remaining stain with oxygen bleach; Ball point—rub with Vaseline or sponge with cleaning fluid, wash in warm water, bleach with oxygen bleach	Same procedure; use hot water; bleach remaining stain
Lipstick	*Rub with cooking fat or Vaseline; wash in warm detergent solution; bleach remaining stain with oxygen bleach	Sponge with solvent; wash in hot detergent solution; bleach
Mildew (light)	Wash; bleach remaining stain by soaking in an oxygen bleach solution; wash in warm detergent water	Wash; bleach remaining stain by soaking in chlorine bleach solution; wash in warm detergent water
Nail polish	Treat with nail polish remover; for acetates, do not use fingernail polish remover containing acetone as it will dissolve the fabric	Same procedure
Paint	Before washing, treat with turpentine or solvent depending on type of paint	Same procedure

(Continued)

* Permanent-press garments or fabrics containing polyester fibers (Dacron, Fortrel, Kodel, Vycron) should not be rubbed with fat or grease. Use cleaning fluid only.

STAIN REMOVAL *(continued)*

Stain	Man-made fabrics, washable silk, wool and noncolorfast cottons	Colorfast cottons and linens
Perspiration	Sponge fresh stain with ammonia, old stain with white vinegar; rinse; wash in warm water with oxygen bleach (if stain persists, dampen stain with lukewarm water and sprinkle with powdered pepsin, let stand 1 hour, brush off powder and wash in warm water; perspiration odors may be removed by soaking garment in salt solution—3 tablespoons salt to 1 quart warm water—or by sponging with Listerine)	Same procedure, or use pepsin, then wash in hot sudsy water
Scorch	Wash; Bleach with mild oxygen bleach	Wash; bleach with chlorine bleach
Tea	Pour boiling water through stain; wash; bleach with oxygen bleach	Same procedure; use chlorine bleach

INFORMATION ON CLOTHING LABELS

In 1972, the federal government required that most articles of clothing had to carry permanent labels with instructions for care and maintenance of the fabric. The labels must reflect washing and drying procedures and any additional instructions needed for proper care. Here is an interpretation of label meanings:

MACHINE WASHABLE APPAREL

When label reads:	It means
Machine wash	Wash, bleach, dry, and press by any customary method including commercial laundering and dry cleaning
Home launder only	Same as above but do not use commercial laundering
No chlorine bleach	Do not use chlorine bleach; oxygen bleach may be used
No bleach	Do not use any type of bleach
Cold wash Cold rinse	Use cold water from tap or cold washing-machine setting
Warm wash Warm rinse	Use warm water or warm washing-machine setting
Hot wash	Use hot water or hot washing-machine setting
No spin	Remove wash load before final machine-spin cycle
Delicate cycle Gentle cycle	Use appropriate machine setting—otherwise wash by hand
Durable press cycle Permanent-press cycle	Use appropriate machine setting—otherwise use warm wash, cold rinse, and short-spin cycle
Wash separately	Wash alone or with like colors

(Continued)

INFORMATION ON CLOTHING LABELS *(continued)*

MACHINE WASHABLE APPAREL

When label reads:	It means
NONMACHINE WASHING	
Hand wash	Launder only by hand in lukewarm (hand comfortable) water; may be bleached; may be dry-cleaned
Hand wash only	Same as above, but do not dry-clean
Hand wash separately	Hand wash alone or with like colors
No bleach	Do not use bleach
Damp wipe	Surface clean with damp cloth or sponge
HOME DRYING	
Tumble dry	Dry in tumble dryer at specified setting— high, medium, low, or no heat
Tumble dry Remove promptly	Same as above, but in absence of cool-down cycle remove at once when tumbling stops
Drip dry	Hang wet and allow to dry with hand shaping only
Line dry	Hang damp and allow to dry
No wring No twist	Hang dry, drip dry, or dry flat only; handle to prevent wrinkles and distortion
Dry flat	Lay garment on flat surface
Block to dry	Maintain original size and shape while drying
IRONING OR PRESSING	
Cool iron	Set iron at lowest setting
Warm iron	Set iron at medium setting
Hot iron	Set iron at hot setting
Do not iron	Do not iron or press with heat
Steam iron	Iron or press with steam
Iron damp	Dampen garment before ironing
MISCELLANEOUS	
Dry-clean only	Garment should be dry-cleaned only, including self-service
Professionally dry-clean only	Do not use self-service dry-cleaning.
No dry clean	Use recommended care instructions; no dry-cleaning materials to be used

FURTHER CLOTHING LABEL GUIDELINES

The following table further interprets the labels to help make washday simpler and more effective and avoid costly mistakes.

When the label says:	Washer setting	Dryer setting	Line dry	Additional precautions
Machine wash, hot—do not bleach	regular cycle, hot water	regular*	yes	Do not bleach under any circumstances
Machine wash, warm** Do not use chlorine bleach	regular cycle, warm water	regular	yes	Use oxygen bleach only
Machine wash, warm—wash inside out, Line dry	regular cycle, warm water	no	yes	Turn inside out before washing
Machine wash warm gentle Tumble dry low	gentle*** cycle, warm water	low	yes	
Hand wash separately, Line dry	no	no	yes	
Hand wash separately Dry flat	no	no	no	
Dry clean only	no	no	no	
Wipe with damp cloth only	no	no	no	

The above wash-water settings are based on typical home conditions and approximate the following ranges:
Hot—130° to 150° F Warm—90° to 100° F Hand—80° to 100° F Cold—less than 80° F

* The term "regular" encompasses terms such as automatic dry, timed dry, special normal, etc.

** The term "warm" encompasses other terms, such as medium, etc.

*** "Gentle" or "delicate" indicates low-speed agitation and shorter washing periods, or permanent press cycles on dryer.

Other Washing Tips

Here are some other fabric care tips that should be kept in mind:

SORT CLOTHES FOR BEST WASHING RESULTS. Always sort clothes according to fabric, color, and soil. Separate delicates from work clothes for proper wash speed, and separate hot-water fabrics from clothes that should be washed in warm or cold water. Never wash noncolorfast clothes with any other fabrics.

Always separate colored clothes from whites to prevent dye transfer. Use mild water temperatures for colors that might fade in hot water. For permanent-press garments, always use the permanent-press cycles on your washer and dryer. If your washer and dryer do not have permanent-press cycles, use warm wash, cold rinse, and gentle cycle settings in the washer and low temperature setting in the dryer.

To determine the proper water temperatures and dryer setting for your fabrics, use the tables on earlier pages as a general guide and consult the instructions included with your washer and dryer.

BALANCE YOUR LOADS FOR BETTER CLEANING. When you wash large items like sheets and tablecloths, try to keep the load balanced with small items like pillowcases and towels. Mixed loads result in better clothes handling in both the washer and dryer.

SOFTEN YOUR WATER FOR BETTER CLEANING. Soap forms scum in hard water, the same kind of scum that forms bathtub rings. And hard water often means poor soil removal that can yellow or gray many types of fabrics. So if the water in your area is hard, always use a packaged water conditioner made for softening, or have a water softener installed. Call your local water department to find out the condition of water in your area.

PICK OUT THE BEST DETERGENT. Phosphate detergents do the most efficient cleaning job because they soften water, break down greasy soil, and hold soil in suspension until it goes down the drain. Nonphosphate detergents may not do as thorough a cleaning job. Clothes may fade and stiffen and a white deposit may be left on some fibers. But if your area prohibits the use of phosphates, or you choose to use a nonphosphate detergent for the sake of ecology, you can approach the cleaning efficiency of phosphate detergents by adding a water conditioner along with your nonphosphate detergent. Low-sudsing and high-sudsing detergents are equally efficient, but you may need to try several brands before you find the one that works best for you.

Always use a low-sudsing detergent in a front-loading washer to prevent a buildup of foamy suds. When washing delicate fabrics, choose a light-duty detergent or soap.

SELECT BLEACH WITH CAUTION. Chlorine bleaches are good for removing stains, but they can damage some fabrics. Never use chlorine bleach on silks, woolens, or on fabrics that are not colorfast. To determine whether or not a fabric is colorfast, snip off a piece of the seam and test for fading in a chlorine bleach solution. Chlorine bleach can cause discoloration to some permanent-press fabrics. When in doubt, always use the oxygen bleaches that are safe for all fabrics. Always dilute bleach before adding to your wash. Use bleach on the entire fabric so any slight fading will be uniform. If your washer has a bleach dispenser, follow the washer instructions.

SOFTEN FABRICS WHILE THEY WASH. Fabric softeners soften clothes in the washer, help reduce lint build-up, and minimize wrinkles and static cling. Most are added during the rinse cycle. If your washer has a fabric-softener dispenser, you can fill the dispenser at the same time you add detergent. Follow the manufacturer's instructions for proper use.

STARCH FABRICS FOR A CRISP FINISH. Spray starches are now available so you can starch while you iron. If you prefer to starch in your washer, follow the instructions included with the starch and your washer. Never starch soiled items, because stains will set. Not all fabrics can be starched, so check garment labels to make sure starch is not harmful to the fabric.

RENEW YOUR WARDROBE WITH DYE. Dye can give faded clothes new life and brightness. Follow instructions included with the dye and your washer. Be sure all stains are removed, and wash clothes before dyeing. Always wash dyed clothes separately to avoid staining other clothes.

Tips on Hanging Wash

Although most wash today is machine dried, some people still prefer to hang it up for drying. Here are some tips on hanging wash:

1. Always start with a clean clothesline. Fold a soapy cloth so that it encircles the line as you draw it along. Follow this with a cloth wrung out in clear water.
2. Sheets, slipcovers, and other large pieces dry faster when you hang them over parallel lines.
3. To prevent plastic tablecloths and shower curtains from sticking together, weight the hems with spring clothes pins.
4. Hang chenille spreads and shag rugs wrong side out so that the tufted surfaces blow against each other. This will raise the pile.
5. Hang towels and linens one-third over the line. This prevents "dog-ears" at the corners and along the edge.

6. Be sure your "drip-dries" are dripping wet. Remember, it's the water that erases wrinkles.
7. After hanging clothes in freezing weather, let them thaw before folding. The fibers may crack if frozen clothes are folded.
8. When drying clothes indoors, place an electric fan on a small table 2 to 3 feet from the garments. Direct flow of air between the lines. Operate at high speed. Tests show that this will save from 2 to 4 hours drying time.

GENERAL STAIN-REMOVAL DIRECTIONS

If you can't identify the exact nature of the stain, try at least to determine whether it is a greasy stain, a nongreasy stain, or a combination of both. Then proceed as follows:

GREASY STAINS ON WASHABLE ARTICLES. Some may be removed merely by regular washing; others by rubbing liquid detergent into the stain, then rinsing with hot water. If this doesn't work, dry the article and apply grease solvent. Repeat if necessary.

If yellow stain remains after solvent treatment, use chlorine or peroxygen bleach.

GREASY STAINS ON NONWASHABLE ARTICLES. Sponge stain well with grease solvent. Dry. Repeat if necessary. Remove any remaining yellow stain as above.

NONGREASY STAINS ON WASHABLE ARTICLES. Some nongreasy stains are removed by regular laundry methods; others are set by them. Sponge stain with cool water; or soak in cool water from 30 minutes to overnight. If stain remains, work a detergent into it, then rinse. If the stain is still there, try chlorine or peroxygen bleach.

NONGREASY STAINS ON NONWASHABLE ARTICLES. Sponge stain with cool water, or force cool water through stain with a small syringe, using sponge under stain to absorb water. If stain remains, rub detergent in it and work into fabric. Rinse. A final sponging with alcohol helps remove detergent and dry fabric. Test alcohol first on fabric. If stain remains, use chlorine or peroxygen bleach.

COMBINATION STAINS ON WASHABLE ARTICLES. Sponge stain with cool water, or soak in cool water for 30 minutes or longer. If stain remains, work detergent into stain. Then rinse and allow to dry. If a greasy stain remains, sponge with grease solvent. Dry. Repeat if necessary. If colored stain remains, use chlorine or peroxygen bleach.

COMBINATION STAINS ON NONWASHABLE ARTICLES. Sponge stain with cool water, or force cool water through stain with small syringe, using sponge under stain. If stain remains, rub detergent on stain and work it into fabric. Rinse spot well with water. Dry. If greasy stain remains, sponge with grease solvent. Dry. Repeat if necessary. If colored stain remains, use chlorine or peroxygen bleach.

Removing Individual Stains

ACIDS. Rinse with water immediately. Apply household ammonia and rinse again.

ADHESIVE TAPE. Scrape off gummy matter carefully with dull knife. Sponge with grease solvent.

AIRPLANE GLUE, HOUSEHOLD CEMENT. Follow directions for mimeograph correction fluid (see below).

ALCOHOLIC BEVERAGES. Follow directions above for nongreasy stains, or sponge the stain with alcohol, if alcohol does not affect the color. Dilute alcohol with 2 parts water before using on acetate. If a stain remains, use a chlorine or peroxygen bleach.

ALKALIS. Rinse with water immediately, then apply vinegar and rinse again.

ANTIPERSPIRANTS, DEODORANTS. Wash or sponge stain thoroughly with detergent and warm water. Rinse. If stain remains, use chlorine or peroxygen bleach. Antiperspirants that contain such substances as aluminum chloride are acidic and may cause fabric damage and change the color of some dyes. You may be able to restore color of fabric by sponging it with ammonia. Rinse thoroughly. Dilute ammonia with an equal amount of water for use on wool or silk.

BLOOD. Follow directions for nongreasy stains. If detergent does not remove stain, put a few drops of ammonia on the stain and repeat with detergent. Rinse. Follow with bleach treatment if necessary.

BUTTER, MARGARINE. Follow directions for greasy stains.

CANDLE WAX, PARAFFIN. Remove excess wax carefully with a dull knife. (Freezing wax with ice cubes helps in scraping process.) Then place the stained area between clean white blotters or several layers of facial tissues and press with warm iron. Remove remaining wax with grease solvent.

CANDY, SYRUP. If chocolate, follow directions for combination stains. For other candy and syrup, follow directions for nongreasy stains. If you need friction, use wool instead of a cloth except on "no-wax," embossed vinyl asbestos, or hard-surface floors; on them use powdered detergent and a plastic scrubbing pad dampened with warm water.

CANNED OR FROZEN FRUIT JUICE. Saturate a cloth with a solution of 1 part glycerine to 3 parts water and place it over the stain for several hours. If the spot remains, rub it gently with scouring powder and a cloth dampened in hot water.

CARBON PAPER. For regular carbon paper, work detergent into stain. If not removed, put a few drops of ammonia on stain and repeat. Rinse well.

For duplicating carbon paper, sponge stain with alcohol. Dilute alcohol with 2 parts water for use on acetate. If stain remains, rub detergent into it. Wash and rinse well. Repeat if necessary.

CHEWING GUM. Scrape off as much as you can with dull knife, a job made easier if you first harden the gum by rubbing it with ice. If stain remains, sponge thoroughly with a grease solvent.

CHOCOLATE AND COCOA. Follow directions for combination stains.

CIGARETTE BURNS. On resilient tile, rub the stain with a cloth dampened with a concentrated solution of detergent and water. For a heavier stain, rub with scouring powder and a piece of steel wool or plastic pad dipped in water. For wood or cork, rub with a cloth coated with a paste of cigar ash and water. For hard-surfaced floors, rub with a cloth dampened in a solution of lemon juice and water.

COFFEE, TEA. With cream, follow directions for combination stains; without cream, for nongreasy stains.

COSMETICS. On washable articles, apply liquid detergent to stain, or dampen stain and rub in detergent to form thick suds. Work in until outline of stain is gone. Rinse. Repeat if necessary.

On nonwashable articles, sponge with a grease solvent as long as any color is removed. If not removed, use method for washable articles.

CRAYON. Follow directions for cosmetics.

DYES. Follow directions for nongreasy stains. If bleach is needed, use chlorine bleach or color remover. A long soak in sudsy water is often effective on fresh dye stains. Another good application for dye stains is to rub with a cloth dampened in a solution of 1 part chlorine bleach and 2 parts water. If this is not effective, use scouring powder and a cloth dampened with hot water.

EGG. Scrape off as much as possible. Follow directions for nongreasy stains.

FINGERNAIL POLISH. Follow directions for lacquer. Nail polish removers can also be used to remove stains. Do not use on acetate, Arnel, Dynel, or Verel without testing to be sure it won't damage the fabric.

FOOD COLORING. Follow directions for nongreasy stains.

FRUIT. Follow directions for nongreasy stains. Sponge fresh stains immediately with cool water. Some fruit stains, including citrus, are invisible on fabric right after they dry, but turn yellow on aging or heating. This stain may be difficult to remove. To remove stains from resilient tile, wood, or cork floors, rub the stain with a cloth dampened in a solution of 1 tablespoon of oxalic acid and 1 pint of water. If you have hard-surface flooring, rub the stain with powdered pumice.

GLUE, MUCILAGE, ADHESIVE. Casein glue: Follow directions for nongreasy stains.

Plastic glue: Wash stain with detergent and water before glue hardens; some types cannot be removed afterward.

Rubber cement: Let dry and rub off as much as you can with cloth. Remove remainder with grease solvent.

Other types of glue and mucilage: Follow directions for nongreasy stains, except use hot water instead of cool.

GRASS, FOLIAGE, FLOWERS. Washable articles: Work detergent into stains, then rinse. If safe for dye, sponge stain with alcohol. Dilute alcohol with 2 parts water for acetate. If stain remains, use bleach. Nonwashable articles: Use same methods, but try alcohol first if it is safe for dye.

GRAVY, MEAT JUICE. Follow directions for combination stains.

GREASE, CAR GREASE, OIL, LARD. Follow directions for greasy stains. On hard surfaces, remove as much as possible with newspaper, paper towels, or a plastic spatula. On resilient tile, rub with a cloth dampened in liquid detergent and warm water. On wood and cork, put a cloth saturated with dry cleaning fluid on the stain for 5 minutes. Then wipe the area dry and wash with liquid detergent and water. On stone, use Stoddard solvent and a soft clean cloth.

ICE CREAM. Follow directions for combination stains.

INK, BALLPOINT. Washing removes some types of ballpoint ink stains, but sets others. To see if stain will wash out, mark a similar piece of fabric with the ink and wash it. If stain remains, treat as follows: for fresh stains, sponge repeatedly with acetone or amyl acetate. Use amyl acetate on acetate, Arnel, Dynel, and Verel. Use acetone on other fabrics. Old stains may also require bleaching.

INK, DRAWING. Black (India ink): Treat as soon as possible. On washable articles, force water through stain until all loose pigment is removed. Wash with detergent, several times if necessary, then soak in warm suds containing 1 to 4 tablespoons of ammonia to a quart of water. Dried stains may need overnight soak.

On nonwashable articles, force water through stain to remove loose pigment. Sponge stain with solution of 1 tablespoon of ammonia per cup of water. Rinse. If stain remains, moisten with ammonia, then work in detergent. Rinse. Repeat if necessary. If ammonia changes color of fabric, sponge first, with water, then moisten with vinegar. Rinse well.

Colors other than black: Follow directions for nongreasy stains. If bleach is needed, use a color remover if it is safe for dye of fabric. If it is not safe, try other bleaches.

INK, MIMEOGRAPH AND PRINTING. For fresh stains, follow directions for greasy stains, or sponge with turpentine. For stubborn stains, follow directions for paint stains.

INK, WRITING. Follow directions for nongreasy stains. Because writing inks vary in composition, it may be necessary to try more than one kind of bleach. Try chlorine bleach on all fabrics for which it is safe. For other fabrics, try peroxygen bleach. A few types of ink may require color removers. If a yellow stain remains after bleaching, treat as a rust stain.

IODINE. Long soaking in cool water may remove it. The quickest way is to wet the stain with a solution containing 1 tablespoon of sodium thiosulfate (photographers' "hypo") in a pint of warm water, or to sprinkle the crystals on the dampened stain. Rinse well.

LACQUER. Sponge stain with acetone or amyl acetate. Use amyl acetate on acetate, Arnel, Dynel, and Verel. Use acetone on other fabrics.

LIPSTICK. Rub with a cloth dampened in liquid detergent and warm water. If you do not get results, rub with steel wool dipped in water and detergent.

MAYONNAISE, SALAD DRESSING. Follow directions for combination stains.

MEDICINES. (See also Iodine, Mercurochrome, Silver nitrate.) Medicines with an oily base, gummy and tarry medicines: Follow directions for greasy stains.

Medicines in sugar syrup or in water: Wash out with water.

Medicines dissolved in alcohol (tinctures): Sponge stain with alcohol. Dilute with 2 parts water for use on acetate.

Medicines that contain iron: Follow directions for rust.

Medicines that contain dyes: Follow directions for dyes.

MERCUROCHROME, MERTHIOLATE, METAPHEN. If washable, soak article overnight in warm detergent solution containing 4 tablespoons of ammonia to each quart of water.

If not washable, and alcohol is safe for the dye, sponge with alcohol as long as any stain comes out. Dilute alcohol with 2 parts water for acetate. If alcohol is not safe, wet stain with liquid detergent. Add a drop of ammonia with a medicine dropper. Rinse.

MILDEW. Wash mildewed article thoroughly. Dry in the sun. If stain remains, treat with bleach. If article cannot be washed, send to a good dry cleaner.

MILK. Follow directions for combination stains.

MIMEOGRAPH CORRECTION FLUID. Sponge stain with acetone or amyl acetate. Use amyl acetate on acetate, Arnel, Dynel, and Verel; use acetone on other fabrics. (*Caution:* Both of these liquids are flammable and are poisonous if swallowed.)

MUD. Let mud dry, then brush well. If spot remains, follow directions for nongreasy stains. Stains from iron-rich clays not removed by this method should be treated as rust stains.

MUSTARD. Washable articles: Rub detergent into dampened stain. Rinse. If stain is not removed, soak article in hot detergent solution for several hours, or overnight. If stain remains, use bleach.

Nonwashable articles: If safe for dye, sponge stain with alcohol. Dilute alcohol with 2 parts water for use on acetate. If alcohol cannot be used, follow treatment for washable articles, omitting soaking.

OIL—FISH-LIVER, LINSEED, MACHINE, MINERAL, VEGETABLE. Follow directions for greasy stains.

PAINT, VARNISH. Treat stains quickly before paint dries. Read the label on the paint container. If a certain solvent is recommended as a thinner, use this in preference to others.

Washable articles: For fresh stains, rub detergent into stain and wash. If stain is dry or is only partially removed by washing, sponge with turpentine. For aluminum paint, trichloroethylene may be more effective. Do not use this solvent on Arnel or Kodel.

While spot is still wet with solvent, work in detergent, soak in hot water overnight. Launder.

Nonwashable articles: Sponge fresh stains with turpentine; for aluminum paint, sponge with trichloroethylene. Do not use the latter on Arnel or Kodel.

If necessary, loosen more of paint by covering stain for 30 minutes or longer with a pad of cotton dampened with the solvent. Repeat sponging.

If stain remains, put a drop of liquid detergent on stain and work it into the fabric with the edge of the bowl of a spoon.

Alternate sponging with turpentine and treatment with detergent as many times as necessary.

On resilient tile, rub with a cloth or piece of steel wool dipped in warm water and liquid detergent. On wood and cork, rub with a cloth dampened in a solution of 1 tablespoon oxalic acid and 1 pint of water.

On a hard-surfaced floor, scrub with a concentrated solution of powdered detergent and water.

PENCIL MARKS. A soft eraser will remove lead pencil and colored pencil marks from some fabrics. If mark cannot be erased, follow directions for regular carbon paper.

For indelible pencil, follow directions for duplicating carbon paper.

PERFUME. Follow directions for alcoholic beverages.

PERSPIRATION. Wash or sponge stain thoroughly with detergent and warm water. If perspiration has changed the color of fabric, try to restore it by treating with ammonia or vinegar. Apply ammonia to fresh stains, rinse with water. If only stain remains, follow directions for greasy stains.

Remove any yellow discoloration with bleach.

RUST. Moisten stain with solution of 1 tablespoon of oxalic acid (*Caution:* poison if swallowed!) in 1 cup warm water. If stain is not removed, heat the solution and repeat. If stain is stubborn, place oxalic acid crystals directly on stain. Moisten with water as hot as is safe for fabric and let stand for a few minutes. Repeat if necessary. (Do not use this method on nylon.) Rinse article thoroughly. If allowed to remain, oxalic acid will damage fabric.

Color removers for dyes can be used to remove rust stains from white fabrics.

For mild rust stains, spread the stained portion over a pan of boiling water and squeeze lemon juice on it. Or sprinkle salt on the stain, squeeze lemon juice on it, and spread in the sun to dry. Rinse thoroughly. Repeat if necessary.

SAUCES, SOUP. Follow directions for combination stains.

SCORCH. If article is washable, follow directions for nongreasy stains. To remove light scorch on nonwashable articles, use hydrogen peroxide.

On heavy fabrics, you may be able to remove surface scorch with very fine sandpaper.

Severe scorch damages the fabric.

SHELLAC. Sponge the stain with alcohol, or soak the stain in alcohol. Dilute alcohol with 2 parts water for use on acetate. If alcohol bleeds the dye, try turpentine.

SHOE POLISH. Because there are so many kinds of shoe polish, no one method will remove all stains. It may be necessary to try more than one of the following methods:

1. Follow directions for cosmetics.
2. Sponge stain with alcohol, if safe for dye in fabric. Dilute alcohol with 2 parts water for use on acetate.
3. Sponge stain with grease solvent or turpentine. If turpentine is used, remove by sponging with a warm detergent solution.

If none of these work, use a bleach.

On resilient flooring, rub with a cloth dampened in a concentrated detergent solution, or use scouring powder, water, and a piece of steel wool. On wood and cork, rub gently with steel wool.

SILVER NITRATE. Dampen stain with water, then put a few drops of tincture of iodine on it. After several minutes, treat as an iodine stain.

Unless stain on silk or wool is treated when fresh, a brown discoloration will remain.

SOFT DRINKS. Follow directions for nongreasy stains.

SOOT, SMOKE. Follow directions for cosmetics.

TAR. Follow directions for greasy stains. To remove tar from hard surfaces, freeze it to brittleness with ice cubes and then scrape it off with a plastic spatula. To remove the tar stain, apply a damp cloth wrapped around a paste made of powdered detergent, calcium carbonate, and water. Leave the paste on the stain for several hours.

TEA. See Coffee.

TOBACCO. For cloth or fabric, follow directions for grass. For other materials, rub with a cloth dampened in a solution of lemon juice and water. If that isn't effective, place a cloth soaked in hydrogen peroxide over the stain, and over that place an ammonia-worked cloth.

URINE. Follow directions for nongreasy stains. If color of fabric has been changed, sponge stain with ammonia. If this does not restore color, sponging with acetic acid or vinegar may help.

If none of these methods work, see directions for medicines and yellowing.

VEGETABLES. Follow directions for nongreasy stains.

YELLOWING, BROWN STAINS. If these are caused by the use of chlorine bleaches on fabrics with some types of wash-and-wear finishes, use one of the following treatments:

For any fabric: Rinse thoroughly with water, then soak for at least 30 minutes in a solution of 1 teaspooon of sodium thiosulfate to each quart of warm water. Rinse thoroughly. To intensify treatment make solution as hot as is safe for the material.

Treatment for white or fast-color fabrics: Rinse thoroughly with water, then use a color remover according to instructions on package.

To remove stains of unknown origin, try as many of the following treatments as necessary, in the order given:

1. Wash.
2. Use a mild treatment of bleach.
3. Use oxalic acid method for rust.
4. Use a strong treatment of bleach.

9

Common Products with Many Uses

CLEANING WITH TRISODIUM PHOSPHATE (TSP)

Need a wall cleaner, a floor-wax remover, a water softener, a detergent for grimy clothes, a cleaner for silverware, your car radiator, or your grandpa's dentures? Just mix trisodium phosphate with the proper amounts of water and you can make them all! Under hundreds of brand names and use names, you have probably been buying and using this versatile chemical right along. By buying it under its own name, or as TSP, and learning how to mix it for its various uses, you not only save money but need store only one product that will do jobs that previously required a dozen.

TSP comes as a white crystalline powder that dissolves completely in hot or cold water and differs from soap in that it makes no suds and leaves no scum. It cleans by emulsifying oil and grease-bound dirt, breaking them down into particles that plain water can wash away.

Although TSP is now harder to purchase by its own name than it used to be, it is still plentiful at dealers in institutional and janitors' supplies, some paint and hardware stores, and from large mail-order firms such as Sears and Montgomery Ward. It is available in packages varying in size from 1 to 100 pounds. You get the same thing by such names as "wax remover" or "denture cleaner," but you pay about one-tenth their price when purchasing TSP.

Here are a few of the many ways you can use it:

WOODWORK. One to 2 teaspoons in a pail of lukewarm water cleans paint. Rinse with a wet cloth and wipe off. Never sprinkle dry TSP on the cloth or on the painted surface to be cleaned. A little stronger or hotter solution will remove high gloss. Don't make it too strong or too hot, however, or it will remove the paint.

FLOORS. TSP will not injure marble, tile, linoleum, or rubber. Will not turn marble yellow or leave floors slippery. Use 1 tablespoon in a pail of water, and clean in usual manner. For thoroughly cleaning unpainted cement or concrete floors, use 2 to 4 tablespoons of TSP in a pail of water, scrubbing the surface with a mop or a long-handled scrubbing brush. Rinse with clear water and let dry.

TILE AND TUBS. Scum on wash bowls, sinks, and bathtubs is undissolved grease or soap deposits made insoluble by the minerals in hard water. Scouring with TSP on a wet cloth will remove it. The powdered chemical will not harm porcelain or ceramic tile, but do not use it to scour other finishes.

RANGES AND REFRIGERATORS. Clean these and other equipment having a finish of baked-on enamel with TSP at a strength of 1 teaspoon to a pail of lukewarm water. Wash your refrigerator inside and out with a cloth wet with the solution. Rinse and wipe dry. Clean gas or electric ranges, washing machines, and enameled steel cabinets the same way.

DISHWASHING. One teaspoon in warm water will give you clean and sparkling dishes without soap. Greasy pans and cooking utensils caked with burned food can be cleaned by boiling in them a solution of about 2 tablespoons of TSP per gallon of water. Do not, however, boil TSP or any other alkaline solution in aluminum pans, as aluminum is corroded and darkened by alkalis. Give this metal a quick wash with warm TSP solution, but do not soak or boil.

CLEANING SILVERWARE. A solution of TSP and an aluminum pan is all you need for a popular no-rub method of cleaning silver tableware. For full directions, see "Cleaning Silver Electrically" on page 268.

LAUNDRY. Soaking clothes for half an hour or overnight in a bath of TSP helps loosen heavy soil and makes subsequent washing easier. TSP in the wash water permits the use of less detergent. It may be used alone to wash delicate fabrics. For further information, see Chapter 8.

CAR-COOLING SYSTEMS. For many years TSP was one of the principal cleaners for car radiators and cooling systems. It is still widely used. For details, see the section entitled "Car-Cooling System Cleaners" to be found on page 282.

GREASE FROM MACHINES. TSP is excellent for removing grease from motors, engines, and other mechanical parts. Use about an ounce in a pail of hot water, and apply with a rough rag or a stiff brush. Rinse with plain water and wipe dry. For cleaning metals before electroplating, use 4 ounces to a gallon of hot water.

PAINT AND VARNISH REMOVER. For one of the cheapest and best, see the next entry.

PAINTBRUSH CLEANER. Especially good for brushes on which the paint has dried hard. To find out how to clean brushes and to remove paint with TSP, see Chapter 2.

DENTURE CLEANER. The Council on Dental Therapeutics of the American Dental Association considers TSP one of the best cleansers for dentures, and many proprietary denture-cleaning preparations consist of TSP alone or with color, flavor, or scent added. For formulas, see Chapter 11.

SODIUM HEXAMETAPHOSPHATE (THE CALGON CONNECTION)

Did you know you could use a popular laundry and dishwashing chemical to soak beans faster, remove scale from inside your steam iron, keep spots off your photo prints and negatives, make your eyeglasses sparkle, tint Easter eggs more evenly, wash your dog?

This chemical-of-many-uses had been a laboratory curiosity for more than a hundred years. Then, in 1929, it was put to its first commercial use as a conditioner of boiler water. Whenever hard water is used in producing steam in heat and power plants, a thick coating of calcium and magnesium salts gradually builds up inside the boilers, drastically reducing their thermal efficiency. Ordinary water softeners precipitate the harmful salts, but leave them as a sludge that has to be removed from time to time.

After long investigation, Dr. R. E. Hall, a Bureau of Mines researcher retained by a chemical company in Pittsburgh, found that the rare chemical, sodium hexametaphosphate, could change all this. Instead of precipitating the offending salts, sodium hexametaphosphate "sequestered" them. That is, it seized them and so tied them in a complex compound with itself that they completely lost their identity and along with that, all their harmful effects. Hall invented the trade name Calgon from "calcium gone," a description of one of the chemical's abilities in softening water.

From conditioning boiler water, it was just a short step to softening water for all kinds of cleaning purposes. Grayness commonly seen on laundered linens, the traditional "bathtub ring," a cloudy film on washed glassware and dishes, all are due to insoluble calcium soap that cannot be washed away by ordinary means. Calgon was put to work on these and other jobs.

During World War II, almost the entire production of Calgon was used by the United States armed forces to help speed ships and for military dishwashing and laundry. Since then, it has found a thousand new jobs in industry and has also come to the grocery store and supermarket as a water conditioner for home laundering (see Chapter 8) and for hand dishwashing. (Calgonite, designed specifically for automatic dishwashers, is a separate product that contains several strong detergents as well as Calgon.)

Besides these two everyday applications, the unique properties of Calgon enable it to do many other things around the house that are not so well known. Here are just a few:

IN THE BATH. Put about 4 tablespoons of Calgon in the bathtub and let it dissolve under the faucet as the tub is filling. Use less soap than usual and get full lather. When finished, there will be no greasy soap film on your skin and no ring around the tub.

BATHROOM SINKS, SHOWERS, TOILET BOWLS. Soap scum and stains in these facilities may be eliminated by rinsing them regularly with a solution of about 1 teaspoon of Calgon to a gallon of water. It disperses and washes away these accumulations and other substances that clog drains.

BATHING YOUR DOG. By using Calgon with soap in the bath and Calgon alone in the first rinse, you can keep your dog's hair softer and glossier. The water conditioner removes dulling film and helps prevent skin irritation. Rinse finally with plain water.

SHAMPOOING YOUR HAIR. What's good for your dog's hair is good for yours, too! Add about 1 teaspoon of Calgon to a gallon of warm water. Thoroughly wet your hair with this solution, then wash it with a mild soap or shampoo preparation. Rinse with what's left of the Calgon solution, and then with plain water.

SHAVING. This will be cleaner and faster if you first wash with conditioned water and soap. After shaving, rinse with conditioned water to remove remaining soap.

HAND DISHWASHING. Conditioned water prevents the formation of a film that dulls and spots dishes. Grease and dirt stay suspended, to finally go down the drain. No ring will form in the dishpan, and dishes, glasses, and silverware will dry spot-free, after rinsing, without wiping. Follow this procedure:

1. Dissolve 2 teaspoons of Calgon in a dishpan of hot water; add more if water is very hard.
2. Add about one-half the usual amount of soap or detergent.
3. Wash glasses first, then silver, and finally dishes.
4. Rinse with hot water.
5. Merely stack to dry; do not towel dry.

Note: Do not use Calgonite for hand dishwashing; this product contains an alkali effective for machine washing but is irritating to the hands.

DISCOLORATION ON ALUMINUM UTENSILS. To remove dark discoloration from inside of aluminum pans, fill with water and add ½ to 1 teaspoon of Calgon. Bring water to boil and simmer for 3 minutes. Because Calgon solution is practically neutral, it will not injure aluminum as solutions of alkaline water softeners or detergents will.

COFFEE POTS. They can be kept free from film and odor by washing them regularly in conditioned water.

ELECTRIC APPLIANCES. Appliances that can't be completely immersed in dishwater respond to Calgon treatment. To clean electric skillets, deep-fat fryers, and electric cookers, follow this method:

1. Scrape the appliance clean or wipe with a paper towel.
2. Fill with water, stir in a tablespoon of Calgon, and add your regular soap or detergent. Boil for 5 minutes.
3. Pour off the soapy water and refill with warm water to rinse. The Calgon will hold any remaining grease in suspension so it can be poured safely down the drain.

CLEANING FRUITS AND VEGETABLES. Unlike any other cleaning aid, Calgon is tasteless and nontoxic. For this reason you can use it to soak and clean fruits and vegetables, with results superior to the use of water alone. Cleaning berries, for instance, is easier with this method. Soak them for 5 minutes in water containing 1 tablespoon of Calgon per gallon, then rinse them in plain water. Soil and most spray residues will rinse away. To remove fine sand and grit from leafy vegetables, separate the leaves and soak and rinse them the same way. Likewise with fresh mushrooms.

QUICK SOAKING FOR NAVY BEANS. These need not be soaked overnight before cooking. Just soak them for several hours in the conditioner bath mentioned for berries and vegetables.

STEAM IRONS. Just as Calgon can remove scale from the boilers of steamships and power plants, it can do so from the inside of your steam iron. At least once a month use a solution of Calgon to remove mineral incrustations from the water reservoir of the iron and to open the steam holes. Pour a solution of 1 teaspoon of Calgon to a cup of water into the iron and set the heat control on cotton. When steam starts coming out, hold the iron at arm's length over the sink and shake gently to circulate the water in the reservoir. Be careful, for the water in the iron is boiling hot! Keep the solution in the iron for about 15 minutes, shaking it several more times. Drain it and fill with tap water. Repeat the above procedure with water alone. Drain and rinse several times. Be sure all the water is out before storing.

EYEGLASSES. They can be kept spotlessly clean by washing them frequently with conditioned water and then rinsing them.

COLORING EASTER EGGS. This can be done with less streaking and spotting if you add a pinch of Calgon to the dye solution. This will help spread the dye more evenly.

SPOTS ON PRINTS AND NEGATIVES. This can be reduced if you add about ¼ teaspoon of Calgon to each quart of developing solution. By reacting with the developer, water-hardness minerals can cause "sludge" or "scum" that produces spots or streaks on paper or film. Conditioned water ties up these minerals, preventing the reaction.

WASHING SODA

Sodium carbonate, in the form of sal soda or washing soda—another old standby—is a more alkaline relative of the bicarbonate. By cutting through oil and grease, sal soda helps in heavy-duty cleaning. As a softener for hard water, it lets you use less of the more expensive soap or detergent to get the same cleaning results with clothes or dishes.

LAUNDRY. For soiled play clothes and greasy work clothes, add ¼ cup of washing soda to the tub or washer and less soap or detergent than usual. The combination will get rid of stubborn dirt better than soap or detergent alone. To clean tub or washer after use, fill with warm water and add ¼ cup of washing soda. Let stand 15 minutes, then drain and rinse.

DISHES, GLASSWARE, POTS AND PANS. For dishes and glassware, add 1 heaping tablespoon of washing soda to the water in your dishpan. Use less soap or detergent. Double the amount of soda for pots and pans. For scouring, apply the granules with a moist cloth or sponge. Do not, however, boil or soak aluminum ware in soda or any other alkaline solution.

RANGES. Clean broilers and clogged-up gas burners by soaking them for a few minutes in hot water to which 2 heaping tablespoons of washing soda have been added. Boiling (not in an aluminum pan, however) hastens the action.

DRAINS AND TRAPS. Washing soda will help keep drains and traps open without endangering a septic tank or corroding plumbing. Pour 3 tablespoons down the drain at least once a week and run very hot water slowly until the granules dissolve.

BARBECUE GRILL. To remove hardened accumulations of grease, apply washing soda dry with a moist, stiff-bristled brush. Rinse and dry.

GARBAGE PAILS. If washed regularly with a solution of ¼ pound of washing soda to a pail of water your garbage pails will stay sanitary.

GARAGE FLOORS. Scatter washing soda generously over grease spots, sprinkle with water, and let stand overnight. Next day scrub with water and hose off.

CAR RADIATORS. See Chapter 7, under "Car-Cooling System Cleaners."

Javelle Water

If you want to remove ink spots on wallpaper, clean a badly discolored porcelain tub, or take up coffee stains from a patio floor, javelle water will do the job and plenty more like it.

The formula for making this popular spot and stain removing solution is: Dissolve half a pound of washing soda in a quart of cold water, then add a quarter pound of chloride of lime, with the lumps crushed. Let the mixture stand until the sediment settles. Draw off the clear liquid, straining it through a fine cloth (not cheesecloth). Put the clear liquid in brown or amber glass bottles, and keep it tightly stoppered.

After using javelle water, be sure to always rinse the cleaned surface with clear water.

BAKING SODA

Bicarbonate of soda or baking soda has been a household standby for more than a century. Your ancestors used it to raise bread and cake, clean pots and clothes, relieve insect bites and sore feet, settle an upset stomach, clean teeth, and gargle throats. On occasion it was also used to smother a fire. Although much more expensive products to perform the same jobs have been developed during the years since, cheap, easily obtainable "bicarb" can still hold its own with the best of them.

Bicarbonate of soda owes its cleaning and sweetening action to the fact that it breaks down slowly into carbon dioxide gas and alkaline sodium carbonate when it is dissolved in water. Heating the solution hastens this decomposition. The evolution of carbon dioxide gas from sodium bicarbonate enables it to raise bread and to put out fires.

Bicarbonate for Cleaning

LAUNDRY. The gentlest of the household-cleaning alkalis, baking soda is easy on delicate fabrics as well as on your hands. As a natural deodorizer, it is especially effective for soaking and washing diapers. Add ½ cup of soda to an ordinary washing-machine load.

REFRIGERATORS AND FREEZERS. For inside surfaces, sprinkle baking soda on a damp cloth and wipe all surfaces including shelves and racks. Rinse with clear hot water and dry. It cuts film and removes stains without scratching. Wash ice trays, crisper boxes, and food containers in a solution of 3 tablespoons of baking soda in a quart of warm water. Rinse in clear hot water and dry. By chemical action the soda removes unpleasant odors.

COFFEE POTS. Wash glass or stainless steel (not aluminum, for any hot alkaline substance will darken or pit this metal) coffeepots in a solution of 3 tablespoons of soda in 1 quart of warm water. Or, if you prefer, run the coffee maker (with aluminum coffee basket removed) through its regular cycle with a solution of the same strength in place of coffee. Rinse in clear hot water and dry well. This will remove film of coffee oils that soap and detergents can't reach.

FOOD AND DRINK CONTAINERS. Vacuum bottles, picnic jugs, ice buckets, lunch boxes, and bread boxes can all be purged of stale odors that might be absorbed by subsequent food by simple soda treatment. Wash containers first in hot soapy water. Sprinkle 2 tablespoons baking soda in each. Partly fill with warm water and wash. Shake bottles well. Rinse in clear hot water. Dry containers but let bottles air dry.

SILVERWARE. Baking soda sprinkled on a damp cloth can pinch-hit for regular silver polish. Rub until tarnish has gone. Rinse well and dry.

PORCELAIN, GLASS, AND PLASTIC. Baking soda cuts soil and grease from all these surfaces without scratching. To clean porcelain or enameled bathtubs and sinks, tiled surfaces, shower curtains, mirrors, glass or plastic dinnerware, sprinkle soda on damp cloth and rub. Rinse with clear hot water and dry.

MARBLE-TOPPED FURNITURE. Wash in a solution of 3 tablespoons of soda in 1 quart of warm water. Let stand a few minutes, then rinse with warm water. For stubborn stains, scour with a paste of soda, then rinse and dry.

COMBS AND BRUSHES. Soak a few minutes in the soda solution mentioned above. This will loosen the dirt particles and oily film for easier cleaning.

BURNED FOOD FROM FRYING PANS. Moisten the pans, if too dry, and sprinkle generously with baking soda. Food then rubs off more easily.

ONION AND FISH SCENT FROM HANDS. Dampen hands and sprinkle baking soda over them. Rub hard. Rinse and dry.

ASH TRAYS. Sweeten and clean with 1 tablespoon soda dissolved in 1 quart of water. Wipe or scrub, rinse, and dry. A sprinkling of dry soda in the bottom of ash trays will prevent smoldering and reduce odor of ashes.

Bicarbonate in Baking

Bicarbonate of soda was the first chemical leavening agent used. It works by reacting with a mild acid to release carbon dioxide gas. This gas forms in the batter or dough and expands during the baking causing the product to raise. Today most cakes, cookies, and hot breads are still leavened by it.

BAKING POWDER. This is merely a combination of baking soda with an acid in powder form, plus an inert powder to keep the other ingredients dry.

Here is one you can put together in a jiffy:

Cream of tartar	2 parts
Baking soda	1 part
Cornstarch	1 part

Stir these ingredients well and sift them together several times to make sure they are thoroughly mixed. The purpose of the cornstarch is to prevent the other two substances from reacting with each other before use because of moisture from the air. If you intend to use the entire batch immediately, you may omit the starch.

BUTTERMILK AND VINEGAR. Before the invention of baking powder, carbon dioxide was released from baking soda by mixing it with sour milk. Today other acid ingredients such as molasses, fruit, buttermilk, or vinegar are combined with baking soda for the same purpose. For most uniform action, the soda is first mixed and sifted with the flour. The acidic substance is added with the liquid ingredients.

As the acid content of vinegar is constant, a fixed proportion of soda to vinegar assures uniform results. This proportion is 1 level teaspoon of soda to 2 tablespoons of vinegar. Since the acidic content of other acid ingredients is apt to vary, the final product may not always be the same. To produce full leavening from 1 teaspoon of baking soda with buttermilk, for instance, may require anywhere from 1 to 1½ cups of the latter. Specific recipes using baking soda may be found in regular cookbooks and also may often be obtained free from soda manufacturers.

Bicarbonate in the Bathroom

UPSET STOMACH. Whenever effervescing tablets or powders will relieve acid indigestion or heartburn, baking soda will usually do just as well because it is the active ingredient in these products. Take ½ teaspoon in ½ glass of water.

GARGLE. Use a solution of the same strength to gargle your mouth and throat. It cleans and sweetens as well as many more costly preparations.

DENTIFRICE. Natural teeth and dentures can be cleaned effectively with baking soda. Just sprinkle a goodly amount on a wet toothbrush and clean as usual.

INSECT BITES. Apply directly as a paste made with a little water. Keep the soda moist by applying a wet cloth. It soothes the stinging and itching.

RASHES AND POISON IVY. For local rashes, apply as for insect bites. When the skin irritation is more general, take a soda bath, using a cup of soda to a tub of warm water.

Bicarbonate Fire Extinguisher

Most dry-powder fire extinguishers owe their effectiveness to carbon dioxide, derived by the action of heat on bicarbonate of soda. On being heated, the bicarbonate decomposes to form sodium carbonate and carbon dioxide. This reaction extracts a large amount of heat from the fire. In addition, the carbon dioxide acts as a smothering agent.

IN THE KITCHEN. Wherever you have a box of baking soda, you therefore have an emergency fire extinguisher. For grease and oil fires around the kitchen range—where water would only spread the blaze—bicarbonate is especially effective. Just break open the box and scatter the powder loosely by the handful. Since soda is itself a cooking ingredient, it cannot harm food and it can be rinsed away once the fire is out.

IN THE CAR AND GARAGE. A box of bicarbonate of soda may also be a lifesaver. It could end a fire in seat cushions, floor mat, engine, or an oil fire on the garage floor, in seconds—without damaging anything it touches. Again, the best way to apply it is to scatter it by the handful, separating the particles as much as possible to form a cloud of powder.

THE MANY USES OF COMMON SALT

Everybody knows that without sodium chloride, or common salt, food is tasteless. Not many know, however, that there are many other uses for salt around the kitchen and home. Here are a few:

Around the Home

WOODEN CLOTHESPINS. These will last longer and will not freeze onto your clothesline in cold weather if you first boil them in a strong solution of salt.

CRACKED EGGS. You can boil eggs without their contents oozing out if you add a teaspoon of salt to each pint of water. The salt in the water increases its density so the osmotic pressure between the fluids inside and outside the egg shell is balanced. This prevents additional fluid from making its way inside the egg and forcing the contents out.

NUT MEATS. If you soak the nuts overnight in salt water before cracking them, the nut meats will come out whole from their shells. The water expands the shells, while the salt prevents the loss of flavor from the meats.

BRASS, COPPER, AND PEWTER. These respond brilliantly to a paste made of salt and vinegar, thickened with flour. Apply the paste, allow to remain for an hour, then rub it off. Wash and polish with a soft cloth. Do not, of course, use this or any other metal cleaner on lacquered objects. Use it only on bare metal.

CUT FLOWERS. You can keep cut flowers longer if you add a little salt to the water in which they stand. The salt resists the growth of decay bacteria.

TO REMOVE A NEW STAIN OR INK SPOT FROM THE CARPET. Pour a mound of table salt immediately on the wet spot. After a few moments brush up the salt and apply more, repeating until the stain has been soaked up and as much as possible of what remains has been bleached. Old spots may be lightened and made less conspicuous by wetting with water and applying a thick coating of salt.

MAKING CREAM WHIP MORE RAPIDLY. Add a pinch of salt to the cream before you begin. The salt strengthens the fat cells.

RUSTY IRONS. If rusty, rough, or sticky from caked starch, irons can be smoothed to a glasslike finish by rubbing with slightly dampened salt applied with a piece of rumpled paper.

SLIP-PROOFING SLIPPERY FISH. Before cleaning, dip your fingers into a dish of salt.

COOKING FOOD FASTER. In a double boiler, add salt to the water in the outer part. The salt raises the boiling point of water.

CLEANING IVORY-HANDLED KNIVES AND PIANO KEYS. Use a mixture of lemon juice and salt. In cleaning piano keys, make sure none of the liquid runs down between the keys.

PATCHING PLASTER. To fill a hole left in a plaster wall by a nail, use equal parts of salt and starch, with just enough water to make a stiff putty. You can paint over this immediately with water or emulsion paints, but you must wait for the stuff to dry before applying oil-solvent paints.

In the Bathroom

EYEWASH, MOUTHWASH, AND GARGLE. Dissolve a scant teaspoon of table salt in a pint of warm water. Because salt water at this concentration has approximately the same density as the body fluids, its action is more soothing than higher or lower concentrations.

TOOTH POWDER. Dry salt, sprinkled on a wet toothbrush, makes a cheap and excellent dentifrice.

HOT-WATER BOTTLE SUBSTITUTE. Pour the salt into a pan and heat it in the oven until it is quite hot. Then pour it into a cotton bag. It will hold its heat for a long time.

Salt for Killing Weeds

Rock salt is one of the oldest and most economical weed killers. Apply it generously where weeds come up in the cracks of sidewalks and beside driveways or any place where unwanted weeds can grow. Spread the dry salt liberally. The first rain will dissolve it completely and the resulting brine will attack the roots and kill the plant.

Use rock salt to prevent the growth of weeds on tennis courts and parking areas. To reduce fire hazards, use it also to remove vegetation from fire lanes, around oil tanks, piles of lumber, and so on. Less is needed to kill tender grass than more stubborn weeds. Under average conditions, about 2 pounds should be used for each square yard. To kill poison ivy, use 4 pounds to the square yard.

Cut high and thick vegetation immediately before or after application. A second application may be needed for the complete eradication of all growth. (*Caution:* Since salt is so effective in making ground sterile, do not use it near grass plots, trees, flower gardens, or vegetable gardens—with one exception, asparagus beds.)

SOAP DOES MORE THAN WASH.

From creating realistic artificial snow for your Christmas tree to detecting gas leaks, from stopping runs in nylon stockings to lubricating stubborn windows and drawers, ordinary household soap may be put to dozens of uses besides the fundamental one of washing with it. Here are a few suggestions:

PATTERNS FOR CASTINGS. Small metal parts for ship and other models can be carved in soap. Having no grain, soap is much easier to carve into small objects than soft wood, the material commonly used for this purpose. Because of its greasy nature, it will not stick to a plaster mold.

PLASTER CASTINGS. These will not stick to rubber or plaster molds that have been lubricated with soap. All you need to do is brush strong soapy water or liquid soap over the inside of the mold before pouring the plaster.

GREASING SCREWS AND NAILS. By rubbing screws and nails on a bar of soap, you make them easier to drive into hard wood. Soaping not only saves work, but also lessens the danger of splitting.

BEFORE TACKLING A DIRTY JOB. Rub wet soap into your hands and scratch some under your fingernails. Let it dry there. When your work is done, the grime will wash off much more easily—and your nails will be perfectly clean!

LEAKS IN GAS-PIPE JOINTS. These are located easily and safely by painting around the suspected joint with soapsuds. Gas flowing through the suds will produce bubbles that will reveal the point of the leak.

DETERMINING WATER SOFTENER NEEDS. Put a measured amount of distilled water in a bottle and, drop by drop, add a strong solution of soap in rubbing alcohol until an even layer of suds is formed when the bottle is shaken. Now empty the bottle, fill it with tap water, and see how much softener must be added to this tap water to give the same result with the same number of drops of the solution.

STICKING DRAWERS. These slide easily after their runners have been rubbed with a moistened cake of soap. The same treatment is effective for doors that stick, the soap being rubbed on the places that scrape. For loosening stubborn windows, rub soap in the jambs and stop strips—if you can move the window enough to get at them.

SUCTION CUPS. These stick better and stay put longer on walls, tile, or woodwork if their edges are rubbed on a wet piece of soap or a soapy cloth before they are applied. If this is done, the cup will also have less tendency to leave an indelible ring on the wall when it is removed.

RETOUCHING PHOTOGRAPHS. If you mix a little soap in the water for moistening the spotting colors, the colors spread more easily on a glossy or oily surface.

RUNS IN NYLON STOCKINGS. Soap can stop runs temporarily. Just moisten the corner of a cake of soap and rub it on the top of the run. This treatment will keep the run from spreading until there is an opportunity to change stockings and make permanent repairs.

PINCUSHION SOAP. A bar of soap makes a handy place to stick needles and pins. What's more, it lubricates them so they will go through stiff fabrics with less effort. In sewing, an occasional jab of the needle into soap helps.

ARTIFICIAL SNOW. For your Christmas tree, "snow" can be made by beating up a thick suds of powdered soap or flakes with an egg beater and applying it to the branches with a spatula or a cake icer. To give it more sparkle, some of the mica or plastic flakes sold as artificial snow may be mixed with the suds, or sprinkled on the branches while the foam is still wet.

MORE USES FOR LINSEED OIL

Besides serving as a smooth-flowing and durable vehicle for paint, varnish, and stain, linseed oil can perform many other useful jobs around the home and shop. It can beautify and protect wood surfaces and keep them from drying out, it can protect metal from moisture, and it can give longer life to rope.

Raw linseed oil may be used where drying time is not important. *Boiled* linseed oil—raw oil containing drying chemicals—should be used where quick drying is desirable. (*Caution:* When practical, burn rags that have been used to apply linseed oil immediately after use; otherwise store them temporarily in covered metal cans or spread them out to dry in a well-ventilated place. The heat produced by the oxidation of the oil may cause exposed piles of rags to catch fire spontaneously.)

Remove excess oil from surfaces that must be handled. Rub to a finger-touch dry to eliminate any stickiness. If they stay sticky, remove the excess with turpentine or mineral spirits. Do not use linseed oil and turpentine mixture on lacquered finishes, since turpentine may dissolve the lacquer.

Never *boil* a mixture of linseed oil and turpentine; it will catch fire!

Uses for Linseed Oil

BREAD BOARDS. After you treat their surfaces, they clean easier. First scrub the board and let it dry thoroughly, then sand the surface smooth. Apply boiled linseed oil with a soft cloth. After 30 minutes rub oil into the wood and wipe off excess. Sand very lightly after it is dry, and let stand at least 24 hours before using.

CHOPPING BLOCKS. To prevent chopping blocks from staining and getting water soaked, give the wood two or three coats of raw linseed oil. Apply each coat liberally and wipe off excess after 2 hours. Then rub well with coarse cloth. Let dry about 48 hours between coats. After long use, another coat may be necessary.

WOODEN TOOL HANDLES. These last longer and keep looking like new if you treat them with a thin coat of linseed oil, and repeat whenever the finish begins to show signs of wear.

LADDERS. To maintain the flexibility and the strength of your ladder and to prevent splintering, coat it at least once a year with boiled linseed oil.

WOODEN HAMMER HANDLES. To prevent loose heads resulting from drying and shrinking of the handles, tighten the head onto the hammer with a wedge. Then stand the hammer on its head in linseed oil. This treatment will keep the hammer head securely in place.

NAILS AND SCREWS. These drive easier if you first dip them in linseed oil. The thin tough coating that the oil forms around them will also help prevent wood rot.

BEFORE GLAZING A WINDOW. Give the wood where the glass is to rest a coat of boiled linseed oil. This will seal the wood and keep it from absorbing oil from the putty. Then spread a thin coat of putty in the sash to form a bed. Lay in the pane, and press gently in place. Drive in glazier's points and apply remainder of putty. If putty is too stiff, add a few drops of linseed oil and knead thoroughly.

BIRD HOUSES. For a bird house with a long-lasting natural-wood finish, first cut all pieces to size. Then soak them for 24 hours in boiled linseed oil. Let the pieces dry before you assemble them.

FLAGPOLE ROPES. Treated with linseed oil, ropes last longer. Wipe new rope with the oil before stringing. If rope is already in place, put a little oil in a pan and draw the rope through it.

TO REMOVE TAR FROM YOUR CAR OR OTHER METAL. Soak spots with raw linseed oil. Allow to stand until soft, then wipe clean with a soft cloth dampened with the oil.

SCREENS AND WINDOWS. Before installing them, touch up unpainted edges with boiled linseed oil to seal the wood and prevent swelling from moisture. Wiping the screen mesh with a mixture of 2 parts boiled linseed oil and 1 of turpentine, applied with a piece of short-nap carpet, will help prevent rust. Remove excess oil and let screen dry before hanging.

STICKING DOORS, DRAWERS, AND WINDOWS. This usually occurs because moisture enters through the raw edges, causing them to warp or swell. To prevent this, apply with a cloth a thin mixture of the 2-to-1 oil-turpentine mixture to the window grooves and to the unpainted edges of the sash, window frame, door, or drawer runners. All should be dry before treatment.

10

Arts and Crafts

ETCHING ON METAL

In etching, a metal plate is first covered with a ground or resist, which is an acid-resisting coating of wax, pitch, or asphaltum. The desired design is scratched through this and the plate is then treated with the etching fluid.

Of the waxes, paraffin is widely used, being cheap and always available. A thin, even coat is produced by pouring the melted paraffin over the plate, which has itself been warmed. Waxes, however, sometimes cause trouble during scribing. If the coating is too cold and hard, it will chip; if too warm, it will pull.

Ready-made asphaltum varnish may prove more satisfactory for most decorative work. When it is allowed to dry hard, it will cut well and leave clear, sharp lines. If asphaltum varnish gets too cold, it may become too stiff to apply. If it is still too thick to spread well at 70° F, thin with a little turpentine.

After etching, varnish may be removed with turpentine.

Etching Solutions

Solutions for etching metal should always be mixed and applied in glass containers or containers heavily coated with asphaltum. Glass photographic trays or baking pans are excellent for flat work. Rectangular, one-piece fish tanks will serve for large work.

Nitric acid is used in etching most metals. For fast etching, this may be used full strength. For slower action, carefully stir 1 part of acid in 1 part of water. When the process is carried out with a diluted solution, it is well to stir occasionally or to rock the tray to remove bubbles and scale that may interfere with even biting. Store the acid and solution in Teflon bottles or in glass bottles with acid-proof caps. (*Caution:* Handle nitric acid with great care; it is extremely corrosive. Wear rubber gloves when mixing or using it; always add the acid to the water, and not vice versa; don't spill or spatter it. If you spill any on your skin, flush immediately with plenty of cold water.)

Etching Copper and Brass

First clean the metal with any available soft abrasive powder, such as whiting or talc, and then wipe the surface with a soft cloth, being careful to remove all fingerprints. Paint all portions not to be etched with an even coat of asphaltum varnish. If a design is to be etched in, coat the entire surface. When the coating is dry, draw or trace the design on the asphaltum with a soft lead pencil. With a sharp scratch awl or other needle-pointed tool, then cut the lines through to the metal.

When ready, lower the piece carefully into the etching bath with plastic tongs. Full-strength, technical-grade nitric acid will etch copper and brass to a depth of about 0.002 inch in 1 minute; for all ordinary purposes the etching will be deep enough in 1 to 1½ minutes. A half-and-half solution will require considerably longer, but should be used where a deep etch is wanted.

Etching Aluminum and Steel

Aluminum is etched in the same way as copper and brass, except that muriatic (hydrochloric) acid is used instead of nitric. Full-strength muriatic acid will etch to a depth of about 0.003 inch per minute. The etching will be slower, but can be kept under better control if the acid is diluted 1 part acid to 2½ to 3 parts water.

An easy way to etch aluminum is to first heat the metal enough to melt paraffin, lay it flat on half-a-dozen thicknesses of newspaper, and flow on a thin coat of the wax. When the coated metal is cold, scratch on the design or lettering, cutting right through the wax film to the metal. Apply the solution to the scratched areas with a small wad of absorbent cotton fastened to the end of a short stick with a rubber band. When the metal has been etched deeply enough, wash thoroughly with water and then remove the wax with boiling water. (*Caution:* Although muriatic acid is not quite as corrosive as nitric acid, it should be handled with the same care. See *Caution* under "Etching Solutions" on page 349.)

Steel may be etched quickly and satisfactorily with a solution made by mixing 1 part muriatic acid with 1 part technical nitric acid. (*Caution:* Be especially careful with this combination, as it is more corrosive than either of the separate acids. If you store it in a bottle, leave the cap loose for the first 15 hours, as during that time it gives off gas.)

Among other applications, you may use this solution for etching names and designs on tools. Clean the metal thoroughly with whiting or other mild abrasive powder and wipe with a cloth. Outline the name or design with asphaltum varnish, or coat the tool all over with asphaltum and scratch the figure in this after it is hard and dry. Then apply a few drops of the solution to the part to be etched and let remain until the etching is deep enough. Rinse with water. After removing the asphaltum with solvent, dry the tool and coat it with oil or other rust preventive.

Etching Pewter

Old-style pewter is difficult to etch because the metal is soft and porous. The new type of pewter so commonly used today for decorative metal working contains a large proportion of tin and may be successfully etched with nitric acid. Follow instructions for etching on copper and brass. With pewter, all the parts that have been etched are left black. In most cases this adds to the effectiveness. If desired, the black can be removed by polishing or buffing.

Cutouts and Silhouettes

To etch cutouts, letters, and silhouettes in copper and brass, use thin metal and clean it with a dry abrasive. Paint all parts that are to be left untouched by the acid with an even coat of asphaltum, including the back and the edges. In designs that are to be etched out to form a picture or a word, a section of one part should join the next part so that the design will not finally fall apart. Irregular lines may be corrected by scraping away the asphaltum after it is thoroughly dry.

Slow etching is advisable in this case, as in all etching where more than 0.002 or 0.003 inch depth is required. Make a bath of 1 part nitric acid to 1 part water. After immersing the prepared plate, watch closely and remove promptly—as soon as the acid has eaten through the metal.

Another method is to coat the entire surface of the metal on both sides with the asphaltum and let dry hard. Outline the letters or design with a soft lead pencil, then scratch only the outline through the coating. In this case only the outline will be attacked. If clean sharp lines have been scratched, the parts will separate when the acid has eaten through.

MAKING JEWELRY AND FILLERS FROM AMALGAMS

Silver Jewelry from Dental Amalgam

Dental amalgam, an alloy of silver and mercury used by dentists for filling teeth, is also an excellent material for making jewelry in the home workshop. With it you can duplicate admired pieces, or you can make ring settings, brooches, watch charms, pendants, earrings, and other pieces of your own design.

Besides an ounce or two of amalgam, which you should be able to get at a dental-supply house, you will need an ounce of mercury to mix with it and increase its workability. You will also need a little plaster of Paris and powdered pumice. With this you can make a number of pieces of jewelry at a cost of not much more than a dollar each.

The simplest way to make a cast is to press the amalgam in a mold made of the plaster.

For an original piece, mix some of the plaster with water and allow it to set until firm and only slightly damp. Then cut the design in its face with an etching tool, knife, or motor-driven hand grinder. For a reproduction of an existing piece, simply grease the piece lightly with petroleum jelly and press it into the damp plaster, leaving it there until the plaster sets.

As soon as the mold has set, mix a little mercury with the silver amalgam to make it pliable. Squeeze out excess mercury through twisted cheesecloth, and then, with the amalgam the consistency of stiff putty, press a little at a time into the plaster mold. Use a wooden clay-modeling tool or any other blunt instrument and pack the amalgam into every corner. Let it set overnight and then carefully pull it from the mold.

When the silver is first taken from the mold, it will be light in color and lusterless. Polishing with pumice and a stiff brush, however, will soon bring out its silver sheen. The amount of polishing controls the degree of luster. Like all silver, amalgam is subject to tarnish, but a little silver polish will restore its shine. Or, if you wish, you can apply a coat of clear lacquer to protect its finish.

Copper Amalgam

A similar amalgam of mercury with copper can also be used to make small pieces of jewelry. In addition, it can be used to fill holes in copper work, to take accurate impressions of small pieces in art and model-making, or to serve as an electrical conducting cement to join connecting wires to carbon brushes.

Although metallic mercury will combine with copper sheet to produce a bright silvery surface, this method cannot be used to produce amalgam in bulk form because the alloying action stops with this surface. You can make a pliable amalgam, however, by combining mercury with finely divided copper obtained by precipitation.

To make copper in this form, suspend several strips of iron or zinc in a solution of either copper sulfate or copper nitrate. The iron or zinc will dissolve, and copper from the solution will precipitate on the strips in the form of a fine powder. Scrape off and collect the powder, and keep adding iron or zinc as long as the solution remains blue.

Place the precipitated copper in a porcelain mortar and wash it well with running water. Then drain it and pour over the copper a solution of mercuric nitrate. (*Caution:* Poison!) Allow this solution to act for about 10 minutes, or until the color of the copper has changed somewhat, and then pour it off. Finally, add to the copper several times its weight of metallic mercury, fill the mortar nearly full of hot water, and knead the mass under the hot water with a pestle.

The kneading will cause the mercury to unite with the copper to form a puttylike amalgam. This can be pressed into a mold, used to fill a hole, or used as a cement. It will form a solid mass of metal as soon as it cools and sets.

METALLIZE BABY SHOES WITHOUT ELECTROPLATING

It is impossible to preserve baby shoes merely by coating them with varnish or enamel. Natural flexibility of the material, changes in temperature and humidity, and possibly mildew will eventually cause the leather or cloth to deteriorate and the coating to crack or chip. For permanent preservation, the shoe material must first be stiffened and sealed against the weather and then given a decorative coat, usually metallic.

If you do not have facilities for electroplating, the following procedure, using both clear and metallic lacquer, provides a similar appearance in a coating that is just as long lasting.

First remove all wax and polish from the shoes with lacquer thinner.

To stiffen the shoes, submerge them for 12 hours in lacquer diluted with an equal amount of lacquer thinner. Cover the container in which this is done to prevent evaporation. Then remove the shoes, let them dry for 1 hour, shape them, and let them dry for another 36 hours. Next dip them for just a few seconds (to prevent softening the sealer coat) in lacquer of full strength and let them dry another 36 hours. Finally spray or brush on metallic lacquer of the desired color.

MODELING AND CASTING ORNAMENTS

Nonhardening Modeling Clay

Kaolin	67 parts
Sulfur	33 parts
Lanolin	60 parts
Glycerine	40 parts

Extra kaolin may be substituted for the sulfur, which acts only as a preservative. Knead all the ingredients together thoroughly. Dry pigments may be worked in to give desired color.

Plastic Molding Materials

A puttylike material that can be used in taking impressions, duplicating rosettes or other raised designs, or for filling cracks in wood can be made of a mixture of plaster of Paris and fine sawdust made into a paste with water containing a little glue.

Another plastic material that is unusually adhesive, dries hard, and can be carved, sandpapered, or colored can be made by mixing:

Whiting	1¼ cups
Linseed oil	2 teaspoons
Clear varnish	3 teaspoons
Thick liquid glue	4 fluid ounces

Mix thoroughly with a spatula or thin-bladed knife. The material can be applied with a brush if a bit more linseed oil is added, or with modeling tools if used stiff. A cookie or cake-icing gun is useful in applying the composition.

This material has many uses. Picture frames, lamp stands, shades, turned vases, shade pulls, and other craft objects can be coated with it to form ropes, scrolls, beads, spatter effects, and so on. It is also useful in filling cracks and in building up small pieces of woodwork that would otherwise require hand carving or delicate fitting.

When dry, the material becomes hard and can be colored with lacquer or colored varnishes. Gold or aluminum bronze powder can be mixed with the plastic material to create metallic colored effects, or it may be dusted on after the material has been applied to an object, thus decreasing the amount of powder needed.

A third plastic material can be made from:

Plaster of Paris	20 parts
White lead	16 parts
Litharge	6 parts
Fine sawdust	4 parts
Liquid glue	

Mix the powders thoroughly and add enough glue to make a paste or slurry that should be rather thin if it is to be applied with a brush, or stiff if it is to be molded or applied with bladed tools.

Cornstarch "Ceramics"

A claylike material that can be used to model toys, knickknacks, and costume jewelry can be mixed in a few minutes from ingredients found in the kitchen:

Cornstarch	1 cup
Bicarbonate of soda (baking soda)	1 pound
Cold water	1¼ cups

Blend cornstarch and baking soda together thoroughly in a saucepan. Mix in the water and place over medium heat for about 4 minutes, stirring constantly until mixture thickens to mashed potato consistency. Turn out on a plate and cover with a damp cloth until cool.

When easy to handle, knead like dough. Work with one portion at a time, wrapping rest in plastic to prevent drying. Knead a few drops of white glue into pieces of clay for added strength. Roll out and cut figures with cookie cutters or a knife, or shape by hand. When joining pieces, lightly moisten facing parts and press together.

Dry objects on waxed paper for about 36 hours, or until hard. Paint with tempera colors. Spray with clear plastic or coat with shellac for shiny, protective finish.

Wax Molds for Plaster Casts

FORMULA 1

Beeswax	4 ounces
Olive oil	1 ounce
Cornstarch	4 ounces

Melt the beeswax over low heat and stir in the olive oil. Sift the starch and then stir in the oil and beeswax until the mixture is as thick as biscuit dough.

The resulting substance will be hard when cold. For use, it must be slightly softened by warming it. When soft enough, dust the object to be copied with talcum powder (French chalk) and press this object carefully into the wax. After cooling again, the object may be removed by tapping the wax. The resulting mold may then be filled with the usual plaster of Paris mixture.

FORMULA 2

Beeswax	4 ounces
Lard	4 ounces
Raw linseed oil	4 fluid ounces
Flour	8 ounces

Melt the beeswax and lard together in a container placed in a pan of hot water. Stir in the linseed oil and then the flour, continuing to stir until all are thoroughly mixed.

FORMULA 3

Paraffin wax	4 ounces
Olive oil	4 fluid ounces
Whiting	8 ounces

Melt the wax as in the previous two formulas (never over an open flame, as it might catch fire) and stir in the whiting. When it has cooled slightly but before it has started to set, dump the mixture on a flat board and knead like dough until the consistency is uniform and pliable.

Parting Medium for Plaster Mold

Tincture of green soap is often the medium applied to a plaster mold to permit the subsequent removal of the cast made in it. Lacking green soap, here is a good substitute:

Place 4 cubic inches of ordinary white soap and 1 tablespoon of olive oil in 1 pint of boiling water. Stir constantly and keep boiling until the soap is completely dissolved. Solution will be hastened if you first shave the soap or cut it into small pieces.

To Hasten or Retard the Setting of Plaster of Paris

To hasten the setting, add ½ teaspoon of salt to each pint of water used in mixing the plaster.

To retard the setting, add 1½ ounces of a saturated solution of borax to each pint of water. This will delay the setting from 15 to 30 minutes, and will make impressions in the plaster harder and sharper.

Coloring Plaster of Paris

Plaster of Paris for ornamental objects may be colored before casting by mixing with water containing household dyes. Royal blue, jade green, scarlet, yellow, purple, and coral, of the Rit brand, all color the plaster in subdued pastels. Use 1 package of dye to each quart of hot tap water. Approximately 4 ounces of this concentrated solution should be mixed with each pound of plaster.

Hardening Plaster Casts

Casts made of plaster of Paris can be hardened by soaking them in a solution made by dissolving 1 part alum in 6 parts hot water. A very small cast should be immersed in the alum water for at least an hour, while larger casts should remain for several days or a week.

If you want to harden just the surface of plaster casts, they may be soaked in melted paraffin or brushed over thoroughly with melted stearin. (*Caution:* Melt either of these in a double boiler; never over an open fire.) When cool and dry, the surface may be given a high polish. If large figures of plaster are to be placed outdoors, you can protect them from the weather by brushing them inside and outside with two or three coats of linseed oil, letting one coat dry before applying the next. Let the last coat of oil dry for 24 hours and then give the plaster a coat of waterproof paint. The cast may now be painted to simulate metal or stone. If properly done, this treatment should be able to withstand the weather for at least two years.

Color Finishes for Plaster Casts

IVORY. Dissolve yellow beeswax (in an amount best judged by experience) in turpentine or mineral spirits. Add a little dry yellow ochre. Apply to the cast with a stiff brush, working quickly as the mixture is rapidly absorbed. Before completely dry, rub the color from high parts of the cast with cheesecloth. Leave color in depressions to give an effect of natural ivory.

ANTIQUE. Apply the same mixture as for ivory, but with the addition of a little dry umber and Paris green. To increase the appearance of age, give the cast a second coat.

POMPEIAN BRONZE. To prevent too much penetration, prime the cast with a thin coat of shellac. Make a thick mixture of lampblack with varnish, add a little copper bronze, then thin to easy brushing consistency with turpentine. The combination should dry without gloss. Using a stiff brush, apply a streaky, uneven coat to the cast. Wipe partly off with cheesecloth. When dry, apply a coating of turpentine in which a little white beeswax and Paris green have been dissolved. When this is dry, polish the highlights very lightly with cheesecloth.

EBONY. Prime with a coat of thin shellac. Make a thick mixture of ivory black with varnish, thin to easy brushing consistency with turpentine, and apply two coats to ensure complete coverage. When dry, apply a coating of white beeswax to the high parts. When this is dry, polish only lightly.

To Clean Plaster Casts

Add enough cornstarch to hot water to make a thick paste. Apply a thick layer of this paste, while still hot, to the cast. Leave overnight to dry. Most of the starch can then be easily broken off, taking the surface dirt with it. The little that remains can be removed with hot water.

Cast Imitation Stone

Anything that can be cast in plaster can be cast in imitation stone, which is really a special mixture of cement. Cast stone is more durable than plaster and can be reproduced just as many times from a given mold. It can be colored with earth pigments to imitate many kinds of real stone.

Here is one common formula:

Portland cement	1 part
Sand	3 parts
Marble dust	
Dry earth colors	
Water	

Another popular formula contains Keene's cement, a harder relative of plaster of Paris made from more thoroughly heated gypsum to which alum or aluminum sulfate has been added:

Portland cement	1 part
White Keene's cement	1 part
Sand	4 parts
Marble dust or chips	
Dry earth colors	
Water	

Both formulas are mixed the same way. First combine the dry ingredients thoroughly on a board of sufficient size. The amount of marble dust or chips to be used depends on the amount of sparkle you want; about 1 part would be an average. The amount of pigment depends on the stone you are trying to imitate and must be determined by making trial batches. Use only earth colors or those sold particularly for coloring cement. Among your choices are red and brown iron oxides, yellow and brown umbers and ochres, and green chromium oxide. For gray or black, you can use lampblack, carbon black, black manganese oxide, or black iron oxide.

Sprinkle one or a combination of these colors into the other dry ingredients as you mix them. When the color appears to be about right, take a little of the mix, stir into it enough water to make a thick paste, and spread it out on an old piece of glass to set. Though it will still be several shades darker than its final color, you should be able to judge in four or five days if the color is satisfactory. If it is not, make what corrections you believe to be needed and test again. In the meantime, keep the main batch of material covered and dry.

When you are sure you have the right combination, mix only enough to meet your requirements for the day. Any excess mixture will set overnight and so be useless. Lay the mixture into a greased mold with a trowel and tamp it down gently with a stick padded on the end with a wad of cloth.

CRAYONS AND PAINTS

How to Make High-Grade Pastel Crayons

Pastel crayons or sticks of higher quality than the average sold in art stores can be made easily and cheaply at home from artists' dry colors held together by a simple gum binder. The famous German chemist, Ostwald, described the method of making them at the beginning of this century. With slight modifications, his method is followed widely by artists today.

The materials you need are dry pigments of desired colors, precipitated chalk for white and to make tints, and a small amount of gum tragacanth and beta-naphthol that you can get from a drugstore or chemical-supply house. Any permanent pigments may be used except poisonous ones that contain lead and arsenic (chiefly lead whites, chrome yellows and greens, Naples yellow, emerald green, cobalt violet). Arsenic would be especially dangerous with pastel, as you get pastel pigments on your hands and breathe their dust.

To make the binder, put about ⅓ ounce of gum tragacanth in a bottle, pour on it a pint of water, and set the bottle overnight in a warm place. The next day, shake the bottle until the gelatinlike mass that has formed in it is dispersed uniformly through the water, then add about ¼ teaspoon of the beta-naphthol as a preservative. Label the bottle Solution A.

Dilute part of this solution with an equal amount of water and put the diluted solution in another bottle labeled Solution B. Dilute another part of Solution A with 3 parts water and bottle it as Solution C. Gum solutions of different strengths are required to compensate for differences in the binding ability of different pigments.

Do your mixing on a slab of glass, marble, or plastic tile, using a moderately flexible spatula as a mixing tool. Begin with white pastels to get an easy introduction to the general procedure. Take about 2 ounces of precipitated chalk and work into this a little more than ½ fluid ounce of Solution C. Rub up the mass with the spatula until it has the consistency of putty. If the mass is so thin it runs, add more chalk; if too thick, add a little more solution. When you can roll it into a ball between your hands without finding it either too sticky or too crumbly, the mass is ready to form into sticks on a sheet of newspaper or paper towel, using either your hand or a small flat stick as a roller. The sticks are then left in a warm place until they are dry and hard.

Sticks can be made similarly with the colored pigments. With these, however, you will have to find by experiment the best combination of binder and pigment. For full-strength colors, use the pigment as it comes. For tints, combine colored pigment with varying amount of chalk. So you will be able to make predictable changes or to reproduce past satisfactory results, keep careful records of quantities used and of combinations of pigment and binder.

In mixing pigments for pastels, remember that the color produced in the final picture will be the same as that of the original dry powders. This color will darken when wet with the solution, but will return to its original value when the pastel stick dries.

Permanent Pigments for Oil Painting

Do you want to be sure you are getting what you think you are when you buy oil colors—long-lasting pigments of precise hue? Time was when certainty was almost impossible. Composition of pigments varied from one manufacturer to another, and identical names were often applied to entirely different products. Since 1942, however, the National Bureau of Standards has published standards of name and composition for the most used and most permanent artists' oil paints. These were chosen by a committee of leading American artists and manufacturers, and are now adhered to voluntarily by most makers of such colors.

The accompanying table lists some of the standard pigments that are commonly used. In several cases a color may also be known by a second name, but the use of a standard name for another pigment of similar color but different composition is not permitted.

Cottage Cheese Casein Paint

For centuries before purified casein became available, artists and others made casein paint from curd cheese—plain cottage cheese made from skim milk without the addition of salt or cream. Some artists still do, getting their uncreamed and unsalted cottage cheese from the delicatessen or supermarket. Here's all you need:

	Parts by volume
Plain cottage cheese	5
Lime putty	1

For directions for making lime putty, see Chapter 2. Stir the lime putty with the cheese and leave for several hours, until the cheese lumps have dissolved completely.

Use limeproof pigments (also listed in Chapter 2) and work up into paste with water. Add to casein solution and dilute with water as you think necessary.

STANDARD OIL-PAINT NAMES AND COMPOSITIONS

Color	Paint name	Pigment composition
White	zinc white	zinc oxide
	flake white	basic lead carbonate
	titanium white	titanium dioxide combined with barium sulfate or zinc oxide
Black	ivory black	carbon from charred animal bones
	lampblack	carbon from condensed smoke
	mars black	ferro-ferric oxide
Blue	ultramarine blue	silicate of sodium and aluminum with sulfur
	cobalt blue	combined oxides of cobalt and aluminum
	cerulean blue	combined oxides of cobalt and tin
	phthalocyanine blue	copper phthalocyanine, made from synthetic organic dye stuff
Brown	raw umber	natural earth that consists chiefly of hydrous oxides and silicates of iron and manganese
	burnt umber	pigment prepared by heating raw umber
	burnt sienna	prepared by heating raw sienna
	burnt green earth	prepared by heating green earth
Green	viridian	hydrous chromic oxide
	green earth	natural earth consisting chiefly of hydrous silicates of iron, aluminum, magnesium, and potassium
	chromium oxide	anhydrous chromic oxide
	phthalocyanine green	chlorinated copper, made from synthetic organic dyestuff
Red	cadmium red	pure cadmium sulfoselenide
	light red	nearly pure iron oxide
	indian red	nearly pure iron oxide
	mars red	artificial ochre, consisting chiefly of iron and aluminum oxides
	alizarin crimson	made from 1-2-dihydroxy anthraquinone and aluminum hydroxide
Yellow	cadmium yellow	pure cadmium sulfide
	cobalt yellow	potassium cobaltinitrite
	mars yellow	artificial ochre, consisting chiefly of hydrous oxides of iron and aluminum
	raw sienna	natural earth consisting chiefly of hydrous oxides and silicates of iron and aluminum
	naples yellow	lead antimoniate
Violet	cobalt violet	anhydrous cobalt phosphate or arsenate
	manganese violet	manganese ammonium phosphate
	mars violet	artificial iron oxide

Paint for Craftwork or Finger Painting

This paint, made easily from kitchen products and household dyes, can be used by the craft worker for finger painting, block printing, screen painting, stenciling, and brayer printing. It can also serve as the binder in making a sawdust molding material of papier-mâché.

Cornstarch	½ cup
Cold water	1 cup
Unflavored gelatin (1 envelope)	¼ ounce
Hot water	2 cups
Mild soap flakes or synthetic detergent	½ cup

Combine cornstarch and ¾ cup of the cold water in a medium-size saucepan. Soak gelatin in remaining cold water. Add hot water to starch mixture and cook over medium heat until mixture comes to a boil and is clear, stirring constantly. Remove from heat; blend in softened gelatin. Add soap or detergent and stir until mixture thickens and soap or detergent is thoroughly dissolved. Makes about 3 cups.

In place of the gelatin, you may use 1 tablespoon of glycerin. If used, combine a full cup of cold water with the cornstarch before cooking. Stir in the glycerin when the mixture is removed from the heat.

To each cup of this base thoroughly stir in 1 teaspoon of household dye. Store in covered jars.

Scarlet, yellow, and royal blue, plus black and brown, are suggested for a basic set of colors. Orange, kelly green, and fuchsia may be added for larger sets. Precipitated chalk or whiting may be used for white.

Save Money on Turpentine

You can save money in buying turpentine for thinning artists' oil colors by buying sealed cans of "pure gum turpentine" in paint, hardware, and food stores. If it bears the seal of the Turpentine Farmers' Association, it is identical with that sold in small bottles at a higher price by artists' supply stores. It is also apt to be fresher. Although still cheaper "wood turpentine" will also serve as a thinner, it has a less agreeable odor.

Transparent Paper for Tracing

Canada balsam	1 ounce
Gum turpentine	1 ounce

Mix these ingredients and apply the resulting liquid to one surface of white, unsized paper, using a small flat brush. If the paper is still too opaque after the coating has dried, apply another coat.

TRANSFERRING NEWSPAPER PRINTS

Transferring pictures and comic strips from newspapers and magazines to plain white paper may provide hours of fun for the youngsters. Here is a simple preparation with which they may do this:

Water	4 ounces
Liquid dishwashing detergent	1 squirt
Turpentine	2 ounces

Put the water into a bottle or jar, add the detergent and turpentine, and shake thoroughly to emulsify the mixture. Brush this liquid uniformly over the picture to be transferred, blot up the surface drops gently with a paper towel. Place the paper on which the picture is to be transferred on a plate, lay the moist picture face down on this, and rub firmly and evenly over the back of it with the bowl of a spoon or with a wallpaper seam roller. On removing the original, a copy of it, in reverse, will be found on the paper beneath. Colored pictures may be transferred, as well as black and white.

HECTOGRAPH DUPLICATING DEVICE

More than half a century before the invention of most of the present office copying machines, small runs of menus, circular letters, club and church notices, and so on were made on a device called the hectograph, a word that means "hundred writing." Because the device—often homemade—is so simple and effective, it still has considerable use for the same purposes.

The operation of the hectograph is based on absorption. The original writing is done on a sheet of bond paper with a water-soluble ink. This sheet is placed face down in contact with the moist surface of a clay, glue, or gelatin composition. The writing is absorbed from the paper and appears in reversed form on the surface. If a sheet of blank paper is then pressed in contact with the surface, the impression is transferred to the paper. When done properly, allowing a little more time of contact for each sheet, at least two dozen good copies may be made. ***(Continued)***

Here is the simplest formula for the pad:

Powdered whiting	16 ounces
Glycerin	4 ounces

Mix 8 ounces of the whiting with the glycerin and beat the mixture thoroughly. Let it stand 12 hours, then mix in the rest of the whiting and knead like dough. When it kneads stiff, set it aside for the glycerin to work through. Again knead well and then put in a shallow rectangular pan and flatten out roughly with your fingers. Finally, make a perfect surface on it by scraping with the edge of a straight stick.

If, on standing, glycerin appears on the surface, sprinkle on some dry whiting and reknead the mixture. Don't wipe off the glycerin. The mixture should be just moist to work best. Add either glycerin or whiting to secure this consistency.

Write or draw what you wish on glazed paper or hard bond paper with ready-made hectograph ink bought at an office stationery supply store (you can also buy special duplicating paper from which you can make the best possible originals and copies) or with homemade ink described below. When the writing is just dry, lay the paper face down on the pad and smooth it flat with a photographic roller or with your hand. Let it remain 3 or 4 minutes, then carefully peel it off. Put on a sheet of blank paper of the same type and smooth it down similarly. Let the first sheet remain just an instant, the next a little longer, and so on until you have either finished your run or the copy is too weak to be satisfactory. Wash off the surface of the pad with a slightly damp cloth to remove the writing and prepare it for fresh copy.

Here is a formula for a glue or gelatin pad, a type more expensive and a little more difficult to make but preferred by many:

"A-Extra" grade glue, or unflavored food gelatin	3 ounces
Water	6½ ounces
Glycerin	18 ounces
Sodium bicarbonate	⅓ ounce

To prepare the composition, follow this procedure:

1. Put cold water in top part of double boiler.
2. Add bicarbonate of soda and stir until dissolved.
3. Add glue or gelatin and let soak 1½ hours.
4. Heat water in lower part of double boiler until mixture in top part has reached 140° F and the glue or gelatin has melted. Don't stir

until free foam has all been released; then stir slowly until the gel is uniformly dissolved in the water.

5. Slowly add the glycerin and stir into solution when the combination has again reached 140° F.
6. Let stand at 140° F until solution clears and cools to 120° F.
7. Pour into 9 × 12-inch pan.

Hectograph Ink

Acetone	2 ounces
Glycerin	5 ounces
Acetic acid (28%)	2½ ounces
Water	12 ounces
Dextrin	½ ounce
Dye	2½ ounces

Use water-soluble dyes: methyl violet, victoria blue, emerald green, or, for red, rhodamine B. First dissolve the dextrin by stirring in hot water. When cool, stir in the other ingredients. (*Caution:* Keep the acetone away from all fire, as it and its vapor are very flammable.)

FROSTING AND ETCHING GLASS

Solution 1

Sodium fluoride	1 ounce
Potassium sulfate	90 grains
Water to make 8 fluid ounces	

Solution 2

Zinc chloride	100 grains
Hydrochloric acid (36%)	1 fluid ounce
Water to make 8 fluid ounces	

Mix the two solutions separately and store them in polystyrene or Teflon bottles (the first one will eat glass). When needed, mix equal amounts of each in a plastic or hard-rubber container. Apply with a pointed stick or a brush, depending on the area to be covered. Rinse after about 30 minutes. A fine mat surface should have been produced. (*Caution:* Wear rubber gloves while handling the solutions and do not breathe the vapors of the mixed solutions.)

Here is another formula for producing a finely etched surface on a glass plate:

Sodium fluoride	60 grains
Powdered gelatin	60 grains
Water	32 ounces

Soak the gelatin in 6 ounces of cold water until it is soft. Dissolve the sodium fluoride (*Caution:* Poison!) in the remainder of the water, heated to 125° F and transferred to a plastic or hard-rubber container, and then add the gelatin solution, stirring until the gelatin is completely dissolved. Coat the resulting liquid uniformly on the glass to be frosted and let it dry thoroughly.

Dip the dry coated glass in a solution made by diluting 1 part concentrated (36%) hydrochloric acid with 30 parts water for 1 minute, and permit to dry without rinsing. After the acid has dried, the coating may be washed off with hot water, leaving a finely etched surface on the glass. (*Caution:* Wear rubber gloves while handling the solutions.)

Imitation Frosted Glass

For uniform frosting: Dissolve ½ ounce of gum arabic in 1 pint of water. Then, with stirring, add Rochelle salts until the water will hold no more. Let stand in a cool place for 12 hours and then filter. Clean the glass thoroughly, lay it flat, and flow on the solution. When dry, coat with thin varnish or lacquer.

For a pattern resembling frost crystals: Dissolve a little dextrin in a strong Epsom salts solution. Apply to the glass as above. As the water slowly evaporates, beautiful crystal patterns develop and cling securely to the glass. When fully developed, they may be protected with a thin coating of varnish or lacquer.

Coloring Glassware

Vases, bottles, bulbs, test tubes, and other glassware intended for decorative or novelty purposes can be frosted with the aid of sodium silicate solution. At the same time, they may be tinted any color by adding a water-soluble dye to the sodium silicate.

The viscid liquid that sticks so firmly to glassware may be painted on or a sufficient quantity may be used to allow the glass to be dipped bodily. If desired, just one part of the glassware may be treated. After being coated and dried, the glass should be immersed for a moment in a boiling hot concentrated solution of Epsom salts or of sal ammoniac and then dried again.

MODIFYING CUT FLOWERS

Dyeing Cut Flowers

Packaged dyes used for dyeing cloth are also suitable for dyeing flowers. Just cut the flower stems on a slant and immerse the stems in a solution of the dye in water.

Only white flowers can be colored the original color of the dye, but many combinations can be made. Yellow flowers can be changed to orange, saffron, green, and other colors. Pink can be changed to lilac, red to purple, and so on through the list of colors and shades.

Changing the Colors of Flowers

The colors of many flowers may be changed chemically. Red roses can be bleached white by exposing them to the fumes from burning sulfur. Because sulfur fumes are irritating, do this outdoors or in a well-ventilated room. Make a little mound of sulfur on a disposable metal pie plate or can cover and place this on a surface that will not burn. After dampening them thoroughly, support the flowers several inches above the sulfur. Then light the top of the sulfur pile and place a carton over everything to act as a fume chamber. The petals often become variegated, making the effect more interesting. The sulfur dioxide produced by the burning reacts with the red coloring matter and changes it to a compound that is colorless or white.

Another way to produce sulfur dioxide is to add a dilute solution of sulfuric acid to sodium sulfite in a glass dish.

Some flowers placed over ammonia fumes also change color. Just support them over a dish of household ammonia, and place a box over everything as before. Many purple flowers turn green when exposed to this gas.

Sun Pictures on Leaves or Fruit

If a monogram, word, or design cut from aluminum foil is coated with varnish and then applied to a mature leaf, or to a fruit that is almost ripe but which has not yet developed color, the parts covered will not be exposed to the sun's rays and so will not develop as fully as the uncovered area. When you later remove the foil, you will find a clear image of itself—a photograph made by nature—on the leaf or fruit. It is important to use a waterproof adhesive such as varnish. Otherwise the cutout may be washed away by rain.

Drying Flowers

The principle of drying flowers is to remove all the moisture and still retain as much of the natural color and form as possible. Since the texture of flowers varies, some will dry better than others. Flowers such as tulips and daffodils have an almost transparent texture when dried, whereas with roses and zinnias, flowers with more substance, the texture does not change appreciably. Of course, you must expect a certain amount of shrinkage to occur in the process of preserving flowers because all the moisture is removed.

As with the texture variations in flowers, so it is with color—some flowers when preserved will retain their natural color, even as vivid as when the plant was growing. White flowers when dried tend to be more cream than white, but candytuft, feverfew, and viburnum mariesi are excellent for drying and appear almost snow-white. You must remember, however, that all colors fade, some more quickly than others as with rugs and draperies. But the fading is so gradual you do not become aware of it. The flowers seem to "age" and the colors become more subtle and blend together. Preserved flowers will lose their color very rapidly if exposed to direct sunlight or if placed in a brightly lighted room. Experience with preserving flowers will help you appreciate these variations in texture, color, and form.

STEPS IN DRYING FLOWERS. One of the easiest ways of drying flowers is to use silica gel and proceed as follows:

1. Pour the silica gel into a cake tin or other sealable container to a depth of 2 inches. Cut the stems to a length of 1 inch and insert flowers face up. Space them so they are not touching.
2. Sprinkle the silica over the flowers until completely covered, gently working it up and around them so contact is made on all parts of the flower.
3. Cover the cake tin or other container with a tight top and seal it with freezer or masking tape. Put it away for 2 to 8 days—in a place where the contents will not be disturbed.
4. To remove the flowers, pour off the mixture slowly until they are

uncovered. Lift out gently and blow away any particles that adhere. Complete the removal of the dust—an artist's brush is recommended.

5. Store flowers away from the light in a sealed air-tight container, to which has been added 3 tablespoons of silica gel. This storing will keep the flowers from wilting so long as warm humid weather persists.
6. When you are ready to make your arrangement, attach to the short flower stem a length of mediumweight florists' wire by spiral wrapping it with green floral tape.

TIMING. Flowers dry in silica gel in anywhere from 2 to 8 days, depending on the texture and maturity of the flower. For instance, the whole stalk of snapdragon is heavy and requires 8 days, while zinnias do best if left in the silica gel 2 or 3 days. Flowers left in the mixture too long tend to fall apart; if not long enough, they take on a crumpled look when exposed to air. Most importantly, if the flowers feel crisp they are usually dry. At this point they should be removed from the mixture but allowed to remain on top of it in a sealed box for another 2 or 3 days.

When blue disappears, maximum moisture content of the silica gel has been reached. Place mixture in heatproof container in 250° F oven. When blue color returns, the silica gel is ready to use again.

LEATHER FOR CRAFT WORK

Leather in many colors may be purchased from handicraft stores or leather companies by whole or half skins, or by the square foot or square inch. Dealers will also cut leather from your pattern, and many of them will furnish project kits of their own design. If much leather is used, it is cheaper to buy whole or half skins.

The best tooling leather is calfskin, but tooling steerhide also works well. Considering economy rather than durability, tooling sheepskin may be used. Calfskin makes excellent billfolds, handbags, coin purses, and cigarette and comb cases. Tooling steerhide makes durable billfolds, key and card cases, bookends, and notebooks. Tooling sheepskin is used for bookcovers, bookmarks, and card-table covers. Pigskin may be tooled in straight lines for letter cases, key cases, and coin purses.

Embossed leathers have designs impressed upon them. Embossed steerhide and cowhide are used for briefcases, notebooks, and camera cases. Sheepskin is sold with fancy embossed designs or imitation grains of expensive leathers, such as ostrich, and is used for coin purses, book covers, and billfolds. Suedes are used for linings, handbags, and belts.

Reptile leathers are used for billfolds, coin purses, and handbags. Ostrich is used for billfolds, coin purses, and book covers. Heavy steerhide, cowhide, and elkhide are used for belts, knife sheaths, and moccasins. "Skiver" is thin leather used only for linings.

Dyeing Leather

Dyes for leather may be water stains, oil stains, acids and oxides, spirit stains, and waterproof drawing inks. The amateur must be very careful if acids and oxides are used since they will burn the leather and cause it to crack if used in too strong solution. Best results will be obtained if commercial dyes are purchased from leather-supply companies.

Before dyeing natural leather, first clean the surface thoroughly. A commercial cleaning solution may be purchased, or a very weak solution of hydrochloric acid may be made by adding 1 part of the acid to 20 parts water. Rub the surface of the leather lightly with a soft cloth dampened with either cleaning solution. Allow the leather to dry slightly before starting to dye it.

Always test the dye on a piece of scrap leather. Flow on the dye with a soft brush. After it has dried, a second coat may be applied if a darker effect is desired. Use a small camel's hair brush to apply dye to all cut edges of leather, being careful not to get dye on the finished surface. Two-tone effects may be obtained by applying spirit dyes to leather that is already colored. Allow ample time for the dye to dry, and polish the surface with a clean, soft cloth.

Finishing Leather Articles

Finish laced edges of leather articles by placing the laced edge on a smooth surface. Tap the lacing lightly with a smooth hammer. Clean and polish natural and dyed leather with saddle soap. Apply a thin coat with a soft, damp cloth and rub the surface lightly. Let it dry a few minutes; then polish with a clean, soft cloth or use a palm of the hand. Work all new leather well between the hands to make it soft and pliable. To produce a high luster, a commercial polishing solution may be applied and the article polished according to directions. Too much wax, however, will cause the leather to become hard and crack.

Recondition used leather articles by cleaning them several times a year or as often as needed. Clean them with saddle soap or some mild white soap. White shoes, if made from a good grade of leather, may be cleaned with saddle soap and then treated with a high grade of white shoe polish, applied according to directions. Slide fasteners on leather articles may be made to move easier if a drop of light oil is applied to the slide. Too much oil will cause the tape to deteriorate. Worn lacing should be replaced immediately with new to prevent excessive wear to the edges.

DECORATIVE CANDLES FROM PARAFFIN

Beautiful decorative candles for holidays and anniversaries can be made easily and inexpensively from household paraffin wax and other items found around the home or obtainable from the local supermarket.

For molds you can use items such as cardboard milk and ice cream containers, plastic containers, cookie cutters, cups, and gelatin molds. To get the hardened wax out in one piece, just make sure that the opening of the mold is the largest part. Grease all molds with cooking oil and chill before pouring wax into them.

Paraffin is flammable, so melt it in a double boiler, with plenty of water in the outer part; never over direct heat.

One way to color the wax is to stir into it shavings from wax crayons. Since the color will lighten as the candle solidifies, add crayon until the wax looks darker than desired.

Another way to color it is to stir into the melted wax 2 teaspoons of powdered Rit household dye for each pound of wax. For brightest results, use lighter shades of dye.

Candlewick can be bought in hobby shops. Or you can make a good wick from carpenters' chalkline, a braided cotton cord that burns well. To slow its burning rate, soak it overnight in a solution of 1 tablespoon of salt and 2 tablespoons of borax in 1 cup of water, and then hang it to dry. To stiffen it, dip it in melted paraffin.

One way to fasten the wick is to tie one end to the middle of a pencil and the other to a small weight. Then lay the pencil across the top of the mold so the weight hangs down in the center and pour the wax around it.

Another way is to insert the wick in a hole melted in the center of the solidified candle by means of a heated wire or ice pick. Then fill around the wick with melted wax.

Whipped wax, or "wax snow," is one form of decoration for your candles. Melt wax in a double boiler. Let cool until a thin film forms on top, and then whip with a fork or an eggbeater until it becomes fluffy like a meringue. Apply this to the candle with a fork while it is still soft. If the candle is colored, leave open spaces for the color to show through. Holiday glitter will stick if sprinkled on the whipped wax while it is still warm and soft.

Flat candles molded of whipped wax in gelatin or cookie molds will float in a bowl of water, making a novel centerpiece.

Scented candles can be made by adding a few drops of perfume, pine oil, or other scent to the melted wax.

To clean pans and utensils, reheat them until wax melts. Pour off excess. Wipe off all the wax you can with a paper towel and with hot soapy water.

DECOUPAGE

The art of decoupage (pronounced day-coo-pazh) was originated by the craftsmen of eighteenth-century Europe in an effort to copy the elaborately engraved and gilded products of Chinese and Japanese lacquer ware. Their discovery, decoupage, involved the arts and crafts technique of applying a cutout print to a desired wood surface and then getting the "picture" to recede into the background by applying many coats of a clear finish. Decoupage is the art of mounting printed pictures or designs on previously finished surfaces, then applying coat after coat of an appropriate clear finish until the picture appears to be part of the surface itself. Although black is traditionally the most popular background color, any solid color is appropriate if it looks well with the print you have chosen. Decoupage can also be used on stained and varnished wood and is ideally suited for antiqued surfaces.

Preparation of Surface

The first step in a decoupage application is to have the wood surface completely smooth and clean. Fill cracks and holes with wood plastic or putty and sand smooth with 6/0 or finer abrasive paper. Apply an enamel undercoat or wood stain base coat in the desired color, which should complement the selected decoupage print. When an opaque finish is desired, at least two coats of enamel and perhaps more may be needed to cover the wood grain. Thoroughly wet-sand between coats. After the enameling dries completely, apply a thin coat of the top finish—clear lacquer, varnish, or special decoupage coating.

On surfaces where the wood grain is to appear, apply a thin coat of the top finish over the stain, and then sand lightly with 6/0 or finer abrasive paper to remove any surface irregularities. Use a tack rag to clean up all sanding debris. When selecting the undercoat material, make certain you know the properties of the final clear top coat. If you choose an undercoat material that tends to soften or lift under a specific coat, you will waste time and effort.

Preparation of Design

Wrapping papers, stationery, prints, and greeting cards are just a few sources for finding suitable designs. Magazine paper is not usually recommended. Lay your designs on a clean piece of waxed paper. Spray lightly several times with the top coat, and allow to dry after each spraying; or brush on one coat of the top finish.

To age a piece of paper money, a square picture, etc., burn the edge by repeatedly jabbing it with a cigarette. If you have a very heavy piece of paper, such as a postcard, which you wish to use, you may strip the paper so that it will not be so heavy and it can be covered more easily with the top finish. To remove the backing paper from the item, put the picture in a pan of lukewarm water and soak. Gently roll off the paper backing a layer at a time, working from center out. If it dries out, put it back in the water. Never strip wedding invitations.

Embossed flowers or raised gold designs may be used most effectively. Make papier-mâché by mixing finely shredded paper tissue with white glue, and pack into back cavity of design. Allow to dry for several days. Black and white etchings may be colored with ordinary colored pencils. Hold the pencil sideways so as not to pierce paper. Color all shadows and line with terra-cotta, coloring in direction of the lines of the drawing. This gives warmth to any color you may put over the terra-cotta. Lightly brush on the top color to set colors.

When cutting paper, use any good cuticle scissors. Learn to turn the paper instead of the scissors. First cut away excess paper, then cut out inside the cuts. Large, intricate pieces may be handled more easily if first cut into sections. Some craftsmen prefer to tear around the print following the shape of the piece, creating a ragged edge. After tearing a print, sand lightly on the reverse side to smooth out the torn edges. While designs with printing on the reverse side should be avoided if possible, they can frequently be sealed by coating the back with white glue slightly diluted with water and allowing them to dry thoroughly. This usually prevents the printing from showing through on the surface of the design.

Gluing on the Design

Remember that decoupage designs must never overlap. Place designs on the object, and make small pencil marks to show the correct placement. Now lay the design face down on a clean piece of waxed paper. Squirt on the white glue, and spread evenly with your fingers from center out. Use enough glue so that the edges do not dry out before you are through spreading. On a large solid design, spread the glue with a damp sponge. Carefully remove the design from the waxed paper and place on the object's surface. Using a damp sponge, press the design in place, then put a clean piece of waxed paper over the design. Use a hard rubber roller, and roll it over the picture in several directions to press out excess glue. Carefully remove the waxed paper, and clean around the edges of the design with a damp sponge. Using a clean piece of waxed paper, roll again and wipe off excess glue. Repeat this until no glue appears when rolled. Glue may leave cloudy spots on the surface, particularly on a dark one. However, the top coats will usually obscure this. Allow design to dry overnight. If any air bubbles appear, slit the bubble with a razor blade. With a toothpick, put glue under the cut edges and roll again. Let dry thoroughly. If your designs extend over the top and down the sides of the object, glue the design on in one piece, and when dry cut along the edge with a razor blade. Sign your work with India ink or paint.

Building Up the Finish

Once the design is glued to the object, the finish building operation can be started. Brush on the first coat of clear lacquer, varnish, or decoupage coating. Allow to dry. If an antique effect is desired, apply the antique glaze, then wipe lightly with a soft cloth. Continue to apply the top coating, sanding very lightly with extra fine sandpaper between coats, and wiping with a soft cloth. Always brush from the center out and check the edges for drips. Do not try to keep brush strokes going in the same direction.

It is impossible to give a set rule for the number of coats needed to sink your design, but a minimum of twelve is usually recommended when using lacquer. Fewer coats are needed with varnish. In either case, the final coat should be rubbed to a satin finish achieved by using 4/0 or finer steel wool. Rub in a circular motion over the entire surface. Do this with a good light beside you so that you can rub away any shiny spots. When the finish is uniformly dull, apply one or two coats of a good quality paste wax, and polish with a clean, soft cloth.

11

Soaps, Cosmetics and Medicines

SOAPMAKING

Pure homemade soap that is superior to many commercial soaps can be made easily from nothing but household lye and leftover fat and grease that ordinarily would be wasted. It is a good cleanser, contains natural glycerin, which is soothing to the skin, and is completely lacking in weight-making fillers.

Six pounds of waste cooking grease and fat from meat scraps, a 13-ounce can of lye, and a few minutes' time will make 9 pounds of fine all-purpose soap at a cost of a few cents for a large bar. By varying the basic formula slightly you can make a special soap to suit every purpose in the house.

As with cooking, the quality of the product will depend on the quality of the ingredients used and the care taken in preparation. Avoid using rancid fat or grease and strain any that is dirty. Measure accurately and watch your temperatures. Use a reputable brand of pure flake lye. Flake lye makes no dust and dissolves easier than powdered lye.

PREPARING FAT. Good soap requires fats that are free from dirt, rancidity, lean meat, salt, and other impurities. Fat rendered from tallows, meat trimmings, and rinds is ready for soap without further treatment. Meat fryings and other refuse fats should be washed as follows:

Add an equal amount of water and bring the combination to the boiling point. Remove from fire; stir, and then add 1 quart of cold water to 1 gallon of the hot liquid. The cold water precipitates foreign substances, and the clean fat rises to the top. Remove the fat when firm.

BASIC SOAP FORMULA. To make 9 pounds of pure, hard, smooth soap suitable for toilet, laundry, or soap flakes, follow this simple recipe:

Cold water	2½ pints
Pure flake lye	1 13-ounce can
Clean fat (tallow or lard, or combination)	6 pounds

Note: Six pounds of fat is about 6¾ pints of liquid fat.

Slowly pour the lye into the water in a Pyrex, iron, or enamel vessel. (*Caution:* Don't spill lye solution on your skin, clothing, or furnishings, as it is extremely caustic.) Stir until the lye is completely dissolved. Then let cool to the correct temperature as shown in the Temperature Table.

Melt fat to clear liquid and let cool to correct temperature as shown in table, or until the fat offers resistance to the spoon. Stir occasionally to prevent crystals from forming. Pour the lye solution into the fat in a thin, steady stream with slow, even stirring. (Rapid addition of lye solution or hard stirring is apt to cause a separation.) A honeylike consistency is formed, which becomes thick in from 10 to 20 minutes.

Pour the thickened mixture into a wooden box that has been soaked in water and lined with clean cotton cloth wet in water and wrung nearly dry. Place in a protecting pan. Cover with a board or cardboard, then with an old rug or blanket to retain the heat while it is texturing out. Leave it alone for 24 hours.

To remove the soap from the mold, lift it by the ends of the overhanging cotton lining. Cut into bars by wrapping the soap with a fine wire and pulling the wire through. Place so air can reach it, but avoid drafts and cold. Aging improves soap. In 10 to 14 days it is ready for use.

TO SAVE SOAP THAT SEPARATES. If soap mixture becomes too hot or too cold, is stirred too hard or not thoroughly mixed, or contains salt, a greasy soap may form at the top while liquid separates out at the bottom.

TEMPERATURE TABLE

Follow these temperatures closely:

Type of Fat	Temperature of Fat	Temperature of Lye Solution
Sweet lard or other soft fat	98° F	77° F
Half lard and tallow	105° F	83° F
All tallow	125° F	93° F

To save the batch, cut or shave the soap into a pot, add the lye solution that has separated and about 5 pints of water. Melt with gentle heat and occasional stirring. Then raise heat and boil gently until it becomes ropy when dropped from the spoon. Pour into mold as mentioned above. Don't worry about too much water—it can be boiled off.

Variations in Soapmaking

Besides all-purpose soap, many other kinds can be made at home. Here are a few:

FLOATING SOAP. Almost any type of soap can be made to float. When the soap mixture becomes thick enough, just fold air into it as egg white would be folded into a cake mixture.

PERFUMED SOAP. You can, of course, scent your soap with small amounts of oils of sassafras, lavender, lemon, almond, rose geranium, or some perfume of your choice. If you do, select one that does not contain alcohol.

A tea made with leaves of rose geranium gives a delightful perfume, and may be colored, if you wish, by adding the extract of blossoms of pink roses or tulips. You can color soap green by adding to the original water a few drops of juice pounded from beet tops. Because all soap absorbs odors, it can be inexpensively perfumed by placing with it the leaves of a favorite flower, or a perfume.

SOAP FLAKES AND POWDER. For flakes, rub three-day-old soap over a vegetable shredder. Stir occasionally while drying. To make powder, first flake the soap and dry in a 150°-F oven. When thoroughly dry, pulverize it.

ROSIN SOAP. A laundry soap that is darker and softer, but which has greater lathering power, can be made by adding rosin. Add 8 ounces of powdered rosin to 5½ pounds of clean fat and heat until the rosin is melted or dissolved in the fat. Cool to 100° F, add the lye solution mentioned above for the basic soap, and cool to 90° F.

SADDLE SOAP. All-tallow soap is often referred to as "saddle soap" because it is an excellent cleaner and preserver of leather. Use 6 pounds of mutton or beef tallow and 2¾ pints of water. Have lye solution 90° F and fat 130° F. This soap will lather better if you substitute 1 pound of lard, coconut oil, or olive oil for that weight of tallow.

GLYCERIN SOAP. Just add about 6 ounces of glycerin to any soap shortly after lye solution has been added.

IMITATION CASTILE SOAP. A high-grade soap that is in many respects superior to real castile soap can be made as follows:

Olive oil	24	ounces
Good grade tallow	38	ounces
Coconut oil	24	ounces
Water	32	ounces
Pure flake lye	13	ounces

Use procedure for basic soap. Pour lye solution into fat when both are 90° F.

LINSEED OIL SOAP. This is a soft soap recommended for washing automobiles and furniture:

Water	2	quarts
Pure flake lye	1	can
Linseed oil	5¾	pounds

Cool lye solution to 90° F and oil to 100° F. Add lye solution a little at a time and combine it well before adding more.

ABRASIVE SOAP. Good for cleaning your hands after any dirty, greasy job. When basic soap mixture thickens add, gradually, 5 to 6 pounds of powdered pumice, emery dust, or tripoli powder and stir until the mixture is thoroughly blended. Mold and cover. Yield: 14 to 15 pounds.

ABRASIVE SOAP PASTE. Another good product for household scouring and mechanics' hands. Shave 3 pounds of basic soap and melt in 3 pints of water. Add 3 ounces of light mineral oil. When thoroughly blended, cool to thick consistency and work in 5 pounds of powdered pumice or tripoli. Keep tightly covered to prevent drying out. Yield: 11 pounds.

JELLY SOAP. This is a convenient and economical soap for use in washing machines and for washing dishes. It melts immediately in hot water and makes thick suds. Cut 1 pound of hard soap into fine shavings and add 1 gallon of water. Boil for about 10 minutes, then transfer to a suitable vessel to cool. Keep covered to prevent drying out.

MECHANIC'S HAND SOAPS. Here is a good cleaner for greasy and grimy hands after work in garage or shop:

Washing soda	1 ounce
Borax	1¼ ounces
Glycerin	½ ounce
Water	13 ounces
Powdered soap	5 ounces
Powdered pumice	7 ounces

Dissolve the washing soda, borax, and glycerin in 3 ounces of the water, and dissolve the powdered soap in the rest of the water. Stir the solutions together. Then stir in the pumice until thoroughly blended.

Note: In this and in similar formulas that call for it, be sure to use powdered soap and not soap powder. Powdered soap is pure soap, although in powdered form, while soap powder is powdered soap combined with powdered alkalies, abrasives, and other builders.

In the following formula, extra sodium carbonate or washing soda acts as a water-softening agent and takes over the cleaning action of part of the soap:

Water	20 ounces
Washing soda	2 ounces
Borax	½ ounce
Powdered soap	2½ ounces
Glycerin	½ ounce
Powdered pumice	10 ounces

Heat the water and dissolve the washing soda, borax, and soap flakes in it. Then add the glycerin with constant stirring. When thickening begins, add the powdered pumice slowly as you continue to stir. Keep stirring until the mixture is smooth enough and thick enough so the pumice will not settle. Then pack it in glass or plastic containers.

Hand-Cleaning Powders

A mild hand cleaner that leaves the hands smooth and soft uses cornmeal as an abrasive and includes sodium perborate as a gentle bleach:

Fine cornmeal	8 ounces
Powdered soap	16 ounces
Powdered borax	12 ounces
Sodium perborate	1½ ounces

Mix thoroughly by stirring and then shaking in a box or passing through a flour sifter several times. For more heavily soiled hands substitute 4 ounces of fine pumice powder for the cornmeal. Use from a flour shaker. Sprinkle on moistened hands, rub, wash, and rinse.

A more powerful cleaner can be made by substituting wood flour (fine sawdust) for the cornmeal and adding a little trisodium phosphate to help cut grease:

Wood flour	10 ounces
Powdered soap	8 ounces
Trisodium phosphate	1 ounce
Borax	1 ounce

Mix and use as described in the previous formula.

Liquid Soap

This can be used from a regular liquid soap dispenser or from a bottle.

Potassium hydroxide	1 ounce
Water	11 ounces
Glycerin	4 ounces
Oleic acid	4 ounces

Dissolve the potassium hydroxide in the water in a stainless steel or heat-resisting glass vessel. (*Caution:* Keep this chemical off your hands and clothing, as it is extremely caustic.) Then mix the glycerin with the oleic acid and add to the solution. Heat to about 172° F, and stir until completely emulsified.

Improvised Liquid Soap

Dissolve any good soap, soap flakes, or powdered soap in hot water, making a thick paste. To each quart of this add a mixture of 1 pint of warm water and ½ pint of ethyl rubbing alcohol. When stirred in, this acts as a clarifying agent. Besides serving as a good liquid soap for general purposes, this preparation also makes a simple and inexpensive shampoo.

Liquid Shampoo

A shampoo comparable to many proprietary brands may be made as follows:

Potassium hydroxide	2¼ ounces
Water	22 ounces
Coconut oil	8 ounces
Ethyl rubbing alcohol compound (70% alcohol)	6 ounces
Perfume	as desired

Dissolve completely the potassium hydroxide in 6 ounces of the water in a stainless steel or heat-resisting glass vessel. (*Caution:* Keep this chemical off your hands and clothing, as it is extremely caustic.) Mix the coconut oil in the top of a double boiler also made of glass or stainless steel, heat it to 158° F and, with constant stirring, add the potassium hydroxide solution. Keep this temperature for about 1 hour, stirring occasionally. Then heat the rest of the water to 158° F and stir into the mixture. Let cool, add the alcohol and, if you wish, the perfume.

COSMETICS

Protective Hand Creams

A mixture of lanolin and castor oil is frequently used on the hands and arms of machinists susceptible to skin trouble caused by constant contact with lubricating oil. This type of "extra skin," however, is not so suitable for those doing general work about the shop, garage, or home.

A good protective cream for all-around use can be made from 1 part by volume of gum acacia (in the form of small globules, or "tears") and 2 parts powdered soap. Put the gum acacia in a widemouthed jar and add only enough water to cover the drops. Cover the jar, and allow to stand overnight. Then stir in the soap to form a thick cream.

Rub this cream well into your hands before starting work. When you have finished, you can easily wash it off along with the dirt.

GLYCERIN HAND LOTION

Gum tragacanth	½ ounce
Boric acid	2 ounces
Water	16 ounces
Witch hazel	16 ounces
Glycerin	8 ounces
Perfume	as desired

Add the gum tragacanth and boric acid to the water and let soak for 12 hours, with occasional stirring. Then add the witch hazel and glycerin and stir or shake well. Strain through clean muslin. If you would like the lotion scented, add perfume to suit.

HAND LOTION

Ethyl rubbing alcohol compound (alcohol 70%)	15 fluid ounces
Water	15 fluid ounces
Soft soap	1 ounce
Glycerin	4 fluid ounces
Perfume	as desired

Mix the rubbing alcohol with the water (use distilled water if your tap water is hard) and dissolve the soft soap in the mixture. Then stir in the glycerin. Add perfume if you wish.

LANOLIN SKIN LOTION

Borax	¼ ounce
White powdered soap	½ ounce

Water	44 ounces
Lanolin	5 ounces
Perfume	as desired

Dissolve the borax and soap in the water, heated to about 110° F. Melt the lanolin separately and then pour into the water solution with vigorous stirring. Finally add perfume, if desired. Shake before using.

COLD CREAM

Heavy mineral oil	200 parts
White beeswax	50 parts
Borax	30 parts
Water	80 parts
Perfume	as desired

Put the oil in the top of a double boiler, add the wax, and heat gently until the wax is melted. Dissolve the borax in the water. Heat both liquids to not more than 150° F. Pour the borax solution into the wax solution steadily with gentle stirring. At this point, blend in a little perfume, if desired. Remove from heat and pour it into glass or plastic containers when it has cooled to 120° F.

A second formula for cold cream substitutes paraffin for part of the beeswax:

Borax	½ ounce
Water	17 fluid ounces
White beeswax	6½ ounces
Paraffin wax	2½ ounces
Heavy mineral oil	21 fluid ounces
Perfume	as desired

Dissolve the borax in water and heat to about 168° F. Mix wax and oil in top of double boiler, raise temperature to 158° F, and stir until wax is melted and combined. Then stir vigorously into the hot borax solution. Keep stirring until mixture cools to about 125° F. Perfume, if desired, may then be mixed in.

PETROLATUM COLD CREAM

Heavy mineral oil	48 fluid ounces
White petrolatum	12 ounces
White beeswax	8 ounces
White ceresin wax	8 ounces
Borax	¼ ounce
Water	12 fluid ounces
Perfume	as desired

Place the petrolatum, waxes, and mineral oil in the top of a double boiler and heat to about 160° F. Stir until the solids have completely melted and combined. Dissolve the borax in the water, heated to the same temperature. Then pour the borax solution into the wax mixture and stir well. Remove from the heat and keep stirring until mixture begins to thicken. Then mix in the perfume.

VANISHING CREAM. A vanishing cream is a greaseless cream that is essentially a stearic acid soap having excess stearic acid suspended in water. The usual pearly appearance is caused by crystallization of the acid. To bring this about, the cream should be allowed to stand a few days after making, stirring it slowly for several minutes each day.

Stearic acid	12½ ounces
Anhydrous lanolin	4½ ounces
Water	30 fluid ounces
White mineral oil	9½ fluid ounces
Potassium carbonate	1 ounce
Perfume	as desired

Melt the stearic acid and the lanolin, mixed with 20 ounces of the water, in the top of a double boiler. Raise the heat to 170° F. Dissolve the potassium carbonate in the remainder of the water, heated also to 170° F. Add this solution to the first mixture. Stir until foaming caused by the reaction of the stearic acid with the carbonate subsides. Then remove from the heat and keep stirring until the mixture thickens. Add perfume at this time, and pour into containers before the cream completely solidifies.

BRUSHLESS SHAVING CREAM

Heavy mineral oil	8 ounces
Diglycol stearate	8 ounces
Water	40 ounces
Perfume	as desired

Heat the mineral oil and diglycol stearate (also called glycostearin) to 150° F in the top of a double boiler. Heat the water separately to the same temperature and stir slowly into the mixture. Let cool to lukewarm and stir in perfume. Keep stirring until at room temperature. Store in jars or tubes.

AFTER-SHAVE LOTION. This is a cooling and astringent solution for use after shaving. Use crystalline boric acid, as supplied for photographic formulas, as the powdered form is more difficult to dissolve.

Boric acid	½ ounce
Ethyl rubbing alcohol compound (70% alcohol)	20 fluid ounces
Water	15 fluid ounces

NAIL POLISH REMOVER. This inexpensive nail polish remover is as effective as any:

Ethyl acetate	1 fluid ounce
Acetone	3 fluid ounces
Cooking oil (corn, soybean, cottonseed, olive)	30 drops

Just stir the ingredients until thoroughly blended, and store in a tightly stopped bottle. The oil is included to prevent the solvents from drying out the nails.

ANTIPERSPIRANT SOLUTION. A simple and effective preparation for the control of perspiration is a solution of aluminum chloride in water. Your druggist may have it already prepared as "aluminum chloride solution, N.F.," or he may make it up for you. Here is the formula, if you want to make it yourself:

Aluminum chloride	2 ounces
Water	8 fluid ounces

Just dissolve the chemical by stirring it in about 6 ounces of water, and then adding enough more water to make 8 ounces. If the solution is cloudy, filter until it becomes clear.

Pat lightly on unbroken skin with a swab of cotton. Repeat two times more, on successive nights. If necessary, repeat again in a week.

This chemical may irritate some skin and may stain clothes if they come in contact with it when wet. Therefore do not rub it in or use it more than necessary. Also let the skin dry thoroughly before letting clothing touch it.

How Hexachlorophene Cuts B.O.

Unpleasant body odor is often the result of by-products of bacteria that live on the skin. It has been found that such bacteria—and hence the odors that they produce—can be almost entirely eliminated by bathing regularly with a soap containing the bacteriostat, or bacteria inhibitor, hexachlorophene. Discovered in the 1940s, this remarkable chemical was the first powerful bacteriostat that was odorless, nonpoisonous, and nonirritating to the skin that could be combined with soap and other cleaning materials without losing its own effectiveness.

Dial soap was the first to introduce hexachlorophene to the general public. Now many other soaps and cleaning agents—as well as many deodorants—contain it, as you can find out from their labels.

A single scrubbing with hexachlorophene soap will have little effect, but daily use for a week should reduce the bacteria on your skin to as little as 5 percent of normal.

Bargains in Talcum Powder

The finest talcum powder is so inexpensive, it would not pay to try to mix your own. Essentially talcum is a native magnesium silicate that has been mechanically milled, ground, sifted, and mixed for many hours to reduce it to an impalpable dust. It owes its usefulness and popularity to its softness, slight greasiness, and its ability to cling to the skin.

If you pay a lot for talcum, you are paying for a brand name or for a drop or two of perfume. To get quality talcum at a bargain price, buy the largest containers of unscented or faintly scented "baby talcum" of any reputable maker. These are often sold as "come-ons" in drugstores and supermarkets.

MOUTHWASHES

Any mouthwash you can buy without a prescription is essentially a liquid with a pleasant taste and odor that is useful for rinsing loose food and debris from your mouth. According to authoritative medical opinion, claims for significant germicidal or antibacterial action by such solutions are baseless. Although it may occasionally be necessary to use medicated solutions containing astringents, germicides, and other special agents, these should be used only under medical supervision to treat definite ailments of the mouth. The normal mouth does not need them, and if used indiscriminately they may do more harm than good.

Most proprietary mouthwashes are slightly alkaline, because alkalies are more effective in removing mucus and saliva. If too strong, however, alkalies will damage mouth and throat tissues. If a mouthwash is acid, on the other hand, it may damage your teeth.

The simplest mouthwash is plain warm water. This wash will be kinder to your mouth and a little more effective in removing debris if you make it approximately isotonic, or the density of your body fluids, by adding a teaspoon of table salt to each pint.

A slightly alkaline mouthwash can be made by dissolving 2 teaspoons of bicarbonate of soda in each pint of water. Or you can use half a teaspoon each of bicarbonate and salt in a pint of water.

If you prefer a flavored mouthwash, try this:

Sodium chloride	1 teaspoon
Sodium bicarbonate	½ teaspoon
Amaranth solution, U.S.P.	40 drops
Peppermint water to make 1 pint of mouthwash	

Peppermint Water

The peppermint water included in the formula above is one of a number of pleasingly flavored waters that have been included in medical preparations down through the centuries chiefly to make them acceptable in aroma and taste. Technically peppermint water is a saturated solution of peppermint oil in distilled water. Because peppermint oil is almost insoluble in water, a tiny amount of oil flavors an amazing amount of solution.

To make peppermint water, add about ½ teaspoon of peppermint oil to 1 quart of water in a 2-quart bottle. Shake the mixture at half-a-dozen intervals during a period of 15 minutes. Stopper the bottle, and set the mixture aside for half a day or longer. Then filter through a filter paper that has first been wetted with water to prevent the excess of oil from going through. Although most of the oil remains behind, you will discover that the water will be saturated with its odor and taste.

TEETH-CLEANING PREPARATIONS

Powders and pastes for cleaning teeth are generally composed of precipitated chalk, salt, bicarbonate of soda, soap, borax, magnesia, glycerin, saccharin for sweetening, flavors and essential oils for taste, water, and color. Some may taste and smell better than others, some contain bleaches that lighten stains faster, and some contain harsher abrasives that remove soil with less brushing. None, however, has value in treating mouth or gum disease or in helping to preserve teeth. If the abrasive in a paste or powder is too hard or too coarse, it cleans teeth faster but also wears down their surface. Recent tests indicate that fluorides in some preparations may be useful in reducing decay, but this is a matter of tooth medication and not of cleaning.

According to the Council on Dental Therapeutics of the American Dental Association, at least 25 percent of all persons could keep their teeth satisfactorily clean by brushing them regularly with plain water. Most of the remainder could do a good job with nothing more than common salt or bicarbonate of soda—or a combination of the two—sprinkled on a wet brush.

If stain still builds up under these simple means, an occasional brushing with a proprietary paste or powder of your choice may help, or you could use one of the following mildly abrasive and inexpensive products you can make yourself.

Inexpensive Tooth Powder

A cheap tooth powder as effective as the most expensive, yet one that will not damage the enamel on your teeth, is simply precipitated chalk you can buy at any drugstore. Plain chalk or flavored chalk was indeed the sole or main ingredient of almost all tooth powders until recent years, and it still holds top place. If you would prefer it flavored, mix thoroughly into it a little oil of wintergreen, spearmint, or peppermint, according to your taste.

Foamy Tooth Powders

If you like foamy or sudsy tooth powders, here is a simple formula of this type:

Precipitated chalk	5 ounces
Sodium bicarbonate	1 ounce
Powdered soap	¾ ounce
Flavor	as desired

Be sure to use powdered soap in this and the next formula, and not soap powder, which is a cleaning preparation made of soap mixed with various "builders." Mix the powders thoroughly and sift them together. If desired, stir in one of the flavors mentioned in the previous formula.

The following foamy powder is a little more complex:

Soluble saccharin	18 grains
Oil of peppermint	½ teaspoon
Oil of cinnamon	¼ teaspoon
Methyl salicylate	1 teaspoon
Precipitated chalk	19 ounces
Powdered soap	1 ounce

Grind and mix thoroughly together the saccharin, oils, and methyl salicylate with about half of the precipitated chalk, and mix the soap with the other half. Then mix the two powders together and sift through a fine sieve.

Denture Cleaners

Dental plates and bridges may be cleaned by brushing them with any of the proprietary tooth powders or pastes, or with the powders just described.

To remove the stains from dentures and to sweeten and disinfect them, they may be soaked in a solution of common household chemicals. These are the same chemicals you would pay a great deal more for if bought under their proprietary names as denture cleaners.

First brush the denture to remove obvious particles, and then let it stand for 15 minutes or overnight in one of the following solutions:

1. Clear household ammonia	4 teaspoons
Water	½ glass
2. Trisodium phosphate	¼ teaspoon
Warm water	½ glass
3. 5% sodium hypochlorite solution (Clorox, Rose-X, Purex, etc.)	½ teaspoon
Water	½ glass

All these preparations are safe for the usual acrylic plastic dentures. Those made of chromium-cobalt alloys should not be left in the sodium hypochlorite solution for more than a few minutes as they may corrode. After soaking, dentures should be rinsed in plain water before using.

A denture cleaner that includes a mild bleaching agent can be made by thoroughly mixing together the following:

Trisodium phosphate	10	ounces
Sodium perborate	5	ounces
Salt	5	ounces

Here is another that does not require soaking, but is used immediately with a brush:

Trisodium phosphate	5	ounces
Cinnamon oil	7	drops

Put the trisodium phosphate in a dry widemouthed bottle. Drop the oil on it, cover the bottle, and shake until the oil is thoroughly mixed with the powder. To use, dissolve a scant ¼ teaspoonful in half a glass of water and brush the denture with the solution. Rinse with plain water.

DENTURE ADHESIVES

Although not recommended by dental authorities for routine use, denture adhesives are often useful in helping a person get used to new dentures, in easing a transitory sore spot, or in preventing dentures from popping out while making a speech.

Most of the proprietary adhesives consist of just one or two common gums, or a combination of them, with the addition of a trace of flavor. The simplest and probably the most widely used is powdered gum tragacanth. Powdered karaya gum may also be used alone, but a few people are sensitive to it. A combination powder, with flavor, may be made as follows:

Powdered gum tragacanth	3	ounces
Powdered karaya gum	1	ounce
Sassafras oil	35	drops

Shake the two powdered gums together in a dry widemouthed bottle until thoroughly mixed. Add the oil and shake again until the oil has blended with the powders. Sprinkle sparingly on the denture, and place in the mouth.

BASIC OINTMENTS

WHITE OINTMENT. This is a bland and basic ointment that may be used either alone or with medication incorporated in it.

White beeswax	1 ounce
Lanolin (wool fat)	1 ounce
White petroleum jelly	20 ounces

Melt the beeswax in the top of a double boiler. Add the lanolin and petroleum jelly and continue to heat until they are also melted. Then remove from heat and stir the mixture until it begins to harden. Pour into widemouthed jars.

BORIC ACID OINTMENT

Finely powdered boric acid	2 ounces
Lanolin	1 ounce
White ointment	17 ounces

Work the boric acid into the lanolin with a spatula until you form a uniform paste. Then similarly work into this the white ointment.

ZINC OXIDE OINTMENT

Finely powdered zinc oxide	3 ounces
Lanolin	1 ounce
White ointment	11 ounces

Preparation is the same as for the formula above.

SULFUR OINTMENT

Precipitated sulfur	2 ounces
Lanolin	1 ounce
White ointment	11 ounces

With a spatula, work the sulfur into the lanolin and about 1½ ounces of the white ointment. Then blend the mixture with the rest of the white ointment.

FOOT POWDER

This preparation is mildly fungicidal and also acts as a drying and soothing agent.

Salicylic acid	½ ounce
Zinc stearate	½ ounce
Boric acid	½ ounce
Powdered talcum	7½ ounces
Cornstarch	10 ounces

Put all these ingredients into a large, dry widemouthed bottle and shake together until thoroughly mixed. Sprinkle between the toes and in the socks. (*Caution:* Some people are sensitive to all preparations containing salicylic acid. If redness and a slight swelling appear within a day, do not continue the use of this powder.)

ALCOHOL FOR MEDICINES AND COSMETICS

Because it is practically impossible for an ordinary individual to get straight ethyl alcohol that is safe for internal use, no formulas requiring it are included in this book. Manufacturers of medical products may obtain pure or specially denatured alcohol by permission, and under the strict control, of the Internal Revenue Service.

The denatured alcohols that are sold for fuel, cleaning, and as a solvent for surface coatings contain extremely poisonous wood alcohol, gasoline, and other denaturants that make them completely unfit for any preparation either to be taken internally or to be applied to the skin.

Vodka as Alcohol

If you want to prepare a medicinal product that requires undenatured ethyl alcohol and you are willing to pay a premium price for it, you can use vodka—provided your formula does not require alcohol of more than 55-percent strength by volume. Present-day American vodka is simply ethyl or grain alcohol ("neutral spirits") diluted with from 45- to 60-percent water. To find the percentage by volume of alcohol in a given vodka, just divide the "proof" number by 2. For percentage by weight, see the accompanying table:

ALCOHOL IN VODKA

Proof	Percent alcohol by volume	Percent alcohol by weight
80	40	33.36
100	50	42.49
110	55	47.24

MEDICINAL DOSES FOR CHILDREN

One long-used and still popular rule for calculating the fraction of an adult dose of medicine that may safely and effectively be given to a child is called *Young's rule,* after the physician who devised it. Usually it is stated simply as "age·over age-plus-12." For example, here is how to calculate the dose for a child of 4:

$$\frac{4}{4 + 12} = \frac{1}{4} \text{ part of an adult dose.}$$

Many physicians disregard age and base a child's dose simply on the proportion of the child's weight to that of an adult, which is set arbitrarily at 150 pounds.

HOW TO READ PRESCRIPTION LATIN

The familiar prescription (from Latin *prae,* before; and *scribere,* to write) is simply an order from a physician, dentist, or other licensed practitioner instructing a pharmacist to compound and dispense certain medication for the patient.

For a number of reasons a prescription is often written in Latin. Three of these are still valid: Because Latin is a dead language, terms in it do not change; Latin is the worldwide language of medicine; and the Latin names of drugs are more definite than the popular terms of the local country. A fourth reason—to conceal from the patient the nature of the ingredients and the instructions for administration—has become dubious with the discovery of amazing new drugs and the vastly increased knowledge of the general public about disease and medicine.

The following glossary of common terms used in prescription Latin is included not only to dispel some of the unwarranted mystery surrounding prescriptions, but to help patients apply them more intelligently.

ALCOHOLIC STRENGTHS

The term "proof" describes the strength of alcohol. In the United States proof is a spirit containing 50-percent alcohol by volume at a temperature of 60° F. This is an arbitrary measurement. Each degree of proof is equal to one-half of one percent of alcohol. Therefore, a spirit of 100 proof contains 50-percent alcohol, and a spirit of 150 proof contains 75-percent alcohol. The trade term for a spirit of more than 100 proof is "overproof" spirit. The accompanying table is a comparison of United States "Proof," British "Sikes," and metric "Gay Lussac."

U.S. proof	British Sikes	Gay Lussac alcohol by volume	U.S. proof	British Sikes	Gay Lussac alcohol by volume	U.S. proof	British Sikes	Gay Lussac alcohol by volume	U.S. proof	British Sikes	Gay Lussac alcohol by volume
0	100.	0	38	66.7	19.0	76	33.5	38.0	113	1.1	56.5
1	99.1	0.5	39	65.8	19.5	77	32.6	38.5	114	0.2	57.0
2	98.2	1.0	40	65.0	20.0	78	31.7	39.0	115	0.7	57.5
3	97.4	1.5	41	64.1	20.5	79	30.8	39.5	116	1.6	58.0
4	96.5	2.0	42	63.2	21.0	80	29.9	40.0	117	2.3	58.5
5	95.6	2.5	43	62.3	21.5	81	29.1	40.5	118	3.3	59.0
6	94.7	3.0	44	61.5	22.0	82	28.2	41.0	119	4.2	59.5
7	93.9	3.5	45	60.6	22.5	83	27.3	41.5	120	5.1	60.0
8	93.0	4.0	46	59.7	23.0	84	26.4	42.0	121	6.0	60.5
9	92.1	4.5	47	58.8	23.5	85	25.6	42.5	122	6.8	61.0
10	91.2	5.0	48	58.0	24.0	86	24.7	43.0	123	7.7	61.5
11	90.4	5.5	49	57.1	24.5	87	23.8	43.5	124	8.6	62.0
12	89.5	6.0	50	56.2	25.0	88	22.9	44.0	125	9.5	62.5
13	88.6	6.5	51	55.3	25.5	89	22.1	44.5	126	10.3	63.0

14	87.7	7.0	52	54.5	26.0	90	21.2	45.0	127	11.2	63.5
15	86.9	7.5	53	53.6	26.5	91	20.3	45.5	128	12.1	64.0
16	86.0	8.0	54	52.7	27.0	92	19.4	46.0	129	13.0	64.5
17	85.1	8.5	55	51.8	27.5	93	18.6	46.5	130	13.8	65.0
18	84.2	9.0	56	51.0	28.0	94	17.7	47.0	131	14.7	65.5
19	83.4	9.5	57	50.1	28.5	95	16.8	47.5	132	15.6	66.0
20	82.5	10.0	58	49.2	29.0	96	15.9	48.0	133	16.5	66.5
21	81.6	10.5	59	48.3	29.5	97	15.1	48.5	134	17.3	67.0
22	80.7	11.0	60	47.5	30.0	98	14.2	49.0	135	18.2	67.5
23	79.9	11.5	61	46.6	30.5	99	13.3	49.5	136	19.1	68.0
24	79.0	12.0	62	45.7	31.0	100	12.4	50.0	137	20.0	68.5
25	78.1	12.5	63	44.8	31.5	O.P.			138	20.8	69.0
26	77.2	13.0	64	44.0	32.0	101	11.6	50.5	139	21.7	69.5
27	76.4	13.5	65	43.1	32.5	102	10.7	51.0	140	22.6	70.0
28	75.5	14.0	66	42.2	33.0	103	9.8	51.5	141	23.5	70.5
29	74.6	14.5	67	41.3	33.5	104	8.9	52.0	142	24.3	71.0
30	73.7	15.0	68	40.5	34.0	105	8.1	52.5	143	25.2	71.5
31	72.9	15.5	69	39.6	34.5	106	7.2	53.0	144	26.1	72.0
32	72.0	16.0	70	38.7	35.0	107	6.3	53.5	145	27.0	72.5
33	71.1	16.5	71	37.8	35.5	108	5.4	54.0	146	27.8	73.0
34	70.2	17.0	72	37.0	36.0	109	4.6	54.5	147	28.7	73.5
35	69.4	17.5	73	36.1	36.5	110	3.7	55.0	148	29.6	74.0
36	68.5	18.0	74	35.2	37.0	111	2.8	55.5	149	30.5	74.5
37	67.6	18.5	75	34.3	37.5	112	1.9	56.0	150	31.3	75.0

(U.P. = Underproof; O.P. = Overproof)

(Continued)

ALCOHOLIC STRENGTHS *(continued)*

The term "proof" describes the strength of alcohol. In the United States proof is a spirit containing 50-percent alcohol by volume at a temperature of 60° F. This is an arbitrary measurement. Each degree of proof is equal to one-half of one percent of alcohol. Therefore, a spirit of 100 proof contains 50-percent alcohol, and a spirit of 150 proof contains 75-percent alcohol. The trade term for a spirit of more than 100 proof is "overproof" spirit. The accompanying table is a comparison of United States "Proof," British "Sikes," and metric "Gay Lussac."

U.S. proof	British Sikes	Gay Lussac alcohol by volume	U.S. proof	British Sikes	Gay Lussac alcohol by volume	U.S. proof	British Sikes	Gay Lussac alcohol by volume	U.S. proof	British Sikes	Gay Lussac alcohol by volume
151	32.2	75.5	164	43.6	82.0	176	54.1	88.0	188	64.6	94.0
152	33.1	76.0	165	44.5	82.5	177	55.0	88.5	189	65.5	94.5
153	34.0	76.5	166	45.4	83.0	178	55.9	89.0	190	66.4	95.0
154	34.9	77.0	167	46.2	83.5	179	56.7	89.5	191	67.3	95.5
155	35.7	77.5	168	47.1	84.0	180	57.6	90.0	192	68.1	96.0
156	36.6	78.0	169	48.0	84.5	181	58.5	90.5	193	69.0	96.5
157	37.5	78.5	170	48.9	85.0	182	59.4	91.0	194	69.9	97.0
158	38.4	79.0	171	49.7	85.5	183	60.2	91.5	195	70.8	97.5
159	39.2	79.5	172	50.6	86.0	184	61.1	92.0	196	71.6	98.0
160	40.1	80.0	173	51.5	86.5	185	62.0	92.5	197	72.5	98.5
161	41.0	80.5	174	52.4	87.0	186	62.9	93.0	198	73.4	99.0
162	41.9	81.0	175	53.2	87.5	187	63.7	93.5	199	74.3	99.5
163	42.7	81.5							200	75.1	100.0

(U.P. = Underproof; O.P. = Overproof)

THE LATIN ON YOUR PRESCRIPTION

Abbreviation or short form	Expanded form	Meaning
a.	auris	ear
aa.	ana	of each
a.c.	ante cibos	before meals
ad	ad	to, up to
add	adde	add
ad lib.	ad libitum	at pleasure
agit.	agita	shake
alb.	albus	white
aq.	aqua	water
b.	bis	twice
bene.	bene	well
b.i.d.	bis in die	twice a day
c.	cum	with
cap.	capiat	let the patient take
caps.	capsula	capsule
caps. amyl.	capsulae amylaceae	wafer-type capsule
chart.	charta	paper, a powder in paper
chart. cerat.	charta cerata	waxed paper
chartul.	chartula	small paper
coch. amp.	cochleare amplum	tablespoonful
or coch. mag.	cochleare magnum	tablespoonful
coch. parv.	cochleare parvum	teaspoonful
collyr.	collyrium	eyewash
d.	dies	a day
d.	dosis	a dose
da	da	give
dieb. alt.	diebus alternis	every other day
disp.	dispensa, dispensetur	dispense
div.	divide	divide
dos.	dosis	a dose
d.t.d.	dentur tales doses	give such doses
ejusd.	ejusdem	of the same
e.m.p.	ex modo praescripto	as directed

(Continued)

THE LATIN ON YOUR PRESCRIPTION (*continued*)

Abbreviation or short form	Expanded form	Meaning
et	et	and
ex aq.	ex aqua	with water
flav.	flavus	yellow
ft.	fiat, fiant	make
gtt.	gutta, guttae	a drop, drops
hor.	hora	an hour
h.s.	hora somni	at bedtime
m.	misce	mix
mitt.	mitte	send
no.	numero	in number
non	non	not
non rep.	non repetatur	do not repeat
O.	Octarius	a pint
ocul.	oculus	the eye
o.d.	oculo dextro	in right eye
o.l.	oculo laevo	in left eye
o.s.	oculo sinistro	in left eye
o.u.	oculo utroque	in each eye
p. ae.	partes aequales	equal parts
p.c.	post cibos	after meals
per	per	by means of
placebo	placebo	to please or satisfy
p.o.	per os	by mouth
p.r.n.	pro re nata	as needed
pro tus.	pro tussi	for the cough
q.i.d.	quater in die	four times a day
q.q.h.	quaqua quarta hora	every four hours
qq. hr.	quaqua hora	every hour
q.r.	quantitas recta	quantity is correct
q.s.	quantum sufficit	a sufficient quantity
R_x	recipe	take
s.	sine	without
s.a.	secundem artem	according to the art
s.c., sub cut.	sub cutem	under the skin
sig.	signa, signetur	label, let it be labeled
s.o.s.	si opus sit	if needed
ss.	semis	half

THE LATIN ON YOUR PRESCRIPTION ***(continued)***

Abbreviation or short form	Expanded form	Meaning
stat.	statim	immediately
s.v.r.	spiritus vini rectificatus	alcohol
tal.	tales	such
t.i.d.	ter in die	three times a day
ut dict.	ut dictum	as directed
v.	vel	or
virid.	viridis	green

12

Household Pests, Fungi, and Bacteria

Some household pests have an incredible ability to escape extinction. Cockroaches, for example, which have been on the earth millions of years longer than man and thrive in all parts of the world, can subsist on any kind of food. Some species of cockroaches prefer man's home to other habitats. Once they enter it, they use countless instinctive tricks to keep from being evicted.

You can help control household pests by systematic housecleaning. You can rid your home of practically all pests, and keep it free of them, by a combination of continuous good housekeeping and the proper use of the right pesticide at the right time. *Note:* Suggestions for insect control are limited to uses in and around the home and do not apply to food-handling establishments. Control of garden and lawn insects is covered in Chapter 13.

GOOD HOUSEKEEPING

It is easier to prevent pests from infesting your home than it is to get rid of them after they are established. Household pests seek available food and places where they may hide and breed. If you eliminate these attractions from your home, the pests will look elsewhere for them.

Here are some basic rules to follow:

1. Practice sanitation. Many household pests live on spilled food and organic matter that has not been completely cleaned up. They breed, multiply, and hide in small areas where food is left available to them—in cracks and crevices in cupboards, walls, and floors; around baseboards; and behind kitchen drawers. They hide in seldom-used storage cabinets, behind washtubs, and around water pipes and toilets.

   Keep these places clean. Frequent scrubbings with hot water and soap or detergent will do the job. (Scrub surfaces *before* treating them with pesticides; do not scrub newly treated surfaces.)
2. Promptly dispose of garbage, bits of food, crumbs, scraps of fabrics, lint, and other waste materials that pests may eat or in which they may breed.
3. Keep all foods in tightly closed containers, and keep the containers clean outside as well as inside. Before purchasing dry foods, examine the packages carefully for evidence of breaks and resultant insect infestation.
4. Don't permit insect pests to hitchhike into your home. Cockroaches and silverfish often enter the house in the crevices of cardboard cartons used in transporting groceries or other materials. Don't leave these containers in the kitchen or basement where the pests may escape to infest your home.
5. Permanently seal up places where pests may enter. You may not be able to close them all, but you can close most. Caulk the openings and cracks around wash basins, toilet bowls, water pipes, drain pipes, and radiator pipes. Fill in the cracks around baseboards and between floorboards. Cover openings where rats or mice may enter. See that windows and doors are tight fitting.
6. Practice pest-prevention measures at all times. Application of pesticide may be needed to supplement good housekeeping. Follow the directions and heed all precautions on the pesticide label.

PESTICIDES AND THEIR APPLICATION

There are many kinds of pesticides, just as there are many kinds of pests. Housekeepers are concerned chiefly with *insecticides* to control insects, *miticides* to control mites, and *rodenticides* to control rodents.

Pesticides may be applied in different forms and different ways to serve various purposes. In order that you may know how to select the right form and apply it properly, read the following explanations:

Surface Sprays

Surface sprays are applied to surfaces in the home where insects are likely to crawl. The spray particles are coarse, and they dampen or wet the surfaces. When the spray dries, a thin deposit of insecticide remains. For several weeks or months, the deposit kills insects that crawl over it.

You may buy these sprays in pressurized containers, or you may buy a liquid insecticide and apply it with a household hand sprayer that produces a continuous coarse spray. (*Caution:* Do not spray oil-base insecticides on asphalt-tile or asphalt-asbestos floors, because they may dissolve the asphalt. They may also soften and discolor some linoleums and some plastic vinyl materials; if in doubt about spraying such surfaces, test the spray on a small, inconspicuous place. If you apply an oil-base insecticide to the cracks in a parquet floor, apply it lightly; an excessive amount may dissolve the underlying cement, and the dissolved cement may stain the floor.)

Space Sprays and Aerosols

Space sprays and aerosols are designed for application into the air. They are especially effective against mosquitoes, houseflies, and other flying insects. They may also be used to penetrate the hiding places of other insects, such as roaches, and drive them into the open where they may be killed with a surface spray or dust.

The particles, or droplets, of a space spray are much finer than those of a surface spray, and float in the air for a time. The particles of an aerosol are finer than those of a space spray, and float in the air for a longer time.

Space sprays leave little residue, and generally should not be used as surface sprays. Aerosols are entirely too fine for surface application.

You may buy space sprays in pressurized containers, or you may buy liquid insecticide and apply it as a space spray with a household hand sprayer having a nozzle that produces very fine particles. Household aerosols are available in pressurized containers.

Some sprays sold in pressurized containers may be labeled for both surface and space applications. If you use one of these products for spraying in the kitchen or pantry, first place cooking and eating utensils, and food, where they will not be contaminated by falling particles.

Before applying a space spray or aerosol, close all windows and doors tightly. Apply the chemical into the air as directed on the container label. After application, leave the room, close the door, and do not reenter for an hour or longer. Breathe as little as possible of the chemicals discharged in space sprays or aerosols. Some people may be allergic to the materials in these sprays or aerosols. Before occupying the room, air it thoroughly.

Dusts

Insecticidal dusts usually contain the same active ingredients as sprays. They are used for surface applications, and may be blown by a household hand duster into cracks, corners, and other places difficult to reach with sprays.

Paintbrush Application

Insecticide may be applied to surfaces in liquid, cream, or paste form with a paintbrush. This method often permits a more accurate placement of the material than does spraying or dusting. It is particularly recommended where only spot treatments are needed.

Cream or paste insecticides are usually available in stores where liquids and dusts are sold.

Poisoned Bait

Poisoned bait, as the name implies, is a bait on which a pest will feed, and to which a pesticide has been added.

In the home, poisoned baits may be used to control rodents and some other pests. Frequently they are more hazardous to humans and pets than other forms of pesticide. If you use a poisoned bait, handle it with extreme care; follow the directions and observe all precautions on the container label.

Buying the Right Pesticide

In this book the active ingredients of pesticides are referred to by their *common* names. You may find that the labels on some pesticide containers in retail stores call the active ingredients by their *chemical* names. The table on page 404 will aid you in buying the right pesticide; it shows the common and chemical name for each active ingredient.

SAFETY WITH PESTICIDES

Poisons for troublesome insects, fungi, and other pests are often poisonous to man and pet animals. They can therefore be dangerous if used

COMMON AND CHEMICAL NAMES OF PESTICIDES

Common name	Chemical name*
Baygon	Propoxur,0-isopropoxyphenyl methylcarbamate
Diazinon	0,0-diethyl 0-(2-isopropyl-4 methyl-6-pyrmidinyl) phosphorothioate
Malathion	S-(1,2-bis[ethoxycarbonyl]ethyl) 0,0-dimethyl phosphorodithioate
Methoxychlor	1,1,1-trichloro-2,2-bis(p-methoxyphenyl)bethane
Perthane	A mixture of diethyl diphenyl dichloroethane (95 percent) and related reaction products (5 percent)
Pyrethrum	Pyrethrum or pyrethrins
Ronnel	0,0-dimethyl 0-(2,4,5-trichlorophenyl) phosphorothioate

* The chemical name shown on the label may not always be exactly as shown here; variation is possible in the arrangement and inclusion of numbers. Other chemical names for other common pesticides are given in Chapter 19.

carelessly. They are safe, however, if you observe a few simple rules:

Use pesticides only when and where needed, and in recommended amounts.

Follow the directions and heed all precautions on the labels. What may be safe with one type may be dangerous with another.

Keep pesticides in closed, well-labeled containers in a dry place, where they will not contaminate food and where children and animals cannot reach them.

While applying a pesticide, be careful not to contaminate water supply, food, dishes, or utensils.

Do not apply oil sprays where they could be ignited by a flame, such as that of a pilot light, or by electric sparks.

Avoid prolonged contact of insecticide with your skin. Some insecticides can be absorbed directly through the skin in harmful quantities.

Do not treat an entire room with insecticides that are meant only for local surface spraying.

High dosages of aerosol mists may be irritating to eyes and lungs. Keep people and pets out of a treated room for at least an hour after the aerosol has been applied.

Wash all exposed parts of the body with soap and water after applying a pesticide.

Dispose of empty pesticide containers at a sanitary land-fill dump, or bury them at least 18 inches deep in a level, isolated place where they will not contaminate water supplies. If you have trash-collection service, thoroughly wrap small containers in several layers of newspaper and place them in the trash can.

Do not smoke while applying pesticides.

CONTROL OF HOUSEHOLD INSECTS

Insects that invade your home may endanger your health, damage household goods, or become a general nuisance. You can control these pests, however, by means of a combination of modern insecticides and proper sanitation.

The table on page 406 will help you choose the proper kind and concentration of insecticide to use against the common pests discussed below.

Ants

Ants may steal into a house unnoticed until their trails become heavily populated. The best way to get rid of them is to follow their trail into their nests, which may be either indoors or outdoors. Then treat the nest with an insecticide such as diazinon or malathion.

You might hasten their eradication by applying a surface or residual spray over the area of their trail. But they may make a new trail that you will also have to spray.

Bedbugs

Thanks to the newer insecticides, bedbugs are not as common in the United States as they once were. But they still may be carried home from theaters, hotels, or public conveyances. They feed largely on human blood, and they usually dine at night.

If bedbugs have recently moved in, they may usually be found along the tufts, seams, and folds of mattresses and sofas. Gradually they spread to crevices in the bedsteads, then they establish themselves in other furniture and cracks or crevices of each room.

Household sprays containing malathion, lindane, ronnel, or pyrethrins fortified with piperonyl butoxide (a chemical that increases their efficiency) are generally effective against bedbugs.

Spray the slats, springs, and frames of beds until they are thoroughly wet. Spray mattresses lightly. (*Caution:* Do not spray mattresses with ronnel or with a spray containing more than 0.1 percent of lindane or 1 percent of malathion.)

HOUSEHOLD PEST-CONTROL TABLE

	Surface sprays*							Aerosols or space sprays					Dusts*		
Insects or pests	**Baygon, 0.5%**	**Carbaryl**	**Diazinon, 0.5%**	**Malathion, 2.3%**	**Methoxychlor, 5%**	**Pyrethrins, 0.2% with piperonyl butoxide**	**Ronnel, 2%**	**Dichlorvos, 0.5%**	**Malathion, 2–3%**	**Methoxychlor, 3%**	**Pyrethrins, 0.1–0.25% with piperonyl butoxide**	**Ronnel, 0.4%**	**Carbaryl**	**Malathion, 4–5%**	**Methoxychlor, 10%**
Ants		X	X	X									X	X	
Bedbugs				X		X	X								
Cockroaches	X		X	X			X							X	
Crickets	X		X	X										X	
Earwigs		X											X		
Firebrats	X		X	X			X							X	
Fleas	X	X	X	X	X	X	X	X	X	X	X		X	X	X
Houseflies				X			X	X	X		X	X			
Millipedes	X	X											X		
Mites				X											
Mosquitoes				X				X	X	X	X				
Pantry pests				X											
Silverfish	X		X	X			X							X	
Spiders	X			X										X	
Ticks	X	X	X	X									X	X	
Wasps		X	X	X				X					X	X	

* Limited areas, such as baseboards, except methoxychlor or pyrethrins.

If necessary, spray other furniture, baseboards, and cracks and crevices in walls and floorboards. Apply spray again in 2 weeks if any bugs remain.

Cockroaches

Among the hardiest and cleverest of household insects, cockroaches destroy food, damage fabrics and bookbindings, and may spread disease by carrying filth on their bodies and legs.

Among about 55 kinds of cockroaches in the United States only 5 kinds can cause trouble in buildings. The rest are outdoor types that cannot develop indoors. If brought in accidentally, they either leave or die.

Cockroaches develop best where there is warmth, moisture, and generally unclean conditions; they grow slowly when this combination of conditions is not present. Thorough cleaning reduces greatly the likelihood of infestation.

Even in a clean house, roaches may enter from outdoors, in infested containers from other buildings, or from adjoining houses or apartments. To keep them out, fill all cracks passing through floors or walls, and cracks leading to spaces behind baseboards and door frames, with plaster, caulking compound, or plastic wood. Pay special attention to spaces around water and steam pipes. When you bring laundry or containers of food into the house, look for hidden roaches and kill any you may find.

Attack whatever cockroaches that remain with an effective insecticide. The most common kind of household cockroach, the German cockroach (also called croton bug and water bug), in some areas has developed resistance to some prescribed pesticides. Diazinon, malathion, or ronnel should be used against this variety. Any of the insecticides checked on the chart will do for the other four kinds.

Use the insecticide of your choice either as a surface spray or as a dust. A combination of spray and dust is effective for severe infestations.

If you use the combination treatment, apply the surface spray first. Allow it to dry. Then apply the dust into cracks and openings difficult to reach with a spray and areas where the dust will not be unsightly. Surface sprays or dusts may be applied with an ordinary household spray gun or dust gun.

A space spray or aerosol mist containing pyrethrum may be used to penetrate deep cracks and crevices and so drive the cockroaches onto surfaces treated with surface spray or dust.

For best results, apply the spray or dust where the roaches hide. You may be able to discover the hiding places by entering a dark room quietly, turning on the light, and watching where they run. Some favorite places are under the kitchen sink and drainboard; inside, around, and under cupboards and cabinets; near pipes and conduits that pass along or through walls; behind window or door frames; behind loose baseboards or molding strips; behind and under refrigerators and ranges; and on closet and bookcase shelves.

When treating cupboards and pantries, take everything from shelves and remove drawers so that food and utensils will not become contaminated.

If the roaches have not disappeared after 3 or 4 weeks, apply the insecticides again, especially if the house is reinfested from outside.

ROACH POWDER. This is a traditional powder for roaches that is still one of the most effective:

Talc	10 ounces
Pyrethrum	5 ounces
Sodium fluoride	5 ounces

Combine the talc and the pyrethrum thoroughly by stirring and sifting, then mix in the powdered sodium fluoride.

Apply with a household powder duster to all places frequented by the roaches. Repeat the treatment after about 4 days and once more after 2 weeks. In this way you will kill newly hatched roaches as well as their parents.

Caution: Sodium fluoride in its concentrated form is extremely poisonous. Wash all utensils carefully after mixing it. Keep the container out of the reach of children. Do not apply it where animals or children may accidentally come in contact with it.

Crickets

Though crickets breed outdoors, they sometimes invade a house. They may chew and otherwise damage clothing.

To keep crickets out, make sure all windows, screens, and doors close tightly. A surface spray containing diazinon or malathion may be applied along baseboards, in cracks, in closets, and other places where crickets may hide. Dusts also may be used in places where they will not be unsightly.

Earwigs

Usually living outdoors, earwigs sometimes crawl into houses or are brought in with flowers, vegetables, or fruit. They are reddish brown, about ¾-inch long, and have a pair of strong forceps on the rear part of the body. They can bite and pinch, and they emit a foul odor when crushed.

Control them by using a surface spray of Carbaryl, diazinon, or malathion along baseboards and across the thresholds of outside doorways. The application of an emulsion spray or dust to the soil near the outside steps also helps keep them out.

Firebrats and Silverfish

These are slender, gray, wingless insects about ½-inch long. They have three slender "tails."

For food, they prefer sugar and starch, and thus love the paste on wallpaper, glue on bookbindings, and starch in cloth.

Control them with diazinon, ronnel, or malathion.

Fleas

You can expect to have fleas in the house if a dog or a cat shares the house with you. If you don't inspect and treat the pet regularly, fleas may become so numerous they may attack you as well as the animal.

The female flea lays her eggs on the pet. They fall off and hatch in chairs, sofas, rugs, carpets, and the pet's bed. The baby fleas grow up and a new horde of adult fleas will soon be extracting blood from pets and people.

Control of fleas starts with good housekeeping. Clean carpets, rugs, upholstered furniture, and other items in infested rooms with a vacuum cleaner and destroy the contents of the vacuum bag. Then apply a surface spray containing diazinon, malathion, methoxychlor, or pyrethrins with piperonyl butoxide to limited areas, such as baseboards and cracks in the floor.

Carpets, rugs, furniture, and places in the house where the pet habitually sleeps may be treated with methoxychlor, diazinon, ronnel, or pyrethrum sprays or with methoxychlor or malathion dusts.

Repeat if necessary in 7 to 10 days.

Fleas on dogs may be treated directly with a dust containing 4 or 5 percent of malathion or 10 percent of methoxychlor. The dust should be rubbed into the fur to the skin. However, there is danger that a dog that licks itself could be poisoned by the dust. Flea collars developed in recent years also have proven successful to protect pets.

Houseflies

These nuisances breed outdoors on decaying organic matter but love to explore indoors and land on people and food, thereby spreading filth with their legs and bodies.

Good sanitation outdoors and proper screening of all doors and windows help to eliminate flies. If you have to use an insecticide inside the house, use a space or aerosol spray containing dichlorvos, malathion, pyrethrins plus a synergist, or ronnel. Be sure the product you buy specifies its use for the control of flying insects, and be careful not to get the spray on food and cooking or eating utensils.

Further control of flies can be had by applying surface sprays to outside garbage cans, door and window frames, screens, and other sites flies frequent. Use malathion or ronnel.

Millipedes and Centipedes

These wormlike creatures have many legs. Except for the house centipede, they normally live outdoors; but heavy rain, extreme dryness, or cold weather may drive them indoors.

Millipedes won't hurt you, but centipedes have a pair of powerful poison claws just behind the mouth that can give you a bad nip that will cause severe pain and swelling. You should therefore keep away from centipedes, especially the big ones. To kill them, apply either Carbaryl or diazinon to all the places where you find them.

Mites

Mites are tiny creatures. The commonest one, the clover mite, infests houses in the fall as cold weather approaches. Some mites also come from rats, mice, and birds and their nests. Others occur in foods, such as cheese and grain.

To control mites, try to find where they are coming into the house and prevent their entry. If they are coming from rats, birds, or their nests, remove these sources of infestation. A residual spray containing malathion can be used to treat infested areas.

Mosquitoes

If you reach for a space spray or aerosol spray to control mosquitoes, be sure it is specifically meant for flying insects. Aerosols or space sprays containing dichlorvos, malathion, or pyrethrins with piperonyl butoxide are suitable.

It will help if you apply a surface spray of malathion, labeled to be nonstaining, to dark and secluded spots under chairs, tables, and beds, in closets, and behind furniture. The residue may be effective for several weeks.

MOSQUITO REPELLENTS. Oil of citronella is one of the most widely used mosquito repellents. It may be used pure or mixed with mineral oil, petroleum jelly, or lanolin in the proportion of 1 part to 5. Almost any oily preparation on the skin repels mosquitoes to some extent.

If you don't like the smell of citronella, try this mixture:

Castor oil	1 ounce
Alcohol	1 ounce
Oil of lavender	1 ounce

Caution: Do not use ordinary denatured alcohol here, or in any other preparation for use on the body. Use U.S.P. 95-percent ethyl alcohol from the drugstore.

Pantry Pests

This category includes several kinds of insects that infest dry-food products kept in pantry or kitchen cupboards. Although often called "weevils," they may actually be small beetles, moth larvae, or true weevils.

Infestations may be controlled by keeping food shelves clean; inspecting food packages for infestation; sterilizing suspected infested dry foods in your oven at about 140° F for 30 minutes; storing uninfested or heat-sterilized dry foods in clean containers with tight-fitting lids; and applying a surface spray of diazinon, household-grade malathion, or pyrethrins with piperonyl butoxide to the shelves.

Remove all items from the shelves before spraying. Allow the spray to dry thoroughly before you replace them.

Scorpions

Normally scorpions live outdoors under lumber piles, rocks, or loose bark on trees. Sometimes, however, they enter the house, where they hide during the day in closets, attics, folded blankets, shoes, and papers. Usually they will not sting unless molested, but when they do their sting is painful and occasionally causes death in infants or young children. If one should bite you, call a doctor at once. While waiting, apply first aid as described in the section on first aid for poisons in Chapter 15.

To control scorpions, use diazinon or Baygon inside as well as outside the house in the places where they may hide.

Spiders

Chiefly apparent by their webs, spiders make many people fearful. Only a few species in the United States are known to be dangerous. (For first aid for spider bites, see section on first aid for poisons in Chapter 15.)

Basements, eaves, porches, and areas under steps are most likely to be infested. The elimination of breeding places outside the house is important in control. Spiders may be killed by malathion or diazinon. Do not spray a spider directly overhead, as it may drop on you and bite.

Ticks

When found in the house, ticks usually have been carried in by family members or the dog. The common brown tick rarely bites people, but its presence is annoying. After feeding on the dog, the brown tick hides around baseboards, window and door casings, curtains, and under the edge of rugs and furniture.

Control of ticks requires treatment of your dog and the infested areas of the house. A veterinarian can treat your dog, or you can do the job yourself by washing the animal with a 0.5 percent water emulsion of malathion. To make this emulsion, combine thoroughly 1½ ounces of malathion 57-percent emulsifiable concentrate with 5 quarts of water.

To get rid of a new brood of ticks around the house, use a surface spray containing diazinon, Baygon, Carbaryl, malathion, or pyrethrin with piperonyl butoxide. Spray it or paint it around baseboards, cracks in the floor and around windows, and on places where the dog usually sleeps. A malathion spray may be applied to rugs, carpets, drapes, or upholstered furniture. Be sure the label says it will not stain.

Wasp

The term "wasp" is applied to hornets, yellow jackets, mud daubers, and other slender-waisted flying insects. These are all beneficial insects that attack and destroy harmful insects found around homes and in gardens. They build nests in trees, under eaves, and in the ground. Some wasps enter buildings in the fall to hibernate.

The trouble with wasps is that they can attack people as well as insects. Hornets and yellow jackets may sting you if you go near their nests. Mud daubers usually will not sting unless you touch them or get them caught in your clothes. (To treat stings of wasps, see the section on first aid for poisons in Chapter 15.) If a person having a history of asthma, hay fever, or other allergy is stung by a wasp, notify his physician immediately.

If wasps build their nests too close to your house or in bushes where children play, you should destroy the nests. Treat the nests at night, and protect exposed areas of the body with cover. The kind of insecticide needed depends on whether the nest is above the ground or in the ground.

Apply a household surface spray containing diazinon, malathion, Carbaryl, Baygon, or Dursban to wasp nests that are in trees and shrubbery or in your house. A spray having a water base is better for this purpose than one having an oil base. Direct the insecticide as closely as possible to the nest opening using a household or a garden-type applicator.

Treat nests in the ground with an insecticide dust containing 4 to 5 percent of malathion. A few puffs of dust directed into the opening of the nest will usually kill the wasps within 24 hours. Put a shovelful of moist soil over the nest hole after the treatment to prevent the wasps from escaping.

CONTROL OF BATS

Sometimes bats enter a home and establish their roost in the attic, in a space between the walls, or in an unused part of an upper story. When this occurs, the bats should be gotten rid of as soon as possible.

These flying mammals stay in their roosts during the day and fly at night in search of insects, on which they feed. Normally bats are harmless, but they are subject to rabies; a bat infected with this often-fatal disease can transmit it to humans. Bats are objectionable also because of the noises they make and the bad odor that emanates from their droppings and urine. This odor persists long after a roost is broken up, and may attract a new colony of bats unless thorough sanitary measures are taken.

To "batproof" a home, first make sure all bats are out of the house. Then cover openings through which they might enter with sheet metal or ¼-inch-mesh hardware cloth. Leave no opening larger than ¼ inch.

It may be necessary to fumigate the infested areas. This operation is dangerous—do not attempt it yourself; employ a professional exterminator. Never handle live bats; you may be exposed to rabies. Also, wear rubber gloves when picking up and destroying dead bats. An exterminator has the experience and equipment needed to bring about successful control of bats.

CONTROL OF RATS AND MICE

Rats and mice destroy or pollute human food, damage property, and carry insects and bacteria that cause disease. If cornered, they will attack people or pets.

To rid your home of rats or mice:

1. Starve them. Leave no food in open places; this includes food in unopened cardboard containers. Place garbage promptly in tightly covered metal containers.

2. Remove their shelter. Keep storage places orderly and clean. Stack stored objects on racks at least 1 foot above the floor. If the house has double walls, make sure spaces are tightly sealed.
3. Kill them. Use bait poisoned with one of the modern anticoagulants, such as warfarin. Follow the directions of the label carefully. Keep the bait out of the reach of children, pets, and livestock.
4. Keep them out. Close all holes in exterior walls. Keep spaces around doors and windows no larger than ¼ inch. Use self-closing devices on doors to the outside that are frequently used.

CLOTHES MOTHS AND CARPET BEETLES

The larvae of clothes moths, and of their lesser known but more abundant relatives the carpet beetles, do great damage to household materials by feeding on them. The adult moths and beetles do no damage.

Female clothes moths and carpet beetles lay soft, white eggs in clothing and household furnishings, in cracks and in other concealed places. Moths lay 100 to 300 eggs, which hatch in 4 to 8 days in summer. Whereas beetles lay about 100 eggs, which hatch in 8 to 15 days in summer. Hatching takes longer in cooler weather.

The larvae of clothes moths and carpet beetles begin feeding as soon as they hatch. They feed on wool, mohair, hair, bristles, fur, feathers, and down. They attack clothing, blankets, rugs, carpets, drapes, pillows, hair mattresses, brushes, and upholstery.

You can rid fabrics of insects and their eggs and larvae by brushing and sunning them, or by having them dry-cleaned.

One of the best ways to protect clothing and blankets against clothes moths and carpet beetles is to spray them with a nonstaining household insecticide containing malathion, pyrethrine, naphthalene flakes, or paradichlorbenzene specifically labeled for mothproofing. You may buy this either in a pressurized container or as a liquid to be applied with a household hand sprayer.

To apply the insecticide, hang the clothing and blankets on a clothesline and spray them lightly and uniformly until their surfaces are moist. Do not soak or saturate. Let sprayed articles dry before you wear or store them.

Spray rugs and carpets every 12 to 18 months with diazinon, malathion, or Baygon.

Spray furniture upholstery and drapes containing wool or mohair with any of the chemicals mentioned above. When sprayed on mattresses, pillows, or upholstered furniture, the chemicals help prevent infestation; they do not kill pests already inside the stuffing.

Note: Do not apply any of these sprays to furs.

PROTECTION IN STORAGE. You can protect woolens and furs by placing paradichlorobenzene crystals or naphthalene flakes or balls (popularly known as moth crystals, flakes, or balls) in the container or closet in which the articles are stored.

The mere odor of these chemicals does not repel the insects and is no guarantee that the concentration of vapor is sufficient to kill them. To be effective in holding the vapor, the container (which may be a chest, box, or garment bag) must be airtight. If you store woolens in a closet without first placing them in containers, see that the closet is tightly sealed.

In a trunk or closet, use 1 pound of crystals, flakes, or balls for each 100 cubic feet of space. As the vapors are heavier than air, the chemicals should be placed near the top of the enclosure.

Articles that are not already infested can be protected without chemicals by storing them in a paper package or a cardboard box, all edges of which are carefully sealed with paper tape.

SOIL TREATMENT FOR TERMITES

Subterranean or ground-nesting termites occur throughout the United States, but most abundantly in the South Atlantic and Gulf Coast states and California. Their chief food is cellulose from wood, and by eating the woodwork of buildings they cause damage totaling millions of dollars every year.

The best way to thwart this damage is to construct buildings so termites can't get into the woodwork. Another way is to treat the soil near the foundations and under concrete slabs with suitable chemicals.

Risks of Infestation

The risk of infestation is greatest beneath buildings having a concrete slab on the ground, a crawl space with inadequate clearance, ventilation, and drainage, or a basement with enclosed porches and terraces where filled earth comes close to the building timbers.

How to Detect Infestations

Telltale signs of subterranean termites are the earthen tunnels built by them over the surface of foundation walls to reach the wood above.

When feeding in wood, the pearly white worker termites make galleries that follow the grain. You can seldom see these on the wood surface, but they may be found by removing weatherboarding or trim boards or by probing with a knife or other tool the places where you suspect the insects are at work. Unlike powderpost beetles, termites do not push out sawdustlike material from their galleries.

Another evidence of termites is the swarming of winged adults early in the spring or fall. Each adult has four silvery wings, which are of equal length and twice as long as the body. Large numbers of detached wings may be found where swarming has taken place, even after the swarm has gone. Winged reproductive termites may be distinguished from winged reproductive ants by their wings and their waistlines. Ants also have two pairs of wings, but of unequal size. Termites have thick waistlines, while ants have thin ones.

Principle of Control

The main objective in termite control is to break contact between the termite colony in the ground and the woodwork in the building. You can do this by removing all wood supports, formboards, debris, and so on from around and beneath the house, and making any necessary changes in the structure of the house to block the passage of termites from soil to wood; by chemically treating the soil; or, better still, by combining these methods.

The suggestions that follow relate chiefly to some of the simpler soil treatments. If properly applied, protection should last several years. Each case of termite trouble, however, requires individual consideration. Some of them may require special equipment and be too complicated for an average homeowner to handle. For such jobs, it may be best to get help from a reliable pest-control man.

Preparation for Treatment

HOUSES WITHOUT BASEMENTS. To control infestations along interior walls or around supporting piers of basementless houses, dig a trench 6 to 8 inches wide and a few inches deep, next to the walls or piers, taking care not to go below the top of the footing. If the land slopes or the footing is more than 12 inches deep, use a crossbar, pipe, or rod to make holes about an inch in diameter and a foot apart from the bottom of the trench to the footing. Dig another trench the same width, but about 12 inches deep, around the outside foundation walls. If necessary, make holes in the trench bottom as described for the inside walls.

HOUSES WITH BASEMENTS. Where termites are coming from beneath the concrete floor in the basement, remove any wood that may extend from the foundation into the ground, treat the soil with poison, and then seal all cracks or holes through which termites might enter. Fill large holes with a dense cement mortar, and small ones with a roofing-grade coal-tar pitch. Where the infestation is located in an expansion joint between the floor and the wall, or around a furnace, make a series of 1-inch holes, about a foot apart, through which a chemical can be poured. Holes along a wall should be made about 6 to 8 inches from it, so as to clear the footing and reach the soil beneath.

Where infestation occurs along exterior foundation walls in houses with full basements, it is necessary to treat the soil to greater depth. Prepare the trench in the same way, but extend the pipe or rod holes right down to the top of the footing. This is especially important in foundations of brick or concrete block where imperfect mortar joints may make termite entry easy.

CONCRETE SLAB ON GROUND. Infestations in houses built with a concrete slab on the ground are the hardest to control, because it is hard to place chemicals in the soil under such floors where they will be effective.

One way to do it is to drill holes about ½ inch in diameter through the concrete slab close to the point where the termites are or where they may be entering. Space the holes about 6 inches from the wall and about 12 inches apart. Be careful, however, not to drill into electrical conduits or plumbing. Apply the chemical through the holes by any means available, although it would be distributed best if applied under considerable pressure.

Dig a trench around the outside foundation walls as described for houses without basements.

Poisons for Termites and How to Prepare Them

The chemicals recommended are all water emulsions. Unlike oil solutions, they will not injure plants when used along exterior foundation walls. Neither will they creep up walls and damage floors, as oil may, when applied along the interior of foundations. The concentrations recommended allow a margin of safety and provide protection for several years.

Caution: Like most pesticides, the chemicals to be mentioned are poisonous to man and other warm-blooded animals and must be handled with care. Do not permit them to come in contact with your skin. Wear rubber or rubberized gloves to protect your hands. If the poison is being applied with pressure through holes in walls or piers, use a plastic face guard so the chemical cannot splash back on your face. If contact with poison occurs, wash the skin immediately with warm soapy water. When the chemical is being applied in an enclosed area, provide a free circulation of air. Never apply these chemicals in places where they might be leached from the soil and enter wells that supply drinking water. Keep children and pets away from areas where the poisons are being prepared and used.

CHLORDANE, 1-PERCENT EMULSION. Chlordane is available as 46- to 48-, or 72- to 74-percent water emulsion concentrates. Prepare the 1-percent emulsion by adding 47 gallons of water to 1 gallon of the 46-percent concentrate, or 95 gallons of water to 1 gallon of the 72-percent concentrate. The ratio is 1 to 47, and 1 to 95, respectively, whether the measure is in gallons or in cupfuls.

Rate of Application

SLAB-ON-GROUND HOUSES. Apply at least 2 gallons of the diluted emulsion for each 5 linear feet of wall, through holes made in the floor or foundation, so it will reach the infested soil. It is advisable to treat around the entire slab and around other openings left for plumbing, and so on. Apply the emulsion at the same rate in the trench made along the exterior foundation walls, if the footing is not more than 15 inches deep. If deeper in some places, apply as directed below for basementless, or crawl-space houses.

HOUSES WITHOUT BASEMENTS. Apply 2 gallons of the diluted emulsion for each 5 linear feet of trench made along the interior of the foundation walls, or around piers or other materials connecting the ground with wood above. Along the exterior foundation walls, including those adjacent to entrance platforms, porches, etc., apply the chemical at the same rate for each foot of depth from the surface to the footing. If the footing is 2 feet deep, for example, increase the dosage to 4 gallons for each 5 linear feet of trench, or if it is 5 feet deep, use 10 gallons for each similar unit. Entrance platforms, sun parlors, and other enclosed areas adjacent to the foundation wall should also be trenched and treated, or have holes bored through the slabs and the chemical applied through them.

BASEMENT HOUSES. Where necessary to treat through the basement floor, apply the chemical in the same manner and at the same rate as recommended for treating the slab-on-ground house. Treat the exterior of the foundation wall the same as mentioned for the basementless house.

Applying Chemicals in Trenches

Pour or sprinkle some of the chemical at the bottom of the trench. Cover with a layer of soil about 6 inches thick. Pour or sprinkle more of the chemical on top of this soil layer. Mix the chemical thoroughly with this layer, and tamp well. Continue to add layers of soil, mixing each with the chemical and tamping as before, until the trench is filled. Do not apply chemicals to frozen or water-soaked soils.

HOW TO GET RID OF POISON IVY

Poison ivy can be destroyed by herbicides, special poisons for plants. The most satisfactory ones for poison ivy, poison oak, and poison sumac are amitrole, ammonium sulfamate, silvex, and formulas containing 2,4-D. These herbicides are sold under their common or chemical names and under various trade names. Workable but less satisfactory herbicides include borax, coal tar creosote oil, fuel oil, kerosene, gasoline, ammonium sulfate, iron sulfate, and common salt.

Any field or garden sprayer, or even a sprinkling can, can be used for applying the spray liquid, but a common compressed air sprayer holding 2 to 3 gallons is convenient and does not waste the spray.

Use moderate pressure giving relatively large spray droplets, rather than high pressure giving a driving mist, because the objective is to wet the leaves of the poison ivy and avoid wetting the leaves of desirable plants.

Apply when leaves are fully expanded, and wet the foliage to the point of runoff. Drench the stems as high as possible when the plants are growing on a wall, and allow the excess spray to run down to the roots.

Because it is extremely difficult to remove all traces of a herbicide from spraying equipment, do not use the same equipment for applying insecticides or fungicides. Otherwise you might injure desirable plants.

Amitrole

Use 2 to 4 pounds of active ingredient per 100 gallons of water. Be careful not to spray on nearby plants. If ivy is growing on a desirable tree, cut ivy stem at ground level in winter (see section on the safe handling of poison ivy in Chapter 15) and treat the sprouts after leaves come out in the spring. If ivy is intertwined with desirable plants, paint the ivy leaves with a long-handled brush. Mix 2 tablespoons of the 50-percent product in 1 quart of water for the paint. Cover at least one-half of the leaves. Amitrole can also be applied dry. (*Caution:* Amitrole kills most lawn grasses. It is slow in action; effects may not show up for 2 or 3 weeks.)

Ammonium Sulfamate

Use 2 to 2½ pounds of the 95-percent product in 3 gallons of water and add a "spreader-sticker," a surface active chemical that helps the spray to stick, spread, and cover. Lacking the latter, a tablespoon of liquid dishwashing detergent will help do the same things. Keep spray off nearby desirable plants. (*Caution:* Ammonium sulfamate sterilizes the soil for several months. To prevent corrosion, do not use near metal pipes and tanks. Whenever possible, use copper, stainless steel, bronze, or aluminum, but not brass, for sprayer parts. Coat other exposed metal parts with acid-resisting paint or rubberized undercoating used on cars.)

Silvex and 2,4-D

Don't be confused if silvex is also labeled as 2,4,5-TP (2-[2,4,5-trichlorophenoxy] proprionic acid). The *P* in this designation distinguishes silvex from its more dangerous relative 2,4,5-T (2,4,5-trichlorophenoxyacetic acid)—a powerful and once widely used herbicide now banned from interstate sales under suspicion of causing birth defects in man and animals. 2,4-D is the short name for 2,4-dichlorophenoxyacetic acid. Follow the manufacturer's recommendations closely in applying these chemicals.

HOW TO CONTROL MILDEW IN THE HOME

Mildew is a thin, musty-smelling growth produced on many household materials by simple plants known as fungi or molds. Though always present in the air, mildew fungi need warmth and moisture and certain types of food substances in order to grow. Given these conditions, they discolor leather, fabrics, paper, and wood. Sometimes they eat into fabrics so severely that the fabrics rot and fall to pieces. Below are measures for the prevention and removal of mildew on walls and household furnishings.

How to Prevent Mildew

1. *Keep things clean.* Soil on articles can supply enough food for mildew to grow when moisture and temperature are right. Greasy films on kitchen walls provide a feast. Most man-made fibers, when clean, will not support mildew growth. Soil on them, however, will do so.
2. *Get rid of dampness.* Take steps to prevent condensation on walls. Remove excess moisture with air conditioners and dehumidifiers. If necessary, get rid of dampness by heating the house for a short time. Use silica gel, activated alumina, or calcium chloride to absorb moisture from the air. Ventilate house, closets, drawers, and musty articles thoroughly when the outside air is drier than that inside.
3. *Get rid of musty odors.* These indicate mold growth and so should be investigated and eliminated as soon as possible. Usually they disappear if the area is well heated and dried. On cement floors and on tiled walls and bathroom floors, get rid of mustiness by scrubbing with a solution of ordinary 5-percent sodium hypochlorite bleach (Clorox, Purex, etc.) diluted ½ to 1 cup to a gallon of water. Rinse with clear water and wipe dry. Keep windows open until surfaces are thoroughly dry. (*Caution:* Work quickly and carefully on plastic and asphalt tile to avoid spotting.)
4. *Keep fabrics dry.* Never let clothing or other fabric articles lie around damp or wet. After washing, dry articles thoroughly and quickly, as slow drying encourages mold. After shampooing a rug, dry it as quickly as possible.
5. *Store with mildew inhibitor.* Certain volatile chemicals, the vapors of which inhibit mold growth (and often keep moths away as well), may be used to protect fabrics during storage. Paradichlorobenzene is one. Scatter crystals of this chemical through folds of garments to be packed in boxes, or hang bags of crystals at the top of garment bags so the heavy vapors settle on the materials being protected. Use about 1 pound of the crystals for each 100 cubic feet of air space. (*Caution:* This chemical damages some plastics. Therefore remove plastic buttons and ornaments from garments and do not use plastic clothes hangers.)
6. *Protect leather goods against mildew.* Sponge leather goods with a 1-percent solution of dichlorophene, hexachlorophene, salicylanilide, or thymol, in denatured or rubbing alcohol. Shoe and luggage stores may have the solutions already prepared. Before sponging, test a small area where it will not show to see if it will change the color of the leather.

How to Remove Mildew

1. *From Textiles.* Remove mildew spots as soon as they are discovered to prevent deterioration of the material. Brush off surface growth outdoors to prevent scattering the spores in the house. Sun and air fabrics thoroughly. If any spots remain, wash fabrics with soap and water, or dry-clean them if unwashable. Rinse well and dry in the sun. If stains persist, moisten them with a mixture of lemon juice and salt and spread the article in the sun to bleach. Or bleach them with sodium perborate bleach or sodium hypochlorite bleach from the grocery store according to directions on the package.
2. *From Upholstered Articles, Mattresses, Rugs.* First remove loose mold from outer coverings by brushing (preferably outdoors) with a broom. Draw out more mold with a vacuum cleaner (if the appliance has a disposable bag, dispose of it immediately). Dry the article by sun and air, fan, electric heater, or by any other means possible. If mildew remains on upholstered articles or mattresses, sponge lightly with thick suds of soap or detergent, and wipe with a clean damp cloth. Sponge mildewed rugs and carpets with thick suds or a rug shampoo, then remove suds with a cloth dampened in clear water. Dry in the sun if possible.
3. *From Leather Goods.* Wipe with a solution of equal parts of denatured or rubbing alcohol and water. Dry in a current of air. If mildew remains, wash with thick suds of a mild soap, saddle soap, or a soap containing a germicide or fungicide. Then wipe with a damp cloth and dry in an airy place.

DISINFECTING AND DEODORIZING WITH HOUSEHOLD BLEACH

Besides its well-known ability to bleach textiles and even to lighten the color of some kinds of wood, ordinary household sodium hypochlorite liquid bleach is also a powerful disinfectant, deodorizer, and stain-removing agent. It is highly effective against all known types of virus and most bacteria. It eliminates odors partly by killing organisms that produce them and partly by chemical combination. On hard, smooth surfaces, its own chlorine odor soon disappears.

Unlike carbolic acid and other chemicals that work primarily on microorganisms, liquid chlorine bleach also reacts with dirt and other contaminants. For strongest action of the bleach as a disinfectant, it is best, therefore, to wash the surface thoroughly before applying it.

TO DISINFECT, DEODORIZE, AND REMOVE STAINS (from sinks, drainboards, dishes, glassware, enamelware, bathtubs, basins, woodwork, tile, porcelain, plastic). First wash surfaces thoroughly. Then wipe with a solution of ¾ cup liquid chlorine bleach to each gallon of warm water. If stubborn stains persist, keep wet for 5 minutes with bleach solution; repeat if necessary. (*Note:* Do not apply with a natural sponge, and do not use on silver, aluminum, steel, or chipped enamelware.)

TO SANITIZE TOILET BOWLS. Cleanse and flush. Then pour in ½ cup liquid chlorine bleach. Swish solution over all inside surfaces. Let stand 10 minutes. Flush. (*Caution:* Do not use ammonia, lye, or other toilet bowl cleaners with liquid chlorine bleach. The combination would release poisonous chlorine gas.)

TO DEODORIZE DRAIN PIPES. Flush with very hot water. Follow by 1 cup liquid chlorine bleach. Let remain 5 minutes; then flush out bleach.

TO HELP MAKE REFRIGERATORS HYGIENICALLY CLEAN. First wash the inside surfaces. Then wipe with solution of ¾ cup liquid chlorine bleach to each gallon of warm water. Rinse, dry, and let air for 30 minutes.

TO REMOVE ODORS OF GARLIC, ONIONS, CABBAGE, OR FISH (FROM YOUR CHOPPING BOARD). Wash board thoroughly, then soak or keep wet for 10 to 15 minutes with a solution of ¾ cup of liquid chlorine bleach to each gallon of warm water. Rinse and dry.

TO STERILIZE SICKROOM DISHES. First thoroughly wash them and then soak them for 5 minutes in a solution of ¾ cup of liquid chlorine bleach to each gallon of hot water. Rinse with hot water and let drain dry. (*Note:* Do not use the bleach on silver, aluminum, steel, or chipped enamelware. Disinfect these by scalding.)

TO DISINFECT A SWIMMING POOL. Each time you fill the pool, use 1 quart of liquid chlorine bleach (sodium hypochlorite 5- to 6-percent solution) for every 6,000 gallons of new water. To determine volume of water in pool when filled, allow 7½ gallons of water for each cubic foot of pool capacity.

If you have a chlorinator, mix the required amount of liquid chlorine bleach with 10 parts water and feed this solution through the device into the main water supply line into the pool. Otherwise mix 8 ounces of liquid chlorine bleach in 5 gallons of water and scatter over a portion of the pool; repeat until the required amount of bleach has been scattered over the entire pool surface.

Usually 1 pint of liquid chlorine bleach per 6,000 gallons of water is enough for daily replenishing. If you have a pool chlorine testing set, check the water daily, adding enough chlorine bleach to maintain a reading of 0.6 to 1.0 part per million.

PURIFYING WATER IN EMERGENCIES

When away from approved water supplies while traveling or camping, or during flood or other disaster conditions at home, you must make sure that available water is safe for drinking. Dysentery, infectious hepatitis, and typhoid fever are among the diseases that can be brought on by polluted water.

The only certain way to remove danger from doubtful water is to purify it yourself. Here are several approved ways to do so:

Purification with Heat

1. Strain water through a clean cloth into a container to remove sediment and floating matter.
2. Boil the water vigorously for at least 1 full minute.
3. The water is ready to use as soon as it is sufficiently cool. If desired, a pinch of salt may be added to each quart of water to improve the taste. Pouring the water back and forth from one clean container to another several times will also do so.

Purification with Chemicals

If boiling is not possible, strain the water as in Step 1 above and purify with any one of the following chemicals that is available:

Sodium hypochlorite laundry bleach containing 5- to 6-percent available chlorine (Clorox, Purex, Rose-X, etc.). Add 2 drops of this solution to each quart of clear water or 4 drops to each quart of cloudy water. If the amount of available chlorine is not stated on the label, add 10 drops to the clear and 20 drops to the cloudy water.

1. Mix thoroughly by stirring or shaking water in container.
2. Let stand for 30 minutes.
3. A slight chlorine odor should still be detectable in the water; if

not, repeat the dosage and let stand for an additional 15 minutes before using.

Tincture of iodine, 2 percent, from medicine chest or first-aid kit. Add 5 drops to each quart of clear water or 10 drops to each quart of cloudy water. Stir, and let stand for 30 minutes, after which time water is safe to use.

Iodine or chlorine tablets from drug or sporting-goods store. Follow instructions on package.

Keep water purified under any of the above methods in clean, closed containers. Use it for cooking, drinking, and for brushing teeth.

CHEMICALS IN SEPTIC TANKS

According to the U.S. Health Service, the operation of septic tanks, used by millions of homes where public sewers are not available, is not at all improved by the addition of disinfectants or other chemicals. By 1967, more than 1,200 products, many containing enzymes, had been placed on the market for use in septic tanks, and extravagant claims have been made for some of them. As far as is known, however, none has been proved of advantage in properly controlled tests.

Some proprietary products that are claimed to "clean" septic tanks contain sodium or potassium lye as the active agent. These may severely damage soil structure and cause accelerated clogging, even though some temporary relief may be experienced at first.

Frequently, however, the harmful effects of ordinary household chemicals are overemphasized. Small amounts of chlorine bleaches, added ahead of the tank, may be used for odor control without adverse effects. If septic tanks are of adequate size, the small amounts of lye or other alkaline chemicals used to clean toilets and drains won't be harmful, either. Neither will soaps, detergents, bleaches, or other household materials as ordinarily used. Moderation, though, should be the rule. Advice of responsible officials should be sought before chemicals arising from a hobby or home industry are discharged into the system.

13

Gardens and Plants

SOIL

Soil is the most important factor in the whole agricultural and horticultural picture. It is far more important than the variety of seeds you plant or the type of culture used. Soil, and the plant nutrients it contains, generally spell the difference between success and failure in every growing operation.

Soil Types

Basically, there are three types of soil:

SANDY SOIL. This has less than 20-percent clay or silt. It loses water quickly, absorbs heat, holds excessive air, and draws out fertilizer elements quickly. To cure this condition, add organic matter, or loam, or fertilizer rich in potash, phosphorus, and manure.

CLAY SOIL. This has very fine particles. It holds too much water—thus remains muddy after a rain. It lacks air. To cure this condition, add sand or fine cinders and organic matter.

LOAM. Loam is the type of soil between sand and clay. It is satisfactory for most plantings.

The type of soil your garden contains and its ability to hold moisture are other keys to good germination. Light or sandy soils need special attention, particularly when small seeds are planted just below the surface. Rapid drying may keep them from getting enough moisture to sprout, even under frequent watering.

To prevent drying, experienced gardeners cover the seed row with a mulch—a layer of organic or inorganic material that reduces evaporation.

Organic materials you can use include grass clippings, straw, ground bark, or sawdust. Burlap sacks or clean plastic also make good mulches but must be removed as soon as seedlings emerge.

Heavy- or clay-type soils pose a different barrier to germination. They resist air movement, retain moisture, and warm up slowly, conditions that encourage seeds to rot. If soil is extremely tight, it may prevent seedlings from emerging.

The only way to improve a heavy soil is to work in generous amounts of compost (decomposed organic material) or conditioners such as peat moss, sawdust, ground bark, or vermiculite.

Soil Nutrients

Plants, like humans, require a balanced diet. Actually, the 13 nutrients essential for plant growth fall into three groups:

Primary nutrients: nitrogen, phosphorus, and potassium.

Secondary nutrients: calcium, magnesium, and sulfur.

Micronutrients: boron, copper, zinc, iron, manganese, molybdenum, and chlorine.

Plants generally use primary nutrients in the heaviest amounts and they're most likely to be deficient. Nitrogen, phosphorus, and potassium are the basis of commercial inorganic fertilizers such as 10-6-4 and 10-10-10. The numbers represent the proportion in which these indispensable elements are present. Thus, the numbers 10-6-4 refer to 10 units or pounds of available nitrogen, 6 units of available phosphorus, and 4 units of potassium.

NITROGEN (N). This is an essential constituent of proteins. An abundant supply of nitrogen results in dark-green foliage and active vegetative growth. However, too much nitrogen causes too rapid growth, softness of tissue, and a general weakness of the plant. A plant in this sort of soil is less resistant to disease, infection, and injury. Also, at flowering time, excess nitrogen causes the plant to resume active vegetative growth, retarding flower and seed formation.

Of course, for vegetables in which leaves, stalks, or stems are the important end product, extra nitrogen should be fed to the soil. In the case of lettuce, for example, an abundance of nitrogen produces soft, crisp leaves. Other vegetables that benefit by extra nitrogen are asparagus, cabbage, leek, chard, and brussels sprouts. Also, nitrogen should be present in lawn soils in a generous amount if you want a rich, heavy carpet of grass. Nitrogen in organic form, such as cottonseed meal, continues its effectiveness over a long period and is helpful in producing outstanding lawns. You can purchase it in the following forms: nitrate of soda, 16-percent nitrogen; cottonseed meal, 6-percent nitrogen; urea, 46-percent nitrogen; dried blood, 10-percent nitrogen; and ammonium sulphate, 20-percent nitrogen.

PHOSPHORUS (P). All plants need phosphorus compounds. These compounds are especially necessary in plants that produce flowers, seeds, and grain. They promote good germination of seed, thrifty seedlings, and general plant vigor. Phosphorus hastens the maturity of plants, too, speeding up flower formation, seeds, and grain. In short, if you want colorful flowers or plump seeds use extra phosphorus. This can be applied separately as acid phosphate, 16 percent; superphosphate, 20 percent; triple superphosphate, 44 percent; and bonemeal, 25 percent. Animal manures are notoriously lacking in phosphorus, yet have been used for generations as fertilizer. That's why gardeners today rely on bagged and packaged fertilizers that carry extra amounts of this important plant food.

POTASH (K). Potash (potassium) is important in the formation and transportation of starch, sugar, and other carbohydrates within plants. The result is plants that produce stiff stalks and have a healthy, disease-resistant growth. However, excess potassium results in an increase in the water content of plants and their resistance to droughts and frost injury, thus delaying their maturity. But potassium is also very important to the root growth of plants. So, if you want large, mealy potatoes, sweet, juicy carrots, tasty beets, or healthy tulip and dahlia bulbs, be sure to feed your soil extra potassium.

SECONDARY NUTRIENTS. These are usually present in good supply. They also get into the soil through other garden products. For example, superphosphate contains some sulfur in addition to phosphorus; limestone, used for correcting acid soil, contains calcium; dolemitic limestone supplies both calcium and magnesium.

MICRONUTRIENTS. Most soils also contain enough micronutrients: boron, copper, zinc, iron, manganese, molybdenum, and chlorine. For regions with micronutrient deficiencies, fertilizer manufacturers often blend micronutrients in with other plant foods.

Soil pH

Soil scientists use the pH scale of 1 to 14 as described in Chapter 16 to identify soils as being acid or alkaline. A pH of 1 is highly acid; a pH of 14 is extremely alkaline. If soil has a pH of 7, it's neutral. Most plants grow best within a pH range of 6 to 7.

A high or low pH blocks growth by tying up soil nutrients, reducing their availability to plants. When plants grow poorly or show signs of a nutrient deficiency, it could mean the pH is too high or too low.

A pH of less than 6 limits availability of phosphorus, nitrogen, potassium, sulfur, calcium, and magnesium. Soil pH of 7.5 or higher ties up phosphorus, iron, manganese, copper, zinc, and boron.

Acid soils are common in humid areas, especially regions with sandy soils. Alkalinity is generally a problem in low-rainfall areas of the West.

You can correct acid soil by adding a calcium source such as ground limestone or dolemitic limestone. To lower the pH of an alkaline soil, add finely ground sulfur, iron sulfate, or aluminum sulfate.

Five pounds of finely ground limestone per 100 square feet of area raises the pH by ½ to 1 unit. To lower the pH by ½ to 1 unit, use ½ pound of ground sulfur or 3 pounds of iron or aluminum sulfate per 100 square feet. Increase these amounts by a third for heavy soil.

Limestone or sulfur should be spaded into the soil well ahead of planting to give them time to take effect. Apply them in fall for spring planting, or in spring for fall-planted plants.

Soil Testing

Soil testing lets you peer beneath the soil surface to determine nutrient levels and pH. It should be the first step you take if you suspect a nutrient shortage or an acid or alkaline soil.

There are two basic ways of testing. Garden centers sell test kits that allow a quick chemical analysis of soil pH and nutrient levels. Test results give you a rough idea of problem areas. But they won't tell you how much fertilizer to apply or the specific amount of limestone or sulfur needed to correct pH.

For a more accurate test, write to the soil-testing laboratory of your state agricultural university. Ask for information on how to take soil samples and pack them for mailing. Once samples are analyzed (usually within 2 to 4 weeks), you'll receive specific recommendations for fertilizing and correcting soil pH.

How to Make Fertilizer by Composting

The purpose of a compost box or heap is to produce fertilizer or plant food through the decay of garbage, weeds, leaves, lawn clippings, sod, manure, or other similar matter. Properly made compost not only enriches the soil chemically, but improves its physical condition. When mixed with clay soil, for instance, it makes it looser and more crumbly, permitting better air circulation and water drainage. When applied to sandy soil, it increases the water-holding capacity.

Make a compost heap by alternating layers of manure or vegetable matter with soil. To hasten decay, scatter a mixture of garden fertilizer and lime, or 2 parts superphosphate, 2 parts hydrated lime, and 1 part ammonium sulfate on each layer of vegetable matter, using about 10 pounds of this mixture for each 100 pounds of material to be treated. When the pile is completed, wet thoroughly with water and cover with soil. The soil is used to absorb the ammonia, which would otherwise escape. Decay proceeds most rapidly when the weather is warm.

Solutions for Hydroponics, or Gardening Without Soil

Raising plants from solutions of chemicals in water has been practiced experimentally for more than a century, but chemiculture on a commercial scale did not begin until 1929, when Dr. William F. Gericke of the University of California first made the suggestion and began the actual promotion. Previously, investigators had used distilled water and expensive laboratory-pure chemicals for their experiments. Gericke proved that tap water and cheap technical and fertilizer-grade chemicals would work just as well; that indeed sometimes they would work even better because of impurities that were themselves beneficial to plant growth. He also coined the now-popular term "hydroponics," and gave impetus to a hobby that spread rapidly.

Since then an extensive investigation of hydroponics has been carried on by the U.S. Department of Agriculture, the agricultural experiment stations of many states and foreign countries, and by commercial growers. The technique has proved especially suited to growing plants in greenhouses and in arid regions where many plants will grow only poorly or not at all. As a hobby, either pure hydroponics or sand culture is ideal. It can be practiced indoors as well as out, and with little more equipment to begin with than a glass or plastic container, a single young plant, and the required solution.

HOW TO CORRECT SOIL PROBLEMS

Need and explanation	Use or correction
LIME: A necessity for all soils. Lack of it makes a soil acid. Oversupply makes a soil alkali.	If pH factor (acidity) is low, add lime, usually in the fall. If soil is "sweet," it has too much lime. Apply a mulch or covering of leaves, sawdust, shavings, peat, or patented remedies containing sulphur or aluminum sulphate.
HUMUS: Result of decomposition of plant or animal residue. Changes structure, texture, water- and air-holding capacity and color of soil.	Add material from compost pile. Spade or plow into soil, preferably in fall.
PEAT MOSS: Decomposed vegetable matter. Adds acidity and organic matter, nitrogen; holds moisture.	Apply as mulch in fall, or work into soil in spring.
AERATION: Carbon dioxide from decaying bacteria must escape or roots will be injured.	Clay soils lack air. Add humus, sand, or cinders. Sandy soils contain too much air, which tends to dry out plants. Add humus. Various plantings require different proportions, so choose accordingly.
COMMERCIAL FERTILIZERS: Package indicates proportion of nitrogen, phosphorus, and potassium content (as 5-10-5) in that order.	Various plantings require different proportions, so choose accordingly.
LIQUID FERTILIZER: Often more effective, speedy in its work, and safer to use than solid fertilizer.	Place fertilizer in a mesh bag and allow it to dissolve in a barrel of water, using 1 gallon of water for each pound of fertilizer. This can be diluted for various purposes.
COMPOST: A pile of a mixture of straw, leaves, weeds, and garden refuse, in 6-inch layers, with fertilizer in each layer. After 3 to 4 months of fermentation it is the equivalent of good manure.	Improve it by adding 60 pounds of sulphate of ammonia, 30 pounds of superphosphate, 25 pounds of potassium chloride, and 50 pounds of ground limestone to ½ ton of wastes.
GREEN MANURE—RYE, ALFALFA, GRASS, COWPEAS, CLOVER, SOY BEANS: Crops grown to be plowed under, to add nitrogen and other plant nutrients to the soil.	Plow in early in fall with fertilizer added.

(Continued)

HOW TO CORRECT SOIL PROBLEMS ***(continued)***

Need and explanation	Use or correction
MULCH—PEAT, LEAF MOLD, HUMUS, STRAW, CORN HUSKS, ETC., MANURES, PAPER, COFFEE GROUNDS, SAWDUST: Inert or organic matter used to cover soil, hold moisture, prevent weed growth, and keep ground cool.	Cover plants (or grass) with mulch in winter, in dry fall, or late spring.
PHOSPHORUS: Many soils lack this essential to plant life.	If lacking, add superphosphate, treble phosphate, or bonemeal.
POTASSIUM: Necessary for strong stems and roots and general plant health. Usually present where there is plenty of organic matter.	If lacking, add potassium chloride, potassium sulphate, manures, or hardwood ashes.
NITROGEN: Normally added to soil from decayed organic matter.	If lacking, add humus or commercial fertilizer—nitrate of soda, sulphate of ammonia, hen or rabbit manure, etc.
OTHER MINERALS—CALCIUM, SULPHUR, MAGNESIUM, IRON, SODIUM, MANGANESE, ALUMINUM: Necessary in small amounts. Usually found in sufficient quantity in soils.	If lacking, add commercial fertilizers containing these elements.

If you want to try it, first read a book on the subject, as different plants, different climate, and water of different composition may require a variation in technique. Here is a formula for a typical nutrient solution:

Ammonium phosphate, monobasic	½ ounce
Magnesium sulfate (Epsom salts)	1½ ounces
Potassium nitrate	2½ ounces
Calcium nitrate	2½ ounces

These are the amounts of major nutrients needed to make 25 gallons of solution. The ammonium phosphate and magnesium sulfate may be of technical grade and the potassium and calcium nitrates of fertilizer grade. In addition, plants require for their growth small amounts of manganese, boron, and iron.

To make a manganese and boron solution, dissolve ⅓ teaspoon of pure manganese sulfate or manganese chloride and 1 teaspoon of drugstore powdered boric acid in 1 gallon of water. Add about 4 teaspoons of this solution to each 1 gallon of the main nutrient solution as you use it.

Make an iron solution by dissolving 1 teaspoon of iron sulfate or iron citrate in 1 quart of water. Add this about twice a week to the nutrient solution in use, at the rate of 1 teaspoon to the gallon.

The following formula has been recommended for making 25 gallons of solution for use in sand culture. It may be improved by adding small amounts of manganese, boron, and iron, as above, as the solution is used.

Ammonium sulfate	½ ounce
Potassium phosphate, monobasic	1 ounce
Magnesium sulfate	2 ounces
Calcium nitrate	8 ounces

PLANTING

Seeds

The best way to get your garden off to a good start is to use "fresh" seed each season. Seed won't keep indefinitely and still retain its power to sprout. If you have seed left from last year, you're better off discarding it and starting with a new supply.

If you planted good quality seed that failed to sprout, it may be due to one or more reasons. Here are key factors that determine whether seed roots or rots.

Soil Temperature

Seeds have a minimum, optimum, and maximum temperature for germination. When you rush the planting season you increase the odds of seed failure, especially for heat-loving crops like corn and beans. Some seeds, such as lettuce, like it cool and refuse to sprout if soil temperature is too warm.

Planting Depth

Planting too shallow or too deep is a frequent cause of poor germination. Even the planting depths recommended on seed packets or in the

HARDINESS OF COMMON VEGETABLES

In this table some common vegetables are grouped according to the approximate times they can be planted and their relative requirements for cool and warm weather.

	Beans, all	Beans, lima	Beans, snap	Beets	Broccoli	Cabbage	Carrots	Chard	Collard	Cucumbers	Eggplant	Kale	Lettuce	Melons	Mustard	Okra	Onions	Parsnips	Peas	Peppers	Potatoes	Radishes	Soybeans	Spinach, common	Spinach, New Zealand	Squash	Sweet corn	Sweet potatoes	Tomatoes	Turnips
EARLY-SPRING PLANTING (cold-hardy plants)																														
Very hardy (plant 4–6 weeks before frost-free date)					X	X							X				X		X		X			X						X
Hardy (plant 2–4 weeks before frost-free date)				X			X	X							X			X				X								
LATE-SPRING OR EARLY-SUMMER PLANTING (cold-tender or heat-hardy plants)																														

Not cold-hardy (plant on frost-free date)		X						X				X	X X	X	X
Requiring hot weather (plant 1 week or more after frost-free date)	X				X	X	X			X				X	
Medium heat-tolerant (good for summer planting)	X			X								X	X X	X	
LATE-SUMMER OR FALL PLANTING, EXCEPT IN NORTH (plant 6–8 weeks before first freeze)		X			X	X	X	X				X			X

RECOMMENDED PLANTING DEPTHS AND ROW SPACING

REQUIREMENT FOR 100 FEET OF ROW				DISTANCE ROWS SHOULD BE APART		
Crop	Seed	Plants	Depth for planting seed	Horse- or tractor-cultivated	Hand-cultivated	Plants in the row
			Inches	*Feet*		
Asparagus	1 ounce	75	1 to 1½	4 to 5	1½ to 2 feet	18 inches
Beans:						
Lima, bush	½ pound		1 to 1½	2½ to 3	2 feet	3 to 4 inches
Lima, pole	½ pound		1 to 1½	3 to 4	3 feet	3 to 4 feet
Snap, bush	½ pound		1 to 1½	2½ to 3	2 feet	3 to 4 inches
Snap, pole	4 ounces		1 to 1½	3 to 4	2 feet	3 feet
Beets	2 ounces		1	2 to 2½	14 to 16 inches	2 to 3 inches
Broccoli:						
Heading	1 packet	50 to 75	½	2½ to 3	2 to 2½ feet	18 to 24 inches
Sprouting	1 packet	50 to 75	½	2½ to 3	2 to 2½ feet	14 to 24 inches
Brussels sprouts	1 packet	50 to 75	½	2½ to 3	2 to 2½ feet	14 to 24 inches
Cabbage	1 packet	50 to 75	½	2½ to 3	2 to 2½ feet	14 to 24 inches
Cabbage, Chinese	1 packet		½	2 to 2½	18 to 24 inches	8 to 12 inches
Carrots	1 packet		½	2 to 2½	14 to 16 inches	2 to 3 inches
Cauliflower	1 packet	50 to 75	½	2½ to 3	2 to 2½ feet	14 to 24 inches
Celeriac	1 packet	200 to 250	⅛	2½ to 3	18 to 24 inches	4 to 6 inches
Celery	1 packet	200 to 250	⅛	2½ to 3	18 to 24 inches	4 to 6 inches
Chard	2 ounces		1	2 to 2½	18 to 24 inches	6 inches
Chervil	1 packet		½	2 to 2½	14 to 16 inches	2 to 3 inches
Chicory, witloof	1 packet		½	2 to 2½	18 to 24 inches	6 to 8 inches
Chives	1 packet		½	2½ to 3	14 to 16 inches	In clusters

Collards	1 packet		½	3 to 3½	18 to 24 inches	18 to 24 inches
Cornsalad	1 packet		½	2½ to 3	14 to 16 inches	1 foot
Corn, sweet	2 ounces		2	3 to 3½	2 to 3 feet	Drills, 14 to 16 inches; hills, 2½ to 3 feet
Cress, upland	1 packet		⅛ to ¼	2 to 2½	14 to 16 inches	2 to 3 inches
Cucumbers	1 packet		½	6 to 7	6 to 7 feet	Drills, 3 feet; hills, 6 feet
Dasheen	5 to 6 pounds	50	2 to 3	3½ to 4	3½ to 4 feet	2 feet
Eggplants	1 packet	50	½	2 to 2½	2 to 2½ feet	3 feet
Endive	1 packet		½	2½ to 3	18 to 24 inches	12 inches
Fennel, Florence	1 packet		½	2½ to 3	18 to 24 inches	4 to 6 inches
Garlic	1 pound		1 to 2	2½ to 3	14 to 16 inches	2 to 3 inches
Horseradish	cuttings	50 to 75	2	3 to 4	2 to 2½ feet	18 to 24 inches
Kale	1 packet		½	2½ to 3	18 to 24 inches	12 to 15 inches
Kohlrabies	1 packet		½	2½ to 3	14 to 16 inches	5 to 6 inches
Leek	1 packet		½ to 1	2½ to 3	14 to 16 inches	2 to 3 inches
Lettuce, head	1 packet	100	½	2½ to 3	14 to 16 inches	12 to 15 inches
Lettuce, leaf	1 packet		½	2½ to 3	14 to 16 inches	6 inches
Muskmelons	1 packet		1	6 to 7	6 to 7 feet	Hills, 6 feet
Mustard	1 packet		½	2½ to 3	14 to 16 inches	12 inches
Okra	2 ounces		1 to 1½	3 to 3½	3 to 3½ feet	2 feet
Onions:						
Plants		400	1 to 2	2 to 2½	14 to 16 inches	2 to 3 inches
Seed	1 packet		½ to 1	2 to 2½	14 to 16 inches	2 to 3 inches
Sets	1 pound		1 to 2	2 to 2½	14 to 16 inches	2 to 3 inches
Parsley	1 packet		⅛	2 to 2½	14 to 16 inches	4 to 6 inches
Parsley, turnip rooted	1 packet		⅛ to ¼	2 to 2½	14 to 16 inches	2 to 3 inches

RECOMMENDED PLANTING DEPTHS AND ROW SPACING *(continued)*

REQUIREMENT FOR 100 FEET OF ROW				DISTANCE ROWS SHOULD BE APART		
Crop	Seed	Plants	Depth for planting seed	Horse- or tractor-cultivated	Hand-cultivated	Plants in the row
			Inches	*Feet*		
Parsnip	1 packet		½	2 to 2½	18 to 24 inches	2 to 3 inches
Peas	½ pound		2 to 3	2 to 4	1½ to 3 feet	1 inch
Pepper	1 packet	50 to 70	½	3 to 4	2 to 3 feet	18 to 24 inches
Physalis	1 packet		½	2 to 2½	1½ to 2 feet	12 to 18 inches
Potatoes	5 to 6 pounds, tubers		4	2½ to 3	2 to 2½ feet	10 to 18 inches
Pumpkins	1 ounce		1 to 2	5 to 8	5 to 8 feet	3 to 4 feet
Radishes	1 ounce		½	2 to 2½	14 to 16 inches	1 inch
Rhubarb		25 to 35		3 to 4	3 to 4 feet	3 to 4 feet
Salsify	1 ounce		½	2 to 2½	18 to 26 inches	2 to 3 inches
Shallots	1 pound (cloves)		1 to 2	2 to 2½	12 to 18 inches	2 to 3 inches
Sorrel	1 packet		½	2 to 2½	18 to 24 inches	5 to 8 inches
Soybeans	½ to 1 pound		1 to 1½	2½ to 3	24 to 30 inches	3 inches
Spinach	1 ounce		½	2 to 2½	14 to 16 inches	3 to 4 inches
Spinach, New Zealand	1 ounce		1 to 1½	3 to 3½	3 feet	18 inches
Squash:						
Bush	½ ounce		1 to 2	4 to 5	4 to 5 feet	Drills, 15 to 18 inches; hills, 4 feet
Vine	1 ounce		1 to 2	8 to 12	8 to 12 feet	Drills, 2 to 3 feet; hills, 4 feet

Sweet potatoes	5 pounds, bedroots	75	2 to 3	3 to 3½	3 to 3½ feet	12 to 14 inches
Tomatoes	1 packet	35 to 50	½	3 to 4	2 to 3 feet	1½ to 3 feet
Turnip greens	1 packet		¼ to ½	2 to 2½	14 to 16 inches	2 to 3 inches
Turnips and rutabagas	½ ounce		¼ to ½	2 to 2½	14 to 16 inches	2 to 3 inches
Watermelons	1 ounce		1 to 2	8 to 10	8 to 10 feet	Drills, 2 to 3 feet; hills, 8 feet

table on pages 436–439 should be used only as a general guide. Also remember that light sandy soils dry rapidly, so seed should be sown slightly deeper than normal. Heavy clay soils retain moisture and warm up slowly, which calls for a slightly more shallow planting depth. You may have to experiment with different planting depths before you strike the proper balance.

CARING FOR THE GARDEN

Watering

In most areas the garden requires a moisture supply equivalent to about an inch of rain a week during the growing season for best plant growth. It requires roughly that amount of watering a week to maintain good production if the moisture stored in the soil becomes depleted and no rain falls over several weeks. An inch of rain is equivalent of about 28,000 gallons on an acre, or 900 gallons on a 30- by 50-foot garden.

Plants give several signals if they get too much or too little water. When thirsty, they wilt (become limp and droop), which severely sets back growth. Too much water forces life-sustaining oxygen out of the soil and stops root growth. If oxygen is cut off too long, plants yellow and die of root rot. Alternate wet and dry periods may cause poor flavor or bitter fruit.

Most raw vegetables contain about 90-percent water, which illustrates the importance of keeping soil evenly moist. The basic rule of supplying moisture is to water "deeply and infrequently." Deep watering encourages maximum root growth.

How often you water depends on soil (light soil drains rapidly, heavy soil more slowly), rainfall, light intensity, temperature, wind, and humidity. Experienced gardeners use a variety of methods to tell them when it's time to water.

The simplest method is to spade up a few spots between rows and feel the soil. A more accurate way of checking for moisture is to use a soil probe or soil-sampling tool. It's the same tool used for taking soil samples for testing and can be found at garden centers or stores that cater to professional gardeners.

When you insert the tube into the ground and pull it out, you remove a column of soil you can easily read. Damp soil in the tube means plant roots have enough moisture. Soil that's muddy and smells foul is too wet. A powdery dry soil needs water immediately.

The top 2 inches of soil should be kept moist when plants are in the seedling stage. Later on, keep soil moist to a depth of 8 to 12 inches.

It is much better to give the garden a good soaking about once a week than to water it sparingly more often. Light sprinklings at frequent intervals do little, if any, good. The best way to apply water, when the soil and slope are suitable, is to run it the length of furrows between the rows until the soil is well soaked. If the soil is very sandy or the surface too irregular for the furrow method, sprinklers or porous irrigating hose must be used.

Controlling Weeds

Weeds rob cultivated plants of water, nutrients, and light. Some weeds harbor diseases, insects, and nematodes that reinfest garden crops in succeeding years.

As soon as the soil can be properly worked after each rain or irrigation, it should be thoroughly hoed or cultivated to kill weeds that have sprouted and to leave the surface in a loose, friable condition to absorb later rainfall. The primary value of hoeing or cultivating is weed control. This cultivation should be shallow so as to avoid injuring the vegetable plant roots that lie near the surface. Although it is desirable to keep the surface soil loose, there is little to be gained by hoeing or cultivating oftener than necessary to keep weeds out of the garden.

In small gardens, weeds can be controlled with black polyethylene mulch supplemented by hand weeding such as pulling, hoeing, and wheel hoeing. Mulching vegetable crops with organic material also is a common practice in small gardens.

The best organic mulches are partially decomposed hay, straw, or grass clippings. The mulch should be applied 4 to 6 inches deep when the plants are about 6 inches tall. Cabbage, tomatoes, and other transplants usually are tall enough soon after they are set in the garden. Not only does mulch control weeds, it also conserves moisture, keeps the soil from packing, and increases the humus necessary for vigorous plant growth.

STODDARD SOLVENT AS WEED KILLER. Ordinary Stoddard solvent makes an excellent herbicide for controlling crabgrass, chickweed, lamb's-quarters, pigweed, and many other broad-leafed weeds and weed grasses in patios and along the margins of walks, roads, and flowerbeds.

Use full strength in a hand sprayer adjusted to give a coarse spray. Thoroughly wet the foliage with the solvent, being careful not to get it on wanted plants. In hot weather, the weeds die the day of treatment. The solvent evaporates quickly and leaves no chemical residue. Repeat the treatment as new weeds appear. Three or four treatments usually control the weeds for the growing season.

PLANTING ANNUALS, PERENNIALS, AND BIENNIALS

Flower	Type	Planting time	Blooming time	Use
Ageratum	an	early spring	summer (mid-July)	border, pots
Alyssum	an, pr	early spring	summer–frost	edge, border
Aster	an, pr	early spring	midsummer–fall	border, cut
Bachelor's button	an	early spring	late spring–summer	bedding, cut
Balsam (lady's slipper)	an	early spring	summer–frost	bedding
Bean (scarlet runner)	an	spring	midsummer–fall	vine, door, porch accent
Calendula	an	spring	summer–frost	bedding, cut
California poppy	an, pr	spring	summer	border, cut
Candytuft	an, pr	spring	late spring–early summer	rock garden, border
Canterbury bell	bn	spring or summer	summer	border, cut
Carnation	pr	spring	everblooming	cut, border, rock garden
Celosia	an	spring	summer–fall	border, cut, dried cut
Cleome	an	spring	early summer–late fall	bed, cut, background
Coleus	pr	anytime	foliage–frost	bedding
Columbine	pr	spring	late spring–summer	border, cut
Coreopsis	pr	anytime	summer–fall	border, cut
Cosmos	an	spring	summer	cut, bed, background
Dahlia	pr	spring	late summer–fall	cut, low-edging
Delphinium	an, pr	spring or summer	spring–summer or late summer–fall	cut, border
Dianthus	an, pr	spring	everblooming	cut, low-edging, border

English daisy	pr	early spring–late fall	early and late spring, summer	bed, low-edging
Four-o'clock	pr	anytime	summer	bedding
Gaillardia	an, pr	anytime	summer–fall	border, cut
Geranium	pr	spring or fall	late spring–summer	rock garden, border
Gloriosa daisy	an, pr	spring or summer	late spring–summer	cut, border, bed
Hollyhock	pr	spring or summer	late spring–early summer or late summer–early fall	background, border
Larkspur	an	early spring–late fall	summer–fall	cut, background
Lupine	an, pr	early spring	summer	border, cut
Marigold	an	spring	everblooming	cut, bedding
Mexican firebush (Kochia)	an	early spring	late summer–fall	background
Morning glory	an	spring	summer–early fall	background, vine
Nasturtium	an	spring	late spring–early summer or all fall	bed, low-edging
Pansy	an	spring or summer	early spring or everblooming	bed, border, low-edging
Petunia	an, pr	early spring	everblooming	bedding
Phlox	an, pr	late fall/early winter	early and late spring, summer	border, cut, bed
Pinks	pr, bn	spring or summer	late spring–summer	border, cut, low-edging
Poppy	an, pr	spring	summer	cut, border
Portulaca	an	early spring	summer, late summer, fall	bed, low-edging, rock garden
Pyrethrum	pr	spring or summer	late spring–early summer	border, cut

Note: an = annual pr = perennial bn = biennial

(Continued)

PLANTING ANNUALS, PERENNIALS, AND BIENNIALS ***(continued)***

Flower	Type	Planting time	Blooming time	Use
Salvia	an, pr	early spring	everblooming	bed, border, cut
Scabiosa	an, pr	early spring	summer, late summer, fall	cut, border
Snapdragon	an, pr	early spring	late spring–early summer or late summer–early fall	cut, bedding
Stocks	an	early spring	summer	cut, bedding
Strawflower	an	early spring	summer	cut, bedding, dried cut
Sunflower	an	early spring	late spring–early summer, summer	cut, background
Sweet pea	an, pr	early spring	early and late spring, summer	cut, vine
Sweet william	an, pr	spring or summer	late spring, early summer	border, cut
Verbena	pr	spring	summer, late summer, early fall, fall	border, cut
Viola	an, pr	spring or summer	everblooming	bed, low-edging
Zinnia	an	spring	everblooming	border, cut

Note: an = annual pr = perennial bn = biennial

PLANTING COMMON HERBS

Herb	Use	Comments
Anise	flavoring, seasoning	annual; at 3-inch thin plants to 14 inches apart
Basil	flavoring, vegetable juice, soups, salads	biennial; produces seeds second year; grows well in house
Beebalm	scent	perennial; hardy
Borage—flowers, leaves	garnish, salads, claret cup	annual, perennial
Catnip	cooking, cats	tends to become a weed
Chives	salads, pot cheese	perennial; ornamental edging plants
Coriander	flavoring bread	annual; gather seeds before they scatter
Cress	mustard, salads	requires running water
Dill	pickling	annual; yellow flower
Fennel	garnish, fish sauce	perennial
Horehound	seasoning, cough remedy	perennial; grows in poor soil
Horseradish	fish	perennial
Lavender	scent, sachets	propagated by cuttings; needs mild climate
Mint	tea, sauces, scent	perennial; it overruns a garden
Mustard	garnish, salads	annual; needs rich soil
Parsley	potatoes, chops	biennial
Peppermint	flavoring	perennial; grows well in house
Rosemary	meats, chicken	propagates by cuttings
Sage	dressing, vegetables, poultry	perennial
Summer savory	vegetable seasoning	annual; aromatic
Sweet basil	aromatic, seasoning	annual; grows from seed
Tarragon	vinegar, salads	perennial; grows well in house
Thyme	seasoning, sandwiches, salads	good as an edging plant
Verbena	with mint leaves for tea	flowers; start indoors in March
Winter savory	flavoring	perennial

Controlling Insects

There are at least 120,000 different kinds of insects in the United States and Canada, but only a few kinds are in any way injurious to man. In fact, many kinds are beneficial. Some of these feed on injurious insects. Without others, plants could not be pollinated and so would have no fruit. Unnecessary use of insecticide often kills beneficial insects that, if allowed to live, would have kept the injurious insects under control.

Do not, therefore, apply an insecticide unless it is necessary to prevent actual damage to flowers or vegetables, or to cure an unhealthful or unpleasant condition in the home.

Very few of the insect pests in your garden will cause appreciable damage unless you have already killed off their parasites and predators with insecticide. If, however, you do have a pest that usually causes serious damage unless an insecticide is used, apply the insecticide when the infestation first appears.

In the flower garden, watch out especially for slugs, cutworms, spider mites, aphids, Japanese beetles and other weevils, lacebugs, and thrips. In the vegetable garden, watch for spider mites, cabbage caterpillars, Colorado potato beetles, and Mexican bean beetles. These are some of the insects likely to need prompt treatment with insecticides. Repeat the treatment in a week or 10 days if infestation continues. Do not treat for soil insects unless you find numbers of cutworms, white grubs, or wireworms when preparing the soil for planting.

You can apply most garden insecticides as a dust or as a spray. Either will give satisfactory control if properly used. Ready-to-use dusts cost more than sprays, but this added cost may be offset by their convenience. In windy weather, sprays are easier to handle than dusts in preventing drift of insecticide to other plants.

No matter which you use, be sure the material contains the correct percentage of active ingredient. Refer to the formulations mentioned here, and also follow the directions on container labels.

USING DUSTS. You can buy ready-to-use dusts at insecticide dealers. If desired, you can get one that contains a fungicide as well as one or more insecticides. Such a "general-purpose" dust is preferred by many gardeners because it kills a larger variety of pests. Or you may wish to obtain two or more dusters and fill each with an insecticide suited for a particular purpose. The plunger-type duster, with a capacity of from 1 to 3 pounds, is the most practicable applicator for the small garden. For a larger garden, a fan- or crank-type duster may be used.

For most uses, purchase dusts that contain the following percentages of active ingredients:

	Percent
Carbaryl	4
Diazinon	2
Dicofol (Kelthane)	2

(Continued)

	Percent
Malathion	4
Methoxychlor	5
Rotenone	¾
Tetradifon	3

Determine from a gardening book or from the insecticide label which material is best suited for a particular insect and plant.

On vegetables, apply an even, light coating of dust at the rate of 1 ounce per 50 feet of row or 125 square feet. On flowers, apply it at the rate of 1 ounce to each 30 feet of row or each 75 square feet of border area. Force dust through the foliage so it reaches both sides of each leaf. Apply dust when the air is still—preferably at dusk or early in the morning.

MIXING AND USING SPRAYS. Few sprays can be purchased ready to use. It is generally necessary to make the spray by mixing water with a wettable powder (WP) or with an emulsifiable concentrate (EC). (*Caution:* Before you buy a powder or concentrate, read the container label to make sure it is prepared for use on plants.)

Spray materials are sold in different strengths. The table on page 448 shows the dilution recommended for general use. If you buy a product in which the percentage of active ingredient differs from that mentioned in the table, mix proportionately more or less of it with water.

When mixing a spray, first break up lumps in the powder or shake concentrate vigorously before measuring. If you use an emulsifiable concentrate, add an equal amount of water to it, and shake or stir thoroughly to make a stable emulsion. Then add this emulsion to the full amount of water and stir until completely mixed.

Do not mix wettable powders and emulsifiable concentrates in the same batch of spray.

Mix a fresh batch of spray for each application. Many spray mixtures deteriorate or otherwise change after standing for only a few hours in a spray tank. Some mixtures may lose their effectiveness against pests; others may cause serious plant injury.

On vegetables, apply 1 quart of spray to each 50 feet of row or 125 square feet. On flowers, apply 2 quarts of spray to each 50 feet of row or to each 75 to 100 square feet of border area. Usually, spraying should be stopped just before the spray starts to run off the foliage. Shake applicator frequently to prevent powder from settling to the bottom of the spray tank.

GUIDE FOR MIXING SPRAYS

Caution: Below is a general listing only. For specific uses and mixing instructions, consult container labels.
(WP means wettable powder and EC means emulsifiable concentrate)

Insecticide	Formulation as bought	Amount to mix with 1 gallon of water
Bacillus thuringiensis (BT)	bacteria culture for caterpillars	½ tablespoon
Benomyl	50-percent WP	½ teaspoon
Carbaryl	50-percent WP	2 level tablespoons
Diazinon	50-percent WP, or 50-percent EC	2 level teaspoons 1 teaspoon
Dicofol (Kelthane)	18.5-percent WP, or 18.5-percent EC	1 level tablespoon 1 teaspoon
Malathion	57-percent EC	2 teaspoons
Methoxychlor	50-percent WP	2 level tablespoons
Pyrethrum	ready-prepared spray	mix with water as directed on container label
Rotenone	derris or cube root powder (5-percent rotenone content)	4 level tablespoons (mix powder with small quantity of water, then add remaining water)
Sulfur	wettable sulfur	3 level tablespoons
Tetradifon	25-percent WP	1 level tablespoon

For small gardens, a plunger-type hand sprayer may be adequate for applying the spray. For larger plantings, a compressed air sprayer with a capacity of from 1 to 5 gallons would be more satisfactory.

FORMULA FOR GENERAL-PURPOSE SPRAY. Here is an excellent general-purpose spray formula:

Methoxychlor, 50-percent WP (wettable powder)	2 level tablespoons
Malathion, 57-percent EC, or dimethoate, 23.4-percent EC (emulsifiable concentrate)	2 teaspoons
Wettable sulfur	2 level teaspoons
Zineb, 65-percent WP	1 level tablespoon
Water	1 gallon

"WEIGHING" INSECTICIDES WITH A SPOON. In preparing small quantities of insecticide, the weight of powders may be determined closely enough by measuring the powders with a tablespoon. Here are the approximate quantities of common powdered insecticides required to weigh 1 ounce:

Carbaryl, WP (wettable powder)	6 level tablespoons
Diazinon, WP	5 level tablespoons
Dicofol, WP	5 level tablespoons
Malathion, WP	4 level tablespoons
Methoxychlor, WP	4 level tablespoons
Sulfur, WP	3 level tablespoons

COMPATIBILITY OF PESTICIDES. Some types of pesticides—insecticides and fungicides—should not be mixed. The following are compatible and may be used together in spray mixtures. Any pesticide on the list can be used with any one or several of the others.

Diazinon	Naled
Dicofol	Pyrethrum
Ferbam	Rotenone
Malathion	Thiram
Maneb	Zineb

Most other pesticides recommended for use on green foliage of plants are also compatible except as follows:

Emulsifiable concentrates of methoxychlor may cause injury to foliage if mixed with sulfur, ferbam, maneb, thiram, zineb, or ziram. Methoxychlor wettable powders are compatible with these fungicides. Mixtures of the fixed coppers (such as basic copper sulfate, copper oxychloride sulfate, and cuprous oxide) with diazinon, ferbam, ziram, maneb, thiram, or zineb may decompose upon standing.

Mixtures of captan with emulsifiable concentrates of methoxychlor, dicofol, or malathion may cause injury to the foliage. Captan is compatible with wettable powders of these insecticides.

GENERAL CONTACT INSECTICIDES. Compounded of only kerosene, laundry soap, and water, the following formula makes a cheap and effective insecticide for general garden use. Prepare it as a stock emulsion to be diluted as needed.

(Continued)

(Continued)

Kerosene	2 gallons
Laundry soap powder or chips	½ pound
Water	1 gallon

Heat the water quite hot and dissolve the soap in it. Remove from flame, but while still hot, add the kerosene very slowly with constant stirring. Continue to stir vigorously until a creamy emulsion is formed.

Diluted with water to a 5-percent emulsion, this formula is effective against red spiders, immature scales, mealybugs, and rose midge larvae in the soil. Diluted to 1 percent, it is effective against thrips, aphids, and ants in the soil. Soil swarming with ants may be rid of these pests without harming plants by soaking with this 1-percent emulsion. Kerosene emulsion should be applied late in the afternoon and the plants thoroughly sprayed with water the next morning before sunrise.

BORDEAUX MIXTURE. One of the oldest fungicides, this mixture is still used to control leaf spot on iris, gray mold on peonies and lilies, dogwood blight, twig blight on yews and junipers, and anthranose and leaf spot on maples and sycamores. It is also useful on potatoes for blight, apples for bitter rot, and on strawberries for leaf spot.

To make a 3-gallon batch:

1. Dissolve 3 tablespoons of copper sulfate fine crystals in 1 gallon of water in a plastic or enameled container large enough to hold the entire mix.
2. Mix 5 tablespoons of spray lime in 1 gallon of water in another container.
3. Pour the lime mixture into the copper sulfate solution, stir well, and then stir in another gallon of water.
4. Pour the combination into the spray tank.

Bordeaux mixture does not keep well after the lime and copper sulfate solutions are mixed, so mix them just before use and stir occasionally while using. The solutions will keep for a long time, however, as separate solutions.

MISCELLANEOUS TIPS.

Slugs. Baits containing metaldehyde are effective and safe in vegetable gardens. Though stale beer is also good.

Cut worms. Carbaryl and diazinon are labeled for cut-worm control.

Labels. *AGAIN, READ THE LABEL BEFORE USING ANY PESTICIDE.*

14

Fire Prevention and Home Security

HOME FIRES: CAUSES AND PREVENTION

What Starts a Fire

Properly controlled, fire is one of the most useful chemical reactions known to man. Manufacturing, transportation, food processing, heating, civilization itself depend upon it. When it gets out of hand, however, fire can be a terrifying destroyer. In the United States, for example, a home is destroyed or damaged by fire every 47 seconds. Every year more than 300,000 Americans are injured by fire; over 12,000 of these victims die. The average cost of treatment for each victim is $8,000. The total cost of fires in the United States exceeds $11 billion a year.

Every ordinary fire is the result of the rapid oxidation of some burnable material. For such oxidation to take place two conditions must be met: first the material must be heated to its kindling temperature; second, there must be sufficient oxygen. If the temperature can be reduced below the kindling point or the oxygen cut off, the fire will stop. The two chief methods of fire extinguishing are, therefore, cooling and smothering. Whether one, the other, or both methods should be used depends upon the type of fire.

The oldest method of reducing the kindling temperature was to soak the blazing material with water. Even today, water is still the most effective, as well as the cheapest and most abundant, agent for putting out large fires of wood, paper, clothing, or other ordinary materials.

Water is a good fire-fighting agent for several reasons. In the first place it won't burn. In the second, water has the ability to absorb more heat from a hot body, weight for weight, than any other common substance. Also, in boiling, water extracts a still greater amount of heat from the burning material. In fact it takes about six times as much heat to boil away 1 pound of water already at the boiling point as it does to bring 1 pound of cold water to that temperature.

Dry chemicals, foam, carbon dioxide, and vaporizing nonflammable liquids put out fire mostly by smothering it.

How Fire Spreads

Fire spreads from one material to another, and from one place to another, in different ways. The most obvious is by contact with the original flame. It can be conducted, however, by something like sheet metal, which by itself will not burn but which may get hot enough to set fire to any flammable material it touches. That is why stovepipes should not be allowed to come in contact with woodwork.

Fire also can be carried by flying sparks or even drafts of hot air. Firemen often find that a fire on a lower floor has made hot air rise through stairways or elevator shafts. This superheated air gathers at the top of the building causing this part to burst into flame although there may be no fire on the floors between.

Finally, the radiation of heat from a burning building may cause a nearby building to catch fire, just as the heat from a bonfire might set your clothes afire, even though the flames didn't touch you.

How to Prevent Fires

Most accidental fires can be avoided with a little care. Firemen have a saying that "a clean building seldom burns." In other words, the majority of fires start in trashpiles, rubbish, or stored odds and ends that accumulate around the house. Closets, attics, and cellars are the main source of home fires, and ordinary good housekeeping is the first line of defense against such fires.

Check your closets, attic, and basement for cast-off articles that would burn easily. These include such things as curtains, draperies, tablecloths, bedclothes, lampshades, coats, suits, dresses, wicker and wooden furniture, rags, and linoleum.

Clean out your storage spaces. You will be surprised at how many burnable odds and ends are really useless to you.

Instead of an attic, many modern homes have an air space between the top floor ceiling and the roof. If your home has such a spot, make sure you can get into it through a trap door. Keep a ladder handy. You won't be able to put out a fire in this space unless you can reach it quickly. Never store anything there.

Whenever you leave your home you can improve its fire resistance by shutting all doors and windows. Closed interior doors will confine a fire to the area of origin for some time and prevent rapid spread within the building. In fact, it is a good idea to sleep with doors closed.

Check Your Electrical Appliances

Many fires happen in homes each day because of faulty or misused electrical equipment. Circuits are overloaded by plugging in too many appliances to a single outlet. An iron is switched on and then forgotten. Flammable material is left in the focus of a radiant heater. Cords are used after the insulation has worn away. Others are stretched under rugs or stapled to baseboards and door frames. If fuses blow frequently, do not replace them with bigger ones, but check your equipment. Your wiring may be overloaded to the point where it could start a fire.

Watch Your Heating Plant

Costly fires may be started by faulty furnaces, stoves, and other heating plants. Some result from too much soot in chimneys. Others are caused by rusted or cracked pipes and fittings. These may be prevented by making sure the chimney is clean and the pipes sound.

Keep magazines, papers, and clothing off radiators and away from open fireplaces or stoves. Do not allow paper lamp shades to touch light bulbs. Enough heat may build up in each of these cases to set the material on fire.

Matches and Careless Smoking Habits

According to the National Board of Fire Underwriters, the careless discarding of lighted matches and smoking materials is responsible for about 30 percent of all fires from known causes. A burning match or tobacco debris recklessly tossed aside may start a disastrous fire taking heavy toll of lives and property.

Here are a few commonsense precautions:

1. Keep all matches out of the reach of small children.
2. Have plenty of ash trays conveniently placed—and keep them clean.

(List continues)

3. Be sure your lighted matches or smokes are completely snuffed out before you discard them.
4. Don't smoke in bed or where No Smoking signs are posted.
5. Don't strike matches in closets, garages, or other places where flammable materials, dust, or vapors may be ignited.

Kerosene and Cleaning Fluids

One in ten fires of known origin is caused by the incautious use of kerosene, gasoline, or other flammable fluids, and by carelessness in handling candles, lamps, open gas jets, torches, and so on. Sloshing or pouring kerosene on wood or coal fires is an example of recklessness.

Using gasoline, naphtha, and other flammable liquids in the house for cleaning causes many tragedies each year. These liquids vaporize when exposed to air and may quickly produce an explosive mixture that is readily ignited by a match, pilot light, sparking motor, or even a static spark developed from rubbing textiles together. Or the quickly spreading vapor may be exploded by a smoker or a fire in another room.

Because of the ever-present danger of fire or explosion from the vapors of flammable cleaning fluids, they should not be used indoors except in the quantities needed to remove small spots, and then only in a well-ventilated room.

Radio and Television Antennas

Fires have been caused in homes by radio and television antennas falling across power lines and causing a short circuit. If possible, install antennas where they cannot fall on such lines if they should topple over. If not, make them substantial enough so that any load of wind, snow, or ice cannot topple them. Place the lead-in conductors at least 6 feet away from any part of a lightning-rod system. Antennas should also be equipped with lightning arresters approved by Underwriters Laboratories and should be properly grounded.

Disposal of Oily Rags

Rags and cotton waste used with linseed or other "drying" oils, or with paint containing such oils, should be burned promptly outdoors or kept in tightly closed metal containers until they can be burned. In drying, such oils combine with oxygen. When this happens on combustible materials of large surface area and poor heat conduction, so much heat may be produced that the materials often take fire spontaneously.

Safety with Natural Gas

Practically all the gas now sold utilities in the United States is natural gas, derived from wells in the ground. Contrary to popular notion, this gas is not poisonous and it has no odor of its own. Asphyxiation from natural gas can occur only when the gas becomes so concentrated that it cuts off the minimum requirement of oxygen. What you smell when you "smell gas" is not the gas itself but a powerful odorizing chemical mixed with the gas to quickly alert you to its presence should there be a leak. Although fires from natural gas do occur, they are usually the result of misuse of equipment or damage to it from an outside cause.

Natural gas will burn in air only when the concentration of the gas is between 4.5 and 14.5 percent by volume. Above and below these limits, it will neither burn nor explode. Ordinarily, however, you have no way of knowing the concentration in an emergency situation. So to be on the safe side, you must follow a few simple rules.

If you have been at home for some time and suddenly smell gas from a nearby source, perhaps a pot has boiled over on the range and put out the flame under it or the hose on a portable burner has sprung a leak or has become detached. In such a case there is little or no danger. Just turn off the gas and open the windows to let the gas diffuse into the outside air. If the gas comes from a leak in a faulty pipe or appliance that you can't turn off, telephone your gas company at once, explain the condition, and follow the advice you are given.

If, on the other hand, your first smell of gas comes to you from a distant room or the floor below, or, after being out for some time you get a strong smell of gas on entering the house, take care! Everything may still be perfectly safe, but you have no way of telling. If you are alone in the house, leave the house at once and telephone the gas company from the nearest neighbor's phone. If there are others in the house, first get them to leave. Do nothing in the house that might cause a flame or spark. Don't light a match or cigarette lighter. Don't turn electric lights or appliances on or off. Don't ring an electric bell. Don't use the home telephone. When the experts from the gas company arrive, they will know what to do. In the meantime, the gas will remain harmless unless some careless person ignites it.

Ventilate Properly for LP Gas

A leak in any system using flammable gases presents a fire hazard. Special precautions must be taken with "LP"—liquefied petroleum or "bottled"—gas because it is heavier than air and so tends to settle to the floor instead of rising, contrary to the more familiar behavior of manufactured or natural gas.

Because of this difference, reduction of hazard with LP gas begins with the proper installation and ventilation of equipment. As it would be difficult to drain away any possible leakage from basements that are wholly underground, LP gas containers should be outdoors and at least 3 feet from basement wall openings.

Drainage for LP gas may be provided by leaving a 2- or 3-inch opening across the top and bottom of the doors to the outside. The floor of the furnace or boiler room must be higher than the surrounding grade; otherwise the gas may accumulate near the floor of this room like water behind a dam. A more positive way to remove the gas may be to use forced ventilation. The exhaust duct should take the air from a point within 2 inches of the lowest part of the floor.

SMOKE AND HEAT DETECTORS

Some 80 percent of all fire fatalities in the home take place during sleeping hours, from 11 P.M. to 6 A.M. When everyone is sound asleep, the smell of smoke and the sight of fire may go undetected until it is too late. For this reason, you need a reliable home early-warning smoke and fire-detector system to ring out an alarm.

There are two basic types of early-warning devices used today in homes: smoke (either ionization or photoelectric) detectors, and heat detectors. Smoke detectors are the most popular and for good reason. Most fire victims die before the flames have reached them. It's not fire but smoke that kills.

Before discussing the different types of smoke and fire detectors, let's take a closer look at the various stages of a fire. Most building fires involve solid fuels and develop in the following stages.

INCIPIENT STAGE. Thermal decomposition of a combustible material produces large quantities of small particles. These are solid and liquid particles (aerosols) composed of unburned carbon, water vapor, and various gases released by the thermal decomposition. Most combustion particles generated in the incipient stage are smaller than one micron (one millionth of a meter). Since the human eye cannot normally see particles smaller than 5 microns, combustion products in the incipient stage are mostly invisible. Ionization smoke detectors react to these small particles.

SMOLDERING STAGE. As a fire in a solid fuel continues to develop, it reaches the smoke or smoldering stage. Combustion has increased to a point where the volume and collective mass of the particles produced is visible as smoke. At this stage of development, heat output has increased but may be insufficient to support continued combustion. Ionization and photoelectric smoke detectors react to smoke from a smoldering fire.

FLAME STAGE. The flame stage is reached when a sufficient quantity of heat is available to ignite the gases and unburned particles liberated by thermal decomposition. When a fire reaches this stage, it generates sufficient energy to become self-sustaining, and will increase in intensity as long as fuel and oxygen are available and temperatures above the kindling stage of the fuel are maintained. Thermal detectors are designed to detect fires in the flame stage.

HIGH-HEAT STAGE. The fourth and final stage of a fire is the high-heat stage that rapidly follows the flame stage. This heat is the energy released by the exothermic chemical reaction of the fire. A fire that reaches this final stage causes the most damage and is the most difficult to extinguish.

Smoke Detectors

As already mentioned, smoke detectors currently available operate on one of two principles: photoelectric or ionization. In the photoelectric detector, a beam of light is projected at an angle to a photocell in a lighttight but not airtight chamber. Since the photocell's view is at an angle to the beam of light, it cannot "see" the light. When smoke enters the chamber, particles in the smoke cause light to be scattered and seen by the photocell. At a calibrated smoke density, the alarm sounds. Because the photoelectric detector reacts only to visible smoke, it is fairly resistant to false alarms.

The ionization-type smoke detector contains a chamber in which a small—and safe—radiation source ionizes air particles between two electrodes, allowing a tiny electrical current to pass since positive ions travel to one electrode, negative to the other. When smoke enters the chamber, the ions attach themselves to the smoke particles. The resulting larger particles travel more slowly, and therefore for a given period of time fewer ionized particles reach the electrodes. This causes a decrease in current flow between the electrodes; at a calibrated level, the alarm sounds.

Some ionization detectors use a dual-chamber principle. Here, a measurement chamber is open to surrounding air; a second reference chamber, which is part of the electrical circuit, is exposed only to air temperature, pressure, and humidity. This system reduces false alarms caused by changing ambient conditions, a problem that has plagued ionization detectors.

In general, photoelectric detectors respond more quickly to smoldering fires with limited heat and little or no open flame, as from a lighted cigarette dropped onto a mattress or sofa. Ionization detectors have a faster response to a clean-burning fire in which flaming is present—when a lighted match is dropped into a full wastebasket or when a Christmas tree catches fire, for example. Since both kinds of fires occur in the home, neither detector is really superior to the other.

Detectors are powered by batteries or by household current. AC-powered smoke detectors are wired directly to a junction box or are plugged into an outlet. In the latter case, a bracket clipped over the plug and screwed to the outlet plate prevents accidental disconnection. Wired-in detectors will avoid this problem, but they are more costly to install.

Battery operation simplifies installation and eliminates the problem of detector deactivation in a blackout or in case of a fire in the home's electric system. But batteries must be replaced annually, and there is the possibility that the homeowner, irritated by the detector's low-battery warning (intermittent beeping), will simply remove the battery and fail to replace it.

Other than battery replacement, there is not much you have to do to keep the detectors in good working order. You should test the unit periodically—some makers say every week, others once a month. You test some by pressing a lever or button, others by blowing smoke into them.

The light source in the photoelectrics must be replaced every 5 or 6 years. There is a warning signal to tell you that the bulb has burned out. Both ionization and photoelectric detectors should be dusted occasionally with a vacuum cleaner.

LOCATION OF SMOKE DETECTORS. Particular attention must be given to choosing a location for the detector. To obtain optimum protection, there are two basic facts to remember: (1) Most residential fire fatalities occur at night when occupants are asleep; and (2) smoke, as well as other combustible products, first tends to rise to the ceiling, then flows out and down the walls. With these points in mind, use the following guidelines when selecting a location for a smoke detector:

1. Locate a smoke detector near sleeping areas. The preferred location is in hallways or areas immediately adjacent to bedrooms so

that the detector will be heard through closed bedroom doors. Further, statistics of the National Fire Protection Association (NFPA) reveal that most fires originate in the kitchen, living room areas, and basement. Therefore, the best location for a smoke detector is between the sleeping area and those locations where a fire is most likely to begin.

2. The detector, if possible, should protect the exit path. Bedrooms are usually farthest from convenient exits. For instance, where there is a long central hallway (20 feet or longer), installation of detectors at each end is recommended. This will help prevent your family from being trapped by dense smoke or flames.
3. Since smoke and other combustible products rise, locate the smoke detector as close to the center of the ceiling as possible, or at the top of a stairway. Remember that stairways provide vertical shafts, like chimneys, for smoke and heat to move up rapidly. Never mount a unit on a ceiling closer than 6 inches from the nearest wall, to avoid dead-air space that could prevent heat from setting off a detector.
4. In mobile homes, in houses with built-in radiant heating in the ceiling, and in rooms with exposed beams, wall mounting of smoke detectors is recommended. Locate the unit no closer than 6 and no further than 12 inches from the ceiling, and at least 1 foot from any corner of the room.
5. Sloped ceilings require placement of smoke detectors within 3 feet of the peak measured horizontally. In the basement, mount the detector flush (not between rafters) on the ceiling within 10 feet of the stairway.

WHERE NOT TO PUT A SMOKE DETECTOR. There are a few locations that should be avoided when selecting a spot for a smoke detector. They include:

Kitchens. While most detectors are designed to ignore normal cooking fumes, burned food or broiling and frying may cause unnecessary alarms. A heat detector is better in this location.

Attics, bathrooms, or closets. Temperature extremes, humidity, or stagnant dead air in these locations may affect the sensitivity of the detector. Also do not install a unit directly outside a bathroom since the excessive moisture escaping from that room could cause unwanted alarms. A heat detector is preferred in such locations.

Near air registers, light fixtures, room air conditioners, or in front of windows. Such locations cause abnormal air currents that could interfere with smoke entering the detector and delay an alarm.

Garages. Automobile exhaust fumes can trigger the alarm. Heat detectors operate better here.

Near fireplaces. If located too close, an improperly vented fireplace may also cause unnecessary alarms.

Unheated mobile homes or unheated rooms. Most detectors are designed to perform best where the ambient temperature does not exceed 100° F (37.8° C) or fall below 40° F (4° C).

LOCATION EXAMPLES. In single-level homes with only one bedroom area, locate the smoke detector in the center of the hallway, between the sleeping area and the rest of the house. When there are two separate bedroom areas, a detector should be installed between each area and the main living section of the house. In mobile homes, locate the detector on an interior wall in the hallway between the living room and the first bedroom door.

In multilevel dwellings, a smoke detector should be located at the head of each stairway. When a doorway is closed at the top of the stairway, creating a dead air space, it is better to locate the unit at the bottom of the stairway. It is also wise to install a detector in bedrooms of occupants who smoke.

Heat Detectors

Heat detectors, in contrast to smoke detectors, alarm only when heat at the detector location reaches a preset level—usually 135° or 200° F. Those rated at 135° F are for most house locations, while those with a rating of 200° F are used in the kitchen (near the oven), in the attic, near the furnace, and similar places where occasional high-temperature conditions occur normally. Some high-temperature heat detectors are rated at only 190° F.

The basic component of a fixed-temperature heat detector is a thermostat that is set at the desired fusing temperature. Actually the unit itself is a compact plastic disc about 2½ inches diameter and approximately 1 inch thick. The average household-model heat detector has a detection range of 10 feet and will protect an area up to 20 by 20 feet when located in the center of that area—that is, in rooms where neither length nor width exceeds 20 feet, mount one detector in the center of the ceiling. Always locate a smoke detector in the same room.

In the case of open-beam and unfinished ceilings (attics, basements, garages, etc.), the flow of heat across the joists is so restricted that the heat-detector spacing across the joist must be reduced to 10 feet apart. The flow of heat in the direction the joists are running is not restricted, so normal spacing (20 feet apart) may be used. In addition always locate a heat detector within 5 feet of walls running parallel to the joist and within 10 feet of walls running at right angles to the joist. Always mount heat detectors on the bottom of the joists—not in the channel between the joists.

Only as a last resort should heat detectors be located on a side wall because activation will be delayed. If absolutely necessary to locate on a side wall, avoid any objects that might further delay activation.

Most heat detectors operate on a low-voltage (12-volt) AC power supply and/or batteries. They are usually of the open-circuit type; that is, the contact must be activated (closed) before the alarm sounds.

Levels of Protection

Generally, a minimum alarm system as just described cannot provide complete assurance of early warning from all potential fire sources. Additional detectors to monitor areas with high fire potential should be considered. In the accompanying table the National Fire Protection Association has defined four levels of protection. Use it as a general guide when selecting detector locations. Also be sure to check local codes and ordinances regarding detector locations. For additional information, write for NFPA Standard No. 74, Household Fire Warning Equipment, National Fire Protection Association, 470 Atlantic Avenue, Boston, Massachusetts 02210.

Level of protection	Smoke-detector location	Additional smoke or heat-detector locations*
1 (optimum)	Between each bedroom area and rest of house; head of basement stairs	Living room, kitchen, furnace room, utility room, basement, each bedroom, attic, dining room, hall, attached garage
2	Between each bedroom area and rest of house	Living room, kitchen, furnace (utility) room, basement, each bedroom, attic
3	Between each bedroom area and rest of house	Living room, kitchen, furnace (utility) room, basement
4 (minimum)	Between each bedroom area and rest of house; head of each stairway to an occupied area	None

* Heat detectors are recommended for kitchens, attics, and garages to avoid nuisance alarms, as explained in the accompanying text.

When installing either smoke or heat detectors, be sure to follow the manufacturer's instructions to the letter for best protection.

WHAT TO DO IF A FIRE STARTS

Big fires in homes usually start from little ones—a match in a wastebasket, blazing grease in an oven or frying pan, a smoldering ironing board cover from a forgotten iron. If you are present when a little fire starts, and act quickly and sensibly enough, you should be able to put it out easily before it can spread farther. The main thing to remember is to work fast but to keep your head.

The very first thing to do if you discover a fire is to quickly size it up. If the fire is so small you are dead sure you can put it out in a few moments, get at it at once. If you have the slightest doubt that it might get out of hand, however, call the fire department immediately—or, better yet, if possible, have someone else call. Give the operator your name, address, location of the fire, and the type of fire—whether trash, flammable liquids, wood, and so on.

If the fire still seems manageable, decide what method to use and try to put it out yourself.

Putting out Fires by Emergency Methods

Although it is recommended that every home have at least one all-purpose fire extinguisher, your home may not and so you must rely on materials at hand. If papers, rags, wood, or similar materials are burning, plain water is probably the handiest and most effective extinguishing agent. Wet the material thoroughly by any means you can find. Pots of water will do, but a quickly rigged garden hose—if you have one and facilities for connecting it—adjusted to a spray rather than a solid stream might wet and smother the fire more quickly. Incidentally, a length of garden hose long enough to reach from an inside faucet to any part of the house might be a more effective safeguard than a small fire extinguisher in this type of fire.

When paint, gasoline, grease in the frying pan, or oil in the engine of your car starts blazing, forget all you know about water as a good extinguishing agent. Water will not mix with oily things. Because it is heavier than most of them, it sinks, causes them to overflow, and thus spreads the flames.

Oil fires must be put out by smothering. Where oil is confined, such as in a pail, a can, or a pan on the stove, this may be done merely by covering the utensil with a pie tin, can cover, or almost anything that is flat and large enough to cover the opening. Even a sheet of cardboard, if slid over the opening deftly enough, can put out an oil fire that looks terrifying.

For smothering larger oil fires, or oil fires that are not confined, carbon dioxide gas or foam (or dry chemicals that liberate carbon dioxide) are the most effective agents. If you have no fire extinguishers containing these, and the fire is not too large, scattering ordinary baking soda over the flames by the handful is almost as effective. (For more information about bicarbonate as a fire extinguisher, see the section on "Baking Soda" in Chapter 9.)

When Clothing Catches Fire

Do not run. If indoors where there are rugs, drop to the floor and roll a rug over yourself. If there are no rugs, use whatever heavy article may be handy—a coat or a blanket. If outdoors, roll on the ground. Remaining in a standing position allows the flame to burn upward over the face. Running would fan the flame and accelerate burning. Use of some heavy article wrapped around the body cuts off the oxygen and more quickly puts out the fire. It also minimizes the extent of body injury.

If Fire Gets out of Control

If you can't control a fire, get yourself and all others in the building away from it before you are trapped. If you don't have time to evaluate the situation, *it is always best to evacuate the family immediately.* If you are not protected with an alarm system, it will be necessary for you to wake everyone up by pounding on walls, hitting two pans against each other, or doing whatever will alert them. Do not stop to dress or gather valuables. Every second counts. Close all doors behind you as you leave. The fire will spread more slowly that way.

Find a wall and follow it around to the door. Keep away from the center of the floor. It is likely to cave in first if there is a fire below. If someone else is in the room and can't find his way out, shout to him from the door. You may be able to guide him to you.

Always keep low in a fire situation. Gases, smoke, and air heated by fire rise. If you are in bed and smell smoke, do not bolt upright because the difference in temperature could make you unconscious. If you must go through a smoky room, crawl. Hold a damp cloth to your nose. Also don't assume that clear air is safe. It could contain carbon monoxide, which affects judgment and can kill.

Be careful of stairs in a burning building. Keep close to the wall and tread lightly. Don't run. Feel with a foot for each step to make sure it will bear your weight before you step on it.

If you can't get down the stairs, you may have to drop from a window. If you are caught on an upper story, you can cut your fall by about 7 feet if you lower yourself out of a window as far as you can before letting go. Or you can use a rope ladder or try to descend to a porch or garage roof by some means such as knotted sheets and blankets.

If you decide that you can't escape by yourself, shut the door to prevent entry of smoke and flames and call for help from a window. Stuff a folded towel under the door to help keep out smoke.

The National Fire Protection Association and the Fire Marshalls Association of North America have developed Operation EDITH, (*E*xit *D*rills *I*n *T*he *H*ome), a home fire-drill program. Its aim is to encourage families to preplan escape routes and have periodic rehearsals for evacuating the house in the event of fire. Everyone should be thoroughly familiar with available exits and alternates. The ideal escape plan should be a direct exit from the bedrooms to the outside of the house. It is important that children be instructed carefully, since their natural tendency is to hide in the event of a crisis. Draw up an escape plan and conduct the drills with your family every 6 months.

Be sure everyone in the house has an emergency escape route. If necessary, consider installing an escape ladder, rearranging bedrooms (put children in rooms with easy escape routes), cutting access door between bedrooms (possibly through a closet), and installing a hall door. (*Note:* If a hall door can be closed, all bedrooms can sometimes share the one best emergency escape exit.)

Determine a meeting place outside the home and insist that everyone meet there should an emergency occur. This can eliminate the tragedy of someone reentering the house looking for a missing member who is perfectly safe. Incidentally, call the fire department as soon as the family is out of the house, and stay on the phone to give them all the information needed. Tragically, some people panic and hang up before giving the address. Be sure everyone knows how to telephone the fire department.

Rescue Tips

Leave rescue work to properly trained and equipped firemen, if they are present. If they are not, take someone with you when you search a burning building. Teamwork is always better. You can search more quickly and thoroughly and you can help each other if necessary. Try to search from the top downward. People who are confused or frightened, especially children, often hide under beds or in closets. Look in every room and in every hiding place you can think of.

If a door is hot to the touch, you can expect to find fire when you open it, so be careful. If the door opens toward you, brace your foot against it and turn the knob gently. An explosive back draft may occur when you open the door. If the door opens away from you, turn the knob, push, and duck to one side until you can see whether flames are going to lash out through it.

Inside a smoke-filled room, keep close to the wall and feel under and on the beds, inside closets, and over large pieces of furniture. If you think the floor won't collapse, cross the room from one corner to another to make sure no one is lying in the center.

If you find an unconscious person, put him on the floor if he isn't already there. Turn him on his back and quickly tie his wrists together. A handkerchief will do. Kneel astride him and put your head between his tied wrists. You can then crawl forward, dragging him beneath you, even though he may be much heavier than you are.

To move an unconscious person downstairs, place him on his back with his head toward the stairs. Put your hands under his armpits so that his head rests on the crook of your arm. Then back down the stairs yourself, letting his feet trail.

FIRE EXTINGUISHERS

The first few minutes of a fire largely determine the amount of damage it will do. In that short time, a portable fire extinguisher may be able to make the difference between a minor annoyance and disaster. But each class of fire calls for specialized action. By using the wrong method or the wrong extinguisher you may do more harm than good.

Classes of Fires

For purposes of fire fighting, fires are classified into four groups:

CLASS A. These are the ordinary penetrating fires in paper, wood, textiles, and so on that call for cooling and quenching by water or the insulating and smothering action of certain dry chemicals.

CLASS B. Burning liquids, such as gasoline, oils, paints, and cooking fats, where smothering action is required. Applying water here would only spread the fire.

CLASS C. Fires in live electrical equipment—motors, switches, appliances, and so on. A nonconducting extinguishing agent must be used on these to prevent injury or even death to the operator. (If burning electrical apparatus can be unplugged, or the switch pulled, a Class C fire can usually be treated as Class A. Therefore, whenever possible, electrical equipment should be deenergized before attacking a Class C fire.)

CLASS D. This is a classification that would rarely, if ever, apply to fires in homes. It includes fires in combustible metals such as magnesium, sodium, and potassium. Neither water nor any ordinary fire extinguisher should be used on these. Special powdered chemicals have been developed that seal the burning surface and smother the fire.

Types of Extinguishers

Portable fire extinguishers come in seven general types, and in sizes that range from hand units about the size of a can of soda to wheeled containers weighing several hundred pounds. Here is a brief rundown of the types and how they work:

WATER EXTINGUISHERS. These include three subtypes:

1. Soda-acid, one of the oldest and most familiar types of extinguisher, contains a solution of bicarbonate of soda and a vial of sulfuric acid. When inverted, the chemicals mix, producing carbon dioxide gas that forces out the solution in a 30- to 40-foot stream. Comes in sizes from 1¼ to 40 gallons, the 2½-gallon size being standard.
2. Pressurized water extinguisher forces out its contents up to 45 feet by means of compressed air. Comes in 1¼- and 2½-gallon sizes. Pressure is restored by connecting to compressed-air line.
3. Pump tank shoots plain water or a special antifreeze mixture from 30 to 40 feet by means of a hand pump. Comes in 1½- to 5-gallon sizes and may be refilled during operation or shut down at any time.

LOADED-STREAM EXTINGUISHER. This works the same as pressurized type but contains a dissolved chemical (potassium acetate) in nonfreezing water solution that makes it effective on Class B as well as on Class A fires.

CARBON DIOXIDE EXTINGUISHER. Consisting of high-pressure cylinder of liquified carbon dioxide gas, this is suitable for only the smallest Class A fires but is excellent for classes B and C. Its special advantage is that it leaves no residue and does no damage to materials on which it is used. It comes in capacities of from 2 to 50 pounds of liquid gas.

REGULAR (ORDINARY) DRY-CHEMICAL EXTINGUISHER. This consists of a container of powdered bicarbonate of soda and a pressure container of carbon dioxide or of compressed nitrogen. The contents are expelled by gas pressure when a valve on a nozzle is opened. Charges range from 1 pound to 350 pounds (the latter on a wheeled cart). The 2¾- and 5-pound sizes of good make are approved by the U.S. Coast Guard for marine use. The one disadvantage of this type of extinguisher is that it leaves a large amount of powder (residue) that must be cleaned up after use.

PURPLE "K" DRY-CHEMICAL EXTINGUISHER. This operates in the same manner as the regular dry-chemical type except that potassium bicarbonate is used in place of bicarbonate of soda. This extinguisher gets its name—purple K—from the color of the powder that it discharges. Charges range from 1 pound to 350 pounds (the latter on a wheeled cart) and like the regular dry-chemical type, it leaves a residue.

MULTIPURPOSE (ABC) DRY-CHEMICAL EXTINGUISHER. This is the only one that Underwriters Laboratories (UL) considers effective against all types of fires. The basic chemical is ammonium phosphate that provides a fire-retardant blanket on materials of Class A fires, acting to smother the fire and to prevent rekindling. Available in sizes from 1 to 20 pounds, the 2½- and 5-pound sizes of good make are approved by the U.S. Coast Guard for marine use. If you have only one fire extinguisher, this type is probably the best choice. Because of its fire-retarding deposit, however, it leaves a cleanup problem even greater than that left by the ordinary powder extinguisher.

How Extinguishers Are Rated

Since the prices for the same type and size of extinguisher may vary considerably, it is wise to be governed by the UL ratings carried on the label of every extinguisher listed by Underwriters Laboratories Inc. Actually, the fire rating of an extinguisher, rather than size, is the guide to its extinguishing ability. As a result of physical testing by UL, fire extinguishers carry on their nameplates a classification consisting of a numeral followed by a letter. The numeral indicates the approximate relative fire-extinguishing potential of the extinguisher on the class of fire, which is identified by a letter. For example, a 1-A fire extinguisher is expected to put out a fire of 50 burning pieces of 20-inch long wood 2×2s. An extinguisher that can cope with fires twice as big gets a 2-A rating, and so on.

Class B extinguisher ratings are not directly related to the amount of fire that can be extinguished by a particular extinguisher, since this is related to the degree of training and experience. Thus, to earn UL's 1-B rating, an extinguisher must discharge effectively for at least 8 seconds and snuff out 3¼ gallons of flaming naphtha in a 2½-square-foot pan. A 10-B extinguisher is rated for a fire about 10 times as large—31 gallons of flaming naphtha in a 25-square-foot pan. Class C extinguishers have no numerical rating because fires are essentially Class A in Class B fires involving energized electrical equipment.

Installation of Extinguishers

Since most home fires originate in the living room and kitchen, at least one extinguisher should be located where it can be quickly reached from both of these rooms. It is best to locate each extinguisher in the path of exit travel so that, if the fire cannot be readily controlled with the extinguisher, there is a good escape route out of the house. In second-floor bedroom areas, the extinguisher should be located in a handy closet or cabinet along the route of exit travel. For basement use, the head of the basement stairs is generally a preferred location; another location would be a basement workshop. When making the actual installation, keep the following points in mind:

1. Mount your extinguisher *upright* in a location that is easy to reach. Clean, dry locations near exits are recommended.
2. Be sure that mounting hardware (screws, rivets, etc.) is of the proper type and size to assure a positive mounting.
3. The extinguisher should be mounted so that the top is not more than 3½ to 5 feet from the floor.
4. Do not locate your extinguisher in an area that will exceed 120° F.
5. Water extinguishers should be protected from freezing (add anti-freeze) unless a loaded stream agent has been added.
6. Do not use any other than the loaded-stream charge recommended by the manufacturer.

Operation and Use of Fire Extinguishers

Mere provision of an extinguisher for your home is useless unless you know how to use it properly and teach your family members how to use

WHICH EXTINGUISHER FOR WHAT FIRE?

Type of extinguisher	Classes of fires A	Classes of fires B	Classes of fires C
Pressurized water	YES Excellent; water saturates material, prevents rekindling	NO Dangerous, actually helps to spread the fire	NO Dangerous to the operator; acts as a conductor
Loaded stream	YES Excellent; saturates material, prevents rekindling	YES Provides smothering action, cools and quenches	NO Liquid is a conductor and should not be used on live electrical equipment
Carbon dioxide	NO Effective on small surface fires only	YES Will not harm food or equipment	YES Excellent; nonconducting, safe for the operator
Regular dry chemical	NO Effective on small surface fires only	YES Excellent; smothers the fire	YES Excellent; nonconducting, smothering film
Purple "K" dry chemical	NO Effective on small surface fires only	YES Excellent; has greatest initial fire-stopping power of the extinguishers listed; smothers fire and prevents reflash	YES Excellent; nonconducting smothering film
Multipurpose (ABC) dry chemical	YES Excellent; forms a smothering film, prevents reflash	YES Excellent; forms a smothering film, prevents reflash	YES Excellent; nonconducting smothering film

it. Be sure you understand the instructions so that there will be no delay if a fire occurs. Before using the extinguisher, carefully read the operating instructions on the extinguisher label. Inform all persons having access to this extinguisher of its operation. The total discharge of extinguisher contents is a matter of *seconds*, therefore any delay should be avoided.

In case of a fire, remember the following facts about the operation of fire extinguishers:

1. The contents are discharged by pressure; do not discharge at a person's face.
2. Hold the extinguisher firmly in an upright position.
3. Stay low to avoid inhalation of smoke and aim discharge just under the flames, using a side-to-side motion sweeping the entire width of the fire. For wall fires, start at the bottom, sweep from side to side, and progress upward. For floor fires, sweep from side to side and move forward as fire diminishes to reach far edge of fire.
4. *Never* move into area where fire was burning even though it appears to have been extinguished. You could be trapped and burned if the fire reflashes.
5. *Never* use water extinguishers on electrical fires.
6. *Never* use extinguishers at distances of less than 6 to 10 feet.

Inspection and Care of Extinguishers

Your extinguisher should be checked once each month or more frequently if necessary to determine that:

1. The pointer on the pressure gauge is in the green operable area.
2. The nozzle opening has not been closed with some foreign object.
3. A ring pull pin is provided to prevent accidental discharge. This pin is secured by means of a plastic wire lockseal. On some models, the carry handle is sealed in place by a tape crossing over the lower portion. Check to make sure that the lockseal is intact. A broken lockseal is an indication of tampering, and there may have been a partial or total loss of contents.
4. Weigh the extinguisher at least every 6 months and if below the weight designated under "Maintenance" on the extinguisher label, the extinguisher should be recharged.

Have your extinguisher recharged or replaced immediately even if only partially discharged. A momentary discharge could cause total loss of pressure. Take your extinguisher to a qualified fire extinguisher service agency for recharging, repairs, or retest. Look for "Fire Extinguishers" in the Yellow Pages of the telephone directory.

Nonrefillable extinguishers should be discarded and a replacement should be obtained immediately for continued fire protection. Do not dispose of a used extinguisher by throwing in a fire. It could explode causing serious bodily injuries.

MAKING FABRICS FLAME RESISTANT

Many home fires that cause crippling burns and loss of life and property start when clothing and other fabrics are accidentally ignited. This hazard is reduced when fabrics are treated to make them flame resistant.

Curtains and draperies for recreation and children's rooms, children's clothing, cloth toys and party decorations, ironing-board covers, and scenery for amateur theatricals are among many items that can be rendered less hazardous by simple treatments you can apply yourself. The items so treated will not be fire*proof*. They will char and possibly glow, but they will not burst into flame and spread the fire to surrounding objects.

The following formulas and methods of application, suggested by the National Bureau of Standards and the U.S. Department of Agriculture, are effective on cotton, linen, and viscose rayon fabrics. The solutions are suitable only for materials protected from outdoor weather. Because the chemicals are water soluble, the treatment must be renewed after each laundering.

Applying Solutions

You can apply flame-retardant solutions by dipping, spraying, or sprinkling. Resin-treated fabrics, and some unused fabrics, resist wetting. To overcome this, add about 1 teaspoon of a wetting agent (any liquid dishwashing detergent will do) to each gallon of solution. Materials must be dry before treatment. Completely wet them with the solution. Do not apply solutions to materials that water would injure. If in doubt, test a small area of the material before treating it.

Preparing Solutions

Four solutions are described on the next two pages. Choose the one best suited to the material you wish to treat. Commercial grades of the chemicals will give as good results as the more expensive reagent or pharmaceutical grades.

FORMULA 1

Boric acid	3 ounces
Borax	7 ounces
Hot water	2 quarts

Dissolve boric acid by making a paste with a small quantity of water. Add this and the borax to the hot water. Stir until the solution is clear. Warm the solution if it becomes cloudy or jellylike from standing.

Fabrics treated with Formula 1 do not flame when exposed to fire. The glow will last about 30 seconds. Materials treated with it may lose their flame resistance in time. Retreat within a year.

Do not use Formula 1 on rayon or resin-treated cotton—sometimes called crushproof, wrinkleproof, or wash-and-wear. For the latter, use Formula 3.

FORMULA 2

Borax	6 ounces
Diammonium phosphate	6 ounces
Water	2 quarts

Add borax and diammonium phosphate to water. Stir until solution is clear. This formula is less flame retardant than Formula 1, but is more glow retardant. It slightly reduces the strength of treated fabrics if not washed out within 3 or 4 months.

FORMULA 3

Diammonium phosphate	12 ounces
Water	2 quarts

Add chemical to water. Stir until solution is clear. Use this formula for resin-treated cotton or rayon fabrics. This formula is less flame retardant than Formula 1, but has good glow retardant properties. It has a greater tendency than Formulas 1 or 2 to weaken a treated fabric if the fabric is stored for long periods.

FORMULA 4

Ammonium sulfate	13 ounces
Water	2 quarts
Household ammonia	small amount

Add ammonium sulfate to water. Stir until solution is clear. Then add enough ammonia to give a faint odor. If fertilizer-grade ammonium sulfate is used, the solution may not be clear. In this case, strain through a cloth before using.

This formula has good glow-retardant properties, but is less flame retardant than Formula 1. It slightly reduces the strength of treated fabrics.

Ironing Treated Fabrics

After applying the solution, allow the fabrics to become nearly dry before ironing. Do not redampen with water. Use a moderately hot iron. If the fabric is wet, or the iron is too hot, the solution may stick to the iron. If it does, wipe the iron with a damp cloth.

FLAMEPROOFING PAPER AND PAPERBOARD

To flameproof paper and paper products in which afterglow may be a problem, the National Bureau of Standards suggests formulas containing diammonium phosphate, a chemical that has superior glow-inhibiting qualities. Here is a suitable formula devised by the Army Quartermaster Corps:

Water	13.2 gallons or 110 parts by weight
Borax	7 pounds or 7 parts by weight
Boric acid	3 pounds or 3 parts by weight
Diammonium phosphate	5 pounds or 5 parts by weight

Heat the water and dissolve the chemicals in it by stirring continuously as they are added. Cool it to lukewarm temperature before application. The addition of about 1/10 part of a wetting agent (liquid dishwashing detergent will do) will help it penetrate the paper. Application may be made by immersion, brush, or spray methods. Enough should be applied, however, so that the weight of the material when dry will have increased about 15 percent. Colors are not ordinarily affected by this solution more than they are by wetting with water, but it is best to test for color fastness before applying it.

The following formula is also effective for paper products:

Diammonium phosphate	10 pounds or 10 parts by weight
Ammonium sulfate	5 pounds or 5 parts by weight
Water	12 gallons or 100 parts by weight

(Continued)

Mix chemicals and water, cool, add wetting agent, and apply as suggested for the formula above. In humid locations, it may be advisable to include 4 or 5 parts of a soluble mildew inhibitor, such as sodium benzoate, sodium propionate, or one of the proprietary fungicides.

MAKING CHRISTMAS TREES FIRE RETARDANT

Although natural Christmas trees cannot be made absolutely fireproof, they can be made flame resistant by several methods.

According to the Forest Products Laboratory of the Department of Agriculture, the most practical, satisfactory, and convenient method of those it has tried is to keep the tree moist, and its needles from discoloring and falling, by standing it in water. The procedure is as follows:

1. Obtain a tree that has been cut as recently as possible.
2. Cut off the end of the trunk diagonally at least 1 inch above the original cut end. Stand the tree at once in a container of water and keep the water level above the cut surface during the entire time the tree is in the house. If the tree is not set up for several days, it should be kept standing in water meanwhile in a cool place.

If started in time, this treatment will prevent the needles from drying out and becoming flammable, and it will also keep them fresh and green. In addition, it will retard the fall of needles of such species as spruce, which loses needles very easily in contrast to balsam fir, which retains its needles even after the branches have become dry.

Keeping Trees Moist and Green

A slightly more complex treatment that requires, in addition to water, several household products plus a trade brand of natural horticultural iron, is claimed by the developers to keep Christmas trees greener and moist longer than water alone. Here is the formula:

Green Garde micronized iron	¼ cup
Hot water	1 gallon
Light corn syrup (Karo, etc.)	2 cups
Sodium hypochlorite solution (Clorox, Purex, Rose-X)	4 teaspoons

Stir micronized iron (obtainable at florists, hardware and garden supply stores) into the hot water. Mix in corn syrup and bleach (the latter helps prevent the formation of algae). Saw about 1 inch from the bottom of the tree trunk to remove clotted resins and to level the base. Pound the base of the trunk with a hammer or axe to crush the fibers. Stand the tree in a holder that holds at least a gallon and pour in the solution. Add tap water daily to keep it filled.

Fire-Retardant Coatings

Additional protection against fire can be provided by the use of fire-retardant coatings if the retention of the natural color of the foliage is unimportant. Here are formulations for three simple ones:

1. (Produces a shiny transparent colorless coating)

	Parts by volume
Sodium silicate (water glass)	9
Water, containing a wetting agent, such as Dreft or Vel, or some liquid dishwashing detergent (1 teaspoon per quart)	1

2. (Produces a cream-colored coating; may be tinted with household dyes)

	Parts by weight
Sodium silicate (water glass)	31
China clay	41
Water (containing wetting agent as in Formula 1)	28

3. (Produces a frosty white coating; may be tinted with household dyes)

	Parts by weight
Water	70
Sodium alginate	1
Monoammonium phosphate	25
China clay	4

To prepare this formula, heat the water to about 180° F, add the sodium alginate, and stir until a uniform gel is obtained. Then add the monoammonium phosphate, heating gently and stirring occasionally until it has dissolved. Finally add the china clay wet with a little water to a thick paste, and stir until it is uniformly distributed throughout the gel.

Applying the Coatings

To appreciably reduce the fire hazard, a heavy coating must be applied of any of the above formulations. One coat will greatly reduce the tendency for flames to spread; two coats are even more effective. Coatings may be applied by either dipping or spraying. It may be necessary to thin the first formula for spray application, in which case more applications are necessary.

Silver effects can be had by spraying an aluminum paint on trees coated with either Formula 2 or Formula 3.

Extra Fire Precautions

In addition to these treatments, all possible precautions against fire should be taken around the Christmas tree, including the elimination of defective electrical connections and the avoidance of the accumulation of combustible decorations on or beneath the tree. The tree should also be placed so that its accidental burning would not ignite curtains or other combustible furnishings or trap the occupants of a room or building.

FIRE-RETARDANT COATINGS FOR WOOD

Many coating materials protect wood against fire in varying degrees. The amount of protection provided depends on the amount and thoroughness of the application and the severity of fire exposure. Most preparations are of value primarily for interior use and are not durable when exposed to weather.

The following have shown good results in laboratory tests:

	Parts by weight
Basic carbonate white lead	41
Raw linseed oil	22.8
Borax	32
Turpentine	3.6
Japan drier	0.6

First work the white lead into part of the oil. Then add the rest of the oil and the other ingredients and stir in thoroughly.

Three or four thick coats, or approximately 1 gallon per 125 square feet of surface, are needed for good protection.

Here is a water-base paint that blisters under fire to produce a non-burning insulating coating:

	Parts by weight
Sodium silicate solution (40–42° Baumé)	11
Kaolin	15
Water	10

Again, three or four thick coats are necessary with four coats covering about 100 square feet.

FIRE-RESISTANT PAINT

No paint can make a surface absolutely fireproof, but this one has proved useful in retarding fire:

	Pounds
Sodium silicate, granular	1½
Sodium aluminate	½
Hydrated lime	½
Powdered asbestos	2

The sodium silicate should be in the form of the granular metasilicate. Dissolve this, along with the aluminate and the lime, by stirring in the smallest possible amount of water. Then stir in the asbestos and add enough additional water to make the paint easy to apply. Dry color may be added if desired. Apply at least two coats.

HOME SECURITY

Your home cannot be made completely secure against a determined professional criminal. On the other hand, a criminal's determination depends on his evaluation of what he can get for the risks he has to take. While the professional carefully evaluates probable rewards and risks before making a move, the amateur tends to act upon what seems to be an opportunity to get anything. The professional aims for homes that promise a reasonable "haul"; the amateur hopes to get "something." With the rising trend of theft by amateurs, almost no house or apartment is too humble not to be a possible target for a burglar.

The security of your home and possessions depends upon the deterrents you place in the way of the prospective housebreaker. You can take two basic types of measures to deter a criminal from entering:

1. Increase his risk.
2. Reduce his idea of what he can get.

Don't Encourage Burglars

Remember, a burglar is taking a gamble whenever he goes on a job. Like any smart gambler, though, he likes to have the odds in his favor. You increase the odds in his favor when you show him what he can get and how much difficulty he will have in getting it. It is a form of protection to keep this kind of information from him. A professional burglar will go to elaborate measures to case a prospective victim to determine what his loot can be and what methods he must use to be successful. Even an amateur may do a fair job of casing before he makes his move. Any burglar, however, picks his intended objectives on the basis of some indication that it will be a worthwhile effort.

A burglary can be well planned or it can be a case of taking advantage of an opportunity and acting with little or no planning and preparation. A phony meter reader, walking off with a TV set after the housewife leaves him for chores in another room, may consider it worth his while for the $100 he could get from the fence. On the other hand, if he sees more articles of value about, he may leave the TV and pay attention to the locks and other security measures with the intent to return when he can get everything of value without being disturbed. If the housewife had asked for identification and/or stayed with the man, the TV set would have been safe and she would have restricted his opportunity to case her home.

There are several things you can do to avoid encouraging burglary:

1. Don't display valuables, especially to strangers. It may help your ego to show them off, but it can also help you lose them. If you display them or can't avoid it, your security measures must be that much more complete. Mark any item of value for identification. A simple diamond-point stylus will provide a permanent marking on any hard material. A would-be burglar will recognize that you have reduced its value when he goes to fence it. Moreover you have added to his risk should he be caught with identifiable stolen goods.

2. Whenever possible, keep strangers out of your home. If they must be allowed entry, stay with them. Restrict their access to those areas of the home where there is a legitimate need for them to be.
3. Request identification of workmen, servicemen, salesmen, etc., and make a note of their names, company, and appearance. Be obvious in letting them know you are doing it.
4. Do not make announcements in public places about your possessions, times you are away from home, planned trips, or even your regular sleeping times.
5. Do not give publications stories about your intended trips, valuable collections, expensive possessions, or any other facts that might cause a burglar to choose you as a prospective victim.
6. Never leave your doors unlocked even when you are at home. Burglars can work amazingly fast and be in and out before you know it, day or night.
7. Put your car in the garage and close the door. Burglars use your car as a guide to your affluence and whether or not you are home. If the car is always behind closed doors, they don't know whether it is there or not and whether you are there or not.
8. Be sure that when you are taking out or putting away valuables there is no one around to see you. Check for a man working on the roof next door, a painter, a man repairing the TV antenna, servants, repairmen, and the like. If strangers are around, don't do anything to draw attention to where you have valuables. The stranger may not be a burglar, but he could pass on the information intentionally or unintentionally.
9. Keep lights on upstairs even when everybody is downstairs. Burglars are as safe in a darkened upper story as they are in an empty house.
10. When you have a party, don't put the guests' furs and purses in an unwatched room. The noise of the party attracts the criminal and covers his activities.

Discourage the Burglar

Whether the burglar knows what possessions you have or only guesses, he can be discouraged from trying to get them. If he has to take too many chances, he will look for an easier target. Your objective is to convince him that your house is too risky to bother with. In doing this you are being obvious. You want him to know that you have taken security measures, but you don't necessarily want him to know exactly what they are. You want to keep him guessing.

The best deterrent is a truly good security system: good locks, alarms, lighting, and security habits. These he will recognize; it's his business to do so. Make sure he does.

1. If you have a burglar-prevention system, advertise that you do. But don't advertise what kind; you are only assisting him if you let him know. Remember, the professional can find ways around most systems if he finds it worthwhile. Use a sign that says "Electronically Protected" but don't use one that names the system. Use a sign that says "Security Lighting System" but not the type or manufacturer. The burglar knows what is on the market and he knows which are a problem to him and which are not.
2. Use good locks. The housebreaker recognizes them. He will not spend the time to overcome a good lock unless he feels he has a lot of time and a lot to gain.
3. Don't give him a place to hide. Keep the accesses to your home exposed to anyone who might be around. Light is his enemy. He is taking a dangerous chance in moving on premises where his movements can be seen. He is taking an even greater chance in working to gain entry where he is exposed for any period of time. Light any access to your home. Use timers or photoelectric switches to ensure that the lights are on during all periods of darkness. Do not allow shrubbery, trees, or other growth to provide cover for the burglar day or night.
4. Don't let the burglar know when you are home and when you are away. Make it appear that you are always home—or may be. Stop the delivery of newspapers, milk, mail, and other items if you are away even for a couple of days, or at least have a trusted neighbor take them in for you. Alert both the neighbors and the police of your absence. Criminals are dissuaded by squad cars slowing to check a residence they are casing or by neighbors checking on unusual cars or callers stopping at a house. Light the interior of your house. A light in the bathroom may cause a burglar to be unsure if anyone is home, but not for long. Do not use small nightlights. Use the normal intensity of light that would be used if the house was in use. Do not leave lights on only where it can be seen that no one is present. Photoelectrically controlled lights can provide protection. Using two or more timers to simulate a normal routine of lighting is best. Placing the TV and radio on timers adds to the effect. Timers can be set differently each time you leave, thereby avoiding a recognizable pattern. Since household timers are quite inexpensive and require no skill to use, you can afford to use them in every room for lights, TV, radio, and even tape recorders with recorded conversations. Do not put the lights and a TV or radio on

one timer. Separate timers can activate the lights, then the sound—and have the sound go off, then the lights. This is a simulation of a more natural routine. The flexibility of these simple-to-use timers provides an effective and economical burglar deterrent.

To design your own timer settings, sit down and make notes of typical routines your family might follow under normal circumstances. Then observe what patterns of usage of lights and sound appliances the routines create. Figure out how many appliances would have to be controlled by timers to simulate a normal day in your home and what their settings would have to be. If your family's habits produce an overly complicated situation, you may need to simplify the pattern you set up with the timers. Take care not to oversimplify, however, and lessen the effectiveness of the timers. Saving the cost of an adequate timing system could cost you more if, in doing so, you tip off a burglar that the home is unoccupied. Change the timers from time to time to produce the effect of different family routines unless your family is unusually rigid in its habits.

5. Be suspicious and be obvious about it. The legitimate salesman, serviceman, or meter reader will not be offended because you require identification or jot down the license number of his auto parked near your home. Should they ask, a simple explanation will satisfy them. On the other hand, if you are being cased, it is unlikely that the criminal will go any farther and risk becoming a suspect to be investigated.

Make Entry Difficult

No matter how good or poor a lock is, it is worthless if it is not locked. Whatever kind of lock you have, use it—day or night—whether you are at home or away.

There is no lock that can't be opened by the burglar who is motivated to get it opened. Some locks can be opened in seconds by an amateur with a tool as simple as a plastic credit card. There are others that would take the most accomplished professional hours to "make," even with the most sophisticated tools of his trade. Your valuables probably don't justify the expense of Fort Knox protection, but they almost certainly justify the expense of locks that can be opened faster with a key than without one.

The most common type of lock—and the most vulnerable to attack—is the spring-latch variety, also called the key-in-knob model. A spring-loaded latch engages automatically and is locked by the doorknob.

Some spring-latch locks have what is called a "dead latch," which is a small metal bar or plunger to automatically lock the latch in place when it goes into the strike. Without this plunger, the National Bureau of Standards says, "it can be a simple matter to stick a thin piece of metal or a credit card between the door and the frame and open the latch bolt."

For additional protection, your best bet is a good deadbolt lock. A deadbolt is a straight bar, usually rectangular, that is squared off at the end and locked only by turning a key or latch. The deadbolt should be at least five-eighths of an inch square, made of steel or solid brass. It should stick out of the lock by a minimum of half an inch.

Equally secure is a dropbolt lock. The bolt in this case is vertical rather than horizontal; it interlocks with strong rings on a specially constructed plate.

The chain lock, allowing you to open the door a few inches and check visitors without undoing the lock, is popular in many areas, but it should not be used as the primary source of security. Once the door is partly open, the chain may be overcome by force or snipped with a wire cutter. A peephole is better for screening callers.

Even the strongest, safest locks won't hold weak doors securely. Hollow-core, wood-veneer flush doors and cheap paneled doors are a breeze to break through; hardboard-faced flush doors and better paneled ones are stronger, but solid or metal-faced doors are safer still. Make sure the door fits snugly in the frame and that the lock's bolt protrudes as far as possible into the frame.

If your door has glass panes in or near it, consider double-cylinder locks, which are opened with a key from inside, too, so a thief can't break the glass, reach in and open the lock. And where a burglar is most likely to come in a window or through a smashed-in door panel, use of double-cylinder locks will limit his haul to what he can take out that way, too.

There is still another way to protect glazed doors; substitute impact-resistant polycarbonate (such as Lexan or Plexiglas) for the glass, or cover the glass with polycarbonate held by extra moldings.

To protect your lock from outside attack, use one whose cylinder is in the door itself, not in the knob (which can be pried off), and cover it with a cylinder guard, bolted through the door.

Windows are a very vulnerable entry to your home. While you can't eliminate breaking the glass for entry (although polycarbonate panes add extra protection), breaking the glass provides extra hazards and trouble for the housebreaker. He would rather not do it. Common window locks can be opened with a butter knife or simple auger tool. If you are going to protect your doors, you owe it to yourself to install window locks that are reasonably burglar proof. Since windows provide ventilation as well as light, be sure you can lock your windows in a partially opened position without leaving room enough for a person to slip in or to reach through and operate the lock. Make sure the windows are not loose in their casements so that they can be easily removed. Particularly vulnerable windows, such as basement windows, may justify bars or grilles (which can be ornamental), but the locks on these should not be neglected.

Commercial hardware is not your only choice, either. Some standard do-it-yourself tricks are described below; you may be able to come up with others.

1. A hole drilled through the lower window sash and a steel bolt or rod can provide a great deal of security against window break-ins. Drill a ½- or ¾-inch hole completely through the lower sash, raise the window about 3 or 4 inches, and then drill through the lower window sash hole into the upper sash. Attach the bolt to the window casing with a long wood screw and a short length of chain. This arrangement permits the window to be raised slightly for air at night without the danger of someone opening it completely while you are asleep. The bolt passing through the lower sash into the upper sash prevents someone from raising the window rapidly against the bolt, breaking the window frame, and gaining entry. (*Caution:* Do not use a wooden dowel, as it may shrink in warm weather and expand in wet thus becoming loose, falling out, or weakening. Use only a steel bolt or rod.)
2. A simple piece of 2×4-inch lumber, with some felt or sponge rubber glued on one end and a metal T screwed to the other end, can provide protection from forced entry through a hall door. The piece of 2×4 can be sawed to the required length, to reach from the closed door to the wall in the hallway. The felt on one end of the 2×4 prevents it from damaging the wall while the metal T on the other end prevents it from slipping out from under the door. Although this bar is obviously unsightly, it is used only during the night or when you are away from home and can leave the house through some other exit. It is simple but extremely effective. When this bar is in place, the door cannot be opened without a complete break-in.
3. This same device can be constructed to work where there is not a wall a short distance across from the doorway. Simply cut the 2×4 ends at 45-degree angles to fit across to a corner wall. Install a regular doorstop at this point along the wall to prevent the 2×4 from slipping. This will give some additional security.

4. Sliding glass doors offer an inviting entryway for burglars. A simple piece of 1×2 or steel rod can be cut and placed in tracks to keep the door from opening, even if the lock is picked or broken. The door can't be opened until the rod is removed. Since there is a danger that a steel rod might accidentally break the glass, a 1×2-inch strip of wood or a broomstick is usually recommended.
5. Aluminum rods with crutch tips can be used for a similar type of protection where wood sliding doors are used. The aluminum rod makes it impossible for the sliding doors to be opened until it is removed. One-inch round head screws can be screwed into the edge of each door to provide holding power to prevent the aluminum rod from slipping out of place.

It is important to remember that increasing the security of windows and doors can compromise fire safety. Any opening that is part of a fire-escape route must be secured in such a way that the security measures can be quickly bypassed or overridden from the inside in the event of fire. A deadbolt lock opened from both outside and inside by a key gives safety from intrusion, but could cost a life if it interferes with quick escape in a fire emergency. For fire safety, it is best to install "panic-proof" locks that open if you twist the inside knob either way—a feature found on many of the better locks.

BURGLAR ALARMS

There are many types of alarms available. Most are electrically controlled. Like locks, alarms are not unbeatable, but they give the burglar one more problem. To be effective, they must be adequately designed to start with and they must work. A label showing that the alarm is listed by Underwriters Laboratories Inc. indicates that sample alarms have met UL standards.

All burglar or security alarms are made up of three basic parts: the detectors or sensors, the control unit, and the alarm itself. The detectors or sensors are electronic or electromagnetic devices to register the presence or action of an intruder. The more common types follow.

Switch Sensors

Electromagnetic devices installed at all entry points that can be reached from the ground. The alarm is triggered when a door or window is opened.

Pressure Mats

Used to protect specific areas. The mats can be hidden under a carpet or rug in a frequently traveled area or near an item of value such as a television set. When someone steps on the mat or exerts other pressure, the alarm is triggered.

Ultrasonic Motion Detectors

Devices that fill the room with sound waves too high for most humans to hear. Any movement in the room disturbs the pattern and sounds the alarm. (*Note:* Some people and most animals are bothered by the high-pitched sounds, so check these sensors at home before buying.)

Infrared Photoelectric Sensors

Project an infrared light beam between two points. Any interruption of the beam triggers the alarm.

The sensors can be connected to the control unit by direct wiring or a wireless system. Either method is effective, according to the Bureau of Standards.

There are two types of alarms, local and remote. The local alarm is the least expensive and is heard only at your home. Its effectiveness depends on the intruder being frightened away or on the neighbors' hearing the sound and calling the police.

The remote alarm transmits a signal to a location away from your home and usually involves a monthly maintenance charge. There are several models of remote alarms:

Automatic Caller

Sends a prerecorded message or signal over telephone lines to someone you choose, such as a relative or an answering service. Its reliability depends on someone answering the call. You will have to check with the telephone company to make sure the system meets its specifications. Do not direct your alarm to the local police department without prior approval.

Direct Connect

Transmits the alarm signal directly to the police department. This type of service provides very good protection, but frequently is not available for the private home owner.

Central Station

Sends the alarm to a private security company that monitors the system, notifies the police, and sends guards to your home.

Make sure pets are removed from protected areas once the system is activated. Do not demonstrate the system to friends just to show it off. Be careful when installing sensors. Some sensors may react to changes in temperature or humidity. The sound of a telephone bell may cause an ultrasonic alarm to send a false signal. Finally, do not operate your alarm on the same electrical circuit as kitchen appliances or your heating or cooling system. The cyclical operation of these appliances may trigger an alarm.

If the manufacturer's instructions are carefully followed, the various alarms can be installed by the average do-it-yourselfer. But obey the law. Be sure the system meets local codes and ordinances and that you have gotten necessary approvals.

Alarms, like locks, are not worth the expense unless you use them. There is a tendency, because of inconvenience, to stop using these systems after a while, especially when you are at home or when you will be gone for only a short while. Burglars do not operate only at night or only in empty homes. Nor do they need more than a short while to do their job.

There is one alarm system that is effective and reliable yet is not likely to become defective—a four-legged one. A watch dog does not have to be a large attack dog to do its job. Attack dogs are dangerous to have around a normal home situation. A watch dog, however, with its bark and possible bite is a very effective deterrent. Training is an important part of its effectiveness. It should bark at strangers entering the yard or coming to the home, but not bark and whine simply because it is left alone. It should be trained so that it can be given the run of the house without damaging it. If the dog must be chained or locked in the basement, its value is diminished. When purchasing a dog for this purpose, it is best to buy a grown dog whose temperament and training can be judged. A puppy's temperament cannot be assessed accurately and the training is likely to be haphazard.

IN CASE YOU ARE BURGLARIZED

Put a personalized identification (such as your social security number) on everything of value that you own. This will enable the authorities to identify any items they recover not only to return them to you but as evidence of their being stolen goods. Moreover, a fence will pay a lot less or nothing for goods that can be identified as stolen. This in turn may dissuade a burglar from taking them because he recognizes their loss in value to him.

List everything of value, including its description, serial number, and other identification markings.

Supply the police with any information you have noted as to suspicious callers, automobiles, phone calls, etc. You may be able to provide a valuable lead.

If you are home when a burglar calls, do nothing to expose yourself to danger. While most burglars are unarmed, they can become desperate when caught. Any of their tools can become a lethal weapon. It is best to leave them alone and make no move to stop them. Your valuables are not more important than your life. Remain calm and notice carefully anything about the individual that may give a clue to the police.

15

First Aid and Safety

PRINCIPLES OF FIRST AID

First aid is the immediate care given to anyone injured or taken suddenly ill. It may be the only care needed, as in the case of minor injuries. Or it may be temporary care given until medical help can be obtained.

The best preparation is a formal course in first aid, such as those offered by the Red Cross. A course, or guidebooks such as those offered by the Red Cross, will teach you what to do as well as *what not to do* (which in many cases is more important). As a basis, though, this chapter offers useful guidelines that can help you save a life, prevent further injury, and even limit the chances for injury-producing accidents.

WHEN IMMEDIATE ACTION IS CRITICAL

You must react promptly if you encounter any or all of the following at the scene of an accident:

1. Danger of further injury (thus the need for emergency evacuation).
2. A victim not breathing or lacking a pulse.

3. Severe bleeding.
4. A case of poisoning.

While you are administering first aid in these instances, direct someone to call for emergency medical help and arrange to transport the victim to a medical facility.

Emergency Evacuation

If the victim's life is endangered from an explosion, poisonous gas, electrical contact, or other immediate peril, he should be moved to a safer place. But first consider whether you can move the victim without being killed, injured, or overcome yourself. When moving an injured person, take care not to cause further injuries. Always move the victim lengthwise rather than sidewise. Avoid doubling the victim up. Once the victim is in a safe place, tend to his breathing, bleeding, poisoning, and shock.

Breathing

If the victim *appears to be unconscious,* do this:

1. Check for consciousness by tapping his shoulders and shouting for his attention.
2. If there is no response, check for breathing.
   a. If he is not breathing, open his airway by rotating his head back with one of your hands on his forehead and the other hand placed under the back of his head and neck. This will open his airway.
   b. Place your ear next to the victim's mouth and nose—listen, feel, and look for breathing. If the victim is now breathing, keep his airway open.

If he is still *not* breathing:

1. Pinch his nose with your fingers.
2. Place your mouth over his mouth, forming a tight seal.
3. Blow four quick breaths into his mouth. (If an obstruction prevents passage of air, remove the obstruction as described in the section "Choking," pages 494–496.)
4. Check with your fingers for a carotid pulse located on either side of the victim's Adam's apple. Use your middle and index finger to check pulse for at least five seconds.
   a. If the victim *has a pulse* and is *still not breathing, begin doing mouth-to-mouth resuscitation.*

b. *If the victim has a pulse and is breathing, monitor both pulse and breathing and get emergency medical help.*

c. *If the victim has no pulse and is not breathing* begin CPR (Cardio-Pulmonary Resuscitation), if you have been trained to do so. This basically involves applying rhythmic pressure to the breastbone with the heel of the hand while alternately administering mouth-to-mouth resuscitation. But to do this effectively, you must be trained by an instructor and have practiced on a manikin. Instruction is available from local chapters of the Red Cross and the Heart Association.

MOUTH-TO-MOUTH RESUSCITATION. Breathe into an adult victim's mouth at a rate of 12 times per minute. To monitor effectiveness of your efforts, watch the victim's chest rise with your breaths and fall as you remove your mouth. With a child, make your breaths shallower, at a rate of 20 per minute.

Continue mouth-to-mouth efforts until the victim begins breathing on his own or until qualified help arrives, or until you can no longer continue. Remember, many victims are revived only after prolonged resuscitation effort.

Bleeding

There are two major categories of wounds: (1) open wounds, with broken skin, and (2) closed wounds, with injury to underlying tissues and no break in the skin.

Open wounds. These can cause heavy loss of blood and, if they do, you need to act quickly to control blood loss and to prevent contamination of the wound.

1. Control the bleeding:
   a. Apply direct pressure with a clean cloth or, if necessary, with your bare hand over the wound.
   b. Elevate the injury while maintaining direct pressure. (But *do not* elevate a limb if you suspect a bone fracture.)
   c. If direct pressure and elevation fail to control bleeding of a limb, then also apply pressure to the appropriate artery to slow blood flow.
      (1) For the arm, apply pressure to the brachial artery between the two muscles along the inside of bone of the upper arm. (Use the flat of your fingers.)
      (2) For the leg, use the femoral artery, located at the leg-hip joint, on top of the pelvis bone. (Use the heel of your hand to slow blood flow.)

BRACHIAL ARTERY

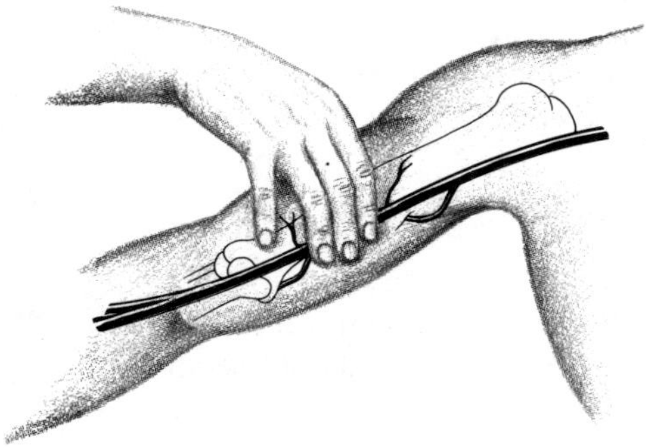

FEMORAL ARTERY

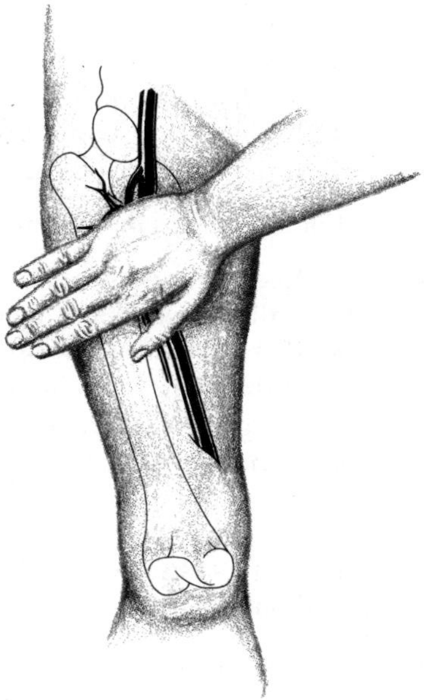

d. If pressure to the artery (combined with direct pressure to the wound and elevation of the limb) fails to stop *heavy flow* of blood, a tourniquet may be needed to prevent death due to blood loss. (*Caution:* A tourniquet is a dangerous device; once applied it should not be loosened or removed except on the advice of a physician. A tourniquet may save a life but it also risks the victim's limb.)

CLOSED WOUNDS. There is little you can do for severe internal wounds, except to make the victim comfortable and obtain emergency medical help fast. *Never* offer fluids to a person if you suspect severe internal injuries. For small closed wounds (bruises that will turn black and blue), apply a cold pack to prevent swelling.

Poisoning

INGESTED POISONS. When poison has been taken through the mouth, do this:

For a *conscious* victim:

1. Dilute the poison with milk or water.

2. Call a poison control center or other medical center for advice. (Be prepared to give this information: amount of poison, victim's age and weight.)
3. Save the poison container label for identification of the poison by medical people.
4. If the victim vomits, save the vomit for laboratory analysis.
5. If the victim loses consciousness, keep his airway open.

For an *unconscious* victim:

1. Keep his airway open.
2. Call for emergency medical help.
3. If the victim is not breathing, give mouth-to-mouth resuscitation. If the victim also has no pulse, a *trained* person should begin cardio-pulmonary resuscitation (CPR).
4. *Do not* give fluids. *Do not* induce vomiting.
5. Save the poison container label for medical people.

INHALED POISONS. If a victim has been overcome by gases, such as carbon monoxide:

1. Remove him to fresh air. Be careful not to be overcome by the gases yourself.
2. If the victim is *not breathing but has a pulse,* give mouth-to-mouth resuscitation.
3. If the victim is *not breathing and has no pulse,* have a *trained* person begin cardio-pulmonary resuscitation (CPR).
4. Obtain emergency medical help.

POISONING FROM STINGS AND BITES (INSECTS, MARINE LIFE). Prevention is vital, especially if you are allergic to specific stings and bites.

What to do:

1. Check for emergency medical identification (bracelet, necklace, and/or card in wallet), indicating an allergic reaction.
2. For minor reactions to bites and stings:
    a. Apply cold packs.
    b. Use soothing lotions such as calamine.
    c. Remove the stinger, if possible.
3. For severe reactions:
    a. If the victim stops breathing, give mouth-to-mouth resuscitation. If the victim also has no pulse, a trained person should begin cardio-pulmonary resuscitation (CPR).

b. Apply a constricting band between the site of the sting and the heart. (*Caution:* Do not apply tightly; tighten only until you can still slip a finger under the band.)
c. Keep the sting or bite area below the level of the victim's heart.
d. Transport the victim to a medical facility as soon as possible.

SNAKE BITES. Prevention of snake bites is the key. In snake season, move with a wary eye and wear protective clothing. Do not step or reach where a snake might be hidden from view.

Of the many kinds of snakes, few are poisonous. And often, bites from poisonous varieties introduce little or no poison into the victim. Still, all bites can lead to infection and should receive prompt medical attention.

What to do:

1. Immobilize the bitten limb and keep it below the level of the heart.
2. Try to identify the type of snake without endangering yourself.
3. Transport the victim to a hospital immediately, while keeping him calm and inactive.
4. If you notice swelling, discoloration, moderate pain, rapid pulse, weakness, nausea, or shortness of breath, apply a constricting band 2 to 4 inches above the area. (Tighten only until you can still slip a finger underneath.)
5. If there are serious reactions such as rapid swelling and numbness, severe pain, slurred speech, shock, or convulsions:
   a. Apply a constricting band 2 to 4 inches above the swelling, if you haven't already done so in response to milder symptoms (again, just tight enough so you can slip a finger underneath).
   b. Make a ½-inch long cut just through the skin over the suspected venom deposit. (*Caution:* Cuts should be made along the long axis of the limb to avoid cutting blood vessels. *Do not* make "X" cuts.)
   c. Apply a snake-bite suction cup or use your mouth to draw venom for at least 30 minutes.
6. If you *cannot* reach a hospital within 4 to 5 hours and *any* symptoms develop, follow procedures described in Item 5, above.

CONTACT WITH POISONOUS PLANTS. Contact with many plants can cause allergic reactions characterized by some or all of the following: itching, redness, rash, headache, and fever. More serious reactions include intense burning, blisters, fever, and severe illness. For relief, do this:

1. Remove contaminated clothing. Wash the affected area thoroughly with soap and water. Apply rubbing alcohol.
2. Apply a soothing skin lotion (such as calamine) if the rash is mild.
3. If the victim has a severe reaction, get medical assistance.

Preventing Plant Poisoning. If it is necessary to work among poisonous plants, you should wear protective clothing. Some protection also may be obtained by first applying a protective lotion. After exposure to plants, wash off the lotion thoroughly with soap and water. Contaminated clothing and tools should also be washed with soap and water to prevent later spread of the poison.

Shock

Shock is a depressed state of all body functions. This is a serious condition and should be watched for in all accidents or injuries. Shock can kill even though the injury may not seem to be life-threatening or even severe. A victim in shock will be weak, and will have a weak rapid pulse and a high breathing rate. The skin may be pale, moist, clammy.

1. Give all necessary first aid for breathing failure, bleeding, or other injury.
2. Keep the victim lying down.
3. Maintain a normal body temperature.
4. Get medical help.

In general, keeping the victim flat will improve his blood circulation. If the victim does not have a neck or back injury, or head or chest injury, raise his feet 8 to 12 inches. Or if the victim has slight difficulty in breathing you can raise the head and shoulders. If medical help is going to be delayed, fluids by mouth will help. (*Caution:* Never give fluids if the victim is unconscious, or if he is vomiting or likely to vomit.) Give a warm solution of salt, soda, and water (1 level teaspoon of salt and ½ level teaspoon of baking soda to each quart of water). Give an adult about ¼ pint (4 ounces) every 15 minutes—less for children.

Choking

Often referred to as a "cafe coronary" because it is frequently mistaken for a heart attack in dining establishments, choking is the sixth leading cause of accidental deaths. And it is the leading cause of accidental death among small children.

COMMON SYMPTOMS. The victim may grasp at his throat. He may be unable to speak, breathe, or cough. He may look terrified and display frantic motions. He may soon turn blue in the face and lose consciousness. By contrast, heart-attack victims may be able to talk or breathe at first. Also, consider that most choking incidents occur when the victim has been eating. If the victim is conscious, you may be able to confirm that he is choking simply by asking him to nod if he is choking.

What to do:

Conscious victim with a complete airway obstruction:

1. Bend him at the waist (seated or standing) and apply four sharp back blows to his spine between the shoulder blades with the heel of your hand.
2. Reach in front of victim, placing your fist thumbside against the victim's abdomen, slightly above the navel and below the tip of the breastbone. Then with your other hand clasped over your fist, administer four quick upward thrusts. These thrusts should be firm enough to force out air from the lungs without being so violent that they injure ribs or other organs.
3. Repeat the back blows and abdominal thrusts until the obstruction is dislodged.

Unconscious victim:

1. With the victim on his back, open his airway by rotating his head back.
2. Attempt to give him four quick breaths, as in mouth-to-mouth resuscitation.
3. If unable to force your breaths into the victim's lungs, *again rotate his head.*
4. Attempt to give four more quick breaths.
5. If unable to get breaths into the victim's lungs this second time, do the following:
   a. As you kneel, quickly roll the front of the victim against your thighs and give four back blows in rapid succession.
   b. Roll the victim onto his back and apply four abdominal thrusts. (To do this, kneel at the victim's side. Use the heel of one hand, fingers pointing toward victim's head, and place the other hand on top, midway between the navel and tip of the breastbone.)
   c. Lift the victim's chin and tongue with one hand and sweep the index finger of your other hand deep into the victim's throat, attempting to hook and dislodge the object.

d. If you do not succeed in clearing the object, repeat the steps you have performed: Attempt four quick breaths; deliver four back blows; administer four manual thrusts; perform finger probes until you can remove the obstruction and/or get air into the lungs.

For infants and small children, follow the above steps (for conscious or unconscious victims as appropriate). However, use less force so as not to cause injury.

BURNS

Chemical Burns

Flush the burned area well with water to dilute and remove the chemical. Do not try to neutralize acid with alkali or alkali with acid. This may do more harm than good. Check with a poison control center for further guidance.

If the chemical has gotten into a person's eye, flush the eye gently but thoroughly with water for at least 20 minutes. Do not use an eyecup. Cover the eye with a sterile compress and get medical attention. If an eye is badly burned, cover both eyes.

Heat Burns

Heat burns are given three classifications: first-degree burns, in which the skin is reddened; second-degree burns, in which skin is reddened and blistered; and third-degree burns, in which the skin and sometimes the underlying tissue is cooked or charred.

The danger to the body does not depend so much on the degree as on the extensiveness of a burn. The severity of a burn is related to the degree and area involved. So a mild burn over a large area can be more dangerous than a second-degree burn of small size. Shock is usually severe in burns over a large area. As a general rule, first-aid for burns involves relief of pain, reduction of the chance of contamination and consequent infection, and the treatment of shock.

If the burn is small, apply cold water to it until the pain is relieved, cover the burn with several sterile gauze pads, piled one on the other, and held in place by a lightly applied bandage. If the skin has broken blisters, do not use cold water but apply the gauze pads without any medication and without causing additional damage.

If the burn is large, and especially if the skin is charred, take extra care. Keep the person quiet and lying down to reduce chances of shock. Cut away clothing from burned area. To prevent contamination, wash your hands thoroughly with soap and water. Do not apply oil, ointment, antiseptic, or any other medication. Cover the burned area with half a dozen or more layers of sterile dry gauze. Treat for shock. Get the victim to a burn-care center as soon as possible.

Sunburn

Ointments and other suntan preparations should be used *only for prevention* of sunburns. If there is redness only, soak the burned area in cold water and cover it with dry sterile dressings. Give as much liquid as possible. Aspirin will help relieve the pain. For a severe sunburn, treat with cold water and get medical attention.

OTHER COMMON PROBLEMS

Cuts, Scratches

These are probably the most frequent home injury. No matter how superficial they may appear, they are potentially dangerous—germs may easily enter the body through the broken skin. They should be treated right away.

Before treating a cut or a scratch, wash your hands thoroughly. Using sterile gauze or a freshly laundered handkerchief or towel, wash the area around the cut or scratch with soap and water. Wash outward from the cut, then wash the cut itself, using soap, water, and sterile gauze. Try to get as much dirt out of the wound as you can. Cover the wound with a sterile compress and fasten in place with a bandage. On very small cuts and scratches, a combined compress and adhesive band will do.

If a cut or scratch has been properly treated, it should not become infected. Infection, however, may possibly show up several days later. Any of these signs is evidence: a reddened, painful area around the wound; pus and red streaks; swelling in the wounded area, chills and fever in the victim.

See a doctor right away if any of these signs appear.

Electric Shock

Symptoms of electric shock are unconsciousness, no breathing, face and lips blue, flushed, or pale, pulse weak or absent. There may also be burns in the area of contact.

If the person is still in contact with the current, the thing to do immediately is to break that contact without endangering yourself. If a switch or plug is near at hand, open the switch or pull the plug. If you cannot do this quickly enough, remove the wire or move the person with a dry wooden pole, rope, or other nonconducting object.

Begin artificial respiration immediately if breathing has stopped. After breathing has been restored, keep the person warm and quiet until professional help arrives. Treat for burns, if necessary, looking for where electricity entered the victim and exited. And treat for shock.

Eye Irritation

Don't try to remove anything more than a windblown object such as dust, dirt, or a small insect. If a particle does not come out readily, let a doctor remove it.

First, try to flush out the particle with warm water (have the person lie on his back and pour plenty of water into the eye; *don't use an eye-cup!*). Blinking during this bath may help. If this doesn't work, pull the eyelid away from the eyeball. With moist sterile gauze or cotton, lift out the particle.

Fainting

Hunger, shock, fatigue, poor ventilation—even seeing or hearing something pleasant or unpleasant—can cause fainting.

To revive a person who has fainted, place him on his back with his head lower than the rest of his body. Loosen all tight clothing and apply cold compresses to his face and forehead. If someone feels faint, have him sit down and put his head between his knees.

Heat Exhaustion

Early symptoms of heat exhaustion, which can be produced by exposure to heat either indoors or outdoors, are weariness, fatigue, and a feeling of faintness. Later the person may break out in profuse, but cold, perspiration; he may turn almost white; his temperature will be normal.

Remove the person to a cool place, have him lie down, and loosen his clothing. Cover him with a light blanket. If he is conscious, give him a saltwater solution (1 teaspoon of salt in ½ glass of water) every 15 minutes. Call a doctor immediately.

Heatstroke

Heatstroke is more serious than heat exhaustion. It demands immediate medical treatment.

The victim of heatstroke will have a fever up to 105° F or even higher. His pulse will be rapid and strong. His face will be flushed and his skin hot and dry. He may even lose consciousness.

Get the person out of the heat source and into a cooler area immediately. Have him lie on his back and remove as much clothing as possible. Apply cold compresses to his head. Cool his body by wrapping him in a sheet and pouring cold water on small portions at a time, or use cold cloths and cold packs. If a tub is available, place him in a tub of cold water. Get medical assistance as quickly as possible.

Nosebleeds

These may occur spontaneously as well as following injury to the nose. Children often have nosebleeds as the result of strenuous exercise, a cold, or high altitudes. In most cases, the bleeding is more annoying than serious.

Often, sitting quietly and leaning forward will stop the bleeding. If this doesn't do it, apply pressure directly at the site of bleeding. If bleeding persists insert into the bleeding nostril a clean pad of gauze (not absorbent cotton) and press firmly on the outside of the nostril. If the bleeding stops, leave the packing in place for a while. If bleeding continues seek medical attention.

Removing Foreign Objects

In small open wounds, wood splinters and glass fragments often remain in the surface tissues or in tissues just beneath the surface. As a rule, such objects irritate only the victim; they do not usually incapacitate a person or cause systemic body infection. They can cause infection, however, if they are not removed. Use tweezers sterilized over a flame or in boiling water to pull out any foreign matter from the surface tissues. Objects embedded just beneath the skin can be lifted out with the tip of a needle that has been sterilized in rubbing alcohol or in the heat of a flame. Foreign objects, regardless of size, that are embedded deeper in the tissues should be left for removal by a physician.

The fishhook is probably one of the more common types of foreign objects that may penetrate the skin. Often, only the point of the hook enters, not penetrating deeply enough to allow the barb to become effective; in this case, the hook can be removed easily by backing it out. If the fishhook goes deeper and the barb becomes embedded, the wisest course is to have a physician remove it. If medical aid is not available, remove the hook by pushing it through until the barb protrudes. Using a cutting tool, cut the hook either at the barb or at the shank and remove it. Cleanse the wound thoroughly and cover it with an adhesive compress. A physician should be consulted as soon as possible because of the possibility of infection, especially tetanus.

Some penetrating foreign objects, such as sticks and pieces of metal, may protrude loosely from the body or even be fixed, such as a stake in the ground or a wooden spike or metal rod of a fence on which the victim has become impaled. Under no circumstances should the victim be pulled loose from such an object. Obtain help at once, preferably from ambulance or rescue personnel who are equipped to handle the problem. Support the victim and the object to prevent movements that could cause further damage. If the object is fixed or protrudes more than a few inches from the body, it should be held carefully to avoid further damage, cut off at a distance from the skin, and left in place. To prevent further injury during transport of the victim, immobilize the protruding end with massive dressings. The victim should then be taken to the hospital without delay.

SAFETY IN THE SHOP

Safety is an important consideration in any shop, and certain safety rules should be stressed. The first one is to be sure that anyone working with hand or power tools is shop oriented, that he knows his way around the shop. Invite the entire family to join you in the planning and building of projects, but be sure you supervise their activity, especially when youngsters are involved.

Safety Rules

1. KNOW YOUR POWER TOOL. Read the owner's manual carefully. Learn each tool's application and limitations as well as the specific potential hazards peculiar to it.

2. GROUND ALL TOOLS. Most power tools are equipped with an approved three-conductor cord and a three-prong grounding-type plug to fit the proper grounding-type receptacle. The green conductor in the cord is the grounding wire. Never connect the green wire to a live terminal.

3. KEEP GUARDS IN PLACE. Use all the safety devices the tool provides. For example, a radial arm saw may have a "splitter" and "antikickback dogs." If you rip a board without them, you may get away with it—but you may not. The tool may hurl the ripping like a deadly spear. Too bad if anyone is standing in its path. A table saw can hurl things too, unless they are properly secured. A drill press has other tricks: it can grab work and become a battering windmill.

4. REMOVE ADJUSTING KEYS AND WRENCHES. Form a habit of checking to see that keys and adjusting wrenches are removed from a tool before turning it on.

5. KEEP WORK AREA CLEAN. Cluttered areas and benches invite accidents. Floor must not be slippery due to wax or sawdust.

6. AVOID DANGEROUS ENVIRONMENTS. Don't use power tools in damp or wet locations. Keep work area well lit. Provide adequate surrounding work space.

7. KEEP CHILDREN AWAY. All visitors should be kept a safe distance from the work area. Also make the workshop kidproof with padlocks, master switches, or by removing starter keys.

8. NEVER FIGHT A TOOL. Don't force it beyond its capability. Don't use it in ways or for purposes for which it is not intended. Don't attempt freehand cuts, or cuts without proper support. If an operation seems to hold special hazards, don't attempt it without thinking for a moment what the price may be.

9. WEAR PROPER APPAREL. Avoid wearing loose clothing, gloves, neckties, or jewelry that could get caught in moving parts. Rubber-soled footwear is recommended for best footing.

10. SECURE WORK. Use clamps or a vise to hold work when practical. It is safer than using your hand and frees both hands to operate the tool.

11. DON'T OVERREACH. Keep proper footing and balance at all times.

12. MAINTAIN TOOLS WITH CARE. Keep tools sharp and clean for best and safest performance. Follow instructions for lubricating and changing accessories.

13. DISCONNECT TOOLS. Before servicing or when changing accessories such as blades, bits, cutters, etc., always disconnect the power cord.

14. AVOID ACCIDENTAL STARTING. Make sure switch is in OFF position before plugging in. Also never leave a running power tool unattended.

15. USE RECOMMENDED ACCESSORIES. Consult the owner's manual for recommended accessories. Follow the instructions that accompany the accessories. The use of improper accessories may cause hazards.

16. DON'T DAYDREAM. If you find yourself daydreaming as you work, snap out of it or postpone your efforts to a time when you feel more alert. When you daydream, you are not thinking of what you're doing. You are also more likely to be startled. Even when you are alert, when you are using a power tool, you are not apt to hear the approach of a visitor. Instruct your family to wait until anyone using a power tool has finished what he is doing and cannot be imperiled in case he is startled.

17. NEVER STAND ON TOOL. Serious injury could occur if the tool is tipped or if the cutting tool is accidentally contacted. Do not store materials above or near the tool so that it is necessary to stand on the tool to reach them.

18. CHECK DAMAGED PARTS. Before further use of the tool, a guard or other part that is damaged should be carefully checked to ensure that it will operate properly and perform its intended function—check for alignment of moving parts, binding of moving parts, breakage of parts, mounting, and any other conditions that may affect its operation. A guard or other part that is damaged should be properly repaired or replaced.

19. DIRECTION OF FEED. Feed work into a blade or cutter against the direction of rotation of the blade or cutter only. Keep out of line of the saw blade, front and rear, and see that no one else ever moves in line with it. This is the area where those

deadly spears are seeking a target. Let only enough blade project on a table saw or portable saw to cut the work. The saw cuts better that way, binding is minimized, and the chances of throwing wood spears are reduced.

20. DON'T FORGET TO THINK. This eliminates most accidents before they happen.

Electricity Cautions

A large sign in a well-known research laboratory carries this warning: "Touch electrical equipment with one hand only."

This is the old one-hand-in-the-pocket trick. It works this way—if you touch a hot line with one hand, the jolt will travel down your arm and through your body to the ground. You'll feel it, but it will not kill you. But if you touch with both hands, the jolt passes up one arm, across your body, and down the other, completing the circuit. The path goes right through your heart.

An insidious thing about electricity is that it can paralyze your muscles. You may not be able to open the hand that clutches a hot wire and let go. You may be conscious but helpless to do anything to save yourself. So avoid getting into such a predicament. Switch off power at the service entry box before you work on a line. Turning power off at the room toggle switch is not enough; sometimes fixtures are incorrectly wired and may be hot even when switched off. The switch may be on the ground line instead of on the hot line.

Ladder Safety

If a ladder has bad rungs, poor footing, or is rickety or improperly slanted, don't climb it until these hazards are corrected. If a ladder slips or moves as you climb, it is not placed properly. If you are using a straight ladder, its base should be away from the supporting wall a distance equal to one quarter of its height.

Before getting on a step ladder, see that it is fully opened and its braces locked. When you get on, don't climb higher than the second step from the top. Never, never stand on the top platform.

In climbing a ladder, carry tools in your pocket, scabbard, or other tote device, but not in your hand. When working on a ladder, try at all times to keep one hand free. You may want to grasp the ladder. If your ladder is set in a doorway, see that the door is open or that it is locked—then no one will bump the ladder and knock you off. Before you move a stepladder, be sure you have not left your hammer on its top. It may come sailing off.

The light weight of magnesium or aluminum ladders is an asset, but the lightness and the metal can also be hazards. A strong wind can blow them down and leave you stranded on a roof. And since magnesium and aluminum conduct electricity, they are risky to use around electric lines and during electrical storms.

Lifting

A back injury may not kill you, but it can give you uncomfortable moments the rest of your life if you slip a disc, tear a ligament, or pull a tendon. The rule for avoiding back injuries when lifting is to bend the knees and keep the back straight. You have to bend your back a little, of course, but minimize it. When you have a lifting job that is just too awkward or heavy, get help—a block and tackle and/or a neighbor.

Menaces Miscellaneous

When you saw, do not use your knee to brace work. When you hammer, hold the nail you are driving only long enough to start it, and make the starting hammer strokes slow and measured so you can't miss. When you drill, keep your hand away from the bit. It may jump. The same goes for a screwdriver, especially one of the wrong size, or one whose tip has become rounded.

Use gloves to protect your hands when handling broken glass or rough masonry.

If your shop is in a basement or attic, and there is a low overhead en route, identify the hazard plainly, so no one could possibly be unaware of it. Avoid having a door that opens onto a downflight of steps. It should open away from the steps. Repair loose or broken steps and handrails as soon as you discover them.

Store inflammables outdoors. Keep oily rags in a sealed can; they sometimes catch fire by spontaneous combustion.

Eye and Face Protectors

You have only two eyes, of course, and replacements are hard to come by. That should be reason enough to protect your eyes whenever you use hand or power tools. And if there is any possibility of facial injuries, you should also use a face protector. Wearing these devices gives you an added benefit—you will work better because you will not be flinching and squinting.

A pair of safety glasses is probably the best choice when you do hand-tool work, power woodworking and metalworking, chipping, light grinding, and similar jobs and *not* "street" glasses with tempered glass lenses, which are shatter-resistant but are not safety spectacles.

The safety glasses you wear should be personally fitted, approved safety spectacles with glass lenses. Rims should fully surround the lenses. If you already wear glasses, the safety lenses can be ground to your prescription. (Of course, if you wear contact lenses, safety specs are a necessity.)

KINDS OF PROTECTION NEEDED

Job	Hazards	Eye/Face protective equipment*
Gas welding, cutting, soldering, brazing	Sparks, molten metal, harmful rays	G with shade #2 lenses for soldering, welding, brazing; for light cutting, shade #3 or #4
Arc or carbon-arc welding of steel	Same	H with shade #10 lens up to and including 5/32-inch electrodes; shade #14 for carbon-arc welding; D under helmet desirable
Chemical and glass handling	Splash, burns, glass breakage	B with F
Chipping, paint scraping	Flying particles	A, B, C, D, or E
Power woodworking	Flying chips, dust	A, B, C, D, or E with F to protect face when necessary
Grinding, power wire-brushing	Flying particles	A, B, C, D, or E; add F for heavy grinding and wire-brushing
Power metalworking (machining)	Flying particles	A, B, C, D, or E
Hand-tool work	Flying particles	A, B, C, D, or E
Dusty operations	Dust particles	B
Visitors in work area	Flying particles	I

* Key:
A. Flexible-fitting goggles
B. Hooded vent flexible-fitting goggles
C. Rigid body cushioned-fitting goggles
D. Safety spectacles with side shields
E. Eyecup safety goggles
F. Face shield
G. Welding goggles
H. Welding helmet
I. Plastic "visitors" spectacles

(Continued)

These safety glasses will withstand considerable impact, unless the lenses are scratched or pitted (such lenses should be replaced). When they do break, safety lenses tend to "spiderweb" and stay put within the rims.

Safety specs with built-in shields offer protection from particles that might hit you from the side. Clip-on side shields are available, but the clip should have a mechanism that cannot be easily dislodged with a blow. Should that happen, the shield itself could cause an eye injury.

Keep a pair of inexpensive plastic safety specs on hand, too, as "visitor" glasses. Everyone who wanders into your work area should also be protected.

Safety glasses are the most comfortable eye protectors for sustained wear, and the best bet for serious do-it-yourselfers. But the flexible-fitting plastic goggles are also suitable for the jobs listed above. You can get goggles with hooded vents, which are useful when you work under extremely dusty conditions or when you handle chemicals.

If there is any chance that you may get hit in the face while working, wear a face shield.

16

Household Chemistry

SPECIAL INKS

Invisible Inks

Invisible or *sympathetic* inks consist of chemical solutions that are colorless when applied, but which become visible when heated or treated with other chemicals. They can be used in performing feats of chemical magic and for writing secret letters to your friends.

An invisible ink that comes ready made is plain lemon juice. Using a clean pen, write or draw with this on ordinary unsized white paper. When dry, this "ink" can't be seen. Hold the paper over heat, however, and the writing magically appears.

Another, and one that gives better results, can be made by adding 10 drops of concentrated sulfuric acid to 1 ounce of water. (*Caution:* Handle the concentrated acid carefully; it is extremely corrosive. In mixing, always add the acid to the water, and not vice versa.) When heated, this ink, previously invisible, turns a deep black.

When gently heated, writing done with a solution of cobalt chloride turns blue.

If sprayed or brushed with a solution of potassium ferrocyanide, writing made with a solution of copper nitrate will become brown.

Writing made with an oxalic acid solution, if similarly treated with a solution of cobalt nitrate, will turn blue.

Writing made with a potassium thiocyanate solution, treated with a solution of ferric chloride, will turn red.

Universal Developer for Invisible Inks

If you have access to a home or school laboratory, you can compound a universal developer that will make almost any secret writing visible. Prepare it by dissolving the following chemicals in 50 milliliters of water:

Potassium iodide	4	grams
Iodine crystals	1/10	gram
Sodium chloride	5	grams
Aluminum chloride crystals (do not use anhydrous aluminum chloride)	4	grams

Apply this solution sparingly to the paper by means of a small wad of cotton dampened with it.

Erasable Ink

Here is a trick ink that you can get rid of instantly in case you don't like what you've written. Just give it a swish with a cloth and it's gone! However, it is quite useless except to astonish friends.

To make it just add 12 drops of tincture of iodine to 3 teaspoons of water, and then stir in a teaspoon of cornstarch. The iodine reacts with the starch to form a deep blue-black color.

Write with a clean pen. Although this ink stands out distinctly, the starch keeps it from penetrating the paper. As soon as it is dry, it can be removed with the above-mentioned swish.

TESTS FOR CHEMICALS, METALS, TEXTILES

Kitchen Tests for Acids and Alkalis

The juice of the chokecherry can be used instead of phenolphthalein solution as an indicator for bases and acids. A water infusion of the berries will turn green when you add an alkali to it and light red when you add an acid. To make the infusion, crush the berries, pour boiling water over them, and, with occasional stirring, let stand for half an hour. Filter or strain out the berries and use the clear liquid.

An infusion of the leaves of purple cabbage, made the same way, can also be used as an indicator. In this case the liquid is red when acid, purple when neutral, and blue turning to dark green as it becomes alkaline.

Test for Gold

The common method used to tell whether an article of jewelry is gold or brass is to touch it with a drop of concentrated nitric acid on the tip of a glass rod. If it is brass or other yellow metal alloy, or if the gold plating has worn off to expose the alloy, the acid will form copper nitrate. If this occurs, the metal and acid will turn blue and a reddish gas will be evolved. If the metal is solid gold, or plated with gold with its coating intact, there will be no reaction at all. (*Caution:* Handle nitric acid carefully. It is extremely corrosive.)

Test for Silver

Sterling silver, silver plate that is intact, and silver coins may be identified positively by means of a test solution suggested by the U.S. Secret Service. It consists simply of 10 grains of silver nitrate and 20 drops of concentrated nitric acid dissolved in 1 ounce of distilled water. (*Caution:* Handle these chemicals with care. Silver nitrate makes black stains on skin and clothing; nitric acid is extremely corrosive.) If you haven't the materials for making this, it can be put up cheaply by a druggist.

To make the test, scrape a small spot on the object to clean it and apply a drop of the solution. If the coin is real, or the object is of sterling silver or plate in good condition, the acid will not change its appearance. If the coin or object is not silver, the solution will blacken it.

Test for White Metals

Many "white" metals, such as ordinary steel, nickel, Monel metal, chromium stainless steel, and "18-8" chromium-nickel stainless steel, look very much alike but vary widely in composition and price and perform quite differently in use. If you want to make sure the metal in your new equipment is what you need and paid for, you can quickly find out with a simple testing kit you can put together for a few cents.

For chemicals, all you need is a few ounces of concentrated nitric acid (*Careful:* very corrosive poison), a like amount of distilled water, and a solution of ¼ ounce of cupric chloride in 2½ ounces of water. For apparatus, you need only three medicine droppers (one for each reagent), a few iron or steel nails, and a small bar or horseshoe magnet.

With this simple equipment you can make a quick and positive identification of eight different metals and alloys, as shown in the accompanying table.

Methods of carrying out the tests are as simple as the equipment. The first test is for magnetic properties, which can be determined by suspending the magnet on a string so it is free to turn, and then bringing the metal to be tested toward it. Monel metal is usually slightly magnetic at room temperatures, but if this quality does not show at once, a bath in ice water or a freezing mixture will cause it to be revealed.

Follow this test with the nitric acid test. Clean the spot where it is to be made with a solution of washing soda or trisodium phosphate and then rinse. Apply 1 or 2 drops of concentrated nitric acid, and wait a few minutes to note the reaction. Then dilute the acid with 3 or 4 drops of distilled water, one drop at a time. If the solution turns green or blue, proceed with the nail test for copper. (*Note:* Between tests, lay the droppers and nails in a clean glass dish, out of contact with each other.)

Keeping the nail in contact with the metal, rub the end of it in the spot of diluted nitric acid. If copper is present in the alloy being tested, it will be deposited either on the nail or on the surface of the metal, under the acid solution.

The purpose of the fourth test is to distinguish inconel—an alloy containing 80-percent nickel, 14-percent chromium, and 6-percent iron from the "18-8" stainless steel that contains 18-percent chromium and 8-percent nickel.

A drop of the cupric chloride in hydrochloric acid is applied, and allowed to remain for 2 minutes. Then add slowly 3 or 4 drops of distilled water, and finally wash off all solutions.

If the sample is "18-8" stainless steel, copper from the cupric chloride solution will be deposited on the metal surface. If the metal is Inconel, copper will not deposit. Only a white spot will indicate where the solution has been applied.

Chemical Humidity Indicator

Artificial flowers and dolls' dresses, impregnated with a chemical that changes color with the humidity, have long been used to indicate the relative amount of moisture in the air. Today, moisture-absorbing agents, such as silica gel, treated with the same chemical are packed in

QUALITATIVE TESTS FOR IDENTIFYING SOME COMMON WHITE METALS AND ALLOYS

MAGNETIC TEST	NITRIC ACID TEST			IRON NAIL TEST FOR COPPER	DROP TEST WITH CUPRIC CHLORIDE IN HYDROCHLORIC ACID	MATERIAL PROBABLY IS
Reaction to magnet	Reaction to concentrated acid	Reaction to acid after dilution	Color of the solution			
Magnetic	reacts slowly	reacts slowly	pale green	no copper plates out	not required	nickel
Magnetic (slightly)	reacts	reacts slowly	greenish blue	copper plates out	not required	monel
Nonmagnetic	reacts	reacts	bluish green	copper plates out	not required	copper-nickel alloy containing less than 60% nickel, e.g. nickel-silver
Magnetic	reacts slowly	reacts	brown to black	not required	not required	steel or cast iron
Nonmagnetic	reacts slowly	reacts	brown to black	not required	not required	"ni-resist"
Magnetic	no reaction	no reaction	colorless	not required	not required	straight chromium stainless steel
Nonmagnetic	no reaction	no reaction	colorless	not required	copper deposits when drop is diluted	chromium-nickel stainless steels, e.g. "18-8"
Nonmagnetic	no reaction	no reaction	colorless	not required	no deposition of copper occurs	inconel

saltshaker caps and canister tops to keep salt and cookies dry. When these agents get too damp, the chemical notifies you by changing color.

The secret of all these devices is cobalt chloride, a chemical whose crystals lose water and turn blue when they are perfectly dry, and combine with water and turn pink when they are moist. To make an indicator, merely soak paper toweling, filter paper, or undyed cotton cloth in a strong solution of cobalt chloride in water and let dry.

You can also use cobalt chloride to work a bit of chemical magic. Soak a handkerchief in a *dilute* solution, and dry. Warm the handkerchief and it becomes bright blue; breathe on it and it becomes pale pink or colorless!

pH TESTS

In addition to its role in testing soil (see Chapter 13), the term "pH" is used commonly in testing aquarium water, in processing foods, in chemical analysis, and in medicine. As described earlier, pH is simply the symbol of a scale, numbered from 0 to 14, that rates water solutions according to their acidity or alkalinity, thus:

pH Relationships

pH value	*Relative acidity or alkalinity*
0 acidity	10,000,000
1	1,000,000
2	100,000
3	10,000
4	1,000
5	100
6	10
7 neutral (pure water)	1
8	10
9	100
10	1,000
11	10,000
12	100,000
13	1,000,000
14 alkalinity	10,000,000

Pure water is given the number 7—right in the middle of the scale—because it contains an equal number of acidic and basic ions and is therefore neutral. As the alkalinity of a solution increases, the pH value goes up; as the acidity increases, the pH goes down. Each step represents an increase or decrease by a factor of 10.

On this scale, the most acid substance is hydrochloric acid, which, in proper concentration, is rated at 0, or 10 million times as *acid* as water. At the other end of the scale is a solution of sodium hydroxide, rated at 14, or 10 million times as *alkaline* as water. Solutions of other substances take their places in between. Here are a few examples:

pH of Common Things

	pH
Hydrochloric acid, normal	0.1
Sulfuric acid, normal	0.3
Oxalic acid, 0.1 normal	1.6
Limes	1.8–2.0
Ginger ale	2.0–4.0
Lemons	2.2–2.4
Swamp peats	2.7–3.4
Apples	2.9–3.3
Grapefruit	3.0–3.3
Bananas	4.5–4.7
Average garden soils	4.5–7.0
Boric acid, 0.1 normal	5.2
Best pH for most plants	6.0–7.0
Cow's milk	6.3–6.6
Drinking water	6.5–6.8
Pure water	7.0
Human blood plasma	7.3–7.5
Sodium bicarbonate, 0.1 normal	8.4
Desert soils	9.0–11.0
Calcium carbonate, saturated	9.4
Ammonia	10.6–11.6
Trisodium phosphate, 0.1 normal	12.0
Sodium metasilicate, 0.1 normal	12.6
Sodium hydroxide, normal	14.0

Approximate measurement of pH may be done with test papers or solutions that change color with different acidity or alkalinity. For instance, familiar litmus paper turns red in solutions of pH less than 7, and turns blue in solutions of more than 7. Phenolphthalein turns red in solutions more alkaline than approximately 9. Chemical-supply houses and garden and aquarium stores can sell you other test papers and solutions that change color at different portions of the scale, also some "universal" papers and solutions that will give color changes for almost the entire scale.

BATTERY POLARITY TESTS

Immerse the bare ends of the leads from the battery about ½ inch apart in a strong solution of salt water. (If the battery is more than about 45 volts, place them farther apart and be sure the parts of the wires you hold are well insulated!) The current will decompose the salt water and in doing so will produce more bubbles about the positive.

You can also test polarity with a homemade color-changing paper. To a strong salt solution add a few drops of phenolphthalein test solution. Soak strips of paper towel or filter paper in this solution and then let the strips dry. When ready to make a test, moisten a strip of the prepared paper and touch the terminal wires to it, again about ½ inch apart (and observing the precautions mentioned above). A pink spot will form around the negative terminal.

BURNING TEST FOR TEXTILES

When nearly all textiles were made of natural materials—wool, cotton, linen, or silk—it was not hard for the housewife to tell by looks and feel just what her clothing, blankets, draperies, and linens were made of. Today, with dozens of new test-tube fibers competing with those original products, determination is far more complex.

A few simple tests, however, can often help solve the mystery. So long as the fibers in a fabric are not so mixed that you can't separate them, the burning test should help you identify several different types of textiles. To perform it, touch the end of a small sample to a match flame; then note the appearance of the burning, the smell, and the nature of the ash.

COTTON AND LINEN, AS WELL AS VISCOSE AND CUPRAMMONIUM RAYON. These most commonly used fabrics all burn rapidly with the familiar odor of burning rags or paper. The ash is small, and after the flame goes out a glowing coal may creep along the unburned material. Because these materials are so similar chemically, further differentiation must be made by appearance or other physical tests. You can distinguish between cotton and rayon by wetting a strand; on pulling, cotton is relatively strong, while rayon breaks easily.

WOOL AND HAIR. These burn more slowly and give off an odor of burnt hair or feathers. Their ash is knobby and cokelike, and the flame stops as soon as the match is removed.

PURE SILK. This burns slowly, with a smell similar to that of wool, and leaves a row of cokelike beads along the edge of the fabric.

WEIGHTED SILK. Silk made heavier by treatment with metallic salts is readily discovered by the burning test. Only the silk fibers burn. A skeleton of black ash is left behind, which retains the structure of the weave.

ACETATE (ACELE, ARNEL). This flames and melts, producing a black ball at the burning edge that hardens when cold.

NYLON. This doesn't really burn at all, although combustible dyes or finishes may cause it to flame slightly. It melts, though, leaving a brown mass at the edge of the material.

MODACRYLIC (DYNEL, VEREL). This is hard to ignite and goes out by itself. It leaves an irregular, hard black bead. Dynel softens if treated with acetone.

POLYESTER (DACRON, FORTREL, KODEL, VYCRON). This is also hard to ignite and is self-extinguishing. It leaves a round and shiny hard black bead, rather than an irregular one, and gives off a pungent odor.

ACRYLIC (ORLON, CRESLAN, ACRILAN, ZEFRAN). This burns readily with a yellow flame having a purple base and orange tip. The flame does not go out by itself. It gives off an acrid odor and leaves a hard black bead.

GLASS FIBERS. These do not burn, but become red hot and may melt into tiny beads if kept in a hot flame.

LYE TEST FOR WOOL

The boiling lye test is the classic method for detecting, and determining the amount of, an adulteration of what is supposed to be pure wool.

Count the threads in a small square of the cloth and then immerse it for exactly 10 minutes in a gently boiling, 5-percent solution of lye.

(*Caution:* Handle lye with care; it is extremely caustic. Prepare and boil the solution in a glass, iron, or stainless steel pot, as it attacks other metals.)

At the end of the 10 minutes, remove what is left of the square of cloth from the solution, rinse it in plain water, and count the remaining threads. Since wool is the only common textile fiber that is dissolved by boiling lye, what is left is cotton or linen, or some other fiber.

ACID TEST FOR WOOL

If you are still in doubt concerning a material that appears to be only part wool, give it the "acid test." Mix 2 drops of concentrated sulfuric acid (*Caution:* Do not spill on clothes or skin) with 100 drops of water and put a drop or two of this 2-percent acid on a piece of the cloth to be tested, allowing it to penetrate the fabric completely. Then place the sample between two sheets of paper and press with a hot iron for 1 minute. If the material contains cotton, the spot where the acid was placed becomes charred. When you rub the charred spot gently between your thumb and forefinger, the cotton falls away and leaves behind it whatever wool the material contains.

TESTING FOR WATER IN GASOLINE

When you buy gasoline for your car or solvents for oil paints and varnishes, are you getting 100 percent of what you expect, or is there water mixed with it? With the help of a powder that can be made easily, you can find out in an instant.

Put an ounce or so of copper sulfate crystals in a small glass baking dish and place the dish in an oven heated to about 490° F. The heat drives the water out of the blue crystals. When all has gone, what remains is anhydrous (waterless) copper sulfate—a pale gray powder. When the powder has cooled, put it in a small bottle having a tight stopper, for use as needed.

To make a test, put a little of the powder into a test tube or small vial and add some of the suspected liquid. Then stopper the tube and give it a few shakes. If the liquid contains water, the copper sulfate will take back the water it lost and once more turn blue. If the liquid is free of water, the powder will remain gray.

COLORING FIREPLACE FLAMES

By soaking fireplace logs in water solutions of certain chemicals and then drying them, or merely by sprinkling the powdered chemicals on the flames, you can conjure up brilliant colors to suit your whim.

Here is a list of some of the chemicals and of the colors they produce:

Strontium nitrate	Red
Common salt	Yellow
Borax	Green
Barium nitrate	Apple green
Copper nitrate	Emerald green
Copper chloride	Bluish green
Calcium chloride	Orange
Lithium chloride	Purple

HEAT AND COLD FROM CHEMICALS

Chemical Heating Bottles

Bottles that become warm when water is added to them operate on well-known physical or chemical principles. Most of these contain iron filings or borings and some salt that becomes chemically active by the addition of water.

One composition that produces mild heat when water is added is:

Iron filings	40 parts
Manganese dioxide	5 parts
Common salt	3 parts

Another:

Iron filings	4 parts
Calcium chloride	2 parts
Powdered sulfur	1 part
Common salt	1 part

One that gives more heat:

Iron filings	24 parts
Copper chloride	10 parts
Ammonium chloride	1 part

Mix the above thoroughly and add about 16 parts of water when ready to start the reaction.

Degrease the iron filings or borings in the above mixtures before using them by washing them with gasoline or painter's naphtha.

Cold from Chemicals

Chemicals that react with water when going into solution cause the water to heat up. Those that merely dissolve absorb heat from the water in doing so and cool it down. You can give a practical demonstration of cold from chemicals by cooling a bottle of soda on a picnic, or at home as an expedient.

All you need is a large fruit-juice can, a turkish bath towel, 1 pound of common photographic hypo, water, and a couple of rubber bands. Fold the towel and wrap it around the sides and bottom of the can for insulation. Then pour in 1 quart of the coldest water you can get, dissolve the hypo in it by rapid stirring, and put in the bottle to be cooled. The temperature of the bottle should go down about 30° F. (The hypo solution need not be wasted. Bottle it and use it for preparing photograph fixing baths.)

A mixture of 50 parts ammonium chloride and 50 parts potassium nitrate, dissolved in 160 parts water, will produce even greater cold. If the ingredients are originally at moderate room temperatures, solution will cause a drop to below 32° F.

THE CHEMICAL ACTIVITY OF METALS

By means of elaborate tests, chemists have arranged all metals in a list according to the ease with which they enter into chemical reactions. This list is variously called the "activity series," the "electromotive series," the "electrochemical series," or the "displacement series," depending upon the use for which it is intended. Starting with the most active, here is the order for the commonest metals:

Li	lithium	C	calcium
K	potassium	Na	sodium

(*List continues on page 520*)

FREEZING MIXTURES

The following, from the Smithsonian Tables, are other mixtures that can produce low temperatures for many processes. The figure in Column A is the number of parts of the substance named in the first column to be added to the parts of the substance in Column B. The next column gives the original temperature of the ingredients, and the last one the final temperature after they are mixed.

Substance	A	B	Initial temp. °C	Resulting temp. °C
Sodium acetate, crystals	85	Water 100	10.7	− 4.7
Ammonium chloride	30	Water 100	13.3	− 5.1
Sodium nitrate	75	Water 100	13.2	− 5.3
Sodium thiosulfate (hypo)	110	Water 100	10.7	− 8.0
Potassium iodide	140	Water 100	10.8	−11.7
Ammonium nitrate	60	Water 100	13.6	−13.6
Calcium chloride	30	Snow 100*	− 1	−10.9
Ammonium chloride	25	Snow 100	− 1	−15.4
Ammonium nitrate	45	Snow 100	− 1	−16.75
Sodium nitrate	50	Snow 100	− 1	−17.75
Sodium chloride (salt)	33	Snow 100	− 1	−21.3
	1	Snow .49	0	−19.7
	1	Snow .61	0	−39.0
	1	Snow .70	0	54.9
Calcium chloride, hexahydrate	1	Snow .81	0	−40.3
	1	Snow 1.23	0	−21.5
	1	Snow 2.46	0	− 9.0
	1	Snow 4.92	0	− 4.0
Alcohol at 4° C	77	Snow 73.00	0	−30.0
		Dry ice**		−72.0
Chloroform		Dry ice		−77.0
	1	Water 0.94	20	− 4.0
	1	Snow 0.94*	0	− 4.0
	1	Water 1.20	10	−14.0
Ammonium nitrate	1	Snow 1.20*	0	−14.0
	1	Water 1.31	10	−17.5
	1	Snow 1.31*	0	−17.5

* Finely shaved ice may be used in place of the snow.

** Dry ice should be broken into small lumps and made into a mush with the alcohol or chloroform. (*Caution:* Don't handle dry ice with your hands; it may freeze your fingers. Use tongs or wear thick gloves. To break it up, put larger pieces in a cloth bag and pound it with a hammer or ice-breaking mallet.)

(Continued from page 518)

Mg	magnesium	Pb	lead
Al	aluminum	H	hydrogen
An	zinc	Bi	bismuth
Cr	chromium	Cu	copper
Fe	iron	Hg	mercury
Ni	nickel	Ag	silver
Sn	tin	Au	gold

Because it acts much the same as a metal in displacement reactions, hydrogen is included as a guidepost. Any metal above hydrogen is more active than hydrogen, and so will displace this gas from such acids as sulfuric and hydrochloric. Metals below hydrogen cannot displace it from any of the acids.

Metallic Plating and the Darkening of Kitchen Pots

This difference in the activity of metals explains many reactions in everyday chemistry. For example, it explains the plating of one metal on another without outside current, described in Chapter 3. When any metal is placed in a solution of a salt of a metal that stands below it, the first metal is dissolved and the second is thrown out of solution in metallic form.

Aluminum pots and pans in the kitchen are often darkened by this swapping of metals. If you cook oatmeal, spinach, or other iron-containing food in an aluminum pot, some of the aluminum changes place with some of the iron, the latter being deposited as a dark coating inside the pot. Although the tidy housewife may scour away this deposit, she needn't do so, for the iron will be removed chemically if some acid food such as tomatoes, rhubarb, or sauerkraut is later cooked in the pot. The iron thus regained is not only harmless but is also a valuable food mineral.

Metals Give Up Electrons Differently

A more specific way to express the activity of metals is to say that they vary in their ability to ionize, or give up electrons. Metals at the top of the list give up electrons more easily than those at the bottom. This difference makes electric batteries possible and explains corrosion and electrolytic action between touching metals.

If two metals of different activity are immersed in a suitable solution and then connected by a wire, electrons will flow through the wire from the more active metal. The farther apart the metals in the series, the greater will be the electromotive force or voltage.

Electrical Activity Explains Corrosion

A similar electrical effect accounts for the accelerated corrosion that often takes place when two metals are in contact in the presence of moisture. This explains why the iron in "tin cans" corrodes more rapidly when the tin plating is broken than if it were not plated at all. It also explains why the iron in zinc-plated, or "galvanized," iron is protected when the zinc coating is damaged. In the latter case, the zinc dissolves, and in so doing forms a protective coating over the iron.

17

Miscellaneous Hints and Formulas

HOW TO CLEAN RECORDS

Modern phonograph records, although much better than discs made a few years ago, are still highly susceptible to dust, dirt, and static electricity. Quality discs have a highly polished surface, and their fine grooves can now carry much more information. For this reason, they must be kept immaculately clean to deliver the best sound with today's more compliant cartridges and much lighter tracking forces.

Lately, there has been a proliferation of products and advice on record care and preservation. A variety of tone-arm-type and hand-held brushes, chemical cleaners, static-reduction devices, and protective treatments are on record store shelves. But, still, one of the best ways to clean records that have become very dirty is to wash them in a mild dishwasher detergent; 2 to 4 drops to 4 pints of lukewarm water in a shallow basin. Dip the record part way into the solution and wipe gently in the direction of the grooves, never across. Use a soft cloth or a cellulose sponge to clean, but be careful to avoid getting the solution on the label. Rinse first under running lukewarm water and then with distilled water. Dry first with a lintless cotton cloth. Finish drying with a disc-washer-type brush, which can be purchased at any record shop. This treatment will remove fingermarks, dust, and grease imbedded in the grooves, and will not leave any deposit of its own to collect further dust.

Antistatic Fluid for Records

Reducing electrostatic charges that build up as discs are handled and played is as important as removing dirt and debris. Fortunately, one of the best antistatic fluids with which to moisten the dust brushes used to clean the grooves of records can be made by mixing 20 parts ethylene glycol with 80 parts water. Applied sparingly, this fluid coats the record with a thin film of moisture that permits the static electricity to leak off.

PREVENT CANDLES FROM DRIPPING

When the water in the following solution evaporates, the solids left behind will form a protective film around the candle.

Epsom salts	2 ounces
Dextrin	2 ounces
Water	13 ounces

Dissolve the Epsom salts and the dextrin in the water. Dip the candles in the solution and then let them dry.

MAKE CUT FLOWERS LAST LONGER

Flowers wilt because they cannot obtain sufficient water through the stems to overcome evaporation through the leaves and flowers. Bacteria multiply in the water, clog, and destroy the stem tubes. Powdered charcoal, salt, camphor, aspirin, or ammonia, added to the water in small quantities, slows bacterial growth.

Another method is the use of liquid chlorine bleach. This also disinfects the water and keeps it sweet-smelling. In addition, it has definite beneficial effects on certain flowers. It tends, for instance, to intensify the color of orchids and chrysanthemums and prevents fading that occurs when asters are kept in plain water. Also, while roses in plain water open rapidly and begin to drop their petals, roses in liquid chlorine bleach solution remain in bud much longer. (This treatment is not recommended, however, for gardenias.)

Make the solution by thoroughly mixing 1 teaspoon of the bleach

(Clorox, Rose-X, Purex, etc.) in each gallon of cold water. Then pour into vases.

To preserve cut flowers longer, cut them early in the morning or after sundown. Cut stems at an angle to increase water intake. Use a sharp knife in preference to shears. Soak thoroughly before arranging. Cut stems and change water daily. Singe ends by wrapping flowers in a bath towel with stems extended. Use Sterno or gas burner.

Hyacinth and narcissus should have jellylike sap squeezed from ends of stem to facilitate their drawing water. Camellias and gardenias take water only through petals. Wrap these in wet tissue to preserve them and spray while on display. Hydrangeas and other flowers with woody stems should have 2 inches of the bottom of the stem pounded. Ferns may be stored in wet newspapers, in a cool, dark place. Water lilies may be forced to remain open by pouring a few drops of warm paraffin in the center, while flower is open.

Cut flowers at proper stage of development—dahlias when fully open; gladiolus when first floret is open; peonies when petals are unfolding; roses before buds open. In general, cut while in bud.

Condition flowers over night. Keep them away from drafts and sunlight. Avoid aluminum containers. Avoid crowding.

DUSTPROOFING TENNIS COURTS

Tennis courts, running tracks, and other bare-earth recreational areas can be made dustproof by sprinkling them with powdered calcium chloride. This chemical absorbs moisture from the air and thus acts as a dirt stabilizer.

FIRE STARTERS

As campfire, outdoor grill, and fireplace starters, short pieces of kindling that have been dipped in melted paraffin wax and allowed to cool are excellent. To be on the safe side, always melt the paraffin in a double boiler, never over an open fire.

MAKE YOUR OWN YOGURT

If you like yogurt, but find it expensive, why not make it yourself at about one-third the cost of the ready-made product?

Dating back to the beginnings of recorded history, yogurt is a solid or semisolid milk product that has become that way chiefly through the action of *Lactobacillus bulgaricus* or other similar friendly bacteria. Yogurt is a tasty, easily digested variation of milk that retains all of milk's food value.

Most commercial yogurt is made from whole milk from which part of the cream has been removed and replaced by dry skim milk. You can make it from whole milk, skim milk, or a combination. For a thicker product, use whole milk with 3 or 4 heaping teaspoons of dry skim milk added to each quart.

To make the first batch of yogurt, you will need a "starter" of 2 or 3 tablespoons of the ready-made unflavored variety for each quart of milk. (Be sure all detergents have been rinsed from containers and utensils.) To kill unwanted bacteria in the milk, first heat it to the boiling point in the top of a double boiler. As soon as the milk has cooled to a lukewarm temperature of about 110° to 115° F, stir in the yogurt and mix it thoroughly. Then either leave the mixture in the top of the double boiler or pour it into glasses or jars that have been prewarmed and which are then placed in a pan of warm water up to their necks. In either case, cover the mixture, and keep the water at lukewarm temperature. As soon as the milk has solidified, which should take about 2 hours, put it in the refrigerator. When cold, it is ready for use.

Subsequent batches of yogurt can be made by using yogurt from the previous batch as a starter. Under ideal conditions, this process can be repeated indefinitely. But when the strain of bacteria gets too weak, you will have to start all over again with a little of the ready-made variety. Again, detergent residues on containers and utensils can kill desirable bacteria, so thorough rinsing is essential.

MAKING LIGHTER FLUID

Cigarette lighter fluid is often simply V.M.&P. Naphtha—a high-grade benzine used for thinning paint and for dry cleaning—put up in small containers with a dispensing spout and sold at from four to eight times the price you would pay for the naphtha under its own name in a supermarket or paint store. For greater convenience in filling a lighter with naphtha, pour some from its original can into a smaller bottle or other container and use a medicine dropper.

MINIMIZING RUST

Rust is a nuisance. If it can't be prevented, it can at least be minimized. In general, paints and lacquers give maximum protection, but these can be applied only to unmachined surfaces. Neutral oil, wax, and grease films provide protection for a limited period ranging from a few weeks to several months. Articles coated with such films may be wrapped in paper, plastic film, or cloth as an additional protection. Metals may be kept corrosion-free with no coating at all if they are packed in a moistureproof wrapping of plastic that contains a packet of silica gel, which is a moisture-absorbing chemical. The following substances may be applied as rust preventives on iron and steel:

ARTICLES PACKED FOR STORAGE OR SHIPMENT
Petroleum jelly
High-viscosity oil (chemically neutral)
Petroleum jelly and oil mixtures

ARTICLES SUBJECT TO HANDLING
Paint and lacquer
Commercial antirust preparations
Soluble-oil emulsions
Chemical films such as oxides and gun bluing
Paraffin wax

Rusty objects can first be cleaned by hand or power wire-brushing, with abrasive cloth, steel wool, abrasive powders and polishes, and by chemical rust solvents.

Mechanical equipment, tools, etc., that are to be taken out of service and stored can be effectively protected from rust by using the following mixture: Heat 1 part powdered rosin and 6 parts lard slowly and with stirring until the rosin is completely melted. Then remove from the fire and thin to a flowing consistency with V.M.&P. naphtha (*Caution:* Flammable!).

Rub this mixture sparingly on the steel, after being sure that the metal is clean and that all rust spots have been removed. A leading manufacturer of chisels has found that tools rubbed lightly with this mixture will resist rust even when immersed for some time in salt water.

If conditions of humidity and condensation are severe, consider the installation of a dehumidifying unit in your shop or where metal objects are stored. Besides stopping rust, a dehumidifier in summer can make working conditions more comfortable and can take the load off air conditioners, or even eliminate the need for them.

During especially humid weather cover power tools with cloth or plastic dust covers. They will help stop condensation of moisture on metal. Bags containing silica gel are also effective in absorbing moisture. Put one in a cabinet or toolbox. In some cases, a little added heat can dry up the moisture. In cool weather, run your heating plant briefly. In confined spaces, a 7½-watt bulb kept burning may do the trick. Even a 25-watter kept burning can pay for its cost with the damage it prevents.

LUBRICATING OIL

A little oil goes a long way toward keeping tools and equipment operating. It is preventive medicine at its best. Keep a checklist on tool maintenance. Every power tool you buy, and many hand tools, will come with suggested maintenance procedures.

As important as oiling is getting the oil where you want it to go. The can that oil comes in is not always the best applicator. A trigger oiler—typically with a 6-inch spout—helps you get oil in the right place. It's the oiler for most household and small jobs. A pump oiler is usually best for machinery. It generally has an 11-inch spout and 1-quart capacity.

Lubricants in your arsenal should include penetrating oil for rusty joints; silicone spray for rubber, metal, and wood; gear-case lubricant for electric tools; and grease for general purposes. You can get all-purpose lithium grease in a dispenser can.

WHAT LUBE TO USE WHERE

Item to be lubricated	Type of lubricant	How often to lubricate
Motors (medium to large)	No. 30 engine oil	twice yearly or each season
Motors (small)	household oil	
Wood, plastic, rubber, and similar nonmetallic parts	silicone in spray, emulsion, or grease form	at first indication of sticking
Gear boxes with fittings	general-purpose grease	twice yearly
Gear boxes with plugs	No. 50 to No. 90 gear oil	as needed; check after each use
Open gears	open-gear grease	keep well coated

(Continued)

WHAT LUBE TO USE WHERE ***(continued)***

Item to be lubricated	Type of lubricant	How often to lubricate
Guns after firing	powder-solvent oil	as needed
Guns for storage	gun oil	
Fishing reels	fine reel or instrument oil	each season; more often if kept wet
Clocks and fine instruments	fine reel or instrument oil	not oftener than once yearly
Locks	silicone or dry graphite	yearly
Hinges	dripless oil or dry moly	as needed or at least yearly
Bearings under heat	dry moly	twice yearly; more often if in continuous service
Bearings (medium duty)	No. 30 engine oil	
Bearings (light duty)	household oil	
Bearings (under abrasive conditions)	general-purpose grease	
Tracks and sliding parts	dry moly, moly jel, or general-purpose grease	twice yearly
Chains and sprockets	moly jel	twice yearly or each season; more often for constant use
Frozen parts	penetrating oil and rust solvent	as needed

A good lubricating oil for household, office, and small-shop appliances that costs only a fraction of so-called "machine oil" can be made by blending medicinal mineral oil or 10-SAE automobile oil with a little kerosene to lower its viscosity. Do not, however, use this (or indeed any ordinary machine oil) on watches or fine clocks. These require special oils that do not gum up even after years of service. For motors of ¼ horsepower and larger, use 20-SAE automobile oil just as it comes.

Dry Lubricant for Wood

Melt ordinary paraffin wax in the top of a double boiler and stir in as much fine flake or powdered graphite as can be easily wetted by the liquid wax. Remove from heat, pour into a square pan, and before the mixture has completely hardened cut into sticks of convenient size.

This lubricant is particularly effective on wood or other nonmetallic substances. Rub it on both of the surfaces that come in contact.

CARE OF OILSTONES

Soak a new stone in oil for several days before using, unless it is of the oil-filled variety. Keep it in a box with a closed cover or wrap it with household plastic wrap and leave a few drops of fresh clean oil on it.

To preserve the flat even surface, sharpen tools on the entire stone surface, turning the entire stone end for end occasionally. A half-and-half mixture of machine oil and kerosene works well on most stones, although a special oil may be bought for the purpose. Some stones, such as those made from natural rock, give best results with water.

With an old cloth, wipe off dirty oil right after using the stone. If the stone gums up or becomes glazed, its cutting qualities can usually be restored with gasoline or petroleum naphtha. Scouring the stone with loose abrasive powder or with sandpaper fastened to a smooth board will sometimes help.

If a silicon-carbide stone becomes clogged, it can be renovated by heating in an oven or over a fire. Place it in an old pan to catch the oil and dirt that will ooze out. Wipe the stone dry while it is hot, then resoak in oil.

If a stone becomes uneven, its flat surface can be restored by grinding on the side of a grindstone or rubbing down with sandstone.

Porous stones may be tempered in their cutting by filling the surface with wax or petroleum jelly.

BUYING AND CUTTING GLASS

Because of improved manufacturing techniques, today's ordinary sheet glass, or "window glass," is remarkably strong and clear and has fine visual qualities. It is made by drawing sheets directly from a bath of molten glass. Although sheet glass does have the optical flatness of plate glass, it is fire-polished and transparent and will ordinarily be the choice for home windows, picture protection, and glass for hotbeds and greenhouses.

Clear plate glass is glass of practically the same chemical composition, but with its surfaces ground and polished for perfect flatness. It is made in thin sizes for mirrors and windows, and in heavy thicknesses for large openings in commercial buildings, glass doorways, partitions, showcases, bookshelves, decorative panels, and so on.

Float glass is a type of flat glass made by a new process. It is flat and parallel like polished plate and may be used for the same purposes.

GLASS FORMS AND SIZES

Use or quality	Thickness (inches)	Maximum size (inches)
	WINDOW GLASS	
Photo	1/16	36 × 50
Picture	5/64	36 × 50
Single strength	3/32	40 × 50
Double strength	1/8	60 × 80
Sheet	3/16	120 × 84
	7/32	120 × 84
	1/4	120 × 84
	3/8	60 × 84
	7/16	60 × 84
Greenhouse	1/8	20 × 24
	CLEAR POLISHED PLATE	
Glazing	1/8	76 × 128
	1/4	127 × 226
Mirrors	1/4	127 × 226
Commercial	5/16	127 × 226
	3/8	125 × 281
	1/2	125 × 281
	3/4	120 × 280
	1	74 × 148
	1 1/4	74 × 148
	FLOAT GLASS	
Glazing mirrors	1/4	122 × 200

Tricks in Cutting Glass

Cutting sheet glass and tubing need not be a shattering experience if you follow a few simple rules of the experts. Actually a glass cutter does not cut glass; it splits it. If the wheel is sharp and it is drawn over the glass at the right speed and pressure, it makes a fine score or groove by slightly crushing or pulverizing the glass under the edge of the wheel. The beveled sides of the wheel act as wedges that push against the sides of the groove and pry the glass apart so that the crack is started. If a crack fails to start in the cutting, tap the scratch with the ball end of the glass cutter to start a crack. Break off a narrow strip along the edges by placing the strip into a notch in the cutter and using the handle as a lever to break off the narrow strip. Glass tubing or rod is cut by nicking the surface with a triangular file.

HOW TO CUT WINDOW OR PICTURE-FRAME GLASS. To cut window or picture-frame glass, proceed as follows:

1. Place several layers of newspaper or a piece of carpet on a firm, level surface and place the glass pane upon this padding.
2. Make certain the glass is clean; dirty glass does not cut well and dulls the cutter.
3. Brush turpentine directly along the line to be cut. This keeps the cutter bearings from gumming and keeps the cutter sharp longer.
4. To make a straight cut, use a straightedge to guide the cutter. A wooden yardstick is ideal, since the wood will not slip as easily on glass as would metal.
5. Lubricate the cutting wheel with a drop of light machine oil, and remove excess.
6. Hold the guide with one hand against the glass and hold the cutter in a vertical position in the other hand. Your forefinger should be extended along the back of the cutter with the tip of the finger down near the wheel.
7. Start the groove at the far end of the guide and draw the cutter toward you. The correct pressure is important, since too much pressure may crack the pane and both too little or too much pressure may make an unsatisfactory groove. If the correct pressure is applied and the cutter is drawn toward you at the right speed, the wheel will make a scratching sound. If the wheel is dull, or too much pressure is applied, the sound will be more like crunching than scratching. (Practice on a piece of scrap glass until you can distinguish the difference.)
8. Draw the cutter over the line once only. If it becomes necessary to correct an imperfect groove, do not use a new cutter for this

purpose; use an old one. Drawing a sharp cutter over a groove the second time dulls it.

9. Make a continuous mark all the way from one edge to the other. If made properly, a slight crack will be visible the complete length of the mark. It is best seen from the side opposite the mark.
10. To part the glass, slide the pane over to the edge of the bench or table so the score mark is parallel to and projecting about ⅛ inch beyond the edge. Holding down the portion resting on the table with one hand, grasp the projecting end between the fingertips and palm of the other hand. Apply a light pressure and the glass will part.

HOW TO CUT PLATE GLASS. Proceed as above, trying particularly to start a continuous crack along the bottom of the groove or the scratch. A sharp cutter and the right pressure will usually start this crack when the groove is scored. If the crack does not appear then, it can generally be started by turning the pane over and tapping against the unscored surface with the end of the cutter handle, directly over the line scored on the other side. A crack that is not continuous can be extended all the way along the groove by such tapping.

HOW TO CUT SAFETY GLASS. This is a sandwich made of a sheet of tough plastic between two sheets of tempered regular glass. To cut it, follow these steps:

1. Score the glass along one surface in the usual way with a glass cutter.
2. Lay the glass on a table with the scored line on top, directly above and parallel with the table edge.
3. While holding down the part of the glass that is on the table with one hand, grasp the overhanging part with the other hand and press down until you see or hear the glass crack along the cut. Or you can secure the part on the table with a board held by two C-clamps, and press on the overhanging part with both hands.
4. Turn the glass over and score a second line exactly opposite the first.
5. Repeat steps 2 and 3 to break the layer of glass on the second side.
6. Work the glass back and forth to break the plastic sheet between the glass sheets. If it doesn't part readily, lay the glass over a small stick or rod, weight down the two sections to spread the cut, and separate the plastic sheet with a razor blade.

HOW TO CUT GLASS TUBING AND ROD. Cut small-diameter glass tubing by first giving it a single sharp nick, at the place desired, with one corner of a triangular file. Then hold the tubing with one hand on each side of the nick, with the nick on the surface directly away from you, and apply pressure as if to bend the ends of the tube toward you. The tube will crack apart at the nick. Cut small-diameter glass rods in the same manner. To cut large-diameter tubing or rods, make a continuous scratch with the file around the entire diameter. (*Caution:* Better wear heavy gloves or wrap your hands with rags when applying pressure to prevent injury if the glass should break in the wrong place.)

Medium for Grinding Glass

Glycerin may be used instead of the usual mixture of turpentine and camphor as a medium in which to suspend emery powder in grinding glass. Glycerin has sufficient body and viscosity to carry the emery well. Because it is water soluble, it is easily washed away when the job is finished.

AQUARIUM CARE

After cleaning a fish tank, or beginning the use of a second-hand one, it is best to sterilize the tank before refilling. One way to do this is to rub all the inside surfaces thoroughly with a damp cloth covered with table salt. Another is to swish around in it for a few minutes a solution of brine, made by dissolving a pound of table salt in about 1½ quarts of warm water. Pour or siphon out the brine before filling with fresh water. A little remaining salt won't hurt most fish.

A third way is to fill the tank with warm water and add ¾ cup of household liquid chlorine bleach to each gallon. Immerse equipment in aquarium for 5 minutes, then pour or siphon out this solution and rinse aquarium and equipment well with plain water. Let air for about 30 minutes before refilling with fresh water.

Removing Chlorine from Aquarium Water

If chlorine in tap water is strong enough to taste or smell, it is harmful to fish. Chlorine can be removed in a number of ways. If you can wait, the cheapest and best way is to let the water stand in open containers for a day or two, thus letting the chlorine diffuse naturally into the air. You can hasten this process to a few minutes by heating the water to about 110° F (don't heat it higher, however, or you may produce undesirable changes in the water). As soon as the water has cooled to 75° or 80° F, it is ready for use.

Removing Chlorine with "Hypo"

You can dechlorinate aquarium water almost instantly by stirring into it a little sodium thiosulfate, or photographer's "hypo." About ½ grain of this chemical will remove the chlorine from 1 to 6 gallons of water, depending on the concentration of the gas. Don't get acid-fixing powder, but just plain sodium thiosulphate or "hypo."

The amount to add to the water is not critical, but don't add more than necessary. A few crystals equivalent in bulk to a 5-grain aspirin tablet should dechlorinate at least 10 gallons of water. Dissolve them in a glass of water and then stir this solution into the bulk of the water until it is thoroughly mixed. If you can still smell chlorine, stir in a little more.

Although you may never be able to use a whole pound of hypo for dechlorinating the water in a small aquarium, you can always share it with your fish-fancier friends, or use it for removing iodine stains (see Chapter 8).

Saving Money on Other Aquarium Chemicals

Tropical-fish clubs and individuals with many or large tanks can also save money by mixing their own solutions of other chemicals used for treating aquarium water or ailing fish. Books on fish care tell you what chemicals to use and in what amounts. Although aquarium stores once supplied the required solid chemicals, you may now have to hunt them down in chemical or photographic supply houses or in a friendly neighborhood drugstore.

To find out whether or not you would save by making your own solutions, just figure out how much of a given chemical you might need in a reasonable time and then compare the cost of the required amount of the chemical as contained in a prepared solution with that of the solid chemical. As a help in doing this, remember that 1 ounce of a 1-percent solution contains about 4½ grains of solid (there are 437½ grains to an ounce, and 7,000 grains to a pound).

In figuring costs, don't let technical terminology mislead you into believing that common and cheap chemicals are rare and expensive ones. "Sodium chloride," for instance, is just common salt; "sodium bicarbonate" is ordinary baking soda; "sodium thiosulfate" is photographic "hypo"; "calcium sulfate" is gypsum or plaster of Paris; "magnesium sulfate" is Epsom salts; while "inert ingredients" generally means either plain water or common salt.

Potassium permanganate, a mild and multipurpose antiseptic used for clearing green water and treating fungus and parasitic diseases of fish, is one chemical on which you can save money by mixing your own solutions. For clearing aquarium water of bacteria and algae, the usual concentration is about 1 grain of permanganate for each 8 gallons of water. To treat fungus disease on fish, you need a stronger solution. The sick fish is held in a net for 1 minute in a solution of 1 grain of the chemical in 1 quart of water.

In a typical, prepared clearing solution, you will get just this 1 grain, mixed with other dry chemicals or dissolved in water. You can save money by buying potassium permanganate in crystal form and mixing your own solutions.

As permanganate solutions work better when freshly made, store this chemical in dry form and mix solutions only when needed. Never add the crystals directly to the tank water. First dissolve them completely in a few ounces of water in a glass and then stir the resulting solution thoroughly into the water in the tank.

Methylene blue, malachite green, and potassium dichromate are other solutions you can mix economically. Methylene blue should be of medicinal or USP grade, and malachite green should be zinc-free and not the type ordinarily used for dyeing. Both may be bought from chemical-supply houses or drugstores. These are more expensive than potassium permanganate; but you don't need much, so just buy an ounce or less, if possible. Potassium dichromate can be bought at a photographic-supply house.

For convenience in use, make 5-percent stock solutions of each of these chemicals by dissolving 22 grains of dry chemical per ounce of water.

Gordon's Tropical Fish Formula

This formula, devised by the late Dr. Myron Gordon, noted geneticist of the New York Zoological Society, makes a nourishing between-live-food snack and is said to be suited to all but very small fish:

Calf's liver	1 pound
Water	1 pint
Baby cereal	14 level tablespoons
Wheat germ	6 level tablespoons
Salt	1 level tablespoon

(Continued)

Cut the liver into ½-inch chunks and remove all the sinewy material. Add to the water and grind to a mash, using a kitchen blender if you have one. Then drain through a fine sieve. Next add gradually the baby cereal and the wheat germ to the mashed liver to make a thick, lumpless paste, blending in the salt at the same time.

For better keeping, package the food in small screw-top glass jars. After filling, and with the covers loosely in place, stand the jars in a pan of water and bring the water to a boil. Then turn off the heat, screw down the caps, and let the jars cool with the water. When the jars have cooled, put them into the refrigerator, where they can be kept for a month or so.

Salt for Sick Fish

Common table salt—the noniodized variety—is an inexpensive and effective remedy for a number of ills of freshwater fish. The salt treatment must be given in a bare tank, however, as a salt solution strong enough to cure fish ailments will kill most aquarium plants.

One of the commonest diseases of fish that responds to salt is caused by a fungus called *Saprolegnia.* It takes the form of a whitish scum, and often appears after the first stages of the disease *Ichthyophthirius,* popularly known as "ICH."

Begin the treatment by putting the fish in a tank or enameled pan containing a salt solution in the proportion of 2 level teaspoons of salt to a gallon of seasoned water. During the next 24 hours, gradually increase the salt concentration to double this amount. If the fish have not visibly improved by the next day, gradually add another 2 teaspoons of salt to the gallon. When the treatment is finished, gradually add fresh water until the salt concentration is quite low before putting the fish back in their regular tank.

Leeches will generally detach themselves from fish if you place the fish in a solution of 3 ounces of noniodized salt in a gallon of water. Leave them for about 30 minutes. Then pick off any remaining leeches with tweezers and paint the sore spots on the fish with mercurochrome.

HEALTH GRIT FOR BIRDS

This combination of calcium and carbon is a necessary staple in the diet of all caged birds. You can buy it already prepared, or you can make it from egg shells and wood charcoal.

Dry several egg shells in the oven until they are light brown. Crush them into a powder by rolling a bottle over them on a flat surface. Powder an equal amount of wood charcoal by the same method and mix the two thoroughly. Place in a bottle cap or a small feeding dish in the bird's cage.

REMOVING ODOR FROM CATS AND DOGS

When your dog smells "doggy" or your cat smells "catty," bathe it with a solution of ½ cup of liquid chlorine bleach to each gallon of lukewarm suds. Rinse and dry. This antiseptic bath aids in ridding animals of odors and helps prevent the spread of infection.

Dog and Cat Repellent Powder

Place the following ingredients in a box or bag and shake together for several minutes. Be careful not to inhale the dust or get it in your eyes. Sprinkle where desired.

Cayenne pepper	1 ounce
Powdered mustard	1½ ounces
Flour	2½ ounces

Dog and Cat Repellent Spray

To keep dogs and cats from outdoor structures of wood, concrete, or stone, spray these with a concentrated solution of moth flakes (naphthalene or paradichlorobenzene) in mineral spirits or painter's naphtha. The solvent will evaporate, leaving crystals of the moth repellent in the structure. For a long time these will give off vapors that are distasteful to animals as well as to moths.

To De-Skunk Animals

To remove the odor from animals that have been sprayed by skunks, use large quantities of tomato juice instead of soap. Or do the washing with tomato pulp, if the juice is not handy.

DRY CELLS

Even when not being used, dry cells will deteriorate with time. What is called the "shelf life" of a battery is the length of time the battery can be stored at room temperature (70° F) and still retain approximately 90 percent of its original capacity.

In general, a dry battery will operate more efficiently at higher temperatures. Its shelf life, however, will be extended if the battery is stored at lower temperatures. This is because the chemical reactions that cause deterioration slow down as temperature is decreased.

Tests made by the Naval Ordnance Laboratory, the National Bureau of Standards, and the military and scientific laboratories of a number of European countries bear this out. According to these tests, unused dry cells lose about 21 percent of their capacity in a year when stored at 70° F. Sealed in moistureproof plastic bags, there is a loss of 11 percent when stored at 40° F, 7 percent at 10° F, and a mere 2.5 percent when stored in a deep freeze at 30° below zero.

To keep dry cells for a long time at peak capacity, wrap them tightly in polyethylene film (heat-sealing joints, if possible) and store them at a temperature of 0° F or below in a freezer. While the cells are frozen, avoid unnecessary handling, as this might crack the internal and external seals, which become brittle at low temperatures. Before using them, allow the cells to warm up to room temperature in their wrappings.

For shorter periods of storage, wrap the cells similarly and keep them in the household refrigerator. In this case, they need not be warmed up before use.

CAR BATTERIES

The relative state of charge of a standard car storage battery can be determined either by measuring the specific gravity of the electrolyte in its cells with a hydrometer, or by measuring their voltage. As a battery hydrometer is cheaper than an accurate voltmeter, the hydrometer method is the one generally used.

The hydrometer is a simple glass barrel syringe enclosing a calibrated float. When a sample of the electrolyte from a battery cell is drawn up by the syringe, the stem of the float projects above the level of the liquid to a degree depending on the liquid's density. The specific gravity is then read directly on a scale inside the stem. (For more about hydrometers and specific gravity, see Chapter 18.)

The specific gravity of a typical fully charged automobile battery is approximately 1,260. In other words, its acid content makes the electrolyte 1.26 times as heavy as plain water. As the battery is discharged, more and more of the acid combines with the plates, diluting the electrolyte and causing it to become lighter. At the same time, voltage drops.

BATTERY CHARGE

To help you check the state of charge of your battery, here are specific gravity and open-circuit voltage readings for a standard battery at 80° F and various states of charge:

State of charge	Specific gravity	Open circuit cell voltage*
100%	1.260	2.10
75%	1.230	2.07
50%	1.200	2.04
25%	1.170	2.01
Discharged	1.110	1.95

* This voltage is given to the nearest hundredth of a volt, and should be taken when a battery is not on charge and is not being discharged. The battery also should not have been charged during the previous 16 hours, as charging produces a higher voltage that may persist for about that length of time.

As specific gravity is also affected by expansion and contraction of the electrolyte caused by changes in temperature, the following corrections should be applied to obtain precise readings:

Above 80° F—Add .004 to the hydrometer reading for each 10 degrees that the electrolyte temperature exceeds 80° F.

Below 80° F—Subtract .004 from the hydrometer reading for each 10 degrees that the electrolyte temperature is below 80° F.

No-Fill, No-Fuss Batteries

In recent time, batteries have been introduced that never need maintenance, not even an occasional check of the water level. Some don't have filler caps, so you can't check the electrolyte if you want to. The new no-maintenance batteries—with or without filler caps—are called different names, and may be made differently inside. But they all share one thing: a claim by the seller that once you have installed one, you never have to do anything to maintain it.

These batteries—either lead-antimony (LA) or lead-calcium (C)—generate electricity by an electrochemical reaction between the plates and the electrolyte. Both types of batteries use lead plates and electrolyte (sulfuric acid and water) to make electricity. Battery plates start life as lead grids. To give the grids rigidity, a hardener is added. Traditionally that hardener has been antimony, but the new generation of batteries uses calcium to harden the grids. After the grids are formed, a lead paste is applied; and the grids are called plates.

To make positive plates, the paste added is in the form of lead peroxide. For negative plates, the paste is in the form of spongy lead. When a cell is discharged by the closing of an external circuit, as in switching on the lights, the sulfuric acid in the electrolyte solution acts on both the positive and negative plates, forming a new chemical compound, lead sulfate. As the sulfate forms, the chemical reaction releases electrons, which flow in the external circuit from the negative to the positive plates. As the discharge continues, the sulfuric acid concentration of electrolyte becomes weaker. The amount of sulfuric acid consumed is in direct proportion to the quantity of electricity generated by the cell.

When the acid in the electrolyte is partially used up, the battery can no longer deliver electricity at a useful voltage, and the battery is said to be discharged. To recharge it, current is passed through the battery in a direction opposite to that of discharge—from positive to negative. For the current to pass in reverse through the battery, it must be at a higher voltage than the normal battery voltage. (That is why the charging system of an automobile with a 12-volt battery is set to deliver in the neighborhood of 13.8 to 15 volts to the battery.) As the current passes through the battery in the direction opposite to that of the discharge, the lead sulfate on the plates is decomposed. Expelled from the plates, it returns to the electrolyte, reforming sulfuric acid, and gradually restoring the electrolyte to original strength. The plates are restored to their original condition, ready to deliver electricity again. Hydrogen and oxygen gases are given off at the negative and positive plates during recharging—the result of the decomposition of water by an excess of charging current not used by the plates. This highly explosive combination of gases is vented to the outside and through the top of the battery. Construction of lead-calcium and lead-antimony batteries is similar. Each battery has six cells, with negative and positive plates in each cell. The number of plates and amount of exposed surface area determine how much energy can be stored. Structural details of other LC and LA batteries may vary somewhat, but all are similar. The two-way charge-discharge process can be repeated some large—but finite—number of times before the active materials in the plates wear out and lose their ability to deliver or hold an electrical charge.

Both batteries use separators between plates to keep plates from touching and short-circuiting. Separators in an LC battery, however, are envelopes that cover positive plates. With an LA battery, separators are just flat sheets. Both separators are microporous, allowing electrolyte to flow through. Flaking lead in an LA battery accumulates in the bottom of the battery case. With LC, it accumulates in envelopes. Plates in LC batteries rest on the bottom of the case, and the electrolyte level can be higher above the plates than with an LA battery, so it can lose more water before battery operation and life are affected. This factor, plus electrochemical differences that make an LC battery more resistant to overcharge, slows water loss sufficiently so that the battery can be made without filler caps.

18

Calculations and Conversions

HOW TO COMPUTE CIRCUMFERENCE, AREA, AND VOLUME

All dimensions should be expressed in terms of the same unit—say in inches or centimeters. The computed areas will then be in terms of square inches or square centimeters, and the volumes in terms of cubic inches or cubic centimeters, and so on depending on the unit used.

Circumference

CIRCUMFERENCE OF A CIRCLE: Diameter times 3.1416.

Area

TRIANGLE: Multiply length of base by height and divide by 2.

SQUARE: Square the length of one side.

RECTANGLE: Multiply the length of the base by the height.

REGULAR POLYGONS

Pentagon (5 sides): Square length of one side and multiply by 1.720.

Hexagon (6 sides): Square length of one side and multiply by 2.598.

Octagon (8 sides): Square length of one side and multiply by 4.828.

CIRCLE: Multiply the square of the radius by 3.1416.

ELLIPSE: Multiply long diameter by short diameter by 0.7854.

SPHERE: Multiply square of the diameter by 3.1416.

CYLINDER: Add area of both ends to the circumference times height.

CUBE: Square length of one side and multiply by 6.

Volume

PYRAMID: Multiply area of the base by the height and divide by 3.

CUBE: Cube the length of one edge.

RECTANGULAR SOLID: Multiply length by width by height.

CYLINDER: Multiply the square of the radius of the base by 3.1416, then multiply by the height.

SPHERE: Multiply the cube of the radius by 3.1416, then multiply by 4 and divide by 3.

CONE: Multiply the square of the radius of the base by 3.1416, then multiply by the height and divide by 3.

WATER WEIGHTS AND MEASUREMENTS

A gallon of water weighs 8.336 pounds and contains 231 cubic inches.

A cubic foot of water contains 7½ gallons, 1,728 cubic inches, and weighs 62.4 pounds.

To find the pressure in pounds per square inch at the base of a column of water, multiply the height of the column in feet by 0.433.

FRACTION EQUIVALENTS IN DECIMALS, MILLIMETERS, SQUARES, CUBES, SQUARE AND CUBE ROOTS, CIRCUMFERENCES AND AREAS OF CIRCLES, FROM 1/64 TO 1 INCH

Fraction*	Decimal	mm	Square	Square root	Cube	Cube root	Circle* circumference	Circle* area
1/64	.015625	.3969	.0002441	.125	.000003815	.25	.04909	.000192
1/32	.03125	.3969	.0009766	.176777	.000030518	.31498	.09817	.000767
3/64	.046875	1.1906	.0021973	.216506	.000102997	.36056	.14726	.001726
1/16	.0625	1.5875	.0039063	.25	.00024414	.39685	.19635	.003068
5/64	.078125	1.9844	.0061035	.279508	.00047684	.42749	.24544	.004794
3/32	.09375	2.3812	.0087891	.306186	.00082397	.45428	.29452	.006903
7/64	.109375	2.7781	.0119629	.330719	.0013084	.47823	.34361	.009396
1/8	.125	3.1750	.015625	.353553	.0019531	.5	.39270	.012272
9/64	.140625	3.5719	.0197754	.375	.0027809	.52002	.44179	.015532
5/32	.15625	3.9688	.0244141	.395285	.0038147	.53861	.49087	.019175
11/64	.171875	4.3656	.0295410	.414578	.0050774	.55600	.53996	.023201
3/16	.1875	4.7625	.0351563	.433013	.0065918	.57236	.58905	.027611
13/64	.203125	5.1594	.0412598	.450694	.0083809	.58783	.63814	.032405
7/32	.21875	5.5562	.0478516	.467707	.010468	.60254	.68722	.037583
15/64	.234375	5.9531	.0549316	.484123	.012875	.61655	.73631	.043143
1/4	.25	6.3500	.0625	.5	.015625	.62996	.78540	.049087
7/64	.265625	6.7469	.0705566	.515388	.018742	.64282	.83449	.055415
9/32	.28125	7.1438	.0791016	.530330	.022247	.65519	.88357	.062126
19/64	.296875	7.5406	.0881348	.544862	.026165	.66710	.93266	.069221
5/16	.3125	7.9375	.0976562	.559017	.030518	.67860	.98175	.076699

21/64	.328125	8.3344	.107666	.572822	.035328	.68973	1.03084	.084561
11/32	.34375	8.7312	.118164	.586302	.040619	.70051	1.07992	.092806
23/64	.359375	9.1281	.129150	.599479	.046413	.71097	1.12901	.101434
3/8	.375	9.5250	.140625	.612372	.052734	.72112	1.17810	.110445
25/64	.390625	9.9219	.1525879	.625	.059605	.73100	1.22718	.119842
13/32	.40625	10.3188	.1650391	.637377	.067047	.74062	1.27627	.129621
27/64	.421875	10.7156	.1779785	.649519	.075085	.75	1.32536	.139784
7/16	.4375	11.1125	.1914063	.661438	.083740	.75915	1.37445	.150330
29/64	.453125	11.5094	.2053223	.673146	.093037	.76808	1.42353	.161260
15/32	.46875	11.9062	.2197266	.684653	.102997	.77681	1.47262	.172573
31/64	.484375	12.3031	.2346191	.695971	.113644	.78535	1.52171	.184269
1/2	.5	12.7000	.25	.707107	.125	.79370	1.57080	.196350
33/64	.515625	13.0969	.265869	.718070	.137089	.80188	1.61988	.208813
17/32	.53125	13.4938	.282227	.728869	.149933	.80990	1.66897	.221660
35/64	.546875	13.8906	.299072	.739510	.163555	.81777	1.71806	.234891
9/16	.5625	14.2875	.316406	.75	.177979	.82548	1.76715	.248505
37/64	.578125	14.6844	.334229	.760345	.193226	.83306	1.81623	.262502
19/32	.59375	15.0812	.352539	.770552	.209320	.84049	1.86532	.276884
39/64	.609375	15.4781	.371338	.780625	.226284	.84780	1.91441	.291648
5/8	.625	15.8750	.390625	.790569	.244141	.85499	1.96350	.306796
41/64	.640625	16.2719	.410400	.800391	.262913	.86205	2.01258	.322328
21/32	.65625	16.6688	.430664	.810093	.282623	.86901	2.06167	.338243
43/64	.671875	17.0656	.451416	.819680	.303295	.87585	2.11076	.354541
11/16	.6875	17.4625	.472656	.829156	.324951	.88259	2.15984	.371223

* Fraction represents diameter.

(Continued)

(Continued)

FRACTION EQUIVALENTS IN DECIMALS, MILLIMETERS, SQUARES, CUBES, SQUARE AND CUBE ROOTS, CIRCUMFERENCES AND AREAS OF CIRCLES, FROM 1/64 TO 1 INCH

Fraction*	Decimal	mm	Square	Square root	Cube	Cube root	Circle* circumference	Circle* area
45/64	.703125	17.8594	.494385	.838525	.347614	.88922	2.20893	.388289
23/32	.71875	18.2562	.516602	.847791	.371307	.89576	2.25802	.405737
47/64	.734375	18.6531	.539307	.856957	.396053	.90221	2.30711	.42370
3/4	.75	19.0500	.5625	.866025	.421875	.90856	2.35619	.441786
49/64	.765625	19.4469	.586182	.875	.448795	.91483	2.40528	.460386
25/32	.78125	19.8438	.610352	.883883	.476837	.92101	2.45437	.479369
51/64	.796875	20.2406	.635010	.892679	.506023	.92711	2.50346	.498736
13/16	.8125	20.6375	.660156	.901388	.536377	.93313	2.55254	.518486
53/64	.828125	21.0344	.685791	.910014	.567921	.93907	2.60163	.538619
27/32	.84375	21.4312	.711914	.918559	.600677	.94494	2.65072	.559136
55/64	.859375	21.8281	.738525	.927024	.634670	.95074	2.69981	.580036
7/8	.875	22.2250	.765625	.935414	.669922	.95647	2.74889	.601320
57/64	.890625	22.6219	.793213	.943729	.706455	.96213	2.79798	.622988
29/32	.90625	23.0188	.821289	.951972	.744293	.96772	2.84707	.645039
59/64	.921875	23.4156	.849854	.960143	.783459	.97325	2.89616	.667473
15/16	.9375	23.8125	.878906	.968246	.823975	.97872	2.94524	.690291
61/64	.953125	24.2094	.908447	.976281	.865864	.98412	2.99433	.713493
31/32	.96875	24.6062	.938477	.984251	.909149	.98947	3.04342	.737078
63/64	.984375	25.0031	.968994	.992157	.953854	.99476	3.09251	.761046
1	1	25.4000	1	1	1	1	3.14159	.785398

* Fraction represents diameter.

DECIMALS TO MILLIMETERS

Decimal	mm	Decimal	mm	Decimal	mm	Decimal	mm
0.001	0.0254	0.260	6.6040	0.510	12.9540	0.760	19.3040
0.002	0.0508	0.270	6.8580	0.520	13.2080	0.770	19.5580
0.003	0.0762	0.280	7.1120	0.530	13.4620	0.780	19.8120
0.004	0.1016	0.290	7.3660	0.540	13.7160	0.790	20.0660
0.005	0.1270	0.300	7.6200	0.550	13.9700	0.800	20.3200
0.006	0.1524	0.310	7.8740	0.560	14.2240	0.810	20.5740
0.007	0.1778	0.320	8.1280	0.570	14.4780	0.820	20.8280
0.008	0.2032	0.330	8.3820	0.580	14.7320	0.830	21.0820
0.009	0.2286	0.340	8.6360	0.590	14.9860	0.840	21.3360
0.010	0.2540	0.350	8.8900	0.600	15.2400	0.850	21.5900
0.020	0.5080	0.360	9.1440	0.610	15.4940	0.860	21.8440
0.030	0.7620	0.370	9.3980	0.620	15.7480	0.870	22.0980
0.040	1.0160	0.380	9.6520	0.630	16.0020	0.880	22.3520
0.050	1.2700	0.390	9.9060	0.640	16.2560	0.890	22.6060
0.060	1.5240	0.400	10.1600	0.650	16.5100	0.900	22.8600
0.070	1.7780	0.410	10.4140	0.660	16.7640	0.910	23.1140
0.080	2.0320	0.420	10.6680	0.670	17.0180	0.920	23.3680
0.090	2.2860	0.430	10.9220	0.680	17.2720	0.930	23.6220
0.100	2.5400	0.440	11.1760	0.690	17.5260	0.940	23,8760
0.110	2.7940	0.450	11.4300	0.700	17.7800	0.950	24.1300
0.120	3.0480	0.460	11.6840	0.710	18.0340	0.960	24.3840
0.130	3.3020	0.470	11.9380	0.720	18.2880	0.970	24.6380
0.140	3.5560	0.480	12.1920	0.730	18.5420	0.980	24.8920
0.150	3.8100	0.490	12.4460	0.740	18.7960	0.990	25.1460
0.160	4.0640	0.500	12.7000	0.750	19.0500	1.000	25.4000
0.170	4.3180						
0.180	4.5720						
0.190	4.8260						
0.200	5.0800						
0.210	5.3340						
0.220	5.5880						
0.230	5.8420						
0.240	6.0960						
0.250	6.3500						

Note: The first pair of columns is longer because the first ten items represent decimals to the thousandths place. Thereafter, decimals are rounded to the nearest hundredths.

TEMPERATURE CONVERSIONS

Temperature in everyday usage may be stated either in degrees Fahrenheit (°F) or in degrees Celsius or centigrade (°C). (Although the term "centigrade" is still often used in the United States, it was recommended by the International Committee on Weights and Measures and the National Bureau of Standards in 1948 that the term be officially changed to "Celsius," after Anders Celsius, the Swedish astronomer who invented the scale.)

Both scales are based on two fixed temperature points, the melting point of ice and the boiling point of water at normal atmospheric pressure.

On the Fahrenheit scale (named after Gabriel Daniel Fahrenheit, who devised it in 1714) the ice point is 32° and the steam point is 212°. The interval between these points is divided into 180 parts or degrees.

On the Celsius scale, the ice point is 0 and the steam point is 100, with the interval between divided into 100 parts or degrees.

By extending their scales beyond the ice point and the boiling point, both systems may be carried down to *absolute zero*, the temperature at which molecular motion ceases, and upward indefinitely as no upper limit to temperature is known.

On the Celsius scale, absolute zero is –273.16 degrees.

On the Fahrenheit scale, absolute zero is –459.69 degrees.

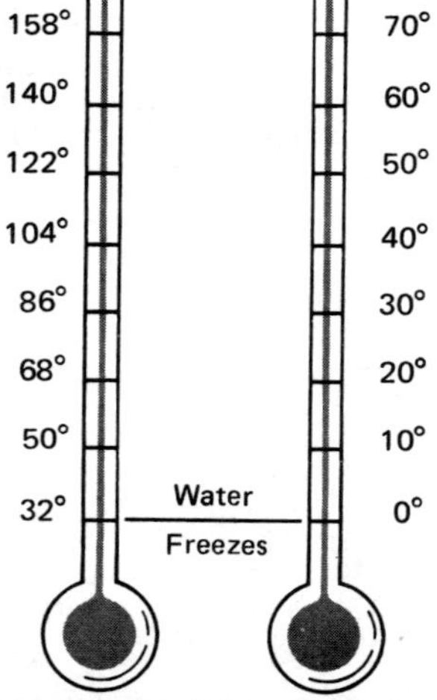

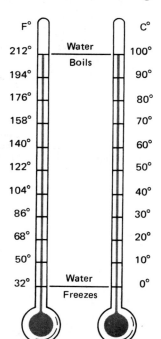

Comparison of Fahrenheit and Celsius scales, showing boiling and freezing point of water

TWO-WAY TEMPERATURE CONVERSION TABLE

°C		°F
−273.16	**−459.69**	
−184	**−300**	
−169	**−273**	−459.4
−157	**−250**	−418
−129	**−200**	−328
−101	**−150**	−238
−73.3	**−100**	−148
−45.6	**−50**	−58
−40.0	**−40**	−40
−34.4	**−30**	−22
−28.9	**−20**	−4
−23.3	**−10**	14
−17.8	**0**	32
−12.2	**10**	50
−6.67	**20**	68
−1.11	**30**	86
4.44	**40**	104
10.0	**50**	122
15.6	**60**	140
21.1	**70**	158
23.9	**75**	167
26.7	**80**	176
29.4	**85**	185
32.2	**90**	194
35.0	**95**	203
36.7	**98**	208.4
37.8	**100**	212
43	**110**	230
49	**120**	248
54	**130**	266
60	**140**	284
66	**150**	302
93	**200**	392
121	**250**	482
149	**300**	572

Find the temperature you want to convert—either Fahrenheit or Celsius (Centigrade)—among the boldface numbers in the center column. Then look to the appropriate column to the left or right to find the temperature you want to convert to.

Fahrenheit to Celsius (or Centigrade)

To convert from degrees Fahrenheit to degrees Celsius, first subtract 32 from the number of degrees F, then multiply the remainder by 5/9 (or 0.556).

Celsius to Fahrenheit

To convert from degrees Celsius to degrees Fahrenheit, multiply the number of degrees C by 9/5 (or 1.8) and add 32.

The Kelvin Scale

There is a third temperature scale that you may often read about but which you may never have occasion to use, unless you are a physicist. It is an absolute temperature scale called the Kelvin scale, after William Thomson, Lord Kelvin. This uses the Celsius unit for its degrees but places its 0 at absolute zero. The ice point then becomes 273.16° K and the boiling point 373.16° K. To convert Celsius to Kelvin, just add 273.16 degrees to the Celsius reading.

PERCENTAGE SOLUTIONS

Ordinarily percentage solutions may be made by dissolving an "X" amount of a chemical in enough water or some other solvent to make 100 parts. It becomes more complicated, however, when you have to dilute a solution of less than 100 percent to make another percent. In such a case, this simple crisscross method will help:

A B D X Y

To figure dilutions by this method:

1. Place the percentage strength of the solution to be diluted at A.
2. Place the percentage of the diluting solution at B. (Water should be entered as zero.)
3. Place the percentage desired at D.
4. Subtract D from A and place the answer at Y.
5. Subtract B from D and place at X.

Then mix X parts of A with Y parts of B to make the percent solution at D.

For example, to dilute 28-percent ammonium hydroxide to make a 5-percent solution:

28 0 5 5 23

Just add 5 parts of 28-percent ammonium hydroxide to 23 parts of water.

HOUSEHOLD WEIGHTS AND MEASURES

Weighing with Coins

Lack small weights for your balance? U.S. coins will serve quite well as substitutes. Here are their *approximate* values:

Dime	40 grains or 2½ grams
Penny	50 grains or 3⅛ grams
Nickel	80 grains or 5 grams
Quarter	100 grains or 6¼ grams
Half-dollar	200 grains or 12½ grams

An ounce equals 437.5 grains, therefore two half-dollars and a dime combined are near enough to serve as a 1-ounce weight.

Measuring with Coins

Ever caught without a ruler when you needed to know the thickness of a board? Money will help. The diameter of a U.S. cent is ¾ inch. Hold a penny against the edge of the stock and you can judge its thickness; ⅝, ¾ inch, or whatever.

Coins are also handy for determining the nominal sizes of steel water pipe. If the inside diameter of a pipe is about half the diameter of a quarter, it is nominal ⅜-inch pipe. If it is somewhat smaller than a dime, it is ½-inch pipe. If a penny fits inside loosely, you have ¾-inch pipe. In 1-inch pipe a quarter will fit loosely, but a half-dollar won't go. If the opening is twice the diameter of a dime, the pipe is 1¼ inches. Combined diameters of a nickel and a penny approximately equal the inside diameter of 1½-inch pipe. A half-dollar and a nickel add up to 2-inch pipe.

Approximate Household Measures

The following will be more accurate if you use standard measuring cups and measuring spoons.

1 teaspoon	⅙ fluid ounce
1 teaspoon	1.33 fluid drams
1 teaspoon	5 milliliters
1 teaspoon	5 medicine droppers
1 teaspoon	75 to 100 drops
1 tablespoon	½ fluid ounce
1 tablespoon	4 fluid drams
1 tablespoon	14.5 milliliters
1 tablespoon	3 teaspoons
1 cup	8 fluid ounces
1 cup	64 fluid drams
1 cup	237 milliliters
1 cup	48 teaspoons
1 cup	16 tablespoons
1 pint (liquid)	16 fluid ounces
1 pint	128 fluid drams
1 pint	473 milliliters
1 pint	96 teaspoons
1 pint	32 tablespoons
1 pint	2 cups
1 medicine dropper	about 20 drops
1 medicine dropper	1 milliliter (approx.)
1 grain	1 drop (approx.)
1 ounce	437.5 grains
1 ounce	28.35 grams
1 fluid ounce	8 fluid drams

1 fluid ounce	30 milliliters
1 fluid ounce	2 tablespoons
1 fluid ounce	6 teaspoons
1 quart (liquid)	0.946 liter
1 liter	1.056 quarts
1 gallon	8.33 pounds of water
1 gallon	231 cubic inches
1 gallon	0.1337 cubic foot
1 cubic foot of water	7.5 gallons

SHORTCUT CALCULATIONS FOR HOME AND SHOP PROBLEMS

Here are a few shortcut calculations for various home and shop problems.

TO DETERMINE PIPE SIZE FROM OUTSIDE DIMENSION. In the nominal sizes from ⅛ through 1 inch, standard, extra-strong, and double-extra-strong pipe measures approximately 5⁄16-inch larger on the outside than its nominal size specification (or so close that the pipe cannot be confused for another size). Simply measure the outside diameter and subtract 5⁄16 inch. Example: if the outside diameter of the pipe measures about 1 5⁄16 inches, 1 5⁄16 minus 5⁄16 gives 1 inch nominal size.

WATER CAPACITY OF PIPES. How much flow a water pipe will deliver depends upon more than its inside diameter (pressure, pipe length, and lift are also involved). But you can quickly compare the capacities of any two pipe sizes if you remember that they vary as the squares of the diameter. That's why pipe with a 1½-inch opening will deliver more than twice as much water as one with a 1-inch opening.

NAIL SIZES. These are pretty arbitrary, but the smaller nails fall into a pattern that can take the strain off your memory. Divide the penny size of a nail by 4 and add ½ inch to get its length in inches; or subtract ½ inch from the inch length of a nail and multiply by 4 to get its size. Thus an 8-penny (8d) nail is 2½ inches long (8 divided by 4 gives

2; 2 plus ½ gives 2½). But remember this works only for nails up to 10 penny (10d) or 3 inches.

WHAT PULLEY SIZE? When stepping up or reducing speed with pulleys, you are dealing with four factors: motor speed, drive-pulley diameter, and driven-pulley diameter. You know three of these factors and you want to find the fourth—the pulley size.

This is the way to figure it: Take the pulley of known diameter and speed (this may be actual or desired speed). Multiply speed by diameter and divide the result by the known diameter or speed (again actual or desired) of the other pulley. The result is the missing figure. For instance, your joiner has a 2½-inch pulley and you want it to turn at about 4,200 rpm. What size pulley should you put on your 1,725-rpm motor to run the joiner at that speed?

Multiply 4,200 by 2½, then divide by 1,725 and you get just over 6. Using a 6-inch pulley on the motor shaft will do the trick for you.

SURFACE SPEED OF SANDER. Revolutions per minute often must be converted into surface feet per minute to give you the recommended speed for a sanding drum or sanding belt (too high a speed will scorch the material being sanded). Knowing the desired surface feet per minute, you can determine the required rpm for the drum or the driven drum on a belt sander. Divide the surface-feet-per-minute figure by the drum diameter in inches multiplied by .262. Once you have the rpm figure, use the preceding pulley formula to get the required belt-driven ratio.

SURFACE FEET OF WORK IN LATHE. Feet per minute for a given spindle speed and work (or tool) diameter can be determined by multiplying ¼ of the speed by the work or tool diameter. For example: For a lathe running 400 rpm, 3-inch work diameter, what is the sfm (surface feet per minute)? Here's how: ¼ of 400 rpm equals 100; 100 times 3 inches gives 300 sfm.

When you want to select a speed to give a desired surface speed, divide desired sfm by work or tool diameter and then multiply by 4. Example: You want 300 sfm for 3-inch work diameter. Find machine speed required this way: 300 divided by 3 inches gives 100; 100 times 4 gives 400 rpm. These mental calculations are accurate to something like 4 percent.

BEAM STIFFNESS. Stiffness refers to how much a beam will bend under a given weight. The formula for determining it is: width multiplied by the cube of the depth.

Comparing a full 2×10 with a full 4×6, you have 2×10×10×10 versus 4×6×6×6, giving a ratio of 2,000 to 846. So although the 4×6 contains more lumber and costs more, it will sag 2⅓ times as much as the 2×10 beam when it is carrying the same load.

BEAM STRENGTH. Comparing the cross-sectional area of two beams does not necessarily give you their relative strength. For example: A full 2×10 joist will take about a 39-percent greater load than a full 4×6, although it weighs and costs one-sixth less. Use the following formula for determining the load-bearing strength: Square the dimension in the direction of the stress, and multiply that figure by the other dimension. In the case of joists, the direction of stress is, of course, through the greater dimension of the beams. With the 2×10 you therefore get 10×10×2, or 200, as against 6×6×4, or 144 for the 4×6. The difference in strength between dressed lumber and its nominal size is so slight that for practical purposes it can be ignored.

CYLINDRICAL TANK CAPACITY. Remember that a circle has approximately three-fourths the area of a square drawn around it, plus 5 percent of this figure. Multiply this total by the height or length of the tank in like units of measurement to get the volume. Convert to cubic feet and multiply the resulting figure by 7½, which is the approximate number of gallons to the cubic foot.

SPHERICAL TANK CAPACITY. A sphere has approximately half the volume of a cube drawn around it, plus 5 percent of the figure arrived at. Again, multiply the cubic footage by 7½ to get gallons.

WEIGHTS OF MATERIALS

Weights of Liquids

The old axiom "a pint's a pound the world around" is a good rule of thumb on which to estimate the weights of liquids. Actually a pint of water weighs just a fraction of an ounce over a pound. Pints of most watery fluids will tip the scale at about a pound. Alcohol, oil, gasoline, turpentine, and similar fluids weigh a little less. Other liquids, such as carbon tetrachloride and glycerin, weigh a little more.

For an approximation of the weight in pounds of a pint of the following liquids, multiply by the first number given. The second number tells you directly the number of pounds per cubic foot.

WEIGHTS OF LIQUIDS

Liquid	Specific gravity	Pounds per cubic foot
Acetone	0.792	49.4
Alcohol, ethyl	0.791	49.4
Alcohol, methyl	0.810	50.5
Benzene	0.899	56.1
Carbon tetrachloride	1.595	99.6
Ether	0.736	45.9
Gasoline	0.66–0.69	41–43
Glycerin	1.26	78.6
Kerosene	0.82	51.2
Linseed oil	0.942	58.8
Mercury	13.6	849
Milk	1.028–0.1035	64.2–64.6
Sea water	0.125	63.99
Turpentine	0.87	54.3
Water	1.0	62.4

The Meaning of Specific Gravity

The number you multiply with in the above table is labeled "specific gravity" (abbreviated sp. gr.). This is simply the ratio of the weight of a substance to that of an equal volume of water at the same temperature. It can also be considered to be the *density* of a substance in terms of grams per milliliter (or cubic centimeter), for in its densest state (at 3.98° C) 1 milliliter of pure water weighs exactly 1 gram.

Knowing the specific gravity of a substance can be useful in many ways. For instance, it can help you to figure out how much of a particular substance you can fit in a bottle, or a packing case, or the trunk of your car; or, turning things around, how much a certain volume of a given substance will weigh. Then again you can often tell one pure liquid from another just by determining its specific gravity. By the same means, you can also determine the concentration of certain acids and salt solutions, the percentage of alcohol in liquors and antifreeze, and even the charge on the battery in your car.

Determining Density with a Hydrometer

Measurement of the specific gravity of liquids is conveniently done with a hydrometer, a simple device of glass that is floated in a sample of the liquid to be tested. The calibrated stem of the hydrometer projects at a height out of the liquid depending upon the liquid's density.

Hydrometers are made with special scales for testing alcohol, milk, oils, sugar solutions, and the relative condition of battery charge. Most hydrometers, however, read either directly in specific gravity or in

(Text continues on page 560)

SPECIFIC GRAVITY CONVERSIONS, READINGS AT 60° F (15.55° C)

Specific gravity	Light Baumé degrees	Heavy Baumé degrees	Pounds per gallon	Gallons per pound
0.6600	82		5.50	0.1818
0.6731	78		5.60	0.1786
0.6863	74		5.72	0.1748
0.700	70		5.83	0.1715
0.7071	68		5.89	0.1698
0.7216	64		6.01	0.1664
0.7368	60		6.14	0.1629
0.7527	56		6.27	0.1595
0.7692	52		6.41	0.1560
0.7685	48		6.55	0.1527
0.8046	44		6.70	0.1493
0.8235	40		6.86	0.1458
0.8434	36		7.03	0.1422
0.8642	32		7.20	0.1389
0.8861	28		7.38	0.1355
0.9091	24		7.57	0.1321
0.9333	20		7.78	0.1285
0.9589	16		7.99	0.1252
0.9722	14		8.10	0.1235
0.9859	12		8.21	0.1218
1.000	10	0	8.33	0.1200
1.007		1	8.38	0.1193
1.014		2	8.46	0.1182
1.021		3	8.50	0.1176
1.028		4	8.56	0.1168
1.043		6	8.69	0.1151
1.058		8	8.81	0.1135
1.074		10	8.94	0.1119
1.090		12	9.08	0.1101

(Continued)

(*Continued*)

SPECIFIC GRAVITY CONVERSIONS, READINGS AT 60° F (15.55° C)

Specific gravity	Light Baumé degrees	Heavy Baumé degrees	Pounds per gallon	Gallons per pound
1.107		14	9.21	0.1086
1.124		16	9.36	0.1068
1.142		18	9.51	0.1052
1.160		20	9.67	0.1034
1.198		24	9.99	0.1001
1.239		28	10.32	0.0969
1.283		32	10.69	0.0935
1.330		36	11.09	0.0902
1.381		40	11.51	0.869
1.436		44	11.96	0.0836
1.495		48	12.45	0.0800
1.559		52	12.99	0.0769
1.629		56	13.57	0.0737
1.706		60	14.21	0.0704

SPECIFIC GRAVITY AND WEIGHTS OF COMMON SOLIDS

Substance	Specific gravity	Weight in pounds per cubic foot
Acrylic plastics	1.18	74
Aluminum, hard-drawn	2.7	168
Asbestos	2.0–2.8	125–175
Asphalt	1.1–1.5	69–94
Basalt	2.4–3.1	150–190
Beeswax	0.96–0.97	60–61
Brass	8.2–8.7	511–543
Brick	1.4–2.2	87–137
Bronze	8.74–8.89	545–554
Cement, portland	1.5	94
Cement, set	2.7–3.0	170–190
Chalk	1.9–2.8	118–175
Clay	1.8–2.6	112–162
Coal, anthracite	1.4–1.8	87–112
Coal, anthracite, piled		47–58

Substance	Specific gravity	Weight in pounds per cubic foot
Coal, bituminous	1.2–1.5	75–94
Coal, bituminous, piled		40–54
Concrete	2.3	145
Copper, hard-drawn	8.89	555
Cork	0.22–0.26	14–16
Earth, dry, loose		65–88
Earth, moist, compacted		95–135
Glass, common	2.4–2.8	150–175
Glass, flint	2.9–5.9	180–370
Gold, wrought	19.33	1207
Granite	2.46–2.76	165–172
Gravel, damp, loose		82–125
Gravel, dry, compacted		90–145
Gypsum	2.31–2.33	144–145
Ice	0.917	57
Iron, cast gray	7.03–7.13	439–445
Iron, wrought	7.8–7.9	487–492
Ivory	1.83–1.92	114–120
Lead	11.0	687
Lime	0.87–1.2	53–75
Magnesium	1.74	109
Marble	2.6–2.8	160–177
Nickel	8.6–8.9	537–556
Paraffin	0.87–0.91	54–57
Phenolic plastic, cast	1.27–1.31	79–82
Platinum	21.37	1334
Polyethylene	0.92	57
Sand, damp, loose		94
Sand, dry, compacted		110
Sandstone	2.14–2.35	134–147
Silver, wrought	10.6	662
Snow, fresh fallen		5–12
Snow, wet, compact		15–20
Steel	7.83	489
Styrene plastic	1.06	66
Tar	1.02	64
Tin	7.29	455
Vinyl plastic	1.4	87
Zinc	7.1	443

degrees Baumé (pronounced *boe-MAY*). The latter system of units was devised in 1768 by the French chemist Antoine Baumé in an attempt to provide a simpler scale. In fact, he devised two scales—one for liquids lighter than water, and one for those heavier. Because the Baumé hydrometer, with its uniformly spaced divisions, was easy to make and easy to read, it caught on quickly and is used for some purposes to this day. The Baumé scale is, though, purely arbitrary and so you often have to convert it into specific gravity to continue your calculations. To help you in this, see the table on pages 557 and 558.

SPECIFIC GRAVITY AND WEIGHTS OF WOODS

Wood, seasoned	Specific gravity	Weight in pounds per cubic foot
Apple	0.66–0.84	41–52
Ash	0.65–0.85	40–53
Balsa	0.11–0.14	7–9
Basswood	0.32–0.39	20–37
Beech	0.70–0.90	43–56
Birch	0.51–0.77	32–48
Blue gum	1.00	62
Box	0.95–1.16	59–72
Butternut	0.38	24
Ebony	1.11–1.33	69–83
Greenheart	1.06–1.23	66–77
Hickory	0.60–0.93	37–58
Ironwood, black	1.08	67
Lignum vitae	1.17–1.33	73–83
Mahogany, Honduras	0.66	41
Mahogany, Spanish	0.85	53
Maple	0.62–0.75	39–47
Oak	0.60–0.90	37–56
Pine, pitch	0.83–0.85	52–53
Pine, white	0.35–0.50	22–31
Pine, yellow	0.37–0.60	23–37
Redwood	0.44	27
Satinwood	0.95	59
Spruce	0.48–0.70	30–44
Teak, African	0.98	61
Teak, Indian	0.66–0.88	41–55
Walnut	0.64–0.70	40–43
Willow	0.40–0.60	24–37

SPECIFIC GRAVITY AND WEIGHT OF GASES

The specific gravity of gases and vapors listed below is based on a system in which the specific gravity of air is 1, the atmospheric pressure normal, and the temperature 32° F or 0° C.

Gas	Weight in pounds per cubic foot	Specific gravity
Acetylene	0.0732	0.907
Air	.0807	1.000
Ammonia	.04813	0.540
Butane, iso	.1669	2.067
Carbon dioxide	.123	1.529
Carbon monoxide	.07806	0.967
Chlorine	.2006	2.486
Ether vapor	.2088	2.586
Ethylene	.07868	0.975
Helium	.01114	0.318
Hydrogen	.00561	0.070
Mercury vapor	.56013	6.940
Methane	.04475	0.554
Nitrogen	.07807	0.967
Oxygen	.08921	1.105
Propane	.1254	1.554
Sulfur dioxide	.1827	2.264
Water vapor	.05028	0.623

ENGLISH AND METRIC SYSTEMS

How Long is a Meter?

You are taught in school that the meter, the unit of length in the Metric System, is roughly 39.37 inches. Scientists who set the standards, however, have to be more precise.

As originally proposed, the meter was to be equal to one 10-millionth part of the quarter-meridian (the distance from the North Pole to the Equator) passing through Paris. To try to find out how long the quarter-meridian really was, two engineer-surveyors spent six years surveying the land between Barcelona and Dunkirk. They calculated the rest. In 1799, based on this work, a standard meter was constructed.

In 1960, the Eleventh General (International) Conference on Weights and Measures redefined the meter in terms of measurements of modern science. Today the standard meter is a unit of length equal to 1,650,763.73 wavelengths in a vacuum of the orange-red radiation of krypton 86 corresponding to the unperturbed transition between the $2p_{10}$ and $5d_5$ levels. No need now to travel to the North Pole to check your meter stick!

Multiplier Prefixes for the Metric or International System

By combining the following prefixes with such basic unit names as meter, gram, liter, volt, ampere, or ohm, you can indicate the multiples and submultiples of the Metric or International System. For example, by combining the prefix "kilo" with "volt," you can get "kilovolt," meaning "1,000 volts"; by combining "milli" with it, you get "millivolt," or "0.001 volt."

Prefix	Abbreviation	Multiplier	
tera	T	10^{12}	or 1,000,000,000,000
giga	G	10^{9}	or 1,000,000,000
mega	M	10^{6}	or 1,000,000
kilo	k	10^{3}	or 1,000
hecto	h	10^{2}	or 100
deka	da	10	or 10
deci	d	10^{-1}	or .1
centi	c	10^{-2}	or .01
milli	m	10^{-3}	or .001
micro	μ	10^{-6}	or .000001
mano	n	10^{-9}	or .000000001
pico	p	10^{-12}	or .000000000001
femto	f	10^{-15}	or .000000000000001
atto	a	10^{-18}	or .000000000000000001

MILLIMETERS TO DECIMALS

mm	Decimal	mm	Decimal	mm	Decimal	mm	Decimal
0.01	.00039	0.06	.00236	0.11	.00433	0.16	.00630
0.02	.00079	0.07	.00276	0.12	.00472	0.17	.00669
0.03	.00118	0.08	.00315	0.13	.00512	0.18	.00709
0.04	.00157	0.09	.00354	0.14	.00551	0.19	.00748
0.05	.00197	0.10	.00394	0.15	.00591	0.20	.00787

mm	Decimal	mm	Decimal	mm	Decimal	mm	Decimal
0.21	.00827	0.61	.02402	1	.03937	41	1.61417
0.22	.00866	0.62	.02441	2	.07874	42	1.65354
0.23	.00906	0.63	.02480	3	.11811	43	1.69291
0.24	.00945	0.64	.02520	4	.15748	44	1.73228
0.25	.00984	0.65	.02559	5	.19685	45	1.77165
0.26	.01024	0.66	.02598	6	.23622	46	1.81102
0.27	.01063	0.67	.02638	7	.27559	47	1.85039
0.28	.01102	0.68	.02677	8	.31496	48	1.88976
0.29	.01142	0.69	.02717	9	.35433	49	1.92913
0.30	.01181	0.70	.02756	10	.39370	50	1.96850
0.31	.01220	0.71	.02795	11	.43307	51	2.00787
0.32	.01260	0.72	.02835	12	.47244	52	2.04724
0.33	.01299	0.73	.02874	13	.51181	53	2.08661
0.34	.01339	0.74	.02913	14	.55118	54	2.12598
0.35	.01378	0.75	.02953	15	.59055	55	2.16535
0.36	.01417	0.76	.02992	16	.62992	56	2.20472
0.37	.01457	0.77	.03032	17	.66929	57	2.24409
0.38	.01496	0.78	.03071	18	.70866	58	2.28346
0.39	.01535	0.79	.03110	19	.74803	59	2.32283
0.40	.01575	0.80	.03150	20	.78740	60	2.36220
0.41	.01614	0.81	.03189	21	.82677	61	2.40157
0.42	.01654	0.82	.03228	22	.86614	62	2.44094
0.43	.01693	0.83	.03268	23	.90551	63	2.48031
0.44	.01732	0.84	.03307	24	.94488	64	2.51969
0.45	.01772	0.85	.03346	25	.98425	65	2.55906
0.46	.01811	0.86	.03386	26	1.02362	66	2.59843
0.47	.01850	0.87	.03425	27	1.06299	67	2.63780
0.48	.01890	0.88	.03465	28	1.10236	68	2.67717
0.49	.01929	0.89	.03504	29	1.14173	69	2.71654
0.50	.01969	0.90	.03543	30	1.18110	70	2.75591
0.51	.02008	0.91	.03583	31	1.22047	71	2.79528
0.52	.02047	0.92	.03622	32	1.25984	72	2.83465
0.53	.02087	0.93	.03661	33	1.29921	73	2.87402
0.54	.02126	0.94	.03701	34	1.33858	74	2.91339
0.55	.02165	0.95	.03740	35	1.37795	75	2.95276
0.56	.02205	0.96	.03780	36	1.41732	76	2.99213
0.57	.02244	0.97	.03819	37	1.45669	77	3.03150
0.58	.02283	0.98	.03858	38	1.49606	78	3.07087
0.59	.02323	0.99	.03898	39	1.53543	79	3.11024
0.60	.02362	1.00	.03937	40	1.57480	80	3.14961

(Continued)

(Continued)

mm	Decimal	mm	Decimal	mm	Decimal	mm	Decimal
81	3.18898	86	3.38583	91	3.58268	96	3.77953
82	3.22835	87	3.42520	92	3.62205	97	3.81890
83	3.26772	88	3.46457	93	3.66142	98	3.85827
84	3.30709	89	3.50394	94	3.70079	99	3.89764
85	3.34646	90	3.54331	95	3.74016	100	3.93701

BOTTLE SIZES

The following is a conversion between alcohol spirit and wine bottle sizes and the new metric bottles:

Old bottle size	Fluid ounces	New bottle size	Fluid ounces
Split	6.4	187 milliliters	6.3
⅘ pint	12.8	375 milliliters	12.7
⅘ quart	25.6	750 milliliters	25.4
1 quart	32.0	1.0 liter	33.8
Magnum	51.2	1.5 liters	50.7
½ gallon	64.0	No conversion (Wineries will be using 50.7 ounces, 1.5 liter size here.)	
Jeroboam	102.4	3.0 liters	101.4
1 gallon	128.0	No conversion (Wineries will be using 101.4 ounces, 3 liter size here.)	

MISCELLANEOUS UNITS OF MEASUREMENT

AGATE. A size of type approximately 5½ point. Also a printing measure of 1⁄14 inch used for column length in periodical advertising.

ANGSTROM (A or λ). This is 0.0001 micron or 1 ten-billionth of a meter. Used in measuring the length of light waves.

ASTRONOMICAL UNIT (A.U.). A unit used in astronomy equal to the mean distance of the earth from the sun (93 million miles).

BARREL (bbl). For liquids except petroleum, 31½ U.S. gallons; for petroleum, 42 gallons. For dry products except cranberries, 105 dry quarts or 7,056 cubic inches; for cranberries, 5,826 cubic inches. An English beer barrel holds 43.23 U.S. gallons.

BOARD FOOT (bd ft). Designates lumber 12 inches by 12 inches by 1 inch, or 144 cubic inches.

BOLT. For measuring cloth, it is 40 yards. For measuring wallpaper, the bolt equals 16 yards.

CABLE'S LENGTH. At sea, 100 to 120 fathoms, or 200 to 240 yards.

CARAT (c). 200 milligrams or 3.086 grains troy. Named from the seed of the carob plant that was once used as a weight in the Mediterranean countries. Used for weighing precious stones. When spelled karat or k or kt, the term means a twenty-fourth part in expressing the proportion of fineness of a gold alloy. For example, a gold alloy containing 18/24 by weight of gold is 18 karats fine.

CHAIN (ch). The length of an actual chain used by surveyors. It is 66 feet, or 1/80 mile long, and is divided into 100 parts called links.

CUBIT. Used thousands of years ago by the Babylonians and Egyptians, the cubit was the first unit of measurement recorded in history. It represented the distance between the elbow and the tip of the extended middle finger. A modified Egyptian cubit—the Olympic cubit—was later used by the Greeks and Romans and was equal to our 18.24 inches. In English measure, the cubit became 18 inches.

ELL. The English ell is 45 inches. In the past and in different communities, the value of the ell has ranged from 24.7 to 48 inches. At present in the Netherlands, the ell is the meter, or 39.37 inches. It is used for measuring cloth.

FATHOM (fath). Originally the distance to which a man could stretch his arms. Now standardized as 6 feet. Used chiefly for measuring cables and depth of water.

FURLONG. In Anglo-Saxon times, the furlong meant what its name said—a furrow's length, or the length of an average furrow plowed by a farmer. Today it means 40 rods or 220 yards.

HAND. Derived from the width of the hand, this measurement is now 4 inches or 10.16 centimeters. Used for measuring the height of horses.

HOGSHEAD (hhd). A wine and other liquid measure, once quite variable but now standardized at 63 U.S. gallons or 238.5 liters.

KNOT. This is not a unit of distance, but a rate of speed of 1 nautical mile an hour. It is therefore not correct to say a ship travels "at 28 knots an hour"; it travels simply "at 28 knots."

LEAGUE. A unit used in different countries and at different times to mean distances varying from about 2.4 to 4.6 miles. In English-speaking countries it now usually means 3 miles—either nautical or statute—but is generally used vaguely or poetically.

LIGHT-YEAR. Nearly 6 trillion miles, the distance light travels in a year at the rate of more than 186,000 miles a second. Used for measuring distances in interstellar space.

LINK. One-hundredth part of a chain, or 7.92 inches. Used by surveyors.

MAGNUM. Wine or spirit bottle holding about ⅖ gallon or the amount such a bottle will hold.

MICRON (μ). One thousandth of a millimeter. Used for scientific measurements.

MIL. One thousandth of an inch. Used especially for measuring the diameter of wire. A circular mil represents the area of a circle 1 mil in diameter. The area of a cross section of wire is generally expressed in circular mils.

NAUTICAL MILE. Theoretically equal to 1 minute or 1/21600 part of a great circle of the earth, or roughly 1⅙ land miles. As the earth is not a perfect circle, various lengths have been assigned to it in different times and places. The British Admiralty mile, for instance, is equal to 6,080 feet or 1,853.2 meters. A U.S. unit, no longer officially used, is 6,080.2 feet or 1,853.248 meters. An international unit equal to 6,076.115 feet or 1,852 meters has been used officially by the U.S. since 1959. The nautical mile is used in both sea and air navigation.

PICA. One-sixth inch or 12 points. Used for measurements in printing and as the name for 12-point type.

PIPE. Wine measure equal to 2 hogsheads.

POINT. Approximately 1/72 inch or 1/12 pica. Used for measuring type size.

QUIRE. Measure for paper quantity—originally 24 sheets, but now usually 25. Twenty quires make a ream.

REAM. Measure for paper quantity—originally 480 sheets, but now usually 500.

ROD. Today a rod equals 5½ yards or 16½ feet. This measure was originally determined in the 16th century by lining up 16 men, left-foot-to-left-foot, as they left church on Sunday morning.

SPAN. An English unit equal to 9 inches or 22.86 centimeters. Derived from the distance between the tip of thumb and the tip of the little finger when both are outstretched.

STONE. A varying unit of weight that in the past has ranged from 4 to 26 pounds avoirdupois. In Great Britain it today has a legal value of 14 pounds.

TOWNSHIP. A division of territory in surveys of U.S. public land, measuring almost 36 square miles. The south, east, and west borders are each 6 miles long. As the latter two follow the meridians of the earth, the north border is a little shorter. Often these geological townships have later become also political townships.

TUN. The capacity of a large cask by the same name—2 pipes, 4 hogheads, or 252 old English wine gallons (which are the same as U.S. gallons).

CONVERSION OF COMMON UNITS

The following table has been compiled especially for this book in the hope that it might make conversions from one measurement unit to another faster and simpler. In it common units of weight, area, volume, power, velocity, and so on are not separated into categories as is often done, but are listed in straight alphabetical order. To use it, just find in the left column the unit you want to convert, then in the middle column the one you want to convert to. Convert merely by multiplying the number of original units by the number you find directly to the right of the second unit.

To convert from such units as spoons, cups, and other household utensils, see earlier section "Approximate Household Measures," and to convert from specialized units and others not commonly used, see "Miscellaneous Units of Measurement." Unless otherwise mentioned, all weight units are avoirdupois, and all volume units (pints, bushels, gallons, etc.) are U.S. Customary units.

CONVERSIONS OF COMMON UNITS

To convert from	To	Multiply by
Acceleration by gravity	centimeters per second	980.665
	feet per second	32.16
Acres	hectares	0.4047
	square chains	10.0
	square feet	43,560.0
	square miles	0.00156
	centiares	100.0
	square yards	119.6
Atmospheres (atm)	inches of mercury	29.921
	feet of water	33.934
	kilograms per square centimeter	1.033228
	pounds per square inch	14.6959
British thermal units (Btu)	calories	0.252
	foot-pounds	778.0
	watt-seconds	1,054.86
Bushels	bushels, imperial	0.968
	cubic feet	1.2445
	cubic inches	2,150.42
	liters	35.2393
	pecks	4.0
	pints, dry	64.0
	quarts, dry	32.0
Calories (cal)	British thermal units	3.9682
	foot-pounds	3,088.4

To convert from	To	Multiply by
Candles per square centimeter	Lamberts	3.142
Candles per square inch	Lamberts	0.4869
Carats	grains	3.086
Centares	square inches	1,549.997
	square meters	1.0
Centigrade, degrees (°C)	Fahrenheit, degrees	$\frac{9}{5} \times °C + 32$
Centigrams (cg)	grains	0.1543
	grams	0.01
Centiliters (cl)	liters	0.01
	ounces; fluid	0.0338
Centimeters (cm)	feet	0.0328
	inches	0.3937
	meters	0.01
Chains (surveyor's)	furlongs	0.10000
	miles, statute	0.01250
	links	100.0
Circle (angular)	degrees	360.0
Circular inch (cir in)	area of a 1-inch-diameter circle	1.0
	circular mils	1,000,000.0
	square inches	0.7854
Circular mil	area of a 0.001-inch-diameter circle	1.0
	circular inches	0.0000001
Circumference of the earth at the equator	miles, nautical	21,600.0
Circumference of the earth at the equator	miles, statute	24,874.5
Cord (cd), of wood, (4 × 4 × 8)	cubic feet	128.0
Cubic centimeters (cu cm)	cubic feet	0.00003531
	cubic inches	0.06102

(Continued)

CONVERSIONS OF COMMON UNITS *(Continued)*

To convert from	To	Multiply by
Cubic centimeters (cu cm)	liters	0.0010
	cubic meter	0.0000010
Cubic decimeters	cubic centimeters	1,000.0
	cubic inches	61.02
Cubic feet (cu ft)	bushels	0.80290
	cords, of wood	0.00781
	cubic centimeters	28,317.08
	cubic inches	1,728.0
	cubic meters	0.0283
	cubic yards	0.0370
	gallons	7.4805
	liters	28.3163
	perch, of masonry	0.04040
Cubic feet of water at 39.1° Fahrenheit (° F)	kilograms	28.3156
	pounds	62.4245
Cubic inches (cu in)	bushels, imperial	0.00045
	bushels	0.00046
	cubic centimeters	16.3872
	cubic feet	0.00058
	cubic meters	0.000016
	cubic yards	0.0000214
	gallons	0.00432
	liters	0.0164
	pecks	0.00186
	pints, dry	0.02976
	pints, liquid	0.0346
	quarts, dry	0.01488
	quarts, liquid	0.0173
Cubic meters (cu m or m^3)	cubic centimeters	1,000,000.0
	cubic feet	35.3133
	cubic inches	61,023.3753
	cubic yards	1.3079
	gallons	264.170

To convert from	To	Multiply by
Cubic millimeters (cu mm or mm³)	cubic centimeters	0.001
	cubic inches	0.00006
Cubic yards (cu yd)	cubic feet	27.0
	cubic inches	46,656.0
	cubic meters	0.7646
Decagrams	grams	10.0
	ounces, avoirdupois	0.3527
Deciliters	bushels	0.284
	gallons	2.64
	liters	10.0
Decameters	inches	393.7
	meters	10.0
Decigrams	grains	1.5432
	grams	0.1
Deciliter	ounces, fluid	0.338
Deciliters	liters	0.1
Decimeters	inches	3.937
	meters	0.01
Degrees (arc)	radians	0.0175
Degrees (at the equator)	miles, nautical	60.0
	miles, statute	69.168
Degrees (deg or °)	minutes	60.0
Dozens (doz)	units	12.0
Drams (dr), apothecaries	grains	60.0
	grams	3.543
	scruples	3.0
Drams, avoirdupois	grains	27.344
	grams	1.772
	ounces, avoirdupois	0.0625
Drams, fluid	cubic inches	0.2256
	milliliters	3.6966

(Continued)

CONVERSIONS OF COMMON UNITS *(Continued)*

To convert from	To	Multiply by
Drams, fluid	minims	60.0
	ounces, fluid	0.125
Dynes	grams	0.00102
Fahrenheit	centigrade, degrees	$\frac{5\,(°F - 32)}{9}$
Fathoms	feet	6.0
	meters	1.8288
	yards	2.0
Feet (ft)	centimeters	30.4801
	fathom	0.16667
	inches	12.0
	links	0.66000
	meters	0.3048
	miles	0.000189
	miles, nautical	0.0001645
	rods	0.06061
	yards	0.3333
Feet of water at 62° Fahrenheit	killigrams per square meter	304.442
	pounds per square foot	62.355
	pounds per square inch	0.4334
Feet per second (fps)	knots	0.5921
	miles per hour	0.6816
Foot-pounds (ft-lb)	British thermal units	0.00129
	calories	0.00032
	meter-kilograms	0.13835
Foot-pounds per minute	horsepower	0.000003
Foot-pounds per second	horsepower	0.000018
Furlongs	chains	10.0
	feet	660.0
	meters	201.17
	miles, statute	0.12500
	yards	220.0

To convert from	To	Multiply by
Gallons (gal)	ounces, U.S. fluid	128.0
Gallons, imperial	gallons, U.S.	1.2009
Gallons (gal), imperial	liters	4.54607
Gallons, U.S.	cubic feet	0.1337
	cubic inches	231.0
	cubic meters	0.0038
	gallons, imperial	0.8327
	liters	3.7878
Gallons, U.S., water	pounds	8.5
Gills	pints, liquid	0.25
Grains	drams, avoirdupois	0.0366
	grams	0.0648
	milligrams	64.7989
	ounces, avoirdupois	0.00229
	ounces, troy and apothecaries'	0.00208
	pounds, avoirdupois	0.00014
	pounds, troy and apothecaries'	0.00017
Grams (g)	dynes	981
	grains	15.4475
	kilograms	0.0010
	milligrams	1,000.0
	ounces, avoirdupois	0.0353
	pounds, avoirdupois	0.0022
Grams per cubic centimeter	kilograms per cubic meter	1,000.0
	pounds per cubic foot	62.4
	pounds per cubic inch	0.03613
Gross	dozen	12.0
Gross, great	gross	12.0
Hands	inches	4.0
Hectares	square meters	10,000
	acres	2.471

(Continued)

CONVERSIONS OF COMMON UNITS *(Continued)*

To convert from	To	Multiply by
Hectograms	grams	100.0
	ounces, avoirdupois	3.5274
Hectoliters	gallons	26.417
	liters	100.0
Hectometers	feet	328.083
	meters	100.0
Horsepower (hp)	kilogram-meters per second	76.042
	foot-pounds per second	550.0
	foot-pounds per minute	33,000.0
	metric horsepower	1.0139
	watts per minute	746.0
Horsepower, metric	horsepower	0.9862
	foot pounds per minute	32,550.0
	foot pounds per second	542.5
	kilogram meters per second	75.0
Inches (in)	centimeters	2.5400
	feet	0.08333
	hands	0.25000
	links	0.12626
	meters	0.0254
	mils	1,000.0
	spans	0.11111
	yards	0.02778
Inches of mercury	feet of water	1.1341
	grams per square centimeter	34.542
	inches of water	13.6092
	pounds per square inch	0.49115
Inches of water	grams per square centimeter	2.537
	inches of mercury	0.07347
	pounds per square foot	5.1052
Kilocycles	cycles per second	1,000.0
Kilogram-meters (kg-m)	pound-feet	7.2330

To convert from	To	Multiply by
Kilogram-meters per second	horsepower	0.01305
	horsepower, metric	0.01333
Kilograms (kg)	grains	15,432.36
	grams	1,000.0
	ounces, avoirdupois	35.2740
	pounds, avoirdupois	2.2046
	tons	0.00110
	tons, long	0.00098
	tons, metric	0.001
Kilograms per cubic meter (kg per cu m or kg/m³)	pounds per cubic foot	0.06243
Kilograms per meter	pounds per foot	0.6721
Kilograms per square centimeter	pounds per square inch	14.22
Kilograms per square meter	pounds per square inch	0.2048
	pounds per square inch	0.00142
Kiloliters (kl)	liters	1,000.0
Kilometers (km)	feet	3,280.8330
	meters	1,000.0
	miles, nautical	0.5396
	miles, statute	0.6214
Kilometers per hour	knots	0.5396
	miles per hour	0.62138
Kilowatt-hours (kwhr)	British thermal units per hour	3,412.75
	horsepower hours	1.3414
Kilowatts (kw)	foot-pounds per minute	0.04426
Knots	feet per second	1.6889
	kilometers per hour	1.8532
	meters per second	0.5148
	miles per hour	1.1516
	nautical miles per hour	1.0

(Continued)

CONVERSIONS OF COMMON UNITS *(Continued)*

To convert from	To	Multiply by
Lamberts	candles per square centimeter	0.3183
	candles per square inch	2.054
Leagues, land	kilometers	4.83
	miles, nautical	2.6050
	miles, statute	3.0
Leagues, marine	kilometers	5.56
	miles, nautical	3.0
	miles, statute	3.45
Links	chains	0.01
	feet	0.66
	inches	7.92
	rods	0.04
	yards	0.22
Liters (l)	bushels	0.0284
	cubic centimeters	1,000.0
	cubic feet	0.035313
	cubic inches	61.02398
	gallons, imperial	0.2199
	gallons, U.S.	0.2641
	pecks	0.1135
	quarts, dry	0.9081
	quarts, liquid	1.0567
Long tons	pounds, avoirdupois	2,240.0
Lumens per square foot	foot-candles	1.0
Lux	foot-candles	0.0929
Megacycles	cycles per second	1,000,000.0
Megameters	meters	100,000.0
Meter-kilograms (m-kg)	foot-pounds	7.2330
Meters (m)	fathoms	0.5468
	feet	3.2808
	inches	39.370
	miles, nautical	0.000541

To convert from	To	Multiply by
Meters (m)	miles	0.000622
	yards	1.0936
Meters per second	knots	1.9425
	miles per hour	2.2369
Microns	inches	0.000039
	meters	0.000001
	mils	0.03937
Miles, nautical	feet	6,080.20
	kilometers	1.85325
	leagues, marine	0.33333
	meters	1,853.2486
	miles, statute	1.1516
Miles per hour (mph)	feet per second	1.4667
	kilometers per hour	1.6093
	knots	0.8684
	meters per second	0.4470
Miles, statute	chains	80.0
	feet	5,280.0
	furlongs	8.0
	kilometers	1.6093
	leagues, land	0.33333
	meters	1,609.35
	miles, nautical	0.86836
	yards	1,760.0
Milligrams (mg)	grains	0.01543
	grams	0.001
Milliliters (ml)	drams, fluid	0.2705
	liters	0.001
	ounces, fluid	0.0338
Millimeters (mm)	inches	0.03937
	meters	0.001
	microns	1,000.0
	mils	39.37
Mils	inches	0.001
	microns	25.4001
	millimeters	0.0254

(Continued)

CONVERSIONS OF COMMON UNITS *(Continued)*

To convert from	To	Multiply by
Minims	drams, fluid	0.01667
Minutes (min)	seconds	60.0
Myriagrams	grams	10,000.0
Myriameters	meters	10,000.0
Ounces (oz), apothecaries'	drams, apothecaries'	8.0
Ounces, avoirdupois	drams, avoirdupois	16.0
	grains	437.5
	grams	28.3495
	ounces, troy and apothecaries'	1.0971
	pounds, avoirdupois	0.0625
Ounces, British fluid	cubic centimeters	28.382
	cubic inches	1.732
Ounces, fluid	millimeters	29.57
Ounces, troy	pennyweights	20.0
Ounces, troy and apothecaries'	grains	480.0
	grams	31.10348
	ounces, avoirdupois	0.91149
Ounces, U.S. fluid	cubic inches	1.805
	drams, fluid	8.0
	gallons	0.00781
	liters	0.0296
Pecks (pk)	bushel	0.25
	cubic inches	537.61
	liters	8.8096
	quarts, dry	8.0
Pennyweights (dwt)	grains	24.0
Perch (of masonry)	cubic feet	24.75
Pints (pt), dry	bushels	0.015625
	cubic inches	33.60
	liters	0.5506

To convert from	To	Multiply by
Pints (pt), dry	pecks	0.0625
	quarts, dry	0.5
Pints, liquid	cubic inches	28,875
	gills	4.0
	liters	0.4732
Poundals	pounds, avoirdupois	0.03113
Pound-feet (lb-ft)	kilogram-meters	0.1383
Pounds (lb), avoirdupois	cubic feet of water	0.0160
	grains	7,000.0
	grams	453.5924
	ounces, avoirdupois	16.0
	poundals	32.1740
	slugs	0.0311
	tons, long	0.00045
	tons, short	0.0005
Pounds per cubic foot (lb per cu ft)	grams per cubic centimeter	0.01602
	kilograms per cubic meter	16.0184
	pounds per cubic inch	0.00058
Pounds per foot	kilograms per meter	1.4882
Pounds per square foot (psf)	inches of water	0.1922
	kilograms per square meter	4.8824
	pounds per square inch	0.00694
Pounds per square inch (psi)	atmospheres	0.0680
	feet of water	2.3066
	grams per square centimeter	70.3067
	inches of water	27.7
	inches of mercury	2.0360
	kilograms per square meter	703.0669
	pounds per square foot	144.0
Pounds, troy and apothecaries'	grains	5,760.0
	kilograms	0.37324

(Continued)

CONVERSIONS OF COMMON UNITS ***(Continued)***

To convert from	To	Multiply by
Pounds, troy and apothecaries'	ounces, troy and apothecaries'	12.0
	pounds, avoirdupois	0.8229
Quadrants	degrees	90.0
Quarts, dry	liters	1.1012
	pecks	0.125
	pints, dry	2.0
	quarts, dry, imperial	0.968
	bushel, U.S.	0.03125
	cubic inches	67.2
Quarts, liquid	cubic inches	57.75
	liters	0.94636
Quintals	grams	100,000.0
	pounds, avoirdupois	220.46
Radians	degrees, arc	57.2958
	minutes, arc	3,437.7468
	revolutions	0.1591
Radians per second	revolutions per minute	9.4460
Ream	sheets	480.0
Ream, printing paper	sheets	500.0
Revolutions	radians	6.2832
Revolutions per minute (rpm)	radians per second	0.1059
Rods	chains	0.25
	feet	16.5
	furlongs	40.0
	links	25.0
	meters	5.029
	yards	5.5
Score	units	20.0
Scruples	grains	20.0
Seconds	minutes	0.01667

To convert from	To	Multiply by
Slugs	pounds	32.1740
Spans	inches	9.0
Square centimeters (sq cm or cm²)	square feet	0.001076
	square inches	0.1550
	square millimeters	100.0
Square chains	acres	0.1
	square feet	4,356.0
	square meters	404.7
	square miles	0.00016
	square rods	16.0
	square yards	484.0
Square decameters	square meters	100.0
Square decimeters	square meters	0.01
Square feet (sq ft)	acres	0.000022988
	square centimeters	929.0341
	square chains	0.00023
	square inches	144.0
	square meters	0.0929
	square rods	0.00368
	square yards	0.11111
Square hectometers	square meters	10,000.0
Square inches (sq in)	circular inches	1.27324
	square centimeters	6.4516
	square feet	0.00694
	square millimeters	645.1625
	square yards	0.00077
Square kilometers (sq km or km²)	hectares	100.0
	square meters	1,000,000.0
	square miles	0.3861
Square links	square feet	0.4356
	square meters	0.0405
	square rods	0.00160
	square yards	0.04840

(Continued)

CONVERSIONS OF COMMON UNITS ***(continued)***

To convert from	To	Multiply by
Square meters (sq m or m²)	centiares	1.0
	square feet	10.7639
	square yards	1.1960
Square miles	square kilometers	2.590
	acres	640.0
	square chains	6,400.0
Square millimeters (sq mm or mm²)	square inches	0.00155
	square meters	0.000001
Square rods	square chains	0.06250
	square feet	272.25
	square links	625.0
	square meters	25.29
	square yards	30.25
Square yards	square chains	0.00207
	square feet	9.0
	square inches	1,296.0
	square links	20.66116
	square meters	0.83613
	square rods	0.03306
Tons, long	kilograms	1,016.0470
	pounds, avoirdupois	2,240.0
Tons, metric	kilograms	1,000.0
	pounds, avoirdupois	2,204.62
	quintals	10.0
Tons of refrigeration	BTU per hour	12,000.0
Tons, register	cubic feet	100.0
Tons, shipping	bushels	32.143
	cubic feet	40.0
Tons, short	kilograms	907.18
	pounds, avoirdupois	2,000.0
Watt-hours	Btu	3.413

To convert from	To	Multiply by
Watts	Btu per hour	3.415
	horsepower	0.00134
Yards (yd)	chains	0.04545
	fathoms	0.50000
	feet	3.0
	furlongs	0.004545
	inches	36.0
	links	0.22000
	meters	0.9144
	miles, statute	0.000569
	rods	0.18182

19

Other Information

RECOMMENDED NAILING PRACTICES

Proper fastening of frame members and covering materials provides the rigidity and strength to resist severe windstorms and other hazards. Good nailing is also important from the standpoint of normal performance of wood parts. For example, proper fastening of intersecting walls usually reduces wall cracking at the inside corners. The schedule below outlines good nailing practices for the framing and sheathing of a well-constructed wood-frame house.

JOINING	NAILING METHOD	NAILS		
		Number	Size	Placement
Header to joist	end-nail	3	16d	
Joist to sill or girder	toenail	2 3	10d or 8d	
Header and stringer joist to sill	toenail		10d	16 inches o.c.
Bridging to joist	toenail each end	2	8d	
Ledger strip to beam, 2 inches thick		3	16d	at each joist
Subfloor, boards 1 × 6 inches and smaller		2	8d	to each joist
1 × 8 inches		3	8d	to each joist
Subfloor, plywood				
At edges			8d	6 inches o.c.
At intermediate joists			8d	8 inches o.c.
Subfloor (2 × 6 inches T&G) to joist or girder	blind-nail (casing and face-nail)	2	16d	

JOINING	NAILING METHOD	NAILS		
		Number	Size	Placement
Soleplate to stud, horizontal assembly	end-nail	2	16d	at each stud
Top plate to stud	end-nail	2	16d	
Stud to soleplate	toenail	4	8d	
Soleplate to joist or blocking	face-nail		16d	16 inches o.c.
Doubled studs	face-nail, stagger		10d	16 inches o.c.
End stud of intersecting wall to exterior wall stud	face-nail		16d	16 inches o.c.
Upper top plate to lower top plate	face-nail		16d	16 inches o.c.
Upper top plate laps and intersections	face-nail	2	16d	
Continuous header, two pieces, each edge			12d	12 inches o.c.
Ceiling joist to top wall plates	toenail	3	8d	
Ceiling joist laps at partition	face-nail	4	16d	
Rafter to top plate	toenail	2	8d	
Rafter to ceiling joist	face-nail	5	10d	
Rafter to valley or hip rafter	toenail	3	10d	
Ridge board to rafter	end-nail	3	10d	
Rafter to rafter through ridge board	toenail	4	8d	
	edge-nail	1	10d	
Collar beam to rafter				
2-inch member	face-nail	2	12d	
1-inch member	face-nail	3	8d	

(Continued)

RECOMMENDED NAILING PRACTICES *(continued)*

Proper fastening of frame members and covering materials provides the rigidity and strength to resist severe windstorms and other hazards. Good nailing is also important from the standpoint of normal performance of wood parts. For example, proper fastening of intersecting walls usually reduces wall cracking at the inside corners. The schedule below outlines good nailing practices for the framing and sheathing of a well-constructed wood-frame house.

JOINING	NAILING METHOD	NAILS		
		Number	Size	Placement
1-inch diagonal let-in brace to each stud and plate (four nails at top)		2	8d	
Built-up corner studs				
Studs to blocking	face-nail	2	10d	each side
Intersecting stud to corner studs	face-nail		16d	12 inches o.c.
Built-up girders and beams, three or more members	face-nail		20d	32 inches o.c.
Wall sheathing				
1 × 8 inches or less horizontal	face-nail	2	8d	at each stud
1 × 6 inches or greater, diagonal	face-nail	3	8d	at each stud
Wall sheathing, vertically applied plywood				
⅜ inch and less thick	face-nail		6d	6-inch edge
½ inch and overthick	face-nail		8d	12 inches intermediate
Wall sheathing vertically applied fiberboard				
½ inch thick	face-nail			1½-inch roofing nail
25/32 inch thick	face-nail			1¾-inch roofing nail (3 inches edge and 6 inches intermediate)
Roof sheathing boards, 4-, 6-, 8-inch width	face-nail	2	8d	at each rafter
Roof sheathing, plywood				
⅜ inch and less thick	face-nail		6d	
½ inch and overthick	face-nail		8d	6 inches edge and 12 inches intermediate

COMMON NAILS REFERENCE TABLE

The "d" in nail sizes means "penny" and is the abbreviation for the Latin denarius, an ancient Roman coin. Originally, 2d, 10d, etc., referred to the cost in pennies for 100 nails. Now it refers to a definite size.

Size	Length (inches)	Diameter guage number	Diameter of head (inches)	Approximate number per pound
2d	1	15	11/64	830
3d	1¼	14	13/64	528
4d	1½	12½	¼	316
5d	1¾	12½	¼	271
6d	2	11½	17/64	168
7d	2¼	11½	11/64	150
8d	2½	10¼	9/32	106
9d	2¾	10¼	9/32	96
10d	3	9	5/16	69
12d	3¼	9	5/16	63
16d	3½	8	11/32	49
20d	4	6	13/32	31
30d	4½	5	7/16	24
40d	5	4	13/32	18
50d	5½	3	½	14
60d	6	2	17/32	11

FINISHING NAILS REFERENCE TABLE

Size	Length (inches)	Diameter gauge number	Diameter of head gauge number	Approximate number per pound
2d	1	16½	13½	1,351
3d	1¼	15½	12½	807
4d	1½	15	12	584
5d	1¾	15	12	500
6d	2	13	10	309
8d	2½	12½	9½	189
10d	3	11½	8½	121
16d	3½	11	8	90
20d	4	10	7	62

CASING NAILS REFERENCE TABLE

Size	Length (inches)	Diameter gauge number	Diameter of head gauge number	Approximate number per pound
4d	1½	14	11	490
6d	2	12½	9½	245
8d	2½	11½	8½	145
10d	3	10½	7½	95
16d	3½	10	7	72

STANDARD WOOD SCREW DIAMETERS

Number	DIAMETER		
	Basic	Maximum	Minimum
0	.006	.064	.053
1	.073	.077	.066
2	.086	.090	.079
3	.099	.103	.092
4	.112	.116	.105
5	.125	.129	.118
6	.138	.142	.131
7	.151	.155	.144
8	.164	.168	.157
9	.177	.181	.170
10	.190	.194	.183
11	.203	.207	.196
12	.216	.220	.209
14	.242	.246	.235
16	.268	.272	.261
18	.294	.298	.287
20	.320	.324	.313
24	.372	.376	.365

DRILL AND BIT SIZES FOR SCREWS

	SHANK OR FIRST HOLES			PILOT OR SECOND HOLES						
				Hardwood		Softwood				
Size of screw	Drill number or letter	Drill size nearest fraction (in inches)	Auger bit size*	Drill number or letter	Drill size nearest fraction (in inches)	Drill number or letter	Drill size nearest fraction (in inches)	Auger bit size*	Auger bit for counter-sink*	Countersink drill number
0	52	1/16		70	1/32	75	1/64		—	32
1	47	5/64		66	1/32	71	1/32		—	20
2	42	3/32		56	3/64	65	1/32		3	16
3	37	7/64		54	1/16	58	3/64		4	4
4	32	7/64		52	1/16	55	3/64		4	B
5	30	1/8		49	5/64	53	1/16		4	F
6	27	9/64		47	5/64	52	1/16		5	L
7	22	5/32		44	3/32	51	1/16		5	O
8	18	11/64	3	40	3/32	48	5/64		6	S
9	14	3/16	3	37	7/64	45	5/64		6	T
10	10	3/16	3	33	7/64	43	3/32		6	X
11	4	13/64	3	31	1/8	40	3/32		7	7/16
12	2	7/32	3	30	1/8	38	7/64		7	29/64
14	D	1/4	4	25	9/64	32	7/64	3	8	33/64
16	I	17/64	5	18	5/32	29	9/64	3	9	37/64
18	N	19/64	5	13	3/16	26	9/64	4	10	41/64
20	P	21/64	5	4	13/64	19	11/64	4	11	45/64
24	V	3/8	6	1	7/32	15	3/16	4	12	49/64

* Standard auger bits are sized by sixteenths of an inch. The number stamped on the square tang represents the diameter of the bit in these units. For example, a Number 3 bit will cut a hole 3/16 inch in diameter, while a Number 4 will cut a 1/4-inch hole.

"POP" RIVET SELECT CHART

Rivet diameter (in inches)	Rivet material	To fit work thickness (in inches)	Rivet diameter (in inches)	Rivet material	To fit work thickness (in inches)
1/8	Aluminum	1/8 short	5/32	Aluminum	3/8 long
1/8	Aluminum (white) rivets	1/8 short	3/16	Aluminum	1/8 short
1/8	Aluminum	1/4 medium	3/16	Aluminum	1/4 medium
1/8	Aluminum	3/8 long	3/16	Aluminum	3/8 long
5/32	Aluminum	1/8 medium	1/8	Steel	1/8 short
5/32	Aluminum	1/4 medium	1/8	Steel	1/4 medium
			1/8	Steel	3/8 long

COMMON STAPLE SIZE AND THEIR USES

1/4-inch leg	5/16-inch leg	3/8-inch leg	1/2-inch leg	9/16-inch leg
Light upholstering, screens, window shades, decorations, valances	Thin insulation, storm windows, draperies, upholstery, heavy fabrics	Weather stripping, roofing papers, light insulation, electrical wires, wire mesh	Canvas, felt stripping, under-layments of carpets, fiberglass	Ceiling tile,* fencing, insulation board, metal lathing, roofing

* Special 9/16-inch staples are also available for ceiling tile.

PIPE DATA AT A GLANCE

Ease of working	Water flow efficiency factor	Type of fittings needed	Manner usually stocked	Life expectancy	Principal uses
THREADED BRASS[1]					
No threading required; cuts easily, but can't be bent; measuring a job is rather difficult	Highly efficient because of low friction	Screw-on connections	12-foot rigid lengths; cuts to size wanted	Lasts life of building	Generally for commercial construction
HARD COPPER					
Easier to work with than brass	Same as brass	Screw-on or solder connections	12-foot rigid lengths; cut to size wanted	Same as brass	Same as brass
SOFT COPPER					
Easier to work with than brass or hard copper because it bends readily by using a bending tool; measuring a job isn't too difficult	Same as brass	Solder connections	Coils are usually soft	Same as brass	Widely used in residential installations

1. Threaded brass is required in some cities where water is extremely corrosive; often smaller diameter will suffice because of low friction coefficient.
2. Flexible copper tubing is probably the most popular; often a smaller diameter will suffice because of its low friction coefficient.
3. Wrought or galvanized iron is recommended if lines are subject to impact.
4. Plastic pipe is the lightest weight of all (weighing roughly one-eighth as much as metal); does not burst in freezing temperatures.

(Continued)

PIPE DATA AT A GLANCE *(continued)*

Ease of working	Water flow efficiency factor	Type of fittings needed	Manner usually stocked	Life expectancy	Principal uses
FLEXIBLE COPPER TUBING[2]					
Easier than soft copper because it can be bent without a tool; measuring jobs is easy	Highest of all metals since there are no nipples, unions, or elbows	Solder or compression connections	3-wall thicknesses: 'K'—thickest; 'L'—medium; 'M'—thinnest; 20-foot lengths or 15-, 30-, or 60-foot coils (except 'M')	Same as brass	'K' is used in municipal and commercial construction; 'L' is used for residential water lines; 'M' is for light domestic lines only (check code before using)
WROUGHT IRON (OR GALVANIZED)[3]					
Has to be threaded; more difficult to cut; measurements for jobs must be exact	Lower than copper because nipple unions reduce water flow	Screw-on connections	Rigid lengths, up to 22 feet; usually cut to size wanted	Corrodes in alkaline water more than others; produces rust stains	Generally found in older homes
PLASTIC PIPE[4]					
Can be cut with saw or knife	Same as copper tubing	Insert couplings, clamps, also by cement; threaded and compression fittings can be used (thread same as for metal pipe)	Rigid, semirigid, and flexible; coils of 100 to 400 feet	Long life; it is rust and corrosion proof	For cold-water installations; used for well casings, septic tank lines, sprinkler systems; check code before installing

1. Threaded brass is required in some cities where water is extremely corrosive; often smaller diameter will suffice because of low friction coefficient.
2. Flexible copper tubing is probably the most popular; often a smaller diameter will suffice because of its low friction coefficient.
3. Wrought or galvanized iron is recommended if lines are subject to impact.
4. Plastic pipe is the lightest weight of all (weighing roughly one-eighth as much as metal); does not burst in freezing temperatures.

Sizes of Wrought Iron, Galvanized Steel, and Copper Pipe

Pipe sizes are generally determined by the inside diameter of the pipe. Does it confuse you, then, to find that to get a pipe about ¼ inch in diameter on the inside and ⅜ inch on the outside you must ask for ⅛-inch pipe? The story behind this anomaly goes back to the days when materials were weaker and pipe of ⅜-inch outside diameter did have an inside diameter of only ⅛ inch. When materials became stronger and walls could be thinner, it was decided to keep the same *outside* diameter so that standard threading tools and fittings could still be used. The inside diameter of threaded iron, steel, and brass pipe therefore became somewhat larger than its nominal size. In the larger sizes the difference is small; in the smaller ones, though, it can confound you.

SIZES OF TYPES K, L, AND M COPPER TUBING

Nominal Size (Inches)	Outside Diameter	Inside Diameter		
	Types K, L, and M	*Type K*	*Type L*	*Type M*
⅜	0.500	0.402	0.430	0.450
½	0.625	0.527	0.545	0.569
¾	0.875	0.745	0.785	0.811
1	1.125	0.995	1.025	1.055
1¼	1.375	1.245	1.265	1.291
1½	1.625	1.481	1.505	1.527

IRON- TO COPPER-TUBE CONVERSION

Since copper tubing has a smooth bore, water flows through it with less resistance than through wrought iron. This feature permits replacement of a heavy iron pipe with a copper tube of smaller diameter. To determine possible replacement sizes involving this factor, check the table below:

Iron pipe size (inches)	Copper tube size	Iron pipe size (inches)	Copper tube size
½	⅜	1¼	1
¾	½	1½	1¼
1	¾	2	1½

DATA ON THREADED METAL

Here are the nominal and approximate actual dimensions of commonly used sizes of standard threaded wrought iron, galvanized steel, and bronze pipe:

Nominal size (inches)	Approximate inside diameter (inches)	Approximate outside diameter (inches)	Threads per inch	Tap drill (inches)
1/8	1/4	3/8	27	11/32
1/4	3/8	17/32	18	7/16
3/8	1/2	11/16	18	37/64
1/2	5/8	13/16	14	23/32
3/4	13/16	1	14	59/64
1	1 1/16	1 5/16	11 1/2	1 5/32
1 1/4	1 3/8	1 5/8	11 1/2	1 1/2
1 1/2	1 5/8	1 7/8	11 1/2	1 47/64
2	2 1/16	2 3/8	11 1/2	2 7/32
2 1/2	2 9/16	2 7/8	8	2 5/8

PIPE SIZES FOR HOME-DRAINAGE SYSTEMS (IN INCHES)

Type of fixture	Lavatory	Tub or shower	Toilet	Sink	Garbage disposal	Dishwasher	Clothes washer
Branch drains Revent lines	1 1/2	1 1/2	3 to 4	1 1/2 to 2	1 1/2 to 2	1 1/2 to 2	1 1/2
Fixture supply lines	3/8	1/2	3/8	1/2	—	1/2	1/2

Note: Main soil stack: 3 to 4 inches. Secondary soil stack: Size of largest branch drain connected to it, in most cases. Basement floor drain: 2 to 4 inches. Building drain: At least the size of main soil stack. Branch building drain: At least the size of largest secondary soil stack emptying into it. Cold-water main line serving both the cold-water system and the hot-water heater: 3/4 inch to 1 inch. Cold- and hot-water main lines serving two or more fixtures: Size of largest branch line served or, if fixtures will be used simultaneously, the next pipe size larger than that used for the largest branch line.

Electricity Consumed by Common Appliances

The accompanying table may help you determine the number and capacity of electrical outlets needed in your home or shop, and to estimate the operating cost of various appliances.

Electric power is charged for by the kilowatt-hour. To find out how long it takes an appliance to use this much electricity, just divide 1,000 by the wattage of the appliance. Using this method, you find you can run a 2-watt clock for 500 hours or a 100-watt lamp for 10 hours on 1 kilowatt-hour. At the other extreme, you discover that a 5,000-watt range oven will consume the same amount of power in 1/5 hour, or 12 minutes.

ELECTRICITY CONSUMPTION: APPLIANCES

	Watts
Air conditioner, room	800 to 1500
Blanket	150 to 200
Blender	250 to 300
Broiler	1200 to 1600
Can opener	80 to 120
Clock	2 to 3
Coffeemaker	600 to 1000
Deep fryer	1200 to 1650
Dishwasher	600 to 1300
Dryer, clothes	4000 to 8700
Fan, portable	50 to 200
Food mixer	120 to 250
Freezer, home	300 to 500
Frying pan	1000 to 1300
Furnace blower	800
Garbage disposal unit	200 to 800
Grill	1000 to 1200
Heat lamp	250
Heater, portable, home	600 to 1650
Heater, portable, home, 230-volt	2800 to 5600
Heating pad	50 to 75
Hot plate, each burner	550 to 1200
Intercom radio	800 to 120
Iron, hand	660 to 1500
Ironer	1200 to 1650
Lamps, fluorescent	15 to 60
Lamps, incandescent	2 up
Microwave oven	800 to 1500
Motors: ¼ horsepower	300 to 400
½ horsepower	450 to 600
1 horsepower	950 to 1000

(continued)

ELECTRICITY CONSUMPTION: APPLIANCES *(continued)*

	Watts
Projector, movie or slide	150 to 550
Radio, transistor	6 to 12
Radio, tube	35 to 150
Range, oven and all burners	8000 to 16000
Refrigerator	150 to 300
Roaster	1200 to 1650
Rotisserie-broiler	1200 to 1650
Sewing machine	60 to 90
Shaver	8 to 12
Stereo	100 to 400
Television	200 to 400
Toaster	550 to 1200
Trash compactor	300 to 500
Vacuum cleaner	200 to 800
Vent hood	125 to 175
Waffle iron	600 to 1100
Washing machine	400 to 800
Water heater	2000 to 5000
Water pump	300 to 700

COPPER WIRE TABLE
(Brown & Sharpe or American Wire Gauge)

		Turns per linear inch		Foot per pound		Ohms per 1000 feet at 68° F
AWG B&S	Diameter in mills	Enamel	Double cotton covered	Bare	Double cotton covered	
1	289.3	—	—	3.947	—	.1264
2	257.6	—	—	4.977	—	.1593
3	229.4	—	—	6.276	—	.2009
4	204.3	—	—	7.914	—	.2533
5	181.9	—	—	9.980	—	.3195
6	162.0	—	—	12.58	—	.4028
7	144.3	—	—	15.87	—	.5080
8	128.5	7.6	7.1	20.01	19.6	.6405

AWG B&S	Diameter in mills	Turns per linear inch		Foot per pound		Ohms per 1000 feet at 68° F
		Enamel	Double cotton covered	Bare	Double cotton covered	
9	114.4	8.6	7.8	25.23	24.6	.8077
10	101.9	9.6	8.9	31.82	30.9	1.018
11	90.74	10.7	9.8	40.12	38.8	1.284
12	80.81	12.0	10.9	50.59	48.9	1.619
13	71.96	13.5	12.0	63.80	61.5	2.042
14	64.08	15.0	13.8	80.44	77.3	2.575
15	57.07	16.8	14.7	101.4	97.3	3.247
16	50.82	18.9	16.4	127.9	119	4.094
17	45.26	21.2	18.1	161.3	150	5.163
18	40.30	23.6	19.8	203.4	188	6.510
19	35.89	26.4	21.8	256.5	237	8.210
20	31.96	29.4	23.8	323.4	298	10.35
21	28.46	33.1	26.0	407.8	370	13.05
22	25.35	37.0	30.0	514.2	461	16.46
23	22.57	41.3	31.6	648.4	584	20.76
24	20.10	46.3	35.6	817.7	745	26.17
25	17.90	51.7	38.6	1031	903	33.00
26	15.94	58.0	41.8	1300	1118	41.62
27	14.20	64.9	45.0	1639	1422	52.48
28	12.64	72.7	48.5	2067	1759	66.17
29	11.26	81.6	51.8	2607	2207	83.44
30	10.03	90.5	55.5	3287	2534	105.2
31	8.928	101	59.2	4145	2768	132.7
32	7.950	113	62.6	5227	3137	167.3
33	7.080	127	66.3	6591	4697	211.0
34	6.305	143	70.0	8310	6168	266.0
35	5.615	158	73.5	10480	6737	335.0
36	5.000	175	77.0	13210	7877	423.0
37	4.453	198	80.3	16660	9309	533.4
38	3.965	224	83.6	21010	10666	672.6
39	3.531	248	86.6	26500	11907	848.1
40	3.145	282	89.7	33410	14222	1069

A mil is 1/1000 (one-thousandth) of an inch.

Measurements of covered wires may vary slightly with different manufacturers.

Wire of size 6 and larger is always stranded. The diameters shown here, however, are those of solid wires of equivalent cross section.

What Size Wire for the Circuit?

The minimum size wire to be used in electrical circuits is determined by both safety and efficiency. In all cases, wiring installations should conform to the rules of the National Electrical Code, which is based on the recommendations of the National Fire Protection Association. This code is concerned only with preventing electrical or thermal hazards that might electrocute somebody or start a fire. Beyond the bare requirements of safety, however, circuits should be designed to not waste too much electricity in the form of useless heat so that they deliver current at the end of the line at a sufficiently high voltage to properly do the job.

WIRE GAUGES FOR FEEDER AND BRANCH CIRCUITS*

	Continuous operation		Noncontinuous operation	
Amperes	Wire size (copper)	Wire size (aluminum)	Wire size (copper)	Wire size (aluminum)
15	14	12	14	12
20	12	10	12	10
25/30	10	8	10	8
35/40	8	6	8	6
45/50	6	4	6	4
60	4	4	4	4
70	4	3	4	3
80	3	2	3	3
90	2	1	3	2
100	1	0	2	1
110	0	00	1	0
125	0	000	1	00
150	00	0000	0	000
175	000		00	0000
200	0000		000	
225			0000	

* American Wire Gauge (AWG) sizes. Continuous loads are those expected to continue for 3 or more hours; noncontinuous loads are those where 67 percent or less of the load is expected to be continuous.

RESISTANCE OF COPPER WIRE

In estimating the resistance of copper wire, it may help to remember several approximate relationships:

Size wire AWG, B&S	Ohms per 1,000 feet	Feet per ohm
10	1	1,000
20	10	100
30	100	10
40	1,000	1

An increase of 1 in AWG or B&S wire size increases resistance 25 percent.

An increase of 2 increases resistance 60 percent.

An increase of 3 increases resistance 100 percent.

ELECTRICAL CONDUCTIVITY OF METALS

With the conductivity of copper rated at 100, here are the relative conductivities of other common metals. All are measured at 68° F or 20° C.

	Relative conductivity
Aluminum	59
Brass	28
Cadmium	19
Chromium	55
Climax	1.83
Cobalt	16.3
Constantin	3.24
Copper, annealed	100
Copper, hard drawn	89.5
Everdur	6
German silver, 18 percent	5.3
Gold	65
Iron, pure	17.7
Iron, wrought	11.4
Lead	7
Manganin	3.7
Mercury	1.66

(Continued)

ELECTRICAL CONDUCTIVITY OF METALS *(continued)*

With the conductivity of copper rated at 100, here are the relative conductivities of other common metals. All are measured at 68° F or 20° C.

	Relative conductivity
Molybdenum	33.2
Monel	4
Nichrome	1.45
Nickel	12–16
Phosphor bronze	36
Platinum	15
Silver	106
Steel	3–15
Tin	13
Tungsten	28.9
Zinc	28.2

WIRING-SIZE DATA (ENCLOSED WIRES)

	Maximum ampere rating	
Wire size	**Types R, RW, RU, T, and TW**	**Types RH and RHW**
14	15	15
12	20	20
10	30	30
8	40	45
6	55	65
4	70	85
3	80	100
2	95	115
1	110	130
0	125	150
00	145	175
000	165	200

CONDUIT SIZE AND AMPERE CAPACITY OF WIRES IN CONDUIT

Number of wires (1 to 9) to be installed in conduit (exact number will vary according to local code)

Wire size	Ampere capacity	½-inch conduit	¾-inch conduit	1-inch conduit	1¼-inch conduit
14	15	4	6	9	9
12	20	3	5	8	9
10	25	1	4	7	9
8	35	1	3	4	7
6	45	1	1	3	4
4	60	1	1	1	3
5	95	1	1	1	3

Extension Cords

The 125-volt all-purpose extension cords for indoor or outdoor use are generally marked type "SJT." Two conductor cords are okay for double-insulated tools with a two-prong plug, but tools with three-prong grounded plugs must be used only with three-wire grounded extension cords connected to properly grounded three-wire receptacles. Current National Electrical Code specs call for outdoor receptacles to be protected with ground-fault detector devices.

When you buy a new extension cord, check the table below or the maker's specs and permanently mark or tag it for capacity. For example, mark a 50-foot cord "13A" to indicate it's good for a maximum 13-ampere load.

HOW TO SELECT THE PROPER EXTENSION CORD

Cord length	Ampere rating for 110–120 V.A.C. tools															
	0-5A	6A	7A	8A	9A	10A	11A	12A	13A	14A	15A	16A	17A	18A	19A	20A
25 feet	18	18	18	18	18	18	16	16	16	14	14	14	14	14	12	12
50 feet	18	18	18	18	18	18	16	16	16	14	14	14	14	14	12	12
75 feet	18	18	18	18	16	16	16	16	16	14	14	14	14	14	12	12
100 feet	18	16	16	16	16	16	16	16	14	14	14	14	14	14	12	12
125 feet	16	16	16	16	16	14	14	14	14	14	14	12	12	12	12	12
150 feet	16	16	14	14	14	14	14	14	14	12	12	12	12	12	12	12

* Wire sizes are AWG (American Wire Gauge); recommendations are minimum allowable. For nameplate ampere ratings that fall between those given here, use the extension cord recommended for the next higher ampere. If the tool has a long supply cord, this should be added when figuring total extension cord length.

REQUIRED CONDUCTOR INSULATION FOR CURRENT-CARRYING CIRCUITS UNDER 6,000 VOLTS

Trade name	Type letter	Insulation	Outer covering	Use
Code	R	code-grade rubber	moisture-resistant, flame-retardant fibrous covering	general use
Moisture resistant	RW	moisture-resistant rubber	moisture-resistant, flame-retardant fibrous covering	general use, especially in wet locations
Heat resistant	RH	heat-resistant rubber	moisture-resistant, flame-retardant fibrous covering	general use
Latex rubber	RU	90-percent unmilled grainless rubber	moisture-resistant, flame-retardant fibrous covering	general use
Thermoplastic	T and TW	flame-retardant thermoplastic compound	none	T—general use TW—in wet locations
Thermoplastic and asbestos	TA	thermoplastic and asbestos	flame-retardant cotton braid	switchboard wiring only
Asbestos and varnished cambric	AVA	impregnated asbestos and varnished cambric	asbestos braid	dry location only

Asbestos and varnished cambric	AVB	same as type AVA	flame-retardant cotton braid	dry location only
Asbestos and varnished cambric	AVL	same as type AVA	asbestos braid and lead sheath	wet location
Slow-burning	SB	three braids of impregnated fire-retardant cotton thread	outer cover finished smooth and hard	dry locations only
Slow-burning weatherproof	SBW	two layers impregnated cotton thread	outer fire-retardant coating	open wiring only

Appliance Grounding

The one electrical problem most often overlooked is improper or inadequate grounding or none at all. It has been estimated by the Injury Control Program of the National Center for Urban and Industrial Health that there are 500,000 household injuries each year as the direct result of accidents with major and portable electrical appliances used in the home. The U.S. Bureau of Vital Statistics lists over 1,000 deaths each year due to electric shock. Proper grounding would have eliminated many of these injuries and deaths.

It has been determined that electric current (amperage), not voltage, is the dangerous ingredient of electricity. Measurements of a 60-Hz, 120-V current and the predicted body reaction are given in the accompanying table:

Current	Effect
0.05 to 2 mA (5/10,000 to 2/1,000A)	Just noticeable
2 to 10 mA (2/1,000 to 10/1,000A)	Slight to strong muscular reaction
5 to 25 mA (5/1,000 to 25/1,000A)	Strong shock, inability to let go
25 to 50 mA (25/1,000 to 50/1,000A)	Violent muscular contraction
50 to 200 mA (50/1,000 to 200/1,000A)	Irregular twitching of the heart muscles with no pumping action (ventricular fibrillation)
100 mA and over (100/1,000A)	Paralysis of breathing

A person's skin, when dry, may have from 100,000 to as high as 600,000 ohms resistance; however, when the skin is wet (such as when perspiring), resistance can drop below 1,000 ohms. Let us assume a technician is working on a 120-V motor with an insulation break leaking current to an ungrounded motor frame. Ohm's law (volts/ohms = amperes) may be used to compute the amount of current received by the technician's body. If his skin is dry, the current would be 120V/100,000 ohms = 0.0012A, or 1.2 mA. This current would be barely noticeable. However, if the technician is perspiring, his skin resistance may be 1,000 ohms or less (with a break in the skin it can be as low as 200 ohms). Using Ohm's law, the current would be 0.12A, or 120 mA (120 V/1,000 ohms = 0.12A). This is more than a lethal current. If the motor frame had been grounded, this leaking current would have bled to the ground, and the fuse or breaker would generally have "blown." Remember, as little as 0.025A at 120 V can kill.

WATTAGE FOR HOME LIGHTING

Room	General area lighting		Local lighting		Remarks
	Bulb	Fluorescent	Bulb	Fluorescent	
Living, dining room	150	60–80	40–150	15–40	For small living rooms
Bedroom	200		40–100		Average size
Bath	100–150	80	Two 60s	Two 20s	Task lights on both sides of mirror
Kitchen	150–200	60–80	60	10 per foot of counter	Fixture over eating area or sink—150-watt bulb, 60-watt fluorescent
Halls, service	75	32			Plus low-wattage night lights
Hall entrance	100	60			
Stairway	75	32			Shielded fixtures at top and bottom controlled by three-way switch
Outdoors, entry and access	40				Wall brackets aimed down
Hall entrance	100	60			
Outdoors, yard	100–150 projector				Controlled from garage and house
Laundry	Two 150s	Two 80s			Placed over washing and ironing areas
Workshop	150	80	60	10 per foot of bench	Task lights aimed at machines
Garage	Two 100s				On ceiling, center of each side of car

AVERAGE FURNITURE DIMENSIONS

Item	Length, inches	Depth-width, inches	Height inches
Dining table	60	42	29
Kitchen table	42	30	30
Card table	36	36	30
Coffee table	36–60	18–24	14–18
Coffee table (round)	36 diam.		15–18
End table	24	15	24
Drum table	36 diam.		30
Lamp table	24 diam.		30
Desk	48	24	30
Secretary	36	24	84
Lowboy	30	18	30
Highboy	36	18	60–84
Breakfront bookcase	48–60	18	78–84
Sofa	72	30	36
Love seat	48	30	36
Occasional chair	27	30	36
Occasional chair (armless)	24	30	30
Wing chair	30	30	36
Dining, desk, folding chair	15–18	15–18	30–36 (seat height 16–18)
Twin bed	78	39	20–24
Double bed	78	54	20–24
Dresser	42–60	22	32–36

BTU IMPUT FOR GAS APPLIANCES

	Approximate input BTU per hour*
Range, free standing	65,000
Built-in oven or broiler unit	25,000
Built-in top unit	40,000
Water heater (quick recovery), automatic storage	
30-gallon tank	30,000
40-gallon tank	38,000
50-gallon tank	50,000
Water heater, automatic instantaneous	
2 gallons per minute	142,000
4 gallons per minute	285,000
6 gallons per minute	428,400
Refrigerator	3,000
Clothes dryer	35,000
Incinerator	32,000

* A *therm* is equal to 10,000 BTUs

RUBBER STOPPER SIZES
(All measurements in millimeters)

Stopper size no.	Fits openings	Top diameter	Bottom diameter	Length
00	10 to 13	15	10	26
0	13 to 15	17	13	26
1	15 to 17	19	15	26
2	16 to 18.5	20	16	26
3	18 to 21	24	18	26
4	20 to 23	26	20	26
5	23 to 25	27	23	26
5½	25 to 26	29	25	26
6	26 to 27	32	26	26
6½	27 to 31.5	34	27	26
7	30 to 34	37	30	26
8	33 to 37	41	33	26
9	37 to 41	45	37	26
10	42 to 46	50	42	26
10½	45 to 47	53	45	26

(Continued)

(Continued)

RUBBER STOPPER SIZES
(All measurements in millimeters)

Stopper size no.	Fits openings	Top diameter	Bottom diameter	Length
11	48 to 51.5	56	48	26
11½	51 to 56	60	51	26
12	54 to 59	64	54	26
13	58 to 63	67	58	26
13½	61 to 70	75	61	35
14	75 to 85	90	75	39
15	83 to 95	103	83	39

Precious Metals

Precious metals are gold, platinum, and silver. Equally expensive, and sometimes used, is palladium. These precious metals may be mixed with or laid over a base metal, usually copper, zinc, tin, antimony, nickel, aluminum, lead, chromium, rhodium, or iron. A mixture of metals is an alloy. The alloy may be used to attain greater durability, hardness, tarnish-resistance, or some special effect. Or it may be used to decrease cost.

Solid (24-karat) gold contains no copper to each 24 parts of gold. This is too soft for most jewelry purposes. But 14-karat gold contains 14 parts gold and 10 parts copper; 10-karat gold contains 10 parts gold, 14 parts copper. Gold-filled metal contains a thin sheet or covering of 12-karat gold, usually (soldered, welded, or brazed on) 1/10th to 1/20th the thickness of the metal. Rolled gold may have a coating of 1/30th to 1/40th the thickness of the metal. Gold-flashed or gold-washed metals may have a gold thickness of 1/100,000th of an inch. Gold-plated metals have a thin layer of gold coated by an electroplating process. White gold, red gold, and green gold are made by adding other metals in the plating process. They may be of solid gold, plated, and so on.

Sterling silver is 92½ percent silver, 7½ percent copper. Pure silver is too soft for ordinary use. Silverplate has a coating of silver over a base metal. Antiqued silver has been oxidized (tarnished) to add to the design.

MOHS' SCALE OF HARDNESS

Minerals, metals, abrasive grits, and other materials are still compared for hardness on the "Mohs' scale," a rating devised in 1820 by Friedrich Mohs, noted German mineralogist. In this scale, talc, the softest mineral, is rated as 1, while diamond, the hardest, is 10. Each mineral on the scale is hard enough to scratch the one below it. Here is the basic scale:

1 talc	6 feldspar
2 rocksalt or gypsum	7 quartz
3 calcite	8 topaz
4 fluorite	9 corundum
5 apatite	10 diamond

Compared with the scale above, here are some values for other materials:

Agate	6–7	Iron	4–5
Aluminum	2–2.9	Jade	7
Amber	2–2.5	Kaolinite	2–2.5
Amethyst	7	Lead	1.5
Anthracite	2.2	Magnesium	2
Asphalt	1–2	Marble	3–4
Brass	3–4	Opal	4–6
Cadmium	2	Osmium	7
Carborundum	9–10	Platinum	4.3
Chromium	9	Pumice	6
Copper	2.5–3	Ruby	9
Diatomaceous earth	1–1.5	Sapphire	9
Emerald	8	Silicon carbide	9–10
Emery	7–9	Silver	2.5–7
Flint	6.8–7	Steel	5–8.5
Garnet	7.5–8.5	Tin	1.5–1.8
Glass	4.5–6.5	Tourmaline	7.3
Gold	2.5–3	Tungsten carbide	9–10
Graphite	0.5–1	Turquoise	6
Gypsum	1.6–2	Wax, 32° F	0.2
		Zinc	2.5

Frequency Range of Voices and Instruments

If your stereo speakers cannot reach down to 20 Hz (formerly *cycles per second*) don't worry too much. No musical instrument except a pipe organ with a 32-foot pipe can go as low. The piano comes next, with its very lowest tone at 27.5 Hz. At the other extreme, the highest fundamental tone of any ordinary musical instrument—shared by the organ, piano, and piccolo—is about 4,186 Hz.

The fundamental frequencies of the singing voice range from about 65 Hz for the lowest tone of the bass to about 1,568 Hz for the highest of the soprano. The harmonics or overtones of both instruments and voices—the extra frequencies that characterize one source of sound from another—extend to about 10,000 Hz, while frequencies in a door squeak, chirping insects, or escaping steam may go beyond 16,000 Hz. It is because of these harmonics that you need good high-frequency response in your hi-fi to get completely natural sound.

To help get a clearer idea of the frequency range of orchestral instruments and human voices, see the accompanying table based on the American standard frequency of 440 Hz for middle A. Where two frequencies are given, the first one is for special instruments.

FREQUENCY RANGE OF VOICES AND INSTRUMENTS

	Frequency in Hz (cycles per second)	
INSTRUMENT	**Lower limit**	**Upper limit**
Organ	16,32	4186
Piano	27	4186
Contra bassoon	30	175
Harp	32	3136
Bass violin	32, 41	262
Bass tuba	41	234
Trombone	51, 82	524
Bassoon	58	623
French horn	61	699
Cello	65	880
Bass clarinet	63, 73	467
E-flat baritone saxophone	69	416
B-flat tenor saxophone	103	623
Viola	131	1318
E-flat alto saxophone	138	831
English horn	164	934

(Continued)

INSTRUMENT	Frequency in Hz (cycles per second)	
	Lower limit	Upper limit
Trumpet	164	1047
Violin	195	2093
Oboe	233	1397
Flute	261	2043
Piccolo	587	4186
VOICE		
Bass	65	294
Baritone	98	416
Tenor	123	1174
Contralto	174	933
Soprano	261	1568

FREEZING POINT OF ANTIFREEZE MIXTURES

ETHYL ALCOHOL–WATER MIXTURES

Percent alcohol by volume	Specific gravity, 60°F	Freezing point	
		°C	°F
3.1	0.9954	− 1.0	30.2
8.5	0.9884	− 3.0	26.6
14.0	0.9822	− 5.0	23.0
20.0	0.9761	− 7.5	18.5
25.0	0.9710	−10.5	13.0
29.5	0.9660	−14.0	6.8
32.5	0.9624	−16.0	3.2
36.0	0.9577	−18.8	− 2.0
40.5	0.9511	−23.6	−10.5
46.3	0.9413	−28.7	−19.7
ETHYLENE GLYCOL (PRESTONE)–WATER MIXTURES			
12.5	1.019	− 3.9	25
17.0	1.026	− 6.7	20
25.0	1.038	−12.2	10
32.5	1.048	−17.8	0

(Continued)

FREEZING POINT OF ANTIFREEZE MIXTURES *(continued)*

ETHYL ALCOHOL–WATER MIXTURES

Percent alcohol by volume	Specific gravity, 60°F	Freezing point °C	Freezing point °F
38.5	1.056	−23.3	−10
44.0	1.063	−28.9	−20
49.0	1.069	−34.4	−30
52.5	1.073	−40.0	−40

TEMPERATURES USEFUL TO KNOW

Degrees Celsius (Centigrade)	Degrees Fahrenheit	
−273	−459.4	Absolute zero
−130	−202	Alcohol freezes
−78.5	−109.3	Dry ice sublimes
−38.9	−38	Mercury freezes
0	32	Ice melts
34.5	94.1	Ether boils
37	98.6	Temperature of human body
60	140	Wood's metal melts
78.5	173.3	Alcohol boils
100	212	Water boils
160	320	Sugar melts
232	450	Tin melts
327	621	Lead melts
658	1,216	Aluminum melts
700	1,292	Dull red heat
800	1,472	Pyrex glass begins to soften
1,000	1,832	Bright red heat
1,083	1,980	Copper melts
1,400	2,552	White heat
1,500	2,732	Temperature of Bunsen flame
1,530	2,786	Iron melts
1,773	3,223	Platinum melts
4,000	7,232	Temperature of electric furnace
6,000	10,800	Temperature of sun's surface

Useful Facts About Rope

The smallest cordage that is technically called "rope" is about ½ inch in circumference and 3/16 inch in diameter.

- *Manila rope* is the strongest and most durable rope made of natural fibers. It is made of abaca, a relative of the banana plant, and commonly called Manila fiber because it is grown almost entirely in the Philippines and shipped chiefly from the port of Manila.

(*Continued*)

ROPE SIZES AND STRENGTHS FOR THREE-STRAND MANILA AND SISAL ROPE WITH STANDARD LAY

(For safe loads, allow at least a 5-to-1 safety factor)

NOMINAL SIZE				MINIMUM BREAKING STRENGTH, POUNDS	
Threads	Circumference (inches)	Diameter (inches)	Weight per 100 Feet (pounds)	Manila	Sisal
6-fine	9/16	3/16	1.47	450	360
6	¾	¼	1.96	600	480
9	1	5/16	2.84	1,000	800
12	1⅛	⅜	4.02	1,350	1,080
15	1¼	7/16	5.15	1,750	1,400
18	1⅜	15/32	6.13	2,250	1,800
21	1½	½	7.35	2,650	2,120
	1¾	9/16	10.20	3,450	2,760
	2	⅝	13.10	4,440	3,520
	2¼	¾	16.30	5,400	4,320
	2½	13/16	19.10	6,500	5,200
	2¾	⅞	22.00	7,700	6,160
	3	1	26.50	9,000	7,200
	3¼	1 1/16	30.70	10,500	8,400
	3½	1⅛	35.20	12,000	9,600
	3¾	1¼	40.80	13,500	10,800
	4	1 5/16	46.90	15,000	12,000
	4½	1½	58.80	18,500	14,800
	5	1⅝	73.00	22,500	18,000
	5½	1¾	87.70	26,500	21,200
	6	2	105.00	31,000	24,800

Useful Facts About Rope *(continued)*

- *Sisal rope* (often made from a related fiber, henequen) is next in importance to Manila rope and is about 80 percent as strong. Its fiber comes from a plant in the century plant family, and was formerly exported from Sisal, Yucatán.

- *Nylon rope,* made from synthetic fibers, is more expensive than Manila rope but about twice as strong. It also has the unique property of being able to stretch about 8 percent and then return to its original length on release of its load. This property makes it extremely useful for long tow lines, or under other conditions where a sudden strong pull might snap an ordinary rope.

- *Dacron rope* is nearly as strong as nylon, is almost impervious to moisture, is a good electrical insulator, and does not stretch at all. It is especially useful for guy lines for antennas, for outdoor clotheslines that stay taut during dry or wet weather, and for other purposes where stretch or electrical conduction would be detrimental.

- *Polyethylene rope,* one of the newest, is about one-third stronger than Manila rope and is the only rope that will float indefinitely on water. Because of this floating ability, polyethylene rope is becoming standard for lifelines and for tow ropes in water skiing.

SHOP, BLUEPRINT, AND OTHER COMMON ABBREVIATIONS

Word	Abbreviation	Word	Abbreviation
Abbreviate	ABBR		
Absolute	ABS	Acoustic	ACST
Accelerate	ACCEL	Actual	ACT.
Acceleration due to gravity	G	Adapter	ADPT
		Addition	ADD.
Accessory	ACCESS.	Adhesive	ADH
Access panel	AP	Adjust	ADJ

Word	Abbreviation	Word	Abbreviation
Advance	ADV	Assemble	ASSEM
After	AFT.	Assembly	ASSY
Aggregate	AGGR	At	@
Air-break switch	ABS	Atomic	AT
Air-circuit breaker	ACB	Attach	ATT
Air-condition	AIR CON.	Audio-frequency	AF
Aircraft	ACFT	Automatic	AUTO
Airplane	APL	Auto-transformer	AUTO TR
Airtight	AT	Auxiliary	AUX
Alarm	ALM	Avenue	AVE.
Allowance	ALLOW	Average	AVG
Alloy	ALY	Back to back	B to B
Alteration	ALT	Baffle	BAF
Alternate	ALT	Balance	BAL
Alternating current	AC	Balcony	BALC
Alternator	ALT	Ball bearing	BB
Altitude	ALT	Baseline	BL
Aluminum	AL	Basement	BSMT
American Standard	AMER STD	Base plate	BP
American Wire Gauge	AWG	Bathroom	B
Ammeter	AM	Bath tub	BT
Amount	AMT	Battery	BAT.
Ampere	AMP	Beam	BM
Ampere hour	AMP HR	Bearing	BRG
Amplifier	AMPL	Bedroom	BR
Anneal	ANL	Bench mark	BM
Antenna	ANTS.	Bent	BT
Apartment	APT	Between	BET.
Apparatus	APP	Between centers	BC
Approved	APPD	Between perpendiculars	BP
Approximate	APPROX	Bevel	BEV
Architectural	ARCH	Bill of material	B/M
Arc weld	ARC/W	Birmingham Wire Gage	BWG
Area	A	Blank	BLK
Armature	ARM.	Blocking	BLKG
Arrange	ARR.	Blower	BLO
Arrester	ARR.	Blueprint	BP
Asbestos	ASB	Board	BD
Asphalt	ASPH	Boiler	BLR

(Continued)

(Continued)

SHOP, BLUEPRINT, AND OTHER COMMON ABBREVIATIONS

Word	Abbreviation	Word	Abbreviation
Both sides	BS	Catalog	CAT
Bottom	BOT	Caulking	CLKG
Bottom chord	BC	Cement	CEM
Brake	BK	Center	CTR
Brass	BRS	Center line	CL
Brazing	BRZG	Center to center	C to C
Break	BRK	Centering	CTR
Breaker	BKR	Centigrade	C
Brick	BRK	Centigram	CG
British Standard	BR STD	Centiliter	CL
British thermal units	BTU	Centimeter	CM
Broach	BRO	Centrifugal	CENT.
Bronze	BRZ	Centrifugal force	CF
Broom closet	BC	Ceramic	CER
Brown & Sharp	B&S	Chain	CH
Brush	BR	Chamfer	CHAM
Building	BLDG	Change	CHG
Building line	BL	Change notice	CN
Burnish	BNH	Change order	CO
Bushing	BUSH.	Channel	CHAN
Bypass	BYP	Check	CHK
Cabinet	CAB	Check valve	CV
Cadmium plate	CD PL	Chemical	CHEM
Calculate	CALC	Chord	CHD
Calibrate	CAL	Chrome molybdenum	CR MOLY
Capacitor	CAP	Chrome vanadium	CR VAN
Capacity	CAP	Chromium plate	CR PL
Cap screw	CAP SCR	Circle	CIR
Carburize	CARB	Circuit	CKT
Case harden	CH	Circuit breaker	CIR BKR
Casing	CSG	Circular	CIR
Cast (used with other materials)	C	Circular pitch	CP
Cast concrete	C CONC	Circulate	CIRC
Cast iron	CI	Circumference	CIRC
Cast iron pipe	CIP	Clamp	CLP
Cast steel	CS	Class	CL
Casting	CSTG	Cleanout	CO
		Clear	CLR

Word	Abbreviation	Word	Abbreviation
Clearance	CL	Control switch	CS
Clockwise	CW	Controller	CONT
Closet	CL	Convert	CONV
Closing	CL	Conveyor	CNVR
Clutch	CL	Cooled	CLD
Coated	CTD	Copper oxide	CUO
Coaxial	COAX	Copper plate	Cop PL
Coefficient	COEF	Cord	CD
Cold drawn	CD	Correct	CORR
Cold-drawn steel	CDS	Corrosion resistant	CRE
Cold rolled	CR.	Corrosion-resistant steel	CRES
Cold-rolled steel	CRS	Corrugate	CORR
Column	COL	Cotter	COT
Combination	COMB.	Counter	CTR
Combustion	COMB.	Counterbalance	CBAL
Common	COM	Counterbore	CBORE
Communication	COMM	Counterclockwise	CCW
Commutator	COMM	Counterdrill	CDRILL
Complete	COMPL	Counterpunch	CPUNCH
Composite	CX	Countersink	CSK
Composition	COMP.	Countersink other side	CSK-O
Compressor	COMPR	Coupling	CPLG
Concentric	CONC	Courses	C
Concrete	CONC	Cover	COV
Condition	COND	Crank	CRK
Conduct	COND	Cross connection	XCONN
Conductor	COND	Cross section	XSECT
Conduit	CND	Cubic	CU
Connect	CONN	Current	CUR
Constant	CONST	Cyanide	CYN
Construction	CONST	Cycle	CY
Contact	CONT	Cycles per minute	CPM
Container	CNTR	Cycles per second	CPS
Continue	CONT	Cylinder	CYL
Continuous wave	CW	Damper	DMPR
Contract	CONT	Dampproofing	DP
Contractor	CONTR	Dead load	DL
Control	CONT	Decibel	DB
Control relay	CR		

(Continued)

(Continued)

SHOP, BLUEPRINT, AND OTHER COMMON ABBREVIATIONS

Word	Abbreviation	Word	Abbreviation
Decimal	DEC	Drawing	DWG
Deep drawn	DD	Drawing list	DL
Deflect	DEFL	Drill	DR
Degree	(°) DEG	Drill rod	DR
Density	D	Drive	DR
Describe	DESCR	Drive fit	DF
Design	DSGN	Drop	D
Designation	DESIG	Drop forge	DF
Detail	DET	Dryer	D
Detector	DET	Duplex	DX
Develop	DEV	Duplicate	DUP
Diagonal	DIAG	Dynamic	DYN
Diagram	DIAG	Dynamo	DYN
Diameter	DIA	Each	EA
Diaphragm	DIAPH	East	E
Differential	DIFF	Eccentric	ECC
Dimension	DIM	Effective	EFF
Dining room	DR	Electric	ELEC
Dioxide	DIO	Electronic air cleaner	EAC
Direct current	DC	Elevation	EL
Directional	DIR	Enamel	ENAM
Discharge	DISCH	Enclose	ENCL
Disconnect	DISC	End to end	E to E
Dishwasher	DW	Entrance	ENT
Distance	DIST	Envelope	ENV
Distribute	DISTR	Equal	EQ
Ditto	DO	Equation	EQ
Division	DIV	Equipment	EQUIP.
Door	DR	Equivalent	EQUIV
Double	DBL	Estimate	EST
Double hung	DH	Evaporate	EVAP
Dovetail	DVTL	Excavate	EXC
Dowel	DWL	Exhaust	EXH
Down	DN	Existing	EXIST
Downspout	DS	Expand	EXP
Drafting	DFTG	Exterior	EXT
Draftsman	DFTSMN	External	EXT
Drain	DR	Extra heavy	X HVY

Word	Abbreviation	Word	Abbreviation
Extra strong	X STR	Flush	FL
Extrude	EXTR	Focus	FOC
Fabricate	FAB	Foot	(′) FT
Face to face	F to F	Foot candle	FC
Fahrenheit	F	Footing	FTG
Fairing	FAIR.	Force	F
Farad	F	Forging	FORG
Far side	FS	Forward	FWD
Feed	FD	Foundation	FDN
Feeder	FDR	Foundry	FDRY
Feet	(′) FT	Fractional	FRAC
Feet board measure	FBM	Frame	FR
Feet per minute	FPM	Freezing point	FP
Feet per second	FPS	Frequency	FREQ
Female	FEM	Frequency, high	HF
Fiber	FBR	Frequency, low	LF
Field	FLD	Frequency, medium	MF
Figure	FIG.	Frequency modulation	FM
Filament	FIL	Frequency, super high	SHF
Fillet	FIL	Frequency, ultra high	UHF
Filling	FILL.	Frequency, very high	VHF
Fillister	FIL	Frequency, very low	VLF
Filter	FLT	Friction horsepower	FHP
Finish	FIN.	From below	FR BEL
Finish all over	FAO	Front	FR
Fireproof	FPRF	Fuel	F
Fitting	FTG	Full size	FS
Fixture	FIX	Furnish	FURN
Flange	FLG	Furred ceiling	FC
Flashing	FL	Fusible	FSBL
Flat	F	Fusion point	FNP
Flat head	FH	Gage or gauge	GA
Flexible	FLEX.	Gallon	GAL
Float	FLT	Galvanize	GALV
Floor	FL	Galvanized iron	GI
Floor drain	FD	Galvanized steel	GS
Flooring	FLG	Galvanized steel wire rope	GSWR
Fluid	FL	Garage	GAR
Fluorescent	FLUOR		

(Continued)

(Continued)

SHOP, BLUEPRINT, AND OTHER COMMON ABBREVIATIONS

Word	Abbreviation	Word	Abbreviation
Gas	G	Henry	H
Gasket	GSKT	Hexagon	HEX
Gasoline	GASO	High	H
General	GEN	High frequency	HF
Girder	G	High point	H PT
Glass	GL	High pressure	HP
Glaze	GL	High speed	HS
Government	GOVT	High speed steel	HSS
Governor	GOV	High tension	HT
Grade	GR	High voltage	HV
Grade line	GL	Highway	HWY
Graduation	GRAD	Holder	HLR
Gram	G	Hollow	HOL
Graphic	GRAPH	Horizontal	HOR
Graphite	GPH	Horsepower	HP
Grating	GRTG	Hose bib	HB
Gravity	G	Hot rolled	HR
Grid	G	Hot-rolled steel	HRS
Grind	GRD	House	HSE
Groove	GRV	Hundred	C
Ground	GRD	Hydraulic	HYD
Gypsum	GYP	I-Beam	I
Half hard	½H	Identify	IDENT
Half round	½RD	Ignition	IGN
Hall	H	Illuminate	ILLUM
Handle	HDL	Illustrate	ILLUS
Hanger	HGR	Impact	IMP
Hard	H	Impedance	IMP.
Hard-drawn	HD	Impregnate	IMPG
Harden	HDN	Inch	(") IN.
Hardware	HDW	Inches per second	IPS
Head	HD	Include	INCL
Headless	HDLS	Increase	INCR
Heat	HT	Indicate	IND
Heater	HTR	Inductance or induction	IND
Heat treat	HT TR.	Information	INFO
Heavy	HVY	Injection	INJ
Height	HGT	Inlet	IN

Word	Abbreviation	Word	Abbreviation
Inspect	INSP	Kip (1000 lb)	K
Install	INSTL	Kitchen	KIT
Instantaneous	INST	Knots	KN
Instruct	INST	Laboratory	LAB
Instrument	INST	Lacquer	LAQ
Insulate	INS	Laminate	LAM
Interchangeable	INTCHG	Lateral	LAT
Intercommunication	INTERCOM	Laundry	LAU
Interior	INT	Lavatory	LAV
Interlock	INTLK	Lead-coated metal	LCM
Intermediate	INTER	Leading edge	LE
Intermittent	INTMT	Left	L
Internal	INT	Left hand	LH
Interrupt	INTER	Length	LG
Intersect	INT	Length over all	LOA
Inverse	INV	Letter	LTR
Invert	INV	Light	LT
Iron	I	Limit	LIM
Iron-pipe size	IPS	Line	L
Irregular	IRREG	Linear	LIN
Jack	J	Linen closet	L CL
Job order	JO	Link	LK
Joint	JT	Liquefied gas	LPG
Joist	JST	Liquid	LIQ
Junction	JCT	Liter	L
Kelvin	K	Live load	LL
Key	K	Living room	LR
Keyseat	KST	Locate	LOC
Kilo	K	Long	LG
Kilocycle	KC	Longitude	LONG.
Kilocycles per second	KC	Lower	LV
Kilogram	KG	Low explosive	LE
Kiloliter	KL	Low frequency	LF
Kilometer	KM	Low pressure	LP
Kilovolt	KV	Low speed	LS
Kilovolt-ampere	KVA	Low tension	LT
Kilovolt-ampere hour	KVAH	Low torque	LT
Kilowatt	KW	Low voltage	LV
Kilowatt-hour	KWH	Lubricate	LUB

(Continued)

(Continued)

SHOP, BLUEPRINT, AND OTHER COMMON ABBREVIATIONS

Word	Abbreviation	Word	Abbreviation
Lubricating oil	LO	Micron	u or U
Lumber	LBR	Microvolt	uV or UV
Lumen	L	Microwatt	uW or UW
Lumens per watt	LPW	Miles	MI
Machine	MACH	Miles per gallon	MPG
Magnet	MAG	Miles per hour	MPH
Main	MN	Milli	M
Male and female	M&F	Milliampere	MA.
Malleable	MALL	Milligram	MG
Manhold	MH	Millihenry	MH
Manual	MAN.	Millimeter	MM
Manufacture	MFR	Milliseconds	MS
Manufactured	MFD	Millivolt	MV
Manufacturing	MFG	Milliwatt	MW
Material	MATL	Minimum	MIN
Material list	ML	Minute	(′) MIN
Maximum	MAX	Miscellaneous	MISC
Maximum working pressure	MWP	Mixture	MIX.
Mean effective pressure	MEP	Model	MOD
Mechanical	MECH	Modify	MOD
Mechanism	MECH	Modulated continuous wave	MCW
Medicine cabinet	MC	Modular	MOD
Medium	MED	Molecular weight	MOL WT
Mega	M	Monument	MON
Megacycles	MC	Morse taper	MOR T
Megawatt	MW	Motor	MOT
Megohm	MEF	Moulding	MLDG
Melting point	MP	Mounted	MTD
Membrane	MEMB	Mounting	MTG
Metal	MET.	Multiple	MULT
Meter (instrument or measure of length)	M	Multiple contact	MC
Micro	u or U	National	NATL
Microampere	uA or UA	National Electrical Code	NEC
Microfarad	uF or UF	Natural	NAT
Microhenry	uH or UH	Near face	NF
Micrometer	MIC	Near side	NS

Word	Abbreviation	Word	Abbreviation
Negative	NEG	Pack	PK
Network	NET	Packing	PKG
Neutral	NEUT	Painted	PTD
Nickel-silver	NI-SIL	Pair	PR
Nipple	NIP.	Panel	PNL
Nominal	NOM	Parallel	PAR.
Normal	NOR	Part	PT
Normally closed	NC	Partition	PTN
Normally open	NO	Pattern	PATT
North	N	Penny (nails)	d
Not to scale	NTS	Perforate	PERF
Number	NO.	Permanent	PERM
Obscure	OB	Permanent magnet	PM
Obsolete	OBS	Perpendicular	PERP
Octagon	OCT	Phase	PH
Ohm	OHM	Phosphor bronze	PH BRZ
Oil-circuit breaker	OCB	Photograph	PHOTO
Oil-insulated	OI	Physical	PHYS
Oil switch	OS	Piece	PC
On center	OC	Piece mark	PC MK
One pole	1 P	Pierce	PRC
Opening	OPNG	Pipe tap	PT
Operate	OPR	Pitch	P
Opposite	OPP	Pitch circle	PC
Optical	OPT	Pitch diameter	PD
Ordnance	ORD	Plaster	PL
Orifice	ORF	Plastic	PLSTC
Original	ORIG	Plate	PL
Oscillate	OSC	Plumbing	PLMB
Ounce	OZ	Pneumatic	PNEU
Outlet	OUT.	Point	PT
Output	OUT.	Pole	P
Outside diameter	OD	Polish	POL
Outside face	OF	Port	P
Outside radius	OR	Position	POS
Out to out	O to O	Positive	POS
Over-all	OA	Potential	POT.
Overhead	OVHD	Pound	LB
Overload	OVLD	Pounds per cubic foot	PCF
Oxidized	OXD		

(Continued)

(Continued)

SHOP, BLUEPRINT, AND OTHER COMMON ABBREVIATIONS

Word	Abbreviation	Word	Abbreviation
Pounds per square foot	PSF	Received	RECD
Pounds per square inch	PSI	Receiver	REC
Power	PWR	Receptacle	RECP
Power amplifier	PA	Reciprocate	RECIP
Power factor	PF	Recirculate	RECIRC
Preamplifier	PREAMP	Reclosing	RECL
Precast	PRCST	Record	REC
Prefabricated	PREFAB	Rectangle	RECT
Preferred	PFD	Rectifier	RECT
Premolded	PRMLD	Reduce	RED.
Prepare	PREP	Reference	REF
Press	PRS	Reference line	REF L
Pressure	PRESS	Refrigerate	REF
Primary	PRI	Refrigerator	REF
Process	PROC	Regulator	REG
Production	PROD	Reinforce	REINF
Profile	PF	Relay	REL
Project	PROJ	Release	REL
Punch	PCH	Relief	REL
Purchase	PUR	Remove	REM
Push-pull	P-P	Repair	REP
Quadrant	QUAD	Replace	REPL
Quality	QUAL	Reproduce	REPRO
Quantity	QTY	Require	REQ
Quart	QT	Required	REQD
Quarter	QTR	Resistance	RES
Quarter hard	¼ H	Resistor	RES
Quarter round	¼ RD	Retainer	RET.
Quartz	QTZ	Retard	RET.
Radial	RAD	Return	RET.
Radiator	RAD	Reverse	REV
Radio frequency	RF	Revise	REV
Radius	R	Revolution	REV
Range	R	Revolutions per minute	RPM
Reactor	REAC	Revolutions per second	RPS
Ream	RM	Rheostat	RHEO
Reassemble	REASM	Right	R

Word	Abbreviation	Word	Abbreviation
Right hand	RH	Shaft	SFT
Ring	R	Sheet	SH
Riser	R	Shield	SHLD
Rivet	RIV	Shop order	SO
Roller bearing	RB	Short wave	SW
Roof	RF	Shunt	SH
Room	RM	Side	S
Room air conditioner	RAC	Siding	SDG
Root diameter	RD	Signal	SIG
Rotary	ROT.	Similar	SIM
Rotate	ROT.	Single-pole, double-throw switch	SPDT
Rough	RGH	Single-pole, normally closed	SPNC
Round	RD	Single-pole, normally open	SPNO
Rubber	RUB.	Single-pole, single-throw switch	SPST
Saddle	SDL	Sink	SK
Safety	SAF	Sketch	SK
Safe working pressure	SWP	Sleeve	SLV
Sand blast	SD BL	Slide	SL
Sanitary	SAN	Slotted	SLOT.
Saturate	SAT.	Small	SM
Schedule	SCH	Smoke	SMK
Schematic	SCHEM	Smokeless	SMKLS
Scleroscope hardness	SH	Socket	SOC
Screen	SCRN	Soft	S
Screw	SCR	Soil pipe	SP
Second	SEC	Solder	SLD
Section	SECT	Solenoid	SOL
Segment	SEG	Sound	SND
Select	SEL	South	S
Semifinished	SF	Space	SP
Semifixed	SFXD	Spare	SP
Semisteel	SS	Speaker	SPKR
Separate	SEP	Special	SPL
Sequence	SEQ	Specific	SP
Serial	SER	Specification	SPEC
Series	SER	Specific gravity	SP GR
Serrate	SERR	Specific heat	SP HT
Service	SERV		
Set screw	SS		
Sewer	SEW.		

(Continued)

(Continued)

SHOP, BLUEPRINT, AND OTHER COMMON ABBREVIATIONS

Word	Abbreviation	Word	Abbreviation
Speed	SP	Tachometer	TACH
Spherical	SPHER	Tandem	TDM
Spindle	SPDL	Tangent	TAN.
Split phase	SP PH	Taper	TPR
Spot-faced	SF	Tar and gravel	T & G
Spring	SPG	Technical	TECH
Square	SQ	Tee	T
Stabilize	STAB	Teeth per inch	TPI
Stainless	STN	Telephone	TEL
Stairs	ST	Television	TV
Standard	STD	Temperature	TEMP
Static pressure	SP	Template	TEMP
Station	STA	Tensile strength	TS
Stationary	STA	Tension	TENS.
Steam	ST	Terminal	TERM.
Steel	STL	Terminal board	TB
Stiffener	STIFF	Terra-cotta	TC
Stock	STK	Terrazzo	TER
Storage	STG	That is	IE
Straight	STR	Theoretical	THEO
Street	ST	Thermal	THRM
Strip	STR	Thermostat	THERMO
Storage	STG	Thick	THK
Structural	STR	Thousand	M
Substitute	SUB	Thread	THD
Suction	SUCT	Throttle	THROT
Summary	SUM.	Through	THRU
Supervise	SUPV	Time	T
Supply	SUP	Time delay	TD
Surface	SUR	Time-delay closing	TDC
Survey	SURV	Time-delay opening	TDO
Switch	SW	Tinned	TD
Symbol	SYM	Toggle	TGL
Symmetrical	SYM	Toilet	T
Synchronous	SYN	Tolerance	TOL
Synthetic	SYN	Tongue and groove	T & G
System	SYS	Tool steel	TS
Tabulate	TAB	Tooth	T

Word	Abbreviation
Total	TOT
Trace	TR
Tracer	TCR
Transfer	TRANS
Transformer	TRANS
Transmission	XMSN
Transmitter	XMTR
Transmitting	XMTG
Transverse	TRANSV
Tread	TR
Truss	T
Tubing	TUB
Tuned radio frequency	TRF
Turbine	TURB
Typical	TYP
Ultimate	ULT
Ultra-high frequency	UHF
Unfinished	UNFIN
Unit	U
United States Gage	USG
United States Standard	USS
Universal	UNIV
Urinal	UR
Vacuum	VAC
Valve	V
Vapor proof	VAP PRF
Variable	VAR
Variable-frequency oscillator	VFO
Velocity	V
Ventilate	VENT
Vent pipe	VP
Versus	VS
Vertical	VERT
Very-high frequency	VHF
Very-low frequency	VLF
Vibrate	VIB
Video-frequency	VDF
Viscosity	VISC
Vitreous	VIT
Voice frequency	VF
Volt	V
Volt-ampere	VA
Voltmeter	VM
Volts per mil	VPM
Volume	VOL
Washer	WASH
Washing Machine	WM
Water	W
Water closet	WC
Water heater	WH
Water line	WL
Waterproof	WP
Watertight	WT
Watt	W
Watt-hour	WHR
Watt-hour meter	WHM
Wattmeter	WM
Weatherproof	WP
Weather stripping	WS
Weep hole	WH
Weight	WT
West	W
Wet bulb	WB
Width	W
Wind	WD
Winding	WDG
Window	WDW
Wire	W
With	W/
Without	W/O
Wood	WD
Woodruff	WDF
Working point	WP
Working pressure	WP
Wrought	WRT
Wrought iron	WI
Yard	YD
Year	YR
Yield point	YP
Yield strength	YS

ABBREVIATIONS FOR COLORS

Amber	AMB	Green	GRN
Black	BLK	Orange	ORN
Blue	BLU	White	WHT
Brown	BRN	Yellow	YEL

CHEMICAL ELEMENTS

Name	Symbol	Atomic weight	Atomic number
Actinium	AC	227	89
Aluminum	Al	26.98	13
Americium	Am	243	95
Antimony	Sb	121.76	51
Argon	Ar	39.944	18
Arsenic	As	74.92	33
Astatine	At	210	85
Barium	Ba	137.36	56
Berkelium	Bk	249	97
Beryllium	Be	9.013	4
Bismuth	Bi	208.99	83
Boron	B	10.82	5
Bromine	Br	79.916	35
Cadmium	Cd	112.41	48
Calcium	Ca	40.08	20
Californium	Cf	251	98
Carbon	C	12.011	6
Cerium	Ce	140.13	58
Cesium	Cs	132.91	55
Chlorine	Cl	35.457	17
Chromium	Cr	52.01	24
Cobalt	Co	58.94	27
Copper	Cu	63.54	29
Curium	Cm	247	96
Dysprosium	Dy	162.51	66
Einsteinium	E	254	99
Erbium	Er	167.27	68
Europium	Eu	152	63
Fermium	Fm	253	100
Fluorine	F	19	9

Name	Symbol	Atomic weight	Atomic number
Francium	Fr	223	87
Gadolinium	Gd	157.26	64
Gallium	Ga	69.72	31
Germanium	Ge	72.60	32
Gold	Au	197	79
Hafnium	Hf	178.50	72
Helium	He	4.003	2
Holmium	Ho	164.94	67
Hydrogen	H	1.008	1
Indium	In	114.82	49
Iodine	I	126.91	53
Iridium	Ir	192.2	77
Iron	Fe	55.85	26
Krypton	Kr	83.80	36
Lanthanum	La	138.92	57
Lawrencium	Lw	257	103
Lead	Pb	207.21	82
Lithium	Li	6.940	3
Lutetium	Lu	174.99	71
Magnesium	Mg	24.32	12
Manganese	Mn	54.94	25
Mendelevium	Mv	256	101
Mercury	Hg	200.61	80
Molybdenum	Mo	95.95	42
Neodymium	Nd	144.27	60
Neon	Ne	20.183	10
Neptunium	Np	237	93
Nickel	Ni	58.71	28
Niobium	Nb	92.91	41
Nitrogen	N	14.008	7
Nobelium	No	254	102
Osmium	Os	190.2	76
Oxygen	O	16	8
Palladium	Pd	106.4	46
Phosphorus	P	30.975	15
Platinum	Pt	195.09	78
Plutonium	Pu	242	94
Polonium	Po	210	84
Potassium	K	39.1	19

(Continued)

CHEMICAL ELEMENTS *(continued)*

Name	Symbol	Atomic weight	Atomic number
Praseodymium	Pr	140.92	59
Promethium	Pm	147	61
Protactinium	Pa	321	91
Radium	Ra	226	88
Radon	Rn	222	86
Rhenium	Re	186.22	75
Rhodium	Rh	102.91	45
Rubidium	Rb	85.48	37
Ruthenium	Ru	101.1	44
Samarium	Sm	150.35	62
Scandium	Sc	44.96	21
Selenium	Se	78.96	34
Silicon	Si	28.09	14
Silver	Ag	107.873	47
Sodium	Na	22.991	11
Strontium	Sr	87.63	38
Sulfur	S	32.066	16
Tantalum	Ta	180.95	73
Technetium	Te	99	43
Tellurium	Te	127.61	52
Terbium	Tb	158.93	65
Thallium	Tl	204.39	81
Thorium	Th	232	90
Thulium	Tm	168.94	69
Tin	Sn	118.7	50
Titanium	Ti	47.90	22
Tungsten	W	183.86	74
Uranium	U	238.07	92
Vanadium	V	50.95	23
Xenon	Xe	131.30	54
Ytterbium	Yb	173.04	70
Yttrium	Y	88.91	39
Zinc	Zn	65.38	30
Zirconium	Zr	91.22	40

NAMES AND FORMULAS FOR CHEMICALS

Popular name	Chemical name	Formula
Alcohol, grain	Ethyl alcohol	C_2H_5OH
Alcohol, wood	Methyl alcohol	CH_3OH
Alum, common	Aluminum potassium sulfate	$AlK(SO_4)_2 \cdot 12H_2O$
Alumina	Aluminum oxide	Al_2O_3
Alundum	Fused aluminum oxide	Al_2O_3
Antichlor	Sodium thiosulfate	$Na_2S_2O_3 \cdot 5H_2O$
Aqua ammonia	Ammonium hydroxide solution	$NH_4OH + H_2O$
Aqua fortis	Nitric acid	HNO_3
Aqua regia	Nitric and hydrochloric acids	$HNO_3 + HCl$
Aromatic spirits of ammonia	Ammonia gas in alcohol	
Asbestos	Magnesium silicate	$Mg_3Si_2O_7 \cdot 2H_2O$
Aspirin	Acetylsalicylic acid	$C_2H_3O_2C_6H_4CO_2H$
Baking soda	Sodium bicarbonate	$NaHCO_3$
Banana oil	Amyl acetate	$CH_3CO_2C_5H_{11}$
Baryta	Barium oxide	BaO
Bauxite	Impure aluminum oxide	Al_2O_3
Bichloride of mercury	Mercuric chloride	$HgCl_2$
Black lead	Graphite	C
Black oxide of copper	Cupric oxide	CuO
Black oxide of mercury	Mercurous oxide	Hg_2O
Bleaching powder	Calcium hypochlorite	$CaOCl_2$
Bluestone	Copper sulfate	$CuSO_4 \cdot 5H_2O$
Blue vitriol	Copper sulfate	$CuSO_4 \cdot 5H_2O$
Boracic acid	Boric acid	H_3BO_3
Borax	Sodium borate	$Na_2B_4O_7 \cdot 10H_2O$
Brimstone	Sulfur	S
Brine	Strong sodium chloride solution	$NaCl\ H_2O$
"Butter of"	Chloride or trichloride of	
Caliche	impure sodium nitrate	$NaNO_3$
Calomel	Mercurous chloride	Hg_2Cl_2
Carbolic acid	Phenol	C_6H_5OH
Carbonic acid gas	Carbon dioxide	CO_2
Caustic potash	Potassium hydroxide	KOH

(Continued)

NAMES AND FORMULAS FOR CHEMICALS *(continued)*

Popular name	Chemical name	Formula
Caustic soda	Dosium hydroxide	$NaOH$
Chalk	Calcium carbonate	$CaCO_3$
Chile saltpeter	Sodium nitrate	$NaNO_3$
Chloroform	Trichloromethane	$CHCl_3$
Chrome alum	Chromium potassium sulfate	$CrK(SO_4)_2 \cdot 12H_2O$
Chrome yellow	Lead chromate	$PbCrO_4$
Copperas	Ferrous sulfate	$FeSO_4 \cdot 7H_2O$
Corrosive sublimate	Mercuric chloride	$HgCl_2$
Cream of tartar	Potassium bitartrate	$KHC_4H_4O_6$
Crocus powder	Ferric oxide	Fe_2O_3
DDT	Dichlorodiphenyl-trichloroethane	$(C_6H) \cdot Cl_2 \cdot CH \cdot CCl_3$
Dry ice	Solid carbon dioxide	CO_2
Dutch liquid	Ethylene dichloride	$CH_2Cl \cdot CH_2Cl$
Emery powder	Impure aluminum oxide	Al_2O_3
Epsom salts	Magnesium sulfate	$MgSO_4 \cdot 7H_2O$
Ethanol	Ethyl alcohol	C_2H_5OH
Ether	Ethyl ether	$(C_2H_5)_2O$
Fluorspar	Natural calcium fluoride	CaF_2
Formalin	Formaldehyde	$HCOH$
French chalk	Natural magnesium silicate	$H_2Mg_3(SiO_3)_4$
Galena	Natural lead sulfide	PbS
Galuber's salt	Sodium sulfate	$Na_2SO_4 \cdot 10H_2O$
Green vitriol	Ferrous sulfate	$FeSO_4 \cdot 7H_2O$
Gypsum	Natural calcium sulfate	$CaSO_4 \cdot 2H_2O$
Hypo	Sodium thiosulfate	$Na_2S_2O_3 \cdot 5H_2O$
Javelle water	Originally potassium hypochlorite solution, now usually sodium hypochlorite solution	$KOCl + H_2O$ $NaOCl + H_2O$
Labarraque's solution	Sodium hypochlorite solution	$NaOCl + H_2O$
Lime, unslaked	Calcium oxide	CaO
Limewater	Calcium hydroxide solution	$Ca(OH_2) + H_2O$
Litharge	Lead oxide	PbO

Popular name	Chemical name	Formula
Lithopone	Zinc sulfide plus barium sulfate	$ZnS + BaSO_4$
Magnesia	Magnesium oxide	MgO
Magnesite	Magnesium carbonate	$MgCO_3$
Marble	Calcium carbonate	$CaCO_3$
Marsh gas	Methane	CH_4
Methanol	Methyl alcohol	CH_3OH
Methylated spirits	Methyl alcohol	CH_3OH
Milk of magnesia	Magnesium hydroxide in water	$Mg(OH)_2$
Minium	Lead tetroxide	Pb_3O_4
"Muriate of"	Chloride of	
Muriatic acid	hydrochloric acid	HCl
Natural gas	Mostly methane	CH_4
Niter	Potassium nitrate	KNO_3
Oil of bitter almonds (artificial)	Benzaldehyde	C_6H_5CHO
Oil of mirbane	Nitrobenzene	$C_6H_5NO_3$
Oil of vitriol	Sulfuric acid	H_2SO_4
Oil of wintergreen (artificial)	Methyl salicylate	$C_6H_4OHCOOCH_3$
Oleum	Fuming sulfuric acid	$H_2SO_4SO_3$
Orpiment	Arsenic trisulfide	As_2S_3
Paris green	Copper aceto-arsenite	$3Cu(AsO_2)_2{\cdot}Cu(C_2H_3O_2)_2$
Pearl ash	Potassium carbonate	K_2CO_3
Peroxide	Peroxide of hydrogen solution	$H_2O_2 + H_2O$
Phosgene	Carbonyl chloride	$COCl_2$
Plaster of Paris	Calcium sulfate	$(CaSO_4)_2{\cdot}H_2O$
Plumbago	Graphite	C
Potash	Potassium carbonate	K_2CO_3
Prussic acid	Hydrocyanic acid	HCN
Pyro	Pyrogalic acid	$C_6H_3(OH)_3$
Quicklime	Calcium oxide	CaO
Quicksilver	Mercury	Hg
Red lead	Lead tetroxide	Pb_3O_4
Red oxide of copper	Cuprous oxide	Cu_2O
Red oxide of mercury	Mercuric oxide	HgO
Red prussiate of potash	Potassium ferricyanide	$K_3Fe(CN)_6$
Rochelle salt	Potassium sodium	$KNaC_4H_4O_6{\cdot}4H_2O$
Rouge	Ferric oxide	Fe_2O_3

(Continued)

NAMES AND FORMULAS FOR CHEMICALS *(continued)*

Popular name	Chemical name	Formula
Sal ammoniac	Ammonium chloride	NH_4Cl
Saleratus	Sodium bicarbonate	$NaHCO_3$
Sal soda	Crystalline sodium carbonate	$NaHCO_3$
Salt	Sodium chloride	$NaCl$
Salt cake	Impure sodium sulfate	Na_2SO_4
Salt of lemon	Potassium binoxalate	$KHC_2O_4 \cdot H_2O$
Saltpeter	Potassium nitrate	KNO_3
Saltpeter (Chile)	Impure sodium nitrate	$NaNO_3$
Salts of tartar	Potassium carbonate	K_2CO_3
Silica	Silicon dioxide	SiO_2
Slaked lime	Calcium hydroxide	$Ca(OH)_2$
Soapstone	Impure magnesium silicate	$H_2Mg_3(SiO_3)_4$
Soda ash	Dry sodium carbonate	Na_2CO_3
Spirit of hartshorn	Ammonia gas in alcohol	
Spirits of salt	Hydrochloric acid	HCl
Spirits of wine	Ethyl alcohol	C_2H_5OH
Sugar of lead	Lead acetate	$Pb(C_2H_3O_2)_2 \cdot 3H_2O$
Sulfuric ether	Ethyl ether	$(C_2H_5)_2O$
Talc	Magnesium silicate	$H_2Mg_3(SiO_3)_4$
TNT	Trinitrotoluene	$C_6H_2CH_3(NO_3)_3$
Toluol	Toluene	$C_6H_5CH_3$
Vinegar	Dilute and impure acetic acid	CH_3COOH
Washing soda	Crystalline sodium carbonate	$NaHCO_3$
Water glass	Sodium silicate	Na_2SiO_3
White arsenic	Arsenic trioxide	As_2O_3
White lead	Basic lead carbonate	$(PbCO_3)_2 \cdot Pb(OH)_2$
White vitriol	Zinc sulfate	$ZnSO_4 \cdot 7H_2O$
Whiting	Powdered calcium carbonate	$CaCO_3$
Wood alcohol	Methyl alcohol	CH_3OH
Xylol	Xylene	$C_6H_4(CH_3)_2$
Zinc white	Zinc oxide	ZnO

THE GREEK ALPHABET

Lower-case letter	Capital letter	Name of letter	English equivalent
α	Α	alpha	a
β	Β	beta	b
γ	Γ	gamma	g
δ	Δ	delta	d
ε	Ε	epsilon	e
ζ	Ζ	zeta	z
η	Η	eta	ē
θ	Θ	theta	th
ι	Ι	iota	i
κ	Κ	kappa	k
λ	Λ	lambda	l
μ	Μ	mu	m
ν	Ν	nu	n
ξ	Ξ	xi	x
ο	Ο	omicron	o
π	Π	pi	p
ρ	Ρ	rho	r
σ	Σ	sigma	s
τ	Τ	tau	t
υ	ϒ	upsilon	u
φ	Φ	phi	ph
χ	Χ	chi	ch
ψ	Ψ	psi	ps
ω	Ω	omega	ō

20

Sources for Materials

As mentioned in the Preface, many chemicals and other raw materials that were once easy to get at the local grocery, paint, hardware, or drugstore may now require a little scouting after.

To save the cost of packing and shipping, it is best first to try to find your materials nearby. The Yellow Pages of your local telephone directory may give you a good start. Look under dealers of chemicals, building materials, industrial hardware, janitor's, photographic, artist's supplies, and so on, depending on the product you need and the field in which it is apt to be used. Sometimes a friendly druggist, or hardware or paint dealer may be willing to refer you to sources of raw materials he once carried but doesn't anymore. Larger photographic dealers may order for you any of a long list of photographic chemicals of a manufacturer they deal with, but which they may not ordinarily stock.

Materials you cannot get locally, you can usually order by mail. In this case, a minimum order is generally required and you must, of course, pay for shipping.

General lists of manufacturers and suppliers of chemicals and related raw materials can be found in the following two annual publications, available in many large libraries:

- OPD *Chemical Buyers Directory* is a part of the subscription to *Chemical Marketing Reporter,* Schnell Publishing Company, Inc., 100 Church St., New York, NY 10007.

- *Chemical Week, Buyers' Guide Issue*, is part of the subscription to *Chemical Week*, McGraw-Hill, Inc., 1221 Avenue of the Americas, New York, NY 10020.

Present sources of a number of hard-to-find materials are mentioned with the materials where they occur in the book. Here are some additional suggestions, along with the names of a few specific dealers, that may help you find more.

GENERAL CHEMICALS

Amend Drug and Chemical Company, Inc., 83 Cordier St., Irvington, NJ 07111. Carries a wide stock of laboratory and industrial chemicals. Convenient for anyone in the New York City area.

Ward's Natural Science Establishment, Inc., P.O. Box 1712, Rochester, NY 14603. Also Ward's of California, P.O. Box 1749, Monterey, CA 93942. This long-established company carries a stock of general chemicals, as well as all kinds of specimens and equipment for the study of biology and earth sciences.

Berg Chemical Company, Inc., 920 E. 132 St., New York, NY 10454. A good source for all sorts of industrial chemicals, including synthetic solvents and detergents, quaternary compounds, pesticides, clays, alcohols, acids and alkalies, Stoddard solvent, and wetting agents.

Eastman Kodak Company, Rochester, NY 14650. Many of the photographic chemicals made by Eastman Kodak may be bought or ordered through dealers handling Kodak products.

Arthur H. Thomas Co., Vine St. at Third, P.O. Box 779, Philadelphia, PA 19105. Will sell from a vast array of laboratory apparatus and supply products to laymen. Will sell chemicals to adults only with a written order from a responsible institution or a qualified scientist, such as a chemist or pharmacist. The catalog is not available to individuals; a request for a catalog must be submitted on a company letterhead in order to be considered.

Harry Ross, 61 Reade St., New York, NY 10007. This pioneer dealer in used microscopes and other laboratory equipment carries a modest line of chemicals for schools and students, and is one of the very few dealers in New York City that still sells chemicals over the counter.

MISCELLANEOUS RAW MATERIALS

H. Behlen & Bro., Inc., 10 Christopher St., New York, NY 10014, founded in 1888, is one of the last big manufacturer-dealers in the country to carry a complete line of raw materials for the wood-finishing trades. Besides the expected pigments, stains, dyes, aniline dyes, solvents, waxes, coated abrasives, and polishes, Behlen sells a wide assortment of often elusive basic products that should be a delight to the do-it-yourselfer. These include acids and alkalies, bronze powders, modeling clay, fibers, gelatin, and a complete line of gold-leafing supplies. There are also dry glues of all types, liquid glues, lacquer (shellac) sticks, and resins such as Mastic Sandarac Copal. Sold only by mail. Literature kit, including catalog, is $1.

WOOD-FINISHING SUPPLIES

For wood-finishing supplies alone, try hardware and paint stores, lumberyards and suppliers of building materials. Craft supply stores that include woodworking are also good sources.

Albert Constantine and Son, Inc., 2050 Eastchester Road, Bronx, NY 10461—its parent company dating back to 1812—carries a complete line of such materials as well as a wide inventory of fine and rare woods for craft work and furniture making. Sells by mail and over the counter. Minimum mail order $5. Catalog 50 cents.

PIGMENTS, STAINS, AND DYES

Founded in 1853, Fezandie & Sperrle, 111 8th Ave., New York, NY 10011, offers the following: dry colors, aniline dyes, stains for wood and for leather, lime proof colors and cement, batik dyes for cotton, silk, and wood and the finest artist pigments. It also sells such specialties as gums, waxes, glues, and glass mullers. Will supply free price lists. Minimum order, $20.00.

Leeben Color & Chemical, 111 8th Ave., New York, NY 10011, manufacturers and custom blenders of food, drug, and cosmetic colors. Also offers a complete line of industrial dyes for soap, detergents, wax, tracer dyes, antifreeze, gasoline, and many other chemical specialty products. Will supply free price lists. Minimum order, $25.00.

Another venerable company, Pylam Products Company, Inc., 95-10 218th St., Queens Village, NY 11429, makes and sells certified food, drug, and cosmetic colors, as well as alcohol, water, wax, and solvent-soluble dyes for coloring candles, soaps, detergents and all sorts of consumer products. Has list for each type of color. Minimum mail order $25.00.

Wolf Paints, 771 Ninth Ave., New York, NY 10019, offers a wide range of paints, stains, pastes, glues, applicators, and other equipment for homeowners, artists, and professional house painters. A catalog is available.

WAXES

Beeswax is still used by leather workers to wax thread, finish belt edges, and so on, and is available from art-and-craft supply stores. This and other waxes—such as carnauba, candelilla, ceresine, ozokerite—used widely in the commercial manufacture of polishes and floor waxes, cosmetics, lubricants, and water-repellents, will probably have to be obtained from special dealers in waxes listed in the Yellow Pages in your phone book or from one of the manufacturers listed below.

Frank B. Ross Co., Inc., 6 Ash Street, Jersey City, NJ 07304. For industrial users of wax, this company publishes a booklet, "Ross Waxes," that contains a wealth of information about the origin of the many natural and synthetic waxes and their physical characteristics and varied uses.

PLASTICS MATERIALS

Castolite Company, Box 391, Woodstock, IL 60098. Liquid plastics and fiberglass for casting, molding, coating, and laminating.

Bel-Art Products Pequannock, NJ 07440. Plastic sheets, tubes, rods, covers, containers, and laboratory ware.

Most craft supply stores also carry liquid casting plastics and a variety of solid forms.

ARTS AND CRAFTS

Besides paints, pastels, canvasses, metals, leather, and other typical arts and crafts materials, artist's and craftworker's supply stores are often a mine of general raw materials that are now often hard to find elsewhere. In larger ones you can get such things as asphaltum varnish (for etching backgrounds), beeswax, liver of sulfur, gold and aluminum leaf, bronze powders, leather dyes, jars, bottles, collapsible tubes, powdered charcoal, modeling and ceramic clays, casting plaster, etc.

If you can't find a local dealer that has what you need, you might try one of these:

Allcraft Tool and Supply Co., Inc., 100 Frank Rd., Hicksville, NY 11801. A complete supply house for jewelry making, electroplating, metalsmithing, silversmithing, enameling on metal, and centrifugal or lost wax casting. Manufactures all types of ovens and workbenches. Also stocks a large selection of books on the above crafts. A catalog is available for $2.50, which is deductible from the first purchase of $10 or more.

Arthur Brown & Bro., Inc., 2 West 46th St., New York, NY 10036. This is probably the largest general artist's supply dealer in America. Sells over the counter and by mail from a large catalog, $1.

Skil-Crafts, 309 Virginia Ave., Box 105, Joplin, MO 64801. Has wide line of arts and crafts materials. Large catalog sent for $2.50.

pH TEST MATERIALS

Papers and liquids that change color to give rough indications of acidity or alkalinity can be bought in garden supply stores and from chemical supply houses. More elaborate equipment for giving more accurate indications can also be bought from the latter sources.

Complete kits for all sorts of pH testing, as well as information concerning methods, can be obtained from the LaMotte Chemical Products Company, P.O. Box 329, Chestertown, MD 21620.

Index